Lecture Notes in Physics

271

Nonlinear Hydrodynamic Modeling: A Mathematical Introduction

Edited by Hampton N. Shirer

Springer-Verlag
Berlin Heidelberg New York London Paris Tokyo

Editor

Hampton N. Shirer
Department of Meteorology
The Pennsylvania State University
University Park, PA 16802, USA

ISBN 3-540-17557-1 Springer-Verlag Berlin Heidelberg New York
ISBN 0-387-17557-1 Springer-Verlag New York Berlin Heidelberg

Printed in Germany

Printing: Druckhaus Beltz, Hemsbach/Bergstr.;
Bookbinding: J. Schäffer GmbH & Co. KG., Grünstadt
2153/3140-543210

Saroja Polavarapu
Mon Feb 27/89

To Daniel and Julia, two of the
greatest kids growing up in a nonlinear world.

PREFACE

These lecture notes provide an introduction to the nonlinear analysis of solutions to hydrodynamic models. Traditionally, at least in the atmospheric sciences, most theoretical study of the properties of the solutions is limited to a linear analysis. The reasoning is that finding the linear modes with the fastest growth rates should yield an adequate understanding of the observed flows. In recent years, however, it has become clear that significant fundamental progress is possible only if a nonlinear approach is taken. With this approach, the finitely many modes are sought that, in the long term at least, carry most of the energy. Although many introductory texts covering the requisite topics of bifurcation, stability, catastrophe theory, etc. exist (e.g., Iooss and Joseph, 1980, or Guckenheimer and Holmes, 1983), most are written from a mathematically formal perspective. An introductory survey of the subject using relatively simple language is needed to provide students of hydrodynamics with sufficient background to read these more mathematical treatments. It is possible to avoid much of the formal mathematical jargon because the necessary basic theorems depend on elementary concepts requiring only undergraduate-level knowledge of differential equations and linear algebra. It is this approach that we adopt here to motivate and describe, without proof, the results and applications of these theorems.

This monograph has a further purpose. As it becomes clear that nonlinear analysis of systems of equations is necessary, it also becomes apparent that the analysis would proceed more easily if the number of equations were small. The pioneer in this area, which is known as low-order modeling, is Professor Edward N. Lorenz of the Massachusetts Institute of Technology. In a series of studies covering a range of fluid responses, he has discovered much about the fundamental nonlinear properties of fluid flow by utilizing various low-order systems of ordinary differential equations. In this monograph, we use his 1963 model of Rayleigh-Bénard convection to illustrate many of the necessary nonlinear concepts and calculations. Although it is a simple matter to write a three- or five-coefficient system of equations, it is often a distinct challenge to write one that is physically relevant. It is natural, then, to ask whether any principles guiding model development could be created, principles whose application would be based on nonlinear mathematical theory. In this monograph, we discuss a preliminary list of seven such principles and we summarize many of the types of calculations that should be carried out to test whether the model results are likely to be physically relevant. The results of these calculations give us a wide variety of information, ranging from the preferred geometrical configuration of the flow to signals that the results are too restrictive and that certain degrees of freedom therefore must be added to the system. Thus we bring a new perspective to nonlinear modeling, a perspective embodied in the concept of metamodeling, or the study of the modeling process itself, and we argue that its application will allow us to create useful and relatively simple-to-analyze nonlinear models of fluid behavior.

The initial manuscript upon which this monograph is based was written in the fall of 1984 by the 11 participants in a graduate meteorology seminar on nonlinear hydrodynamics at The Pennsylvania State University. This seminar was organized by Professors John A. Dutton and Hampton N. Shirer; the students were Dr. Steven B. Feldstein, Mr. Ronald Gelaro, Mr. R. Wayne Higgins, Mr. Paul A. Hirschberg, Mr. Mark J. Laufersweiler, Mr. Jon M. Nese, Mr. Robert J. Pyle, Mr. Arthur N. Samel, and Mr. David J. Stensrud. Each participant was asked to give a lecture on one or more topics and then to organize their material into a chapter for a set of notes. These original chapters were used by the 14 participants in the fall of 1985 seminar, who gave lectures from and critically reviewed the initial manuscripts. On the basis of these reviews, the notes were completely reorganized and rewritten in the form presented here.

The chapters of the monograph are divided into four main groups--Chapters 1 to 3 introduce the basic concepts of modeling and review the creation, development, and analysis of nonlinear models; Chapters 4 to 10 discuss various aspects of time-independent, or stationary, solutions to the models; Chapters 11 to 14 review the behavior of temporally periodic solutions; and Chapters 15 to 18 survey more complicated temporal flows and the analysis of their properties.

Here we briefly summarize the major topics of each chapter. In Chapter 1, we discuss models and their purposes and we outline the seven modeling principles; four we regard as fundamental to all models, with the remaining three being intermediate their branching properties can be determined via a power series analysis of the differential system. Finally, in Chapter 14, we show how to extend the notion of asymptotic stability to one for temporally periodic solutions, and then we review the three principal types of temporal solutions that bifurcate from the periodic ones.

In the remaining four chapters of the monograph, we consider more complicated temporal, or chaotic, flows; these flows have been proposed to model one form of turbulence commonly observed in fluids. Several proposed routes along which a flow might evolve toward a turbulent state are discussed in Chapter 15. Some measures of the complicated structures of the chaotic solutions are introduced in Chapter 16. In Chapter 17, we present a quite general review of the properties of the solutions to some of the differential equations of atmospheric flows, and then we propose two ways that optimum models might be created. Finally, in Chapter 18, we return to a discussion of the elements of the modeling process that provide the necessary concepts underlying metamodeling.

An undertaking of this magnitude would not be possible without the tireless efforts of a large number of people. We are especially grateful to Professor Robert Wells whose advice led to major improvements in the discussion throughout the monograph. Professor Wells thoroughly read the entire manuscript and offered a large number of extremely helpful suggestions. In addition, his help was essential in implementing the Alexander-Yorke continuation method discussed in Chapter 10 as well as in calculating the Lyapunov dimensions in Chapter 16. We thank Professor John A. Dutton, who reviewed and offered many useful comments on each chapter, as well as Dr. Harry W. Henderson and Mrs. Tracy H. Hirschberg, who offered many critical comments on the material in some of the chapters. Also, Professor Peter Kloeden kindly gave us his notes from which Section 13.2 was written.

All of the authors helped to critique and proofread the manuscript; several, especially Mr. R. Wayne Higgins, Mr. Paul A. Hirschberg, Mr. Mark J. Laufersweiler, and Mr. Jon M. Nese, helped considerably with the host of other mundane tasks. Also, we thank the fall 1985 participants in the graduate seminar for their comments that led to greatly improved organization of the material: Ms. Shuyi Chen, Ms. Sharon Douglas, Dr. Steven B. Feldstein, Mr. R. Wayne Higgins, Mr. Paul A. Hirschberg, Mrs.

ones that must be incorporated eventually. We describe the modeling process in more detail in Chapter 2, where we show how solutions to a simple model of a physical system may possess the qualities outlined in the four fundamental principles. Then, in Chapter 3, we review the Galerkin method for creating low-order dynamical systems, or truncated spectral models, whose behavior we investigate in subsequent chapters.

Normally we begin analyzing nonlinear models by first studying their stationary solutions. We show in Chapters 4 and 5 how determination of the asymptotic stability properties of the stationary solutions may be used to identify the critical values of the forcing at which transitions or bifurcations between stationary solutions occur. Acceptable branching behavior is modeled by forms that satisfy certain physically imposed constraints, and we review these in Chapter 6. In order that the solutions to the models correspond to observed flows, some of the response parameters, such as cell aspect ratio, must take preferred values, and the methods used to find these values are covered in Chapter 7.

We begin in Chapters 8 and 9 to consider the three intermediate modeling principles, that is we investigate whether model behavior is sensitive to additional possible degrees of freedom. First, in Chapter 8, we show how to identify the forcing parameters necessary for describing adequately all types of transitions; in addition, we note how to identify the forcing effects that might serve as candidates for any of the identified parameters not already in the problem as it was originally posed. Hierarchies of transitions are observed in many laboratory flows, and we see in Chapter 9 how these can be modeled via secondary branching. We complete our consideration of stationary solutions in Chapter 10, where we present a numerical algorithm for determining all stationary solutions to a low-order model.

Certainly other types of solutions are possible, and in Chapters 11 to 14 we consider temporally periodic ones. In Chapter 11, we discover how the creation of these solutions is signaled by a type of stability exchange known as Hopf bifurcation; in addition, we review the acceptable forms of these branching solutions. As with stationary solutions, the observed characteristics of the periodic solutions can be related to the preferred values of certain response parameters, and we discuss how to find their values in Chapter 12. Although periodic solutions cannot always be obtained analytically, we show in Chapter 13 that some of

Tracy H. Hirschberg, Mr. Mark J. Laufersweiler, Mr. Jon M. Nese, Mr. Robert J. Pyle, Mr. Shou-Ping Wang, Mr. Morris L. Weisman, and Mr. Chidong Zhang.

The following people helped develop the figures: Dr. Hai-Ru Chang (Chapter 9), Dr. John A. Dutton (Chapters 1,17), Dr. Steven B. Feldstein (Chapters 4,14), Mr. Ronald Gelaro (Chapters 5,10), Mr. R. Wayne Higgins (Chapters 3,5,8), Mr. Paul A. Hirschberg (Chapters 6,9,14), Mr. Mark J. Laufersweiler (Chapters 2,7,9), Mr. Jon M. Nese (Chapters 15,16), Mr. Robert J. Pyle (Chapters 7,11,13,14), Dr. Hampton N. Shirer (Chapters 2,4,9,10,11,13,14), Mr. David J. Stensrud (Chapter 12, Appendix B), and Dr. Robert Wells (Chapters 7,8,10,14,15,16,17). We also thank Mr. Robert J. Pyle for supplying the symbolic output in Tables 3.1 and 3.2 and Dr. Hai-Ru Chang for providing the 11-coefficient model used in Chapter 16.

Mrs. Delores Corman and Mrs. Nancy Warner typed and retyped the apparently endless versions of each chapter. We deeply appreciate their skillful work and good humor throughout the lengthy project. Also, we are indebted to Mr. Vic King who excellently drafted the large number of figures.

Finally, this work could not have been completed without the partial funding provided by the National Science Foundation through Grants ATM 81-13223 and ATM 83-07213, and by the National Aeronautics and Space Administration through Grant NAS 8-36150.

HAMPTON N. SHIRER
December 1986

TABLE OF CONTENTS

CHAPTER 1

MODELING: A STRATEGY FOR UNDERSTANDING

JOHN A. DUTTON

Science is the process by which humans attempt to comprehend, predict, and perhaps control the environment in which they find themselves. It proceeds on a number of levels, sometimes sequentially and sometimes simultaneously. Modeling is the heart of the scientific enterprise, for it links together the phases of the scientific endeavor.

The basic strategy of science is to convert facts or intuition gained by observing objects or natural processes in our surroundings into conceptual and quantitative structures that encourage and permit extrapolation of knowledge to new circumstances. We effect this strategy by constructing models of the phenomena that capture our interest.

Models, then, in a preliminary description, are devices that mirror nature in some sense by embodying empirical knowledge in forms that permit inferences, preferably quantitative, to be derived from them. Many branches of science have evolved to a level in which the models employed are explicitly mathematical, perhaps systems of differential equations, that can be treated in an axiom and theorem formulation. In others, true theoretical study is not yet possible because the essential state variables have not yet been perceived or invented.

This chapter is an introduction to the main concepts of modeling, which is a way of codifying knowledge about our world; in a companion chapter, Chapter 18, we examine metamodeling, which is the study of the process of modeling itself.

We shall first examine the role of modeling in scientific progress, and then consider modeling in the context of the Earth Sciences, emphasizing the dynamics of fluid systems -- the atmosphere and ocean -- in part because modeling is more advanced in atmospheric and oceanic sciences than it is in the other Earth Sciences. We shall find that although enough has been done that we can take a formal view of our accomplishments, many challenges remain. The hope and motivation of the present approach is that the formal study of models and modeling may stimulate the development of higher-level and more effective strategies for future work.

1.1 Modeling Motivations and Issues

Scientific study of a natural object or phenomenon proceeds through a number of usually distinct but interactive phases. They can be described as (see box below for accompanying definitions):

- Exploration and discovery
- Observation
- Formulation of descriptive or empirical models
- Development and verification of theories or inferential models concerning the state variables and their evolution
- Simulation and prediction of phenomenological behavior
- Modification of phenomenological behavior in the physical world

The first two phases may be described, perhaps loosely, as pre-modeling stages; the next two explicitly involve the development, refinement, and verification of models. The last two stages are made possible by the existence of reliable and efficacious models.

The interaction of the phases of science is illustrated in Fig. 1.1. Empirical knowledge is developed by exploration, discovery, and observation, and is then codified in descriptive models or by theoretical assimilation and summary. Quantitative understanding embodied in theories can be converted into models that foster the quantitative inferences of simulation and prediction. The attempt to

DEFINITIONS

Theory --

A speculative or established explanation accounting for known facts or phenomena, often expressed in the physical sciences in a symbolic or mathematical form that emphasizes the evolution of state variables describing the system of interest.

Descriptive Model --

A representation of structure or process in a descriptive, graphical, or statistical form.

Inferential Model --

An implementation of a theory in a form that fosters inference, especially quantitative, about a specific collection of phenomena or processes.

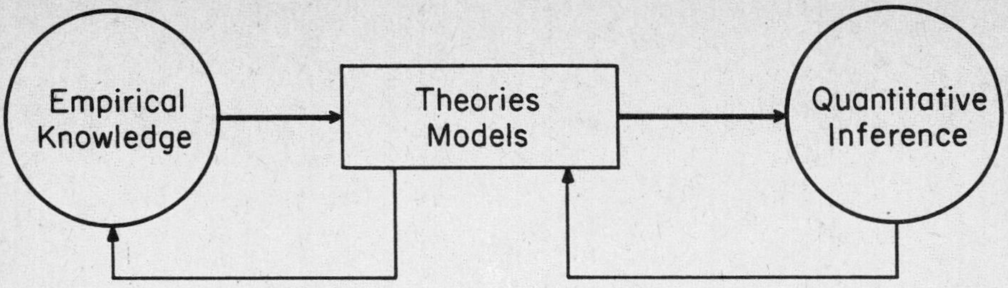

Fig. 1.1 The interactions of the phases of science.

formulate or validate theories and models stimulates new observations and the simulations or predictions produced by preliminary versions of models usually indicate the need for revision or for more pertinent observations. As shown, the process proceeds with interactions between the phases, with theorizing and modeling being the integrative endeavor.

1.1.1 Earth system modeling. The Earth Sciences have long been concerned with models of specific phenomena or entire subsystems of the Earth System, implicitly expecting that perhaps someday these models would become components in a system model of broader scope, one that explicitly accounted for the interactions between the phenomena and processes that determine the evolution of the entire planet. Today we have begun to take a global view, intrigued by the possibility of constructing an Earth System model by working from global concepts to modular components.

Contemplation of the prospects for modeling the Earth System reveals that one of the major problems is the vast range of scales that must be resolved. Many of the processes in which we are interested, such as condensation of water or carbon fixation by vegetation, occur on the molecular level. Yet we need to achieve a global perspective to understand the System.

The major subsystems of the Earth are the atmosphere, the ocean, the crust and mantle, the cryosphere, and the terrestrial and oceanic biosystems. These major subsystems interact through the exchange of energy and momentum, and through the major biogeochemical cycles, including those involving water, carbon, nitrogen, and sulphur. The fact that the interactions between the subsystems and the chemical cycles occur over broad ranges of temporal and spatial scales presents the crucial and formidable challenge of Earth System Science.

For example, the processes shaping the Earth System occur in five broad bands of time scales:

- Millions of Years. Mantle convection and the motion of the tectonic plates, mountain building and vulcanism, the evolution of life and the associated development of the present chemical composition of the atmosphere all occur on scales measured in millions of years.
- Thousands of Years. The oscillations between ice ages and interglacial periods, with the associated changes in chemical concentrations and the distribution of biological species, occurred, apparently, in response to the variations in the Earth's orbit around the sun that proceed in cycles of tens of thousands of years.
- Decades to Centuries. The changes that threaten the viability of the planet -- changes in climate, chemical composition of the atmosphere, patterns of surface aridity or acidity, and terrestrial biological systems -- must be resolved soon for a period including the next few centuries.
- Days to Seasons. Weather phenomena, eddies in ocean currents, seasonal growth and melting of ice caps and glaciers, surface runoff and weathering, and the annual cycle of plant growth are all confined to time scales regulated by the annual cycle of solar insolation. A large part of the feedback from biogeochemical cycles occurs through the alteration of the radiative processes that supply energy to the major subsystems.
- Seconds to Hours. The fluxes of mass, momentum, and energy between the land, the ocean, the ice, the atmosphere, and the biota are all dominated by processes having time scales that are less than one day. Over the land and the ocean these exchanges occur through the medium of turbulent transports that are themselves responsive in part to diurnal cycles in heating rates.

Earth System Science extends across this range of scales, attempting to integrate the causes and effects from both the longer-scale and shorter-scale processes that drive and shape the processes within one of the bands.

This representation reveals that there are two distinct problems to consider in modeling the Earth System. The first is to find a proper formulation for the interactions between systems -- such as atmospheric and oceanic exchanges of heat or exchanges of nutrients between plants and soil. The second is that in order to develop a model appropriate to one of the temporal bands we must find ways to simulate appropriately its interactions with the other bands, it being immediately evident that we cannot hope to develop any model that individually spans the entire range of temporal variation in the Earth System. We have evidently, a hierarchy of scales in which the more slowly evolving processes may be considered fixed relative to intermediate scales; the more rapidly evolving processes cannot be resolved explicitly but must be treated with statistical or parametric approaches. With this observation in mind, we can construct a diagram (Fig. 1.2) of a generic model of one or more Earth System components within a spectral band.

This resolution of spectral bands is perhaps most familiar in atmospheric models. For prediction on scales of 24 hours, we can take the external energy fluxes as fixed, but for prediction over intervals of ten days we must include evolving

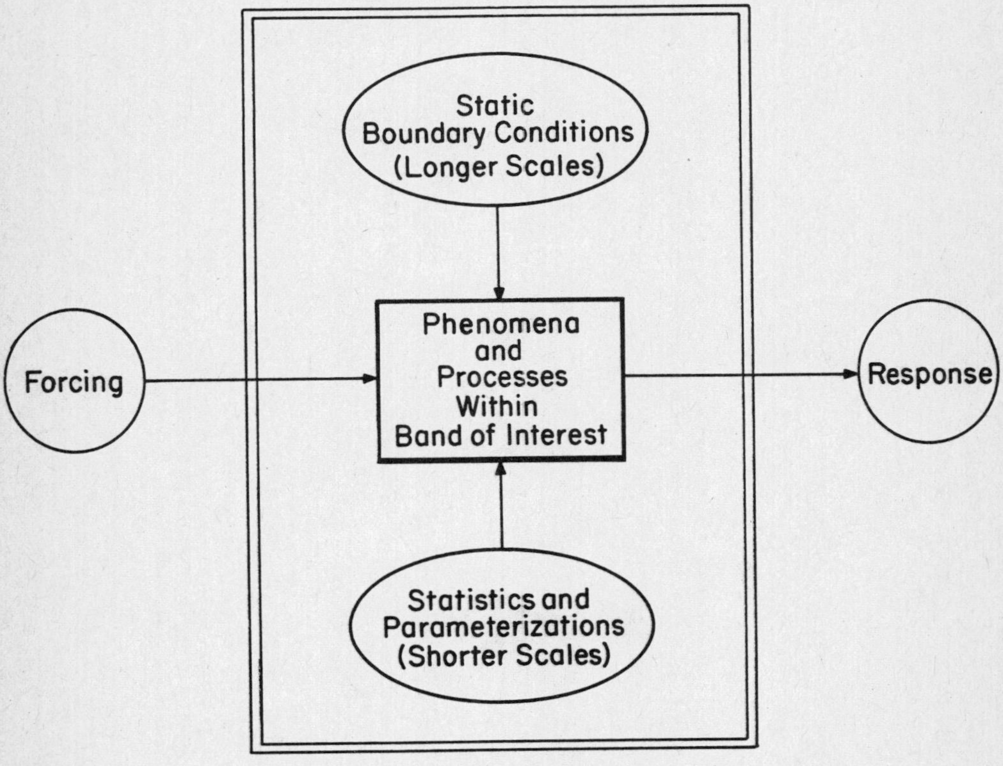

Fig. 1.2 Elements of a model of flow within the Earth System.

boundary heat exchanges. For climate models, the orbital variations of the latitudinal distribution of solar heating become relevant. For models of turbulent processes, the flows in the atmosphere whose shears drive the smaller-scale flows can themselves be taken to be invariant.

These considerations illustrate the fundamental conflict in modeling: we shall have to compromise between accuracy and simplicity. Accuracy requires including the interactions between the various time scales and the various systems; simplicity requires that they be neglected or parameterized in order that we have tractable models. Much of the effort in modeling is devoted to resolving this conflict.

Models are conceptual, analytical, or numerical structures that we use to study scientific questions. For the Earth System and for its components, the scientific issues include determining how equilibrium states are controlled by external conditions, how effects are related to causes, how instabilities are created and released, and the extent to which prediction is possible.

The goals of Earth System modeling are to formulate these questions in sufficiently precise terms that they can be attacked rigorously and to develop the models that will allow us to examine them with confidence. The motivation for modeling, then, is to determine how our world works and what its future might be.

An evident impediment to the development of successful Earth System models is the diversity of the modeling capabilities of the several disciplines involved. The models of geophysical fluid dynamics provide examples of subsystem models that must be linked to create an Earth System model.

1.1.2 Motivations for modeling in geophysical fluid dynamics. The atmospheric and oceanic sciences are unique among the Earth Sciences in having available theoretically derived systems of equations describing the evolution of state variables. Thus the motivations and challenges in modeling are quite different from those that prevail in the disciplines in which much of the effort is still aimed at developing or discovering suitable quantitative representations of the processes of interest.

The Navier-Stokes equations, the First Law of Thermodynamics, the equations of mass conservation for air and water or for water and salt, and the equation of state provide a basic mathematical model whose behavior emulates that of the atmosphere or ocean. The discipline that studies the foundations and implications of this system applied to rotating domains is known as geophysical fluid dynamics; it emphasizes the larger-scale flows in the Earth System, but it is necessarily concerned with smaller-scale and turbulent phenomena as well.

Since a basic and reliable mathematical model is already available, the modeling effort in geophysical fluid dynamics concentrates on developing appropriate derivative or approximate forms of equations and using them to establish results, to perform simulations that will enhance our understanding of the evolution of flows, or to enable predictions to be made.

The examination of fluid flows suggests that the significant scientific questions can be collected into groups that concern:

- Regime selection
- Maintenance of balances
- Prediction

Resolving the questions associated with each of these topics is the motivation for modeling in hydrodynamics.

Fluid flows, being nonlinear in nature, may exhibit quite different regimes of response to varying intensities of the forcing that drives them. In many cases, the transition from one regime to another occurs in response to infinitesimal variation in a controlling parameter.

An early but still definitive example is the transition from laminar to turbulent flow in a pipe that occurs as the dimensionless Reynolds number exceeds a critical value. With scaling of the equations of motion to make them dimensionless, the Reynolds number appears as the ratio of the inertial (or nonlinear) forces to viscous forces and thus indicates the physical phenomenology involved in the transition.

The behavior of fluids heated from below and thus rendered convectively unstable has long been of interest and continues to provide unresolved challenges. Figure 1.3, taken from Krishnamurti (1973), depicts the flow regimes determined experimentally as the Rayleigh and Prandtl numbers of a convective flow are varied. The Rayleigh number is a ratio of the adverse temperature difference driving the flow to the viscous effects retarding it; the Prandtl number measures the relative

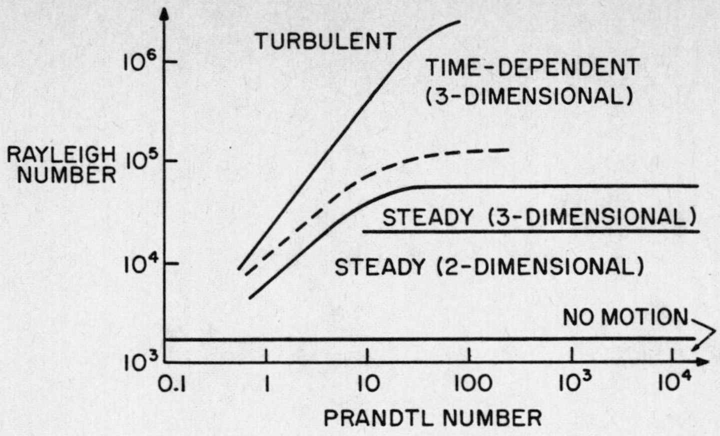

Fig. 1.3 Regimes of flow observed in Rayleigh-Bénard convection experiments (after Krishnamurti, 1973).

efficiency of the dissipation of momentum to that of heat. In general, heat is transferred conductively until convection appears at a critical value of the Rayleigh number. The initially steady, cellular convection then becomes temporally varying as the forcing is further increased, exhibiting increasingly complex periodic flow until the transition to turbulence occurs. We might summarize these observations by saying that the fluid exhibits motionless, steady, periodic, multiply periodic, and turbulent behavior as the forcing is increased -- there are four major changes in regime.

The response diagram for the flow of a liquid confined to a rotating annulus that is heated differentially on the vertical walls provides another demonstration of the complexity of fluid flow. Figure 1.4 (Fowlis and Hide, 1965) shows that at small rotation and heating rates, the flow is a symmetric convective overturning. As the rotation or heating rate is increased, the flow becomes asymmetric, with waves reminiscent of those in the midlatitude atmosphere becoming responsible for quasi-horizontal heat transport. At large heating or rotation rates, the response becomes an intense symmetric circulation.

These examples reveal two characteristics of fluid flow. It generally becomes more complicated as the forcing increases -- a situation we might describe quantitatively by saying that the energy is distributed over wider wavenumber bands.

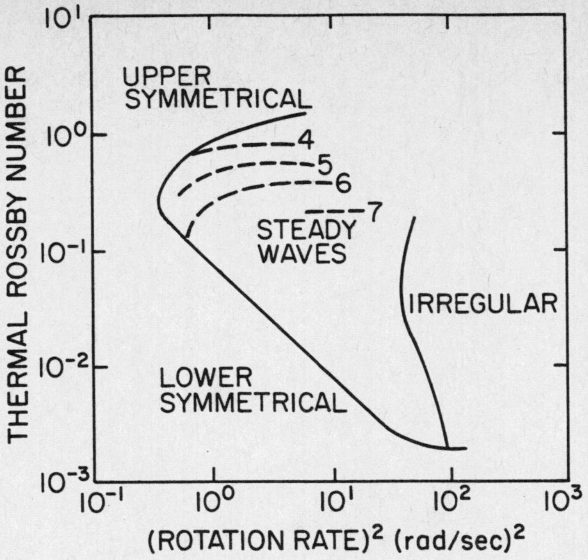

Fig. 1.4 Regimes of flow observed in horizontally heated rotating annulus experiments (after Fowlis and Hide, 1965).

Concomitantly, it becomes more difficult to make accurate predictions of the temporal evolution of the flow within a specific response regime.

In fluid flows, the energy supplied or released by the forcing is transported and converted by the flow into various forms until eventually it is effectively lost through the action of the dissipative forces. Thus the individual regimes have associated with them specific balances or evolutionary equilibria of energy conversion processes; one of the motivations of modeling is to understand how these balances are maintained and how they differ between flow regimes. The determination of which balances of forces or which energy conversion processes dominate within a regime is the essential step in developing reduced or simplified systems of equations appropriate to the various regimes (e.g. Chapter 15 in Dutton, 1986).

Although simulation of flow properties, either analytically or numerically, is an essential component of both theoretical and practical studies throughout fluid dynamics, the operational prediction of future states given an initial state is still confined to meteorology and is motivated by a variety of sociological and economic factors. The reduction of the systems of equations to approximate and simplified forms appropriate to specific atmospheric regimes has been an essential component in the development of successful prediction techniques. The present demands for accurate atmospheric predictions and the anticipated demands for accurate simulation of oceanic phenomena augment the intellectual challenges of predicting fluid flows with a sense of urgency.

1.1.3 Modeling issues in geophysical fluid dynamics. Atmospheric and oceanic flows present, themselves, a vast range of scales in both time and space. In the atmosphere, the dominant energy containing structures are of sizes that may be scaled with the radius of the Earth. The dissipation at the end of the turbulent spectral tail occurs on scales of millimeters or less. Thus the ratio of largest to smallest spatial scales is of the order of 10^{10}; temporal variations appear in the range from seasons to fractions of seconds, giving a ratio of largest to smallest scales of at least 10^8.

The existence of these vast ranges has led to the essential modeling strategy of separating the flows by spectral band and invoking the scheme presented above of isolating a range of interest by treating larger scales as steady and parameterizing the effects of the smaller scales. While this strategy allows us to cope with certain problems, it creates others that cannot be circumvented. The application of the strategy is also dependent to some degree on the flow regime of interest.

Thus models of the transition from conductive to steady cellular flow can be effected by resolving only the small number of spectral components that dominate the steady flow and neglecting the rest. Flows that contain a strong turbulent component, however far removed spectrally from the energy-containing features, require that the effects of that turbulence in creating local instabilities and in dissipating energy be included. Presently available computer resources do not permit numerical models to operate across the required spectral ranges and, even if they did, the inherent and unavoidable difficulties of a wide range of time scales that would appear make direct modeling impossible. Thus the modeler is faced with the necessity of departing from the direct application of the equations of motion and creating new models that summarize the effects of turbulence in interactions with the spectral bands of interest. Closing the resulting systems of equations necessitates expressing the effects of the turbulence as a function of the explicit variables of the model, despite the fact that there is no demonstration that such a representation is universally valid.

The fact that processes at small scales can interact with larger-scale processes to modify the evolution of the flow is a consequence of the inherent nonlinearity of the flow. In essence, all phenomena in the flow affect all other phenomena to some degree, regardless of spectral band. There are two consequences. The first is that the effects of the small scales must be treated statistically, since they cannot be resolved explicitly. The second is that the unavoidable errors in initial conditions render deterministic prediction of flow structure possible only over temporal ranges short enough that interactions with small-scale structures do not accumulate to effect large-scale changes.

The strategy of isolation by spectral band has received new emphasis in recent years with the increasing interest in spectral models of fluid flow. In such models, the variable fields are expanded in Fourier representations, and the equations of motion are used to obtain a system of equations governing the evolution of the Fourier coefficients. Upon truncation of the Fourier representation to a finite number of terms, the evolution of the flow is represented by the changing values of the Fourier coefficients. When ordered, they become components of a vector in a phase space whose dimension is determined by the truncation and thus the flow evolution corresponds to motion of a point in the phase space.

The predictability question may now be phrased relative to the divergence of the images in phase space of two points that were neighbors initially. Because of nonlinearity, the images of the initial points will separate eventually in the general case, and hence the corresponding patterns in physical space will be quite different. Prediction in the usual sense is thus impossible.

Study of the phase space behavior of fluid dynamical models reveals, however, that the images of all initial conditions are asymptotically confined to structures of smaller dimension than the phase space itself. These structures are known as strange attractors; attractors because all initial points are attracted to them, strange because of their complicated and challenging properties.

The motivations for modeling and the issues that have appeared lead us to an explicit program for geophysical fluid dynamical modeling. It has two components:

- Develop a hierarchical series of models that will correctly resolve the phenomenological sequence involved in the transition from simple to turbulent flows as the forcing rate is increased.
- Develop mathematical methods that will characterize the topology and the topological dynamics of the strange attractors of fluid flows, thereby leading to new concepts of modeling and predictability in geophysical fluid dynamics.

Current efforts in these directions are proceeding in most cases with spectral models truncated to include rather limited numbers of coefficients. This approach raises the crucial question of determining the topological relations between the solutions of the spectral models as the number of coefficients increases and the relations between the topologies of such solutions and those of the original initial value problem based on the partial differential system.

This monograph is concerned with the mathematical and philosophical issues that arise in attempting to proceed along the path indicated above. From the mathematical viewpoint, we are concerned with efficacious methods for converting questions about partial differential equations into questions about topological structures and their evolution and then finding ways to answer those questions despite the inherent nonlinearities we encounter.

To set the stage for the discussion of the mathematical issues and methods in the chapters that follow, we turn first in Section 1.2 to a characterization of models and their purposes, and then in Section 1.3 to a development of some principles for constructing effective models.

From the philosophical viewpoint, we are concerned with the process of modeling. In attempting to formalize some of its main characteristics, we are led in Chapter 17 to metamodeling considerations in which we contemplate our own efforts at modeling.

1.2 Models: Types and Purposes

Modeling is the crucial element in scientific endeavor because it is the process by which we pass from observation to prediction. In constructing models, we attempt to produce replicas of our environment in forms that enhance understanding and foster quantitative inference. With models we can simulate physical processes and perform experiments that offer insight into the evolution of the physical world. Models may then provide a rational basis for making decisions.

Because of the importance of models in science, it is worthwhile to examine them from an abstract viewpoint, to attempt to isolate the essential components of the modeling process. We begin with a definition, and then examine the purposes of models and the various forms in which they appear.

1.2.1 Definition of a model. In modeling, we seek to create a replica of the prototype object or process that is more manageable intellectually than the original. In doing so, we seek economy of representation while maintaining adequate complexity. Thus the essence of modeling is to strip away the nonessential elements, a procedure that usually involves separation of processes by both temporal and spatial scale. Interactions with physical or logical neighbors may be simplified or eliminated. Obviously, such simplifications would depend strongly on the goals implicit in the motivation of the model.

We focus the discussion by offering a formal definition:

> A model is a reduced and parsimonious representation of a physical, chemical, or biological system in an abstract mathematical, numerical, or experimental form.

This definition emphasizes the process of reduction and simplification -- the retention of only essential elements -- that is the key to modeling. It also mirrors the phases of science discussed in Section 1.1, suggesting that observation must be followed by selection and synthesis, culminating in the formulation of the relevant properties in a mathematical or abstract form that can be used as the basis for analytical solutions or numerical algorithms suitable for computer simulation.

1.2.2 Purposes of models. Modeling is such an integral part of scientific investigation that the motivations for constructing models are not often stated explicitly. Models have a number of purposes and functions:

1. Organize and document knowledge

   Models are usually the most effective way of organizing and integrating knowledge about a phenomenon or a process. Thus the Norwegian cyclone model encapsulates the essence of the structure of the midlatitude cyclone. The models of spectral ranges (such as the -5/3 inertial subrange in turbulence) summarize the consequences of diverse processes. And of course, the equations of motion are the ultimate model of fluid motion, permitting us to simulate any aspect of the flow if we can but use them effectively.

2. Reveal links between cause and effect

Models allow us to solve direct problems of determining what effects result from specified causes and help us to understand indirect problems of determining what causes have produced the effects we observe. In some cases these inferences are made from structural models, such as the cyclone model, and in other cases from models, such as the equations of motion, that are explicit statements of the relations between cause and effect based on rates of change induced by present structure and pattern.

3. Test understanding: reveal issues for research and observation

The process of modeling involves both construction and verification, for a model untested in independent and varied circumstances is but a speculation about reality. Thus the process of verification of a model often reveals lacunae in knowledge, oversights in observations, and blunders in interpretation. In eliminating error in a model, we increase our understanding. The interactive process of model improvement and verification reveals the issues that must be attacked by observation and additional research.

4. Predict changes in structure as forcing or essential parameters vary

Nonlinear systems, such as atmospheric or oceanic flows, often exhibit dramatically different responses as external conditions are varied. Usually, these changes in structure occur as critical values of essential parameters are exceeded. Thus an important purpose of a mathematical or numerical model of a system is to mirror and predict these crucial changes in response regimes and to provide understanding of the physical imperatives that control the transitions.

5. Provide forecasts of evolutionary behavior

Attempting to know the future is a human compulsion often well-served by models. Many of the predictive models we use are intuitively perceived relations between cause and effect, as in subjective methods of predicting weather from sky conditions or in the statements of most likely outcome used in medicine or in the social sciences. Others are formal and mathematical forms converted to numerical form in order to obtain solutions to initial value problems with computers, as in the complex numerical weather prediction endeavors now extant -- some of them involving a million lines of computer code.

6. Test modeling strategies

Finally, the development and verification of specific models allows us to ascertain whether our modeling strategy is adequate to the task at hand. The results obtained with preliminary or trial versions of models indicate whether we are proceeding in the right direction. They may tell us whether we have identified the crucial issues and whether our plan for resolving them is likely to succeed.

Models, then, are aids to thinking. They permit our minds to analyze and understand complex parts of the environment by reducing the overwhelming detail and variety to comprehensive structures or forms. Our perception of the world around us is gained through models; we cope with the enormity of it all by reducing it to models, be they diagrams, equations, or computer code. Models, we might say, are the key to knowledge and the anchor of sanity.

1.2.3 Types of models. Models appear in various forms, but can be categorized in general by the primary purpose they serve and the degree of sophistication inherent in their formulation.

1. Organizational models

Observations of structure are often reduced by abstraction and summarized in composite form as organizational models. These models abound in thinking about natural processes, and often are expressed as drawings. The Norwegian cyclone and frontal pattern model is again a good example, as are the sketches of the circulation system in a leaf, the motions of crustal convection and plate tectonics, and the model of a model shown in Fig. 1.5.

2. Kinematical models

In the language of physics, kinematics is concerned with geometrical relations that are valid in all cases, independent of the forces that are applied. Extending the terminology, we refer to kinematical models as those that summarize geometrical or analytical invariants in the environment. The

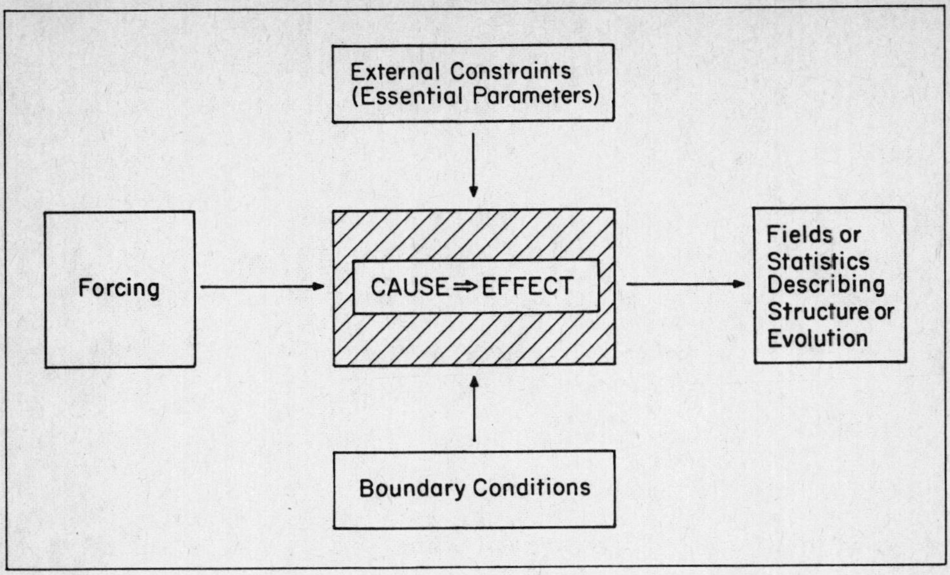

Fig. 1.5 An organizational model representing a simulation model.

equation of mass conservation in fluid dynamics is an example of such a model, as is the equivalent formulation in other fields of models in which fluxes, sources, and sinks must balance. Kinematical models often provide a pathway to determining the state variables and relations among them that are necessary to formulate more sophisticated models.

3. Dynamical models

Continuing the analogy with physics, we refer to dynamical models as those that specify which patterns of evolution will be followed in response to the forcing. The classical dynamical model, of course, is Newton's statement that acceleration equals specific force. Dynamical models usually appear as differential equations, but other formulations, specifically variational forms, are possible.

Dynamical models have two important characteristics. The first is that the state variables of the system must be known in order to formulate an explicit dynamical model. In some fields the state variables are well-known and can be derived from first principles. In others, especially in biology, it is not at all clear what the state variables describing macrostates should be, even though the molecular processes might be well understood.

The second is that dynamical models allow us to convert observed patterns into understanding or prediction of processes. This conversion of pattern to process is an essential one: our observations are almost always of patterns of the state variables, be they patterns evident in satellite imagery or inferred from analysis of point observations. Our interest, however, centers on the rates and intensities of processes; dynamical models allow us to examine processes given the patterns that they produce.

Because of their relation to processes, the appropriate state variables for a model may be scale-dependent. In atmospheric science we can produce effective large-scale models with the classical state variables, but encounter difficulties with proper representation of turbulent processes. In biology we comprehend molecular structure and process, but do not yet know how to represent processes on the scale of a forest stand.

Dynamical models take different forms depending on the purpose they are intended to serve. Among the possibilities are:

- Predictive Models -- designed to make predictions of future events from knowledge of present conditions. These models are usually based on sound dynamical principles but are structured with the sole aim of producing useful and accurate predictions over a specific temporal range.
- Representational Models -- designed to simulate the evolution of a system of interest. Accuracy of representation is important in these models, but the necessary concentration on detail that renders them accurate may cloud the understanding of the interactions of processes that might be gleaned from them. An important function of these simulation models is that they allow us to perform experiments through simulation of systems whose behavior we cannot, or dare not, modify.
- Abstract Models -- designed to contribute to knowledge of structure and balances through concentration on essential

elements and the elimination of as many degrees of freedom as possible. These models in fluid dynamics are often cast in spectral form and are now used in studies of regime selection and stability. Abstract models, when successful, enhance understanding of the main interactions in somewhat restricted settings even though the details necessary for a complete picture of a broad range of phenomena may be neglected.

1.2.4 Experimental models. An obviously attractive way to study a natural system that is daunting in its original scales is to create a smaller version that can be manipulated in a laboratory. The success of the attempt usually depends on how well the geometrical and dynamical relationships in the original can be reproduced in the laboratory version through appropriate scaling. Even though truly equivalent models can be obtained only rarely on smaller scales, the behavior of roughly equivalent systems can be most revealing. Observational results from experimental models often suggest theoretical approaches or conclusions that can be verified for the natural system through mathematical or numerical approaches.

This brief analysis of the purposes and types of models reveals the breadth and complexity of the modeling endeavor. Such a categorization may be helpful in determining the goals and objectives we have in mind in developing or studying a particular model. Most importantly, it is clear that different models are appropriate to different tasks. There are different and equally valid ways of looking at the physical world around us. We learn by comparing and contrasting a variety of views and perceptions, including those offered by different models.

1.3 Principles for Constructing Effective Models

Models, as devices for documenting knowledge and simulating the realities of the physical world, must be developed from the material at hand, be it observations or equations. In all cases, as pointed out in the definition given in Section 1.2, the aim is to simplify the actual complexity while retaining effectiveness.

There are two basic approaches to developing models and they proceed in quite different directions. In the top-down design of a model, we determine overall structure as a broad outline based on assessment of goals and specifications -- we proceed from the general to the specific. The required components are identified and the linkages with other components determined. No attention is given, at this stage, to how the submodels are to be specified or implemented. The model in effect is represented as a collection of modular elements that would interact by exchanging information along specified channels. The modularity is important, for each of the components can be created and tested subsequently without disturbing the overall structure of the model.

In the bottom-up approach, the initial efforts are directed toward obtaining correct simulations of the components that will eventually be combined. Thus an interactive atmosphere and ocean model might be started by producing appropriate but independent models of the atmospheric and oceanic circulations. Because of its emphasis on phenomenology and process, science usually proceeds from specific to general in creating models of natural phenomena. There are obvious advantages to ensuring that the component parts are adequately understood and represented before broadening the scope of the model, but there are also dangers that the modules do not perform the functions required in a broader setting.

Perhaps the most effective way to proceed is to combine the two approaches. There is little point in attacking a modeling problem unless there is some knowledge of the components and a top-down approach, however intellectually sound it may appear, may distort reality and may omit components or interactions that are in fact essential. In contrast, an approach that works upward from the most detailed level is likely to lack the sense of direction imposed by a broader view or motivation and may be deflected in undesirable directions.

Modeling, regardless of the approach, is always a process of compromise between the tractability of simplicity and the complexity of reality. Still, there are some guidelines that help to ensure that a model is effective.

A model should:

1. <u>Possess adequate complexity</u>

   The level of complexity in a model must be adequate for the intended purpose. Although extremely simple models are appealing, they are not effective or useful if they oversimplify. The level of complexity in a model must be determined by the context and perhaps by experimentation. It is not useful to study fluid states without accounting for dissipation and it is not very revealing to study the long-term statistics of a turbulent fluid isolated from external forcing. Nevertheless, there are phenomena and there are transitions in structure that apparently can be represented with reasonable veracity by quite simple models.

2. Possess conservation properties

Any model, however reduced, should exhibit appropriate versions of the classical physical conservation properties relating to mass and energy and other quantities such as momentum or vorticity in hydrodynamic models.

3. Emphasize the energy-containing features

Although an important consequence of nonlinearity is the interaction between features of quite different spatial scales, a model should normally emphasize the energy-containing features in the range of spatial scales to which it applies. Since the phenomenology is dominated by these scales, they usually are of central interest and the relevant processes represented in the model are viewed relative to them.

4. Maximize the information per component or degree of freedom

It is important to realize that not all representations of a phenomenon with a model that possesses N components or degrees of freedom are equally effective. Hence it follows that we should strive to have models whose components conform to the physical situation and thus maximize information.

5. Represent situations that occur with finite probability

There is a danger in developing simple models that we specify a configuration that is impossible or occurs only with zero probability. We do not want our model of a falling coin to allow only for the case in which it lands on its edge. Thus models in which the viscosity is zero represent impossible configurations and a model of convection that only permits vertical temperature gradients represents an improbable situation. It is, in other words, advisable to allow for the small but real effects we find in the physical world.

6. Preserve overall structure under sufficiently small perturbations

Except for models that are rigorously derived from first principles, we cannot expect to determine from observational data the precise structure of a model or the exact values of the constants within it. Hence models should be designed to accommodate this uncertainty by being insensitive to perturbations in the form of the model. We should doubt the applicability of a model in which the qualitative behavior of solutions depends on the exact values of external parameters such as the acceleration of gravity or internal parameters such as the coefficient of viscosity. This modeling requirement corresponds to the mathematical property of structural stability.

7. Preserve structure under extension to more complex forms

Since models are a reduction of reality, it is likely that we shall want to extend them to a broader range of applicability once a simpler case is understood. Thus the model should be constructed so that it can be extended to more complex forms or to include more degrees of freedom. This notion suggests that a simple model should be a subset of a larger model that is applicable to a reduced range of conditions.

This brief list of desirable qualities of a model may help to guide our efforts, but it clearly does not tell us how to construct effective models. In some ways that is necessarily a cycle of trial, verification, and revision. Nevertheless, these desirable qualities of models do offer some strategic goals.

CHAPTER 2

A SIMPLE NONLINEAR MODEL OF CONVECTION

HAMPTON N. SHIRER

In Chapter 1 we noted that there are seven modeling principles for guiding the development of an effective low-order model of a physical system. The first four of these principles, which we review below, may be regarded as the fundamental ones, because they describe requirements that all models should meet, while the other three may be regarded as intermediate ones because they describe how to ensure that the model results are not sensitive to inclusion of more degrees of freedom. In an orderly development of a hierarchy of models, we first use the four fundamental principles to direct the creation of the simplest possible model, and then we use the other three principles to guide the specification of appropriate larger models. However, we must always remember that the ultimate test of the adequacy of a model is accomplished by comparing its results with observations or by comparing the properties of its solutions with those of the complete system.

One of the physical systems we study throughout this monograph is classical Rayleigh-Bénard convection. The smallest effective model of its time-dependent states is the three-component Lorenz (1963) model. In this chapter, we verify this statement by examining the Lorenz model in the light of the four fundamental principles. These principles are that a model of a hydrodynamic flow should

- possess adequate complexity;
- obey suitable conservation properties, or preserve relevant energetics;
- emphasize the dominant, or energy-containing, features;
- represent the maximum information per component.

Extensions of the Lorenz model that are necessary in order to capture the additional important nonlinear characteristics of convection are discussed in Chapters 8 and 9.

A fascinating result we find as we proceed through this monograph is that certain forms recur in the solutions to many different models. This leads to the conclusion that these forms may be canonical for nonlinear hydrodynamic systems. As the Lorenz model of Rayleigh-Bénard convection contains nonlinear stationary solutions that exhibit one of these typical forms, the trident, this model serves as a useful one for illustrating the above modeling principles. During the discussion, we define some of the terminology and describe the point of view that we adopt in analyzing nonlinear problems. Along the way, we pose some questions that we address in later chapters.

2.1 Essential Features of Convection

We begin by reviewing some properties of shallow convective flows revealed by observations and theoretical deductions. In Section 2.2 we base the development of the Lorenz model on this summary.

2.1.1 Observed characteristics. When a fluid such as water is heated uniformly from below and cooled uniformly from above, then heat is transported vertically by conduction. At first there is no motion apparent in the fluid and the temperature varies linearly with height from the temperature T_{oo} at the bottom to the temperature T_1 at the top; the difference between the two temperatures is given by $\Delta_z T = (T_{oo} - T_1)$. However, when the value of $\Delta_z T$ is increased above a critical value $(\Delta_z T)_c$, two-dimensional motion having a single dominant wavelength L in the horizontal and a single wavelength $2z_T$ in the vertical develops (Fig. 2.1a). When the value of $\Delta_z T$ is expressed in a more universal form by means of a Rayleigh number Ra (defined in (2.28)), we find (as shown in Fig. 1.3) that motion appears when the value of Ra exceeds a corresponding value Ra_c that is independent of the Prandtl number P (defined in (2.29)) (Krishnamurti, 1970a,b). The intensity of this temporally steady circulation is proportional to $(Ra - Ra_c)^{1/2}$, a fact that can be deduced from an analysis of the equations of motion (Chandrasekhar, 1961). Finally, because the action of the convection is to transport warm fluid upward and cold fluid downward, a net warming in the upper half and a net cooling in the lower half of the domain is seen, as shown in Fig 2.1b. This net temperature deviation from the conductive profile does not vary horizontally and has a vertical wavelength of z_T. A successful low-order model must represent the above observed features.

2.1.2 The Boussinesq system. Some other important properties of convection can be determined from analysis of the partial differential equations that describe the convective flow. The appropriate set of approximate equations is obtained by neglecting certain terms in the complete set of the equations of motion. The approximations that lead to the equations (2.10)-(2.12), which are known as the

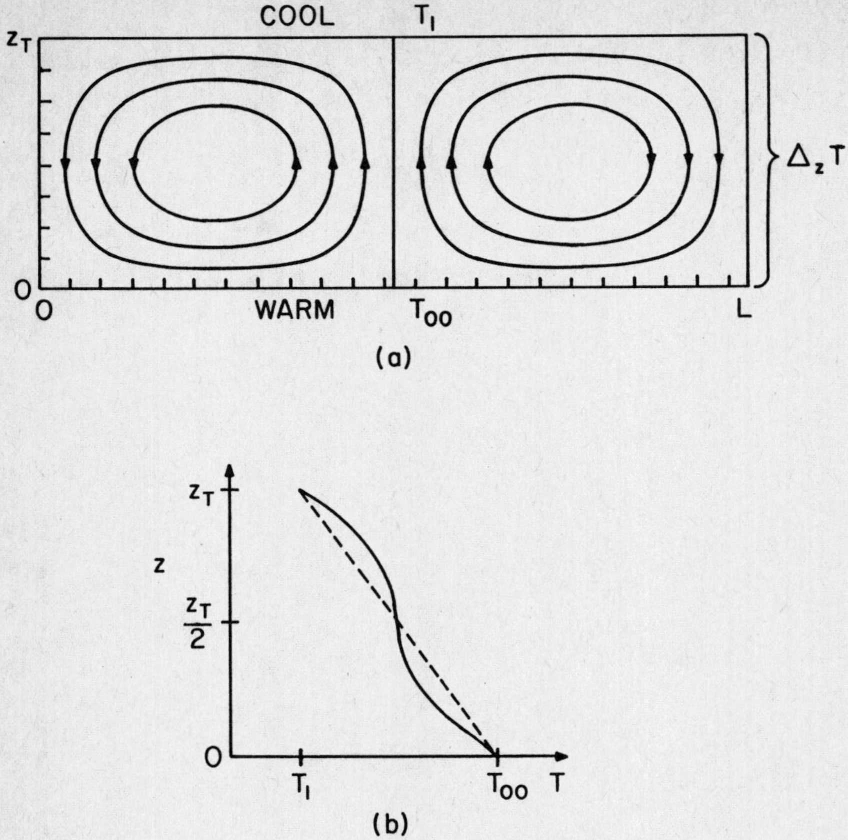

Fig. 2.1 Cross section of convection for small supercritical values of Ra (a) and net warming and cooling produced by convective transports (b). In (b) the dashed line is the conductive temperature profile (2.3) and the solid line is the profile produced by the convection.

shallow Boussinesq equations, are discussed thoroughly in Chapter 13 of Dutton (1976) and Chapter 15 of Dutton (1986). Here we briefly summarize the fundamental simplifications.

In the Boussinesq system, convection is regarded as a perturbation superimposed on a conductive basic state; however, we do not neglect a priori products of perturbations as in a linear analysis. The conductive state, denoted by a subscript o, is given by

$$\underset{\sim}{v}_o = 0 \quad , \tag{2.1}$$

$$\rho_o = \rho_{oo} \quad , \tag{2.2}$$

$$T_o(z) = T_{oo} - \Delta_z T\,(z/z_T) \quad , \tag{2.3}$$

$$p_o(z) = p_{oo} - \rho_{oo}\, g\, z \quad , \tag{2.4}$$

in which $|\Delta_z T|\,|z/z_T| \ll T_{oo}$. The two-dimensional convective state, denoted by primes, is given by

$$\underset{\sim}{v}'(x,z,t) = \underset{\sim}{v}(x,z,t) - \underset{\sim}{v}_o \quad , \tag{2.5}$$

$$\rho'(x,z,t) = \rho(x,z,t) - \rho_{oo} \quad , \tag{2.6}$$

$$T'(x,z,t) = T(x,z,t) - T_o(z) \quad , \tag{2.7}$$

$$p'(x,z,t) = p(x,z,t) - p_o(z) \quad . \tag{2.8}$$

The three primary approximations used to convert the equations of motion to the Boussinesq system are

1) Compression is negligible and so the continuity equation is replaced by $\nabla\cdot\underset{\sim}{v}' = 0$.
2) The equation of state has the form typical of liquids, which are incompressible fluids: that is, $\rho = \rho_{oo}[1 - (T - T_o)/T_{oo}]$ can be expressed in the normalized form $\rho'/\rho_{oo} = - T'/T_{oo}$.
3) The pressure gradient force can be linearized via

$$-\frac{1}{\rho}\nabla p - g\underset{\sim}{k} \cong -\frac{1}{\rho_{oo}}\left(1 - \frac{\rho'}{\rho_{oo}}\right)\left(\nabla p' + \frac{\partial p_o}{\partial z}\underset{\sim}{k}\right) - g\,\underset{\sim}{k}$$

$$\cong -\frac{1}{\rho_{oo}}\nabla p' + g\,\frac{T'}{T_{oo}}\,\underset{\sim}{k} \quad , \tag{2.9}$$

in which we have used $1/\rho = 1/[\rho_{oo}(1+\rho'/\rho_{oo})] \cong (1-\rho'/\rho_{oo})/\rho_{oo}$ and the above normalized form for the equation of state.

With these approximations introduced, the <u>two-dimensional Boussinesq system</u> is

$$\frac{\partial \underset{\sim}{v}'}{\partial t} + \underset{\sim}{v}'\cdot\nabla\underset{\sim}{v}' = -\frac{1}{\rho_{oo}}\nabla p' + g\,\frac{T'}{T_{oo}}\,\underset{\sim}{k} + \nu\nabla^2\underset{\sim}{v}' \quad , \tag{2.10}$$

$$\frac{\partial T'}{\partial t} + \underset{\sim}{v}'\cdot\nabla T' = \frac{\Delta_z T}{z_T} w' + \kappa\nabla^2 T' \quad , \tag{2.11}$$

$$\nabla\cdot\underset{\sim}{v}' = 0 \quad , \tag{2.12}$$

in which ν is either the molecular viscosity for fluids or the (constant) eddy viscosity for the atmosphere and κ is either the molecular or (constant) eddy thermometric conductivity.

Because the flow is two-dimensional, a convenient change of variables is found by noticing that the continuity equation (2.12) implies that the velocity components u' and w' can be determined from a stream function ψ via

$$u' = -\frac{\partial\psi}{\partial z} \quad , \tag{2.13}$$

$$w' = \frac{\partial\psi}{\partial x} \quad . \tag{2.14}$$

These definitions ensure that the fluid is nondivergent because

$$\nabla\cdot\underset{\sim}{v}' = \frac{\partial}{\partial x}\left(-\frac{\partial\psi}{\partial z}\right) + \frac{\partial}{\partial z}\left(\frac{\partial\psi}{\partial x}\right) = 0 \quad . \tag{2.15}$$

The pressure gradient term can be eliminated from the system when the equation of motion is converted into a vorticity equation. Upon defining

$$-\eta = \frac{\partial w'}{\partial x} - \frac{\partial u'}{\partial z} = \nabla^2\psi \quad , \tag{2.16}$$

we obtain

$$\frac{\partial}{\partial t}(\nabla^2\psi) + J(\psi,\nabla^2\psi) = \frac{g}{T_{oo}}\frac{\partial T'}{\partial x} + \nu\nabla^4\psi \quad , \tag{2.17}$$

$$\frac{\partial T'}{\partial t} + J(\psi,T') = \frac{\Delta_z T}{z_T}\frac{\partial\psi}{\partial x} + \kappa\nabla^2 T' \quad , \tag{2.18}$$

in which we have used $\nabla^4\psi = \nabla^2(\nabla^2\psi)$ and the Jacobian is

$$J(f,g) = \frac{\partial f}{\partial x}\frac{\partial g}{\partial z} - \frac{\partial f}{\partial z}\frac{\partial g}{\partial x} \quad . \tag{2.19}$$

The antisymmetric properties of J, in which $J(f,g) = -J(g,f)$, are powerful ones to exploit in any analysis of the properties of the solutions to (2.17)-(2.18).

2.1.3 Dimensionless forms. An advantageous next step is to convert the equations into dimensionless forms. This is not done in order to find small terms that can be neglected; that elimination has been carried out in the conversion of the original set of equations into (2.10)-(2.12). Instead, the variables are normalized in a way that produces a system having the fewest possible dimensionless parameters. The process of nondimensionalization is by no means unique, and the particular transformations that are used depend on the goals of the study. In this monograph we consider two different dimensionless forms of the Boussinesq equations--the one introduced by Shirer and Dutton (1979) and the one used by Lorenz (1963). The first one is more general because it may be used to form models representing flows having an arbitrary number of horizontal and vertical wavenumbers, while the second one is limited to cases for which only one horizontal wavenumber is considered. Producing dimensionless equations, however, does not eliminate important parameters from a system, although this process may hide them from view. Consequently, it is possible to miss some important behavior that depends upon these hidden parameters (see Chapter 7); thus, formulation of too elegant a system may lead an unwary investigator to incorrect conclusions. It is also possible that some essential parameters governing the transitions do not appear in any possible set of the dimensionless parameters. This phenomenon occurs because certain physical effects are not included in the original dimensional system. In this case, some mathematical techniques, discussed in Chapter 8, are needed to help locate the missing parameters.

In developing a suitable set of definitions for converting dimensional to dimensionless forms, we often choose as length scales the ones implied by the cyclic nature of the flow. For both the Shirer and Dutton (1979) and Lorenz (1963) systems, we convert our original domain $0 \leq x \leq L$, $0 \leq z \leq z_T$ to a dimensionless form $0 \leq x^* \leq 2\pi$, $0 \leq z^* \leq \pi$ by using the definitions

$$x = x^* L/(2\pi) \quad , \tag{2.20}$$

$$z = z^* z_T/\pi \quad . \tag{2.21}$$

Because the decay of a perturbation of the conductive solution is controlled by the energy loss owing to viscous and thermal dissipation, we usually choose a diffusive time scale. For the Shirer and Dutton or general form we put

$$t = t^* z_T L/(2\pi^2\kappa) \quad . \tag{2.22}$$

For the stream function, we use

$$\psi = \psi^*\kappa \quad , \tag{2.23}$$

and for the thermal perturbation, we set

$$T = T^*\nu\kappa T_{oo}\,\pi^3/(g\, z_T^3) \quad . \tag{2.24}$$

Substitution of (2.20)-(2.24) into (2.17)-(2.18) leads to the general dimensionless system

$$\frac{\partial}{\partial t^*}(\tilde{\nabla}^2\psi^*) + J(\psi^*,\tilde{\nabla}^2\psi^*) - P\frac{\partial T^*}{\partial x^*} - \frac{P}{a}\tilde{\nabla}^4\psi^* = 0 \quad , \tag{2.25}$$

$$\frac{\partial T^*}{\partial t^*} + J(\psi^*,T^*) - Ra\frac{\partial \psi^*}{\partial x^*} - \frac{1}{a}\tilde{\nabla}^2 T^* = 0 \quad , \tag{2.26}$$

in which

$$\tilde{\nabla}^2(\ \ ) = a^2\frac{\partial^2}{\partial x^{*2}}(\ \ ) + \frac{\partial^2}{\partial z^{*2}}(\ \ ) \quad , \tag{2.27}$$

and $\tilde{\nabla}^4\psi^* = \tilde{\nabla}^2(\tilde{\nabla}^2\psi^*)$; with the scaling (2.20)-(2.21), we note that $J(f^*,g^*)$ is obtained from (2.19) by simply affixing asterisks to the variables f,g,x, and z. In (2.25)-(2.26) we have introduced three dimensionless parameters: the Rayleigh number

$$Ra = \frac{g\Delta_z T\, z_T^3}{\nu\kappa T_{oo}\pi^4} \quad , \tag{2.28}$$

the Prandtl number

$$P = \nu/\kappa \quad , \tag{2.29}$$

and the domain aspect ratio

$$a = 2z_T/L \quad . \tag{2.30}$$

For the Lorenz form we use (2.20)-(2.21) to scale the spatial variables, but introduce the definitions

$$t = t^* \, z_T^2/[\pi^2\kappa(1+a^2)] \quad , \tag{2.31}$$

$$\psi = \psi^* \, (1+a^2)\kappa/a \quad , \tag{2.32}$$

$$T = T^* \, (1+a^2)^3\pi^3 T_{oo}\nu\kappa/(a^2 g \, z_T^3) \quad . \tag{2.33}$$

The domain aspect ratio a, which is often considered to be an important parameter of the problem because it gives the shape of the convective cell (Chapter 7), is incorporated into the dimensionless forms so that the variable a finally appears in only one term of the spectral system. Substitution of (2.20)-(2.21) and (2.31)-(2.33) into (2.17)-(2.18) yields the Lorenz system (Shirer and Wells, 1983, Chapter 3)

$$\frac{\partial}{\partial t^*}\tilde{\nabla}^2\psi^* + J(\psi^*,\tilde{\nabla}^2\psi^*) - P(1+a^2)\frac{\partial T^*}{\partial x^*} - \frac{P}{(1+a^2)}\tilde{\nabla}^4\psi^* = 0 \quad , \tag{2.34}$$

$$\frac{\partial T^*}{\partial t^*} + J(\psi^*,T^*) - r\frac{\partial \psi^*}{\partial x^*} - \frac{1}{(1+a^2)}\tilde{\nabla}^2 T^* = 0 \quad , \tag{2.35}$$

in which the normalized Rayleigh number r is

$$r = \frac{g\Delta_z T \, z_T^3 a^2}{T_{oo}\nu\kappa(1+a^2)^3\pi^4} \quad . \tag{2.36}$$

For there to exist unique solutions to either (2.25)-(2.26) or (2.34)-(2.35), we must introduce appropriate boundary conditions to create a well-posed initial/boundary value problem. Because (2.25) contains a fourth-order operator $\tilde{\nabla}^4(\;)$ and (2.26) contains a second-order operator $\tilde{\nabla}^2(\;)$, we must specify six conditions on the vertical boundaries and six on the horizontal ones. Typically we are guided by our knowledge of the physical setting. In this chapter we examine a flow that is confined to a box whose boundaries are rigid and stress-free. Because the heating is applied at only the top and bottom boundaries, we assume that these vertical boundaries are perfectly conducting and that the lateral boundaries are nonconducting. The appropriate boundary conditions are then:

lateral boundaries

$$\left.\begin{aligned} &\text{rigid:}\quad u^*(0,z^*) = u^*(2\pi,z^*) = 0 \\ &\text{stress-free:}\quad \frac{\partial w^*}{\partial x^*}(0,z^*) = \frac{\partial w^*}{\partial x^*}(2\pi,z^*) = 0 \\ &\text{nonconducting:}\quad \frac{\partial T^*}{\partial x^*}(0,z^*) = \frac{\partial T^*}{\partial x^*}(2\pi,z^*) = 0 \end{aligned}\right\}, \tag{2.37}$$

vertical boundaries

$$\left.\begin{aligned} &\text{rigid:}\quad w^*(x^*,0) = w^*(x^*,\pi) = 0 \\ &\text{stress-free:}\quad \frac{\partial u^*}{\partial z^*}(x^*,0) = \frac{\partial u^*}{\partial z^*}(x^*,\pi) = 0 \\ &\text{conducting:}\quad T^*(x^*,0) = T^*(x^*,\pi) = 0 \end{aligned}\right\}. \tag{2.38}$$

For application to the partial differential equations, we must express the boundary conditions on the velocity components in terms of the stream function ψ^*. Because $u^* = -\partial\psi^*/\partial z^*$ vanishes along the lateral boundaries and $w^* = \partial\psi^*/\partial x^*$ vanishes along the vertical boundaries, we conclude that ψ^* must be equal to a (possibly different) constant on each boundary. But because these constants must match at each corner, we discover that the value of ψ^* must be the same on each boundary. For convenience we set the constant to zero so that the rigid boundary conditions become

$$\psi^*(0,z^*) = \psi^*(2\pi,z^*) = \psi^*(x^*,0) = \psi^*(x^*,\pi) = 0 \quad . \tag{2.39}$$

A similar argument shows that the stress-free boundary conditions can be written as

$$\tilde{\nabla}^2\psi^*(0,z^*) = \tilde{\nabla}^2\psi^*(2\pi,z^*) = \tilde{\nabla}^2\psi^*(x^*,0) = \tilde{\nabla}^2\psi^*(x^*,\pi) = 0 \quad . \tag{2.40}$$

Finally, the thermal boundary conditions are

$$\frac{\partial T^*}{\partial x^*}(0,z^*) = \frac{\partial T^*}{\partial x^*}(2\pi,z^*) = T^*(x^*,0) = T^*(x^*,\pi) = 0 \quad . \tag{2.41}$$

A different set of boundary conditions is needed if we consider flows whose circulation patterns propagate horizontally and so are not confined to the box (see Chapters 11 and 12). We still view the flow as occurring in a box, but now fluid can enter the box through one lateral boundary and leave through another. In this case we replace the lateral boundary conditions (2.37) with cyclically continuous ones; as before we need six conditions, and some natural ones are

$$\left.\begin{aligned}
&u^*(0,z^*) = u^*(2\pi,z^*) = -\frac{\partial\psi^*}{\partial z^*}(0,z^*) = -\frac{\partial\psi^*}{\partial z^*}(2\pi,z^*) \\
&w^*(0,z^*) = w^*(2\pi,z^*) = \frac{\partial\psi^*}{\partial x^*}(0,z^*) = \frac{\partial\psi^*}{\partial x^*}(2\pi,z^*) \\
&\frac{\partial u^*}{\partial x^*}(0,z^*) = \frac{\partial u^*}{\partial x^*}(2\pi,z^*) = -\frac{\partial^2\psi^*}{\partial x^*\partial z^*}(0,z^*) = -\frac{\partial^2\psi^*}{\partial x^*\partial z^*}(2\pi,z^*) \\
&\frac{\partial w^*}{\partial x^*}(0,z^*) = \frac{\partial w^*}{\partial x^*}(2\pi,z^*) = \frac{\partial^2\psi^*}{\partial x^{*2}}(0,z^*) = -\frac{\partial^2\psi^*}{\partial x^{*2}}(2\pi,z^*) \\
&T^*(0,z^*) = T^*(2\pi,z^*) \\
&\frac{\partial T^*}{\partial x^*}(0,z^*) = \frac{\partial T^*}{\partial x^*}(2\pi,z^*)
\end{aligned}\right\} \quad . \tag{2.42}$$

The vertical boundary conditions are

$$\psi^*(x^*,0) = \psi^*(x^*,\pi) = \tilde{\nabla}^2\psi^*(x^*,0) = \tilde{\nabla}^2\psi^*(x^*,\pi) = 0 \quad , \tag{2.43}$$

and

$$T^*(x^*,0) = T^*(x^*,\pi) = 0 \quad . \tag{2.44}$$

In the literature, the misleading label for the boundary condition (2.43) is simply "free" (e.g. Chandrasekhar, 1961), which is not to be confused with the meteorological use of the term "free" to refer to bounding material surfaces on which $\omega = dp/dt = 0$.

2.1.4 Deduced properties. One of the properties we expect the low-order model to have is that the dominant sources and sinks of energy are represented accurately. Accordingly, it is useful to determine from the partial differential equations (2.25)-(2.26) or (2.34)-(2.35) the equation governing the rate of change of energy. We normally require that the energy be nonnegative, and this is most conveniently accomplished if it is defined using quadratic forms. Positive constants can be introduced into the definitions if they lead to simplifications of the expressions.

If we recall with the aid of (2.13)-(2.14) and

$$\tilde{\nabla} = \underset{\sim}{i}a \frac{\partial}{\partial x^*} + \underset{\sim}{k} \frac{\partial}{\partial z^*} \quad , \tag{2.45}$$

that $|\underset{\sim}{v}^*|^2 = |\tilde{\nabla}\psi^*|^2$, then the appropriate definitions for kinetic energy KE and available potential energy AE are

$$KE = \frac{1}{2} \int_0^{2\pi}\int_0^{\pi} |\tilde{\nabla}\psi^*|^2 \, dz^*dx^* \quad , \tag{2.46}$$

and

$$AE = \frac{1}{2} \int_0^{2\pi}\int_0^{\pi} PT^{*2} \, dz^*dx^* \quad . \tag{2.47}$$

We observe that, owing to the boundary conditions (2.39)-(2.40), we have

$$\begin{aligned} \int_0^{2\pi}\int_0^{\pi} \psi^*J(\psi^*,\tilde{\nabla}^2\psi^*)dz^*dx^* &= \int_0^{2\pi}\int_0^{\pi}\Big[\frac{\partial}{\partial x^*}\Big(\frac{\psi^{*2}}{2}\frac{\partial}{\partial z^*}\tilde{\nabla}^2\psi^*\Big) - \psi^{*2}\frac{\partial^2}{\partial x^*\partial z^*}\tilde{\nabla}^2\psi^* \\ &\quad - \frac{\partial}{\partial z^*}\Big(\frac{\psi^{*2}}{2}\frac{\partial}{\partial x^*}\tilde{\nabla}^2\psi^*\Big) + \psi^{*2}\frac{\partial^2}{\partial x^*\partial z^*}\tilde{\nabla}^2\psi^*\Big]dz^*dx^* \\ &= \int_0^{\pi}\frac{\psi^{*2}}{2}\frac{\partial}{\partial z^*}\tilde{\nabla}^2\psi^* \, dz^*\Big|_0^{2\pi} - \int_0^{2\pi}\frac{\psi^{*2}}{2}\frac{\partial}{\partial x^*}\tilde{\nabla}^2\psi^* \, dx^*\Big|_0^{\pi} = 0 \quad , \end{aligned} \tag{2.48}$$

and by a similar argument that

$$\int_0^{2\pi}\int_0^{\pi} T^*J(\psi^*,T^*) \, dz^*dx^* = 0 \quad . \tag{2.49}$$

Thus the rate of change of total energy E = KE + AE is given by

$$\frac{\partial}{\partial t^*}(KE+AE) = GA - DI \quad , \tag{2.50}$$

in which the energy generation rate GA and the dissipation rate DI are defined by

$$GA = \int_0^{2\pi}\int_0^{\pi} (1+Ra)P\frac{\partial\psi^*}{\partial x^*}T^* \, dz^*dx^* \quad , \tag{2.51}$$

$$DI = \int_0^{2\pi}\int_0^{\pi} \frac{P}{a}\left(|\tilde{\nabla}^2\psi^*|^2 + |\tilde{\nabla}T^*|^2\right) dz^*dx^* \quad , \tag{2.52}$$

for the generalized system (2.25)-(2.26) and

$$GA = \int_0^{2\pi}\int_0^{\pi} (1+a^2+r)P \frac{\partial\psi^*}{\partial x^*} T^* \, dz^* dx^* \quad , \tag{2.53}$$

$$DI = \int_0^{2\pi}\int_0^{\pi} \frac{P}{(1+a^2)} (|\tilde{\nabla}^2\psi^*|^2 + |\tilde{\nabla}T^*|^2) \, dz^* dx^* \quad , \tag{2.54}$$

for the Lorenz system (2.34)-(2.35). We notice from (2.52) or (2.54) that the dissipation rate DI depends on the squared gradient of the temperature, and so we expect that DI would also depend on the squared gradient of the velocity components. Instead, we find that DI depends on the squared magnitude of the vorticity. However, it is easy to show using the dimensionless forms of (2.13)-(2.14) and $\tilde{\nabla}\cdot\underset{\sim}{v}^* = 0$ that $|\tilde{\nabla}^2\psi^*|^2 = |\tilde{\nabla}u^*|^2 + |\tilde{\nabla}w^*|^2$, and so DI actually has the expected form. The expressions for GA and DI are very similar in both (2.51)-(2.52) and (2.53)-(2.54), and both yield the same definitions in the dimensional variables. Because normally T^* and $w^* = \partial\psi^*/\partial x^*$ are positively correlated, we have $GA \geq 0$; it is evident from (2.52) or (2.54) that $DI \geq 0$ as well. Thus, the energy of the perturbation decays if $DI > GA$, and the energy increases if $GA > DI$. The transition between these two cases occurs when $GA = DI$, a condition necessary for a stationary, or time-independent, nonzero convective solution to exist (see Section 6.1).

We note from either (2.51)-(2.52) or (2.53)-(2.54) that the boundary between decay and growth is independent of P, a result having its origins in the judicious inclusion of P in the definition (2.47) for AE. Thus, the only way that GA could increase sufficiently in value that it exceeds the value of DI is for the magnitude of Ra to exceed some critical one Ra_c (or for r to exceed r_c). We conclude that Ra_c or r_c would be independent of P, and this is what is observed (Fig. 1.3). We expect then that perturbations of the conductive solution would damp when $Ra < Ra_c$ or $r < r_c$ and so the conductive solution would be stable. As $t \to \infty$ we expect that this solution would be observable, but because the rate of damping could be slow, we do not know how long we might have to wait before the magnitude of the perturbation would be small enough to be negligible. (If we have to wait too long, then the time scales built into the original Boussinesq equations might no longer be valid and the results of the model would be questionable). When $Ra > Ra_c$ or $r > r_c$, we expect

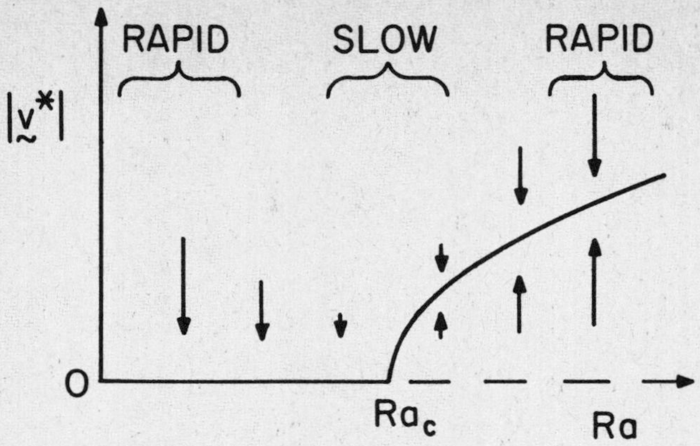

Fig. 2.2 Bifurcation diagram showing the magnitudes of the stationary solutions as functions of Ra. Stable solutions are denoted by solid lines, unstable ones by dashed lines.

that perturbations would amplify, and the conductive solution would be unstable, hence unobservable, at least as $t \to \infty$.

If we recall that the amplitude of the convective solution is proportional to $(Ra - Ra_c)^{1/2}$, then we can display the expected form of the solution on a bifurcation diagram (Fig. 2.2), in which the magnitudes of the time-independent solutions are displayed as functions of the Rayleigh number Ra. Solid lines denote stable solutions, dashed lines unstable ones. The lengths of the arrows indicate the expected temporal behavior of the perturbations of the conductive solution. We note that the stationary solution changes abruptly but smoothly at $Ra = Ra_c$; because the solution splits, or bifurcates, there, we refer to Ra_c as a bifurcation point. Moreover, the convective solution inherits stability from the conductive one as the value of Ra increases past Ra_c. In general, a transition from one solution to another is expected to occur at a bifurcation point, but as we see in Chapters 5 and 6, such transitions may be either smooth or sudden and depend on the form of the new solution.

Also, we note that perturbations decay or grow slowly when the value of Ra is near that of Ra_c, but rapidly when the value of Ra is far from that of Ra_c. Indeed, the rates of decay or growth are very close to exponential, implying that solutions to the equations linearized about a known solution might provide useful information.

In fact, a theorem ensures that the bifurcation points can be determined from study of the linear problem: At least two solutions meet at a bifurcation point when at least one component of the linear solution neither grows nor decays. Here we outline how we use this theorem to find the value of Ra_c, and we discuss it further in Chapter 5.

We consider the behavior of small deviations of the conductive solution, which here is $\psi^* = T^* = 0$. We assume that these deviations and their spatial derivatives are small in magnitude; then we may neglect the Jacobians because they have quadratic forms, with magnitudes therefore being much smaller than those of the linear terms. The linearized version of (2.25)-(2.26) is then

$$\frac{\partial}{\partial t^*} \tilde{\nabla}^2 \psi^* - P \frac{\partial T^*}{\partial x^*} - \frac{P}{a} \tilde{\nabla}^4 \psi^* = 0 \quad , \tag{2.55}$$

$$\frac{\partial T^*}{\partial t^*} - Ra \frac{\partial \psi^*}{\partial x^*} - \frac{1}{a} \tilde{\nabla}^2 T^* = 0 \quad , \tag{2.56}$$

in which $|\psi^*| \ll 1$, and $|T^*| \ll 1$. Because the above system is linear with constant coefficients in each of x^*, z^*, and t^*, it has solutions of the form

$$\psi^*(x^*,z^*,t^*) = \hat{\psi} \exp[(\lambda_r + i\lambda_i)t^* + imx^* + inz^*] \quad , \tag{2.57}$$

$$T^*(x^*,z^*,t^*) = \hat{T} \exp[(\lambda_r + i\lambda_i)t^* + imx^* + inz^*] \quad , \tag{2.58}$$

in which m is the integral wavenumber in the horizontal and n is the integral wavenumber in the vertical; the case m = n = 1 is shown in Fig. 2.1a. The conductive solution is stable if the perturbations decay; this situation occurs provided that $\lambda_r = Re(\lambda) < 0$. In contrast, the solution is unstable if $\lambda_r > 0$. Upon substitution of (2.57)-(2.58) into (2.55)-(2.56), we find that the amplitudes $\hat{\psi}$, $\hat{T}$ must satisfy the pair of homogeneous equations

$$-(\lambda_r + i\lambda_i)(m^2a^2 + n^2)\hat{\psi} - imP\hat{T} - \frac{P}{a}(m^2a^2 + n^2)^2\hat{\psi} = 0 \quad , \tag{2.59}$$

$$(\lambda_r + i\lambda_i)\hat{T} - im\, Ra\, \hat{\psi} + \frac{1}{a}(m^2a^2 + n^2)\hat{T} = 0 \quad , \tag{2.60}$$

in which we have canceled the exponential forms from each equation. This system has a nontrivial solution $\hat{\psi}$, $\hat{T}$ only if the determinant of the coefficients vanishes, that is if

$$\begin{vmatrix} -(\lambda_r+i\lambda_i)(m^2a^2+n^2) - \frac{P}{a}(m^2a^2+n^2)^2 & -imP \\ -im\,Ra & \lambda_r+i\lambda_i+\frac{1}{a}(m^2a^2+n^2) \end{vmatrix} = 0 \quad , \tag{2.61}$$

where the first column multiplies $\hat{\psi}$ and the second $\hat{T}$,

or upon expansion if

$$(\lambda_r+i\lambda_i)^2(m^2a^2+n^2) + (\lambda_r+i\lambda_i)[(\frac{P+1}{a})(m^2a^2+n^2)^2] + \frac{P}{a^2}(m^2a^2+n^2)^3 - Ra\,m^2P = 0 \quad , \tag{2.62}$$

which yields

$$(\lambda_r+i\lambda_i) = -\frac{(P+1)}{2a}(m^2a^2+n^2) \pm \frac{1}{2a}\left[(P-1)^2(m^2a^2+n^2)^2 + 4Pm^2a^2Ra/(m^2a^2+n^2)\right]^{1/2} \quad . \tag{2.63}$$

The corresponding calculation for the Lorenz system (2.34)-(2.35) gives

$$(\lambda_r+i\lambda_i) = -\frac{(P+1)(m^2a^2+n^2)}{2(1+a^2)} \pm \frac{1}{2(1+a^2)}\left[(m^2a^2+n^2)^2(P-1)^2 + 4Pr(1+a^2)^3m^2/(m^2a^2+n^2)\right]^{1/2} \quad . \tag{2.64}$$

We note that the discriminant in (2.63) or (2.64) is positive and so $\lambda_i = 0$; the minus root always gives $\lambda_r < 0$, but the plus root vanishes in (2.63) if

$$Ra = Ra_c = (m^2a^2 + n^2)^3/(m^2a^2) \quad , \tag{2.65}$$

and in (2.64) if

$$r = r_c = \frac{(m^2a^2+n^2)^3}{m^2(1+a^2)^3} \quad . \tag{2.66}$$

The Lorenz model is usually only formulated for the case $m = n = 1$ (Fig. 2.1a), for which (2.66) simplifies to

$$r_c = 1 \quad . \tag{2.67}$$

The fact that the value of the bifurcation point depends on that of the cell aspect ratio ma, an observation we exploit in Chapter 7, is apparent only from the version in (2.65); consequently, the generalized dimensionless forms are preferred when the effects of varying cell aspect ratio ma are studied. As we discover in Chapter 7, additional analysis is needed to conclude that the expected circulation would have horizontal wavenumber $m = 1$ and vertical wavenumber $n = 1$, as depicted in Fig. 2.1a. When $Ra > Ra_c$, or $r > r_c$, we find that $\lambda_r > 0$, and so the deviations grow exponentially. They do not grow infinitely large, however, because eventually the nonlinear terms become important. With the low-order models discussed in Section 2.2, we are able to calculate the amplitudes of the nonlinear convective solutions as well as to determine their stabilities. As an important part of the analysis, we verify that the corresponding value of Ra_c in one model is the same as (2.65), and that r_c in the other model is the same as (2.67).

2.2 The Lorenz Models

To develop either form of the model, we seek functions for the variables ψ^* and T^* that capture the energy containing modes; owing to the cyclic nature of the domain, we find that trigonometric functions suffice (see Section 3.2). But we do not wish to include more terms than absolutely necessary in order to describe the developing convective flow. To determine the optimum form, we use the observations outlined in Section 2.1.1. In addition, we note that the terms in (2.68), (2.71) and (2.72) below were the only ones remaining in some long-term temporal integrations of a larger seven-component model developed by Saltzman (1962). It was this result that Lorenz (1963) exploited in his study.

For the velocity variable, we use the fact that circulations having single dominant harmonics of wavenumber $m = 1$ in the horizontal and $n = 1$ in the vertical occur to write

$$\psi^*(x^*,z^*,t^*) \sim \psi_{11}(t^*) \sin x^* \sin z^* \quad , \tag{2.68}$$

which corresponds to

$$u^*(x^*,z^*,t^*) \sim -\psi_{11}(t^*) \sin x^* \cos z^* \quad , \tag{2.69}$$

$$w^*(x^*,z^*,t^*) \sim \psi_{11}(t^*) \cos x^* \sin z^* \quad . \tag{2.70}$$

Because the w^* and T^* fields are positively correlated, we find from (2.70) that the thermal perturbation must include

$$T^*(x^*,z^*,t^*) \sim T_{11}(t^*) \cos x^* \sin z^* \quad , \tag{2.71}$$

and we expect that $\psi_{11} T_{11} > 0$ in order that $\overline{\psi^* T^*} > 0$. But we recall that the convective flow serves to heat the upper portion of the fluid and to cool the lower portion and that this heating pattern is independent of x^*. Thus, we consider representations of the form $T^* \sim \sin(kz^*)$ with $k = 1,2,\ldots$; only even values of k could produce the correct heating distribution, and the case $k = 2$ best reproduces the pattern shown in Fig. 2.1b. Hence, an additional temperature component must be

$$T^*(x^*,z^*,t^*) \sim T_{02}(t^*) \sin(2z^*) \quad . \tag{2.72}$$

Here we expect that $T_{02} < 0$ for the net heating pattern to be correct. We note that (2.68)-(2.72) are suitable choices because they satisfy the boundary conditions (2.39)-(2.41).

Having deduced the forms for the dominant components of ψ^*, T^*, we assume that they are the only ones and write the generalized expansions as

$$\psi^*(x^*,z^*,t^*) = \psi_{mn}(t^*) \sin(mx^*) \sin(nz^*) \quad , \tag{2.73}$$

$$T^*(x^*,z^*,t^*) = T_{mn}(t^*) \cos(mx^*) \sin(nz^*) + T_{0,2n}(t^*) \sin(2nz^*) \quad , \tag{2.74}$$

in which the observed case corresponds to $m = n = 1$. Recalling that the domain is $0 \leq x^* \leq 2\pi$ and $0 \leq z^* \leq \pi$, we may use the Galerkin technique discussed in Chapter 3 to convert the Boussinesq system (2.25)-(2.26) to a three-component ordinary differential system. To produce the equation for the rate of change $\dot{\psi}_{mn}$ of ψ_{mn}, we substitute (2.73)-(2.74) into (2.25), multiply the result by $\sin(mx^*)\sin(nz^*)$, and finally integrate the result over the domain. We perform similar calculations to produce the $\dot{T}_{mn}$ and $\dot{T}_{0,2n}$ equations. The resulting system of equations is

$$\dot{\psi}_{mn} = \frac{Pm}{(m^2a^2+n^2)} T_{mn} - P\left(\frac{m^2a^2+n^2}{a}\right)\psi_{mn} \quad , \tag{2.75}$$

$$\dot{T}_{mn} = mn\,\psi_{mn}\,T_{0,2n} + m\,Ra\,\psi_{mn} - \left(\frac{m^2a^2+n^2}{a}\right)T_{mn} \quad , \tag{2.76}$$

$$\dot{T}_{0,2n} = -\frac{1}{2}\,mn\psi_{mn}T_{mn} - \frac{4n^2}{a}\,T_{0,2n} \quad , \tag{2.77}$$

in which the overdot denotes a temporal derivative. The thermal advection term $J(\psi^*,T^*)$ is represented by the quadratic forms in (2.76) and (2.77), the energy generation terms by the first linear ones in (2.75) and (2.76) and the dissipation terms by the last ones in (2.75)-(2.77). Thus the Lorenz model contains representatives of all terms in (2.25)-(2.26) except $J(\psi^*,\tilde{\nabla}^2\psi^*)$. Terms representing this Jacobian are in the Saltzman (1962) model, but proved in some cases to be unimportant; they are considered further in Chapter 9.

The version of (2.75)-(2.77) discussed by Lorenz (1963) is obtained by setting

$$\psi^*(x^*,z^*,t^*) = \sqrt{2}\,X(t^*)\sin x^* \sin z^* \quad , \tag{2.78}$$

$$T^*(x^*,z^*,t^*) = \sqrt{2}\,Y(t^*)\cos x^* \sin z^* - Z(t^*)\sin(2z^*) \quad , \tag{2.79}$$

so that only the observed case $m = n = 1$ is considered. The factors of $\sqrt{2}$ are included so that the resulting equations are simpler; the negative sign in front of Z in (2.79) is chosen so that a positive value of Z gives the correct net heating pattern (Fig. 2.1b). The resulting spectral system, obtained from (2.34)-(2.35), is

$$\dot{X} = -PX + PY \quad , \tag{2.80}$$

$$\dot{Y} = -XZ + rX - Y \quad , \tag{2.81}$$

$$\dot{Z} = XY - bZ \quad , \tag{2.82}$$

in which

$$b = 4/(1+a^2) \quad . \tag{2.83}$$

We now investigate the effectiveness of the Lorenz model as measured by the four fundamental principles that were reviewed at the beginning of this chapter.

2.2.1 Energetics of the models. We develop the forms for the energies KE and AE in the Lorenz systems in a way analogous to that used in the partial differential equations (2.25)-(2.26) and (2.34)-(2.35). Because the integration over the domain has been performed already in the creation of either Lorenz model, the appropriate forms for KE and AE in the low-order models do not contain integrals. To see this fact, we combine (2.46) and (2.73) to obtain

$$KE = \frac{1}{2}\int_0^{2\pi}\int_0^{\pi} |\tilde{\nabla}\psi^*|^2 dz^* dx^* \sim \frac{1}{2}|(m^2a^2+n^2)^{1/2}\psi_{mn}|^2 \sim \frac{1}{2}(m^2a^2+n^2)\psi_{mn}^2 \quad , \qquad (2.84)$$

and combine (2.47) and (2.74) to find

$$AE = \frac{1}{2}\int_0^{2\pi}\int_0^{\pi} P\, T^{*2} dz^* dx^* \sim \frac{1}{2} P\, T_{mn}^2 + P\, T_{0,2n}^2 \quad . \qquad (2.85)$$

Thus, we have

$$\frac{d}{dt^*}(KE+AE) = \frac{d}{dt^*}\left[\frac{1}{2}(m^2a^2+n^2)\psi_{mn}^2 + \frac{1}{2} P\, T_{mn}^2 + P\, T_{0,2n}^2\right]$$

$$= mP(1+Ra)\psi_{mn}T_{mn} - \frac{P}{a}\left[(m^2a^2+n^2)^2\psi_{mn}^2 + (m^2a^2+n^2)T_{mn}^2 + 8n^2T_{0,2n}^2\right] \quad . \qquad (2.86)$$

For the model (2.80)-(2.82), we have

$$KE \sim \frac{1}{2}(a^2+1)\, X^2 \quad , \qquad (2.87)$$

$$AE \sim \frac{1}{2} P\, Y^2 + \frac{1}{2} P\, Z^2 \quad , \qquad (2.88)$$

and so

$$\frac{d}{dt^*}(KE+AE) = \frac{d}{dt^*}\left[\frac{1}{2}(a^2+1)X^2 + \frac{1}{2} PY^2 + \frac{1}{2} PZ^2\right]$$

$$= P(1+a^2+r)\, XY - \frac{P}{(1+a^2)}\left[(1+a^2)^2 X^2 + (1+a^2)Y^2 + 4Z^2\right] \quad . \qquad (2.89)$$

Using the facts that for spectral models $|\partial\psi^*/\partial x^*| \sim m\psi^*$, $|\tilde{\nabla}^2\psi^*|^2 \sim (m^2a^2+n^2)^2\psi^*$, and $|\tilde{\nabla}T^*|^2 \sim (m^2a^2+n^2)T^*$, we may compare (2.86) with (2.50)-(2.52) and (2.89) with

(2.53)-(2.54) to see that the energy generation and dissipation expressions have identical forms in the Lorenz and original systems. Thus, both the Lorenz systems capture the essential energetics properties, as required.

2.2.2 Stability properties of the conductive solution. We next verify that the value of the critical Rayleigh number Ra_c or r_c is correct and that the conductive solution is stable for $Ra < Ra_c$ or $r < r_c$, and unstable for $Ra > Ra_c$ or $r > r_c$. Here the conductive solution is given by $\psi_{mn} = T_{mn} = T_{0,2n} = 0$ or $X = Y = Z = 0$ and so to obtain the equations linearized about the conductive solution, we need only to drop the nonlinear terms $\psi_{mn}T_{0,2n}$ and $\psi_{mn}T_{mn}$ from (2.76)-(2.77) or XZ and XY from (2.81)-(2.82). As before, this system has solutions of the form $\psi_{mn} \sim \hat{\psi}_{mn}\exp(\lambda t^*)$, $T_{mn} \sim \hat{T}_{mn}\exp(\lambda t^*)$, and $T_{0,2n} \sim \hat{T}_{0,2n}\exp(\lambda t^*)$; moreover, the conductive solution is stable when $\mathrm{Re}(\lambda) < 0$.

Solutions to the linearized form of (2.75)-(2.77) obey

$$\dot{\psi}_{mn} \sim \lambda\hat{\psi}_{mn}e^{\lambda t^*} = \{\frac{Pm}{(m^2a^2+n^2)}\hat{T}_{mn} - P(\frac{m^2a^2+n^2}{a})\hat{\psi}_{mn}\}e^{\lambda t^*} \quad , \tag{2.90}$$

$$\dot{T}_{mn} \sim \lambda\hat{T}_{mn}e^{\lambda t^*} = \{m\,Ra\,\hat{\psi}_{mn} - (\frac{m^2a^2+n^2}{a})\hat{T}_{mn}\}e^{\lambda t^*} \quad , \tag{2.91}$$

$$\dot{T}_{0,2n} \sim \lambda\hat{T}_{0,2n}e^{\lambda t^*} = \{-\frac{4n^2}{a}T_{0,2n}\}e^{\lambda t^*} \quad , \tag{2.92}$$

in which $\lambda = \lambda_r + i\lambda_i$ is a complex number. This system has a nontrivial solution only if

$$\begin{array}{ccc} \hat{\psi}_{mn} & \hat{T}_{mn} & \hat{T}_{0,2n} \end{array}$$
$$\begin{vmatrix} -P(\frac{m^2a^2+n^2}{a}) - \lambda & \frac{Pm}{(m^2a^2+n^2)} & 0 \\ m\,Ra & -(\frac{m^2a^2+n^2}{a}) - \lambda & 0 \\ 0 & 0 & -\frac{4n^2}{a} - \lambda \end{vmatrix} = 0 \quad . \tag{2.93}$$

The characteristic equation governing the stability of the conductive solution is a cubic polynomial equation in the characteristic exponent λ:

$$-(\frac{4n^2}{a} + \lambda)[\lambda^2+(\frac{m^2a^2+n^2}{a})(P + 1)\lambda - \frac{m^2P}{(m^2a^2+n^2)}Ra + P(\frac{m^2a^2+n^2}{a})^2] = 0 \ . \tag{2.94}$$

The roots of (2.94) are

$$\lambda = \begin{cases} -\,4n^2/a \\ -\,(P+1)\left(\dfrac{m^2a^2 + n^2}{2a}\right) \pm \dfrac{1}{2a}\left[(P-1)^2(m^2a^2+n^2)^2 + 4Pm^2a^2Ra/(m^2a^2+n^2)\right]^{1/2} \end{cases} . \tag{2.95}$$

No change in stability can be linked to the first exponent $-4n^2/a < 0$ since it is independent of Ra. But the other two exponents are identical to those (2.63) obtained from the analysis of the partial differential system. The corresponding calculation (see Section 4.2.1) for the stability of the conductive solution (2.80)-(2.82) yields (cf. (4.34)-(4.35)):

$$\lambda = \begin{cases} -\,b \\ -\,\dfrac{(P+1)}{2} \pm \dfrac{1}{2}\left[(P-1)^2 + 4rP\right]^{1/2} \end{cases} . \tag{2.96}$$

The last two expressions in (2.96) are identical to those in (2.64) for the partial differential equations when $m = n = 1$. We conclude that not only is the value of Ra_c or r_c the same as that in the original system, but, as required, the conductive solution is stable when $Ra < Ra_c$ or $r < r_c$.

2.2.3 Convective solutions. Because $\lambda = 0$ at the bifurcation point $Ra = Ra_c$ and because $\partial\lambda/\partial Ra \neq 0$ at $Ra = Ra_c$, then a standard theorem of bifurcation theory (see Chapter 5 of Iooss and Joseph, 1980) states that the new branching solution is stationary (time-independent). With there being an infinite number of values Ra_{mn} of $Ra_c(m,n)$, one for each pair of positive integers m and n, the theorem implies that there are an infinite number of branching stationary solutions, each one emanating from one of the bifurcation points (Fig. 2.3). These convective solutions have wavenumber m in the horizontal and n in the vertical and they meet the conductive solution at the appropriate value of Ra_c. The generalized Lorenz model (2.75)-(2.77) may be used to find the forms for all of these branches in one calculation. As we note in Chapter 9, evidence for the validity of this application of (2.75)-(2.77) is given by Saltzman (1962) and Rabinowitz (1968).

We obtain the convective solutions by setting the temporal derivatives in (2.75)-(2.77) to zero and finding nonvanishing solutions of

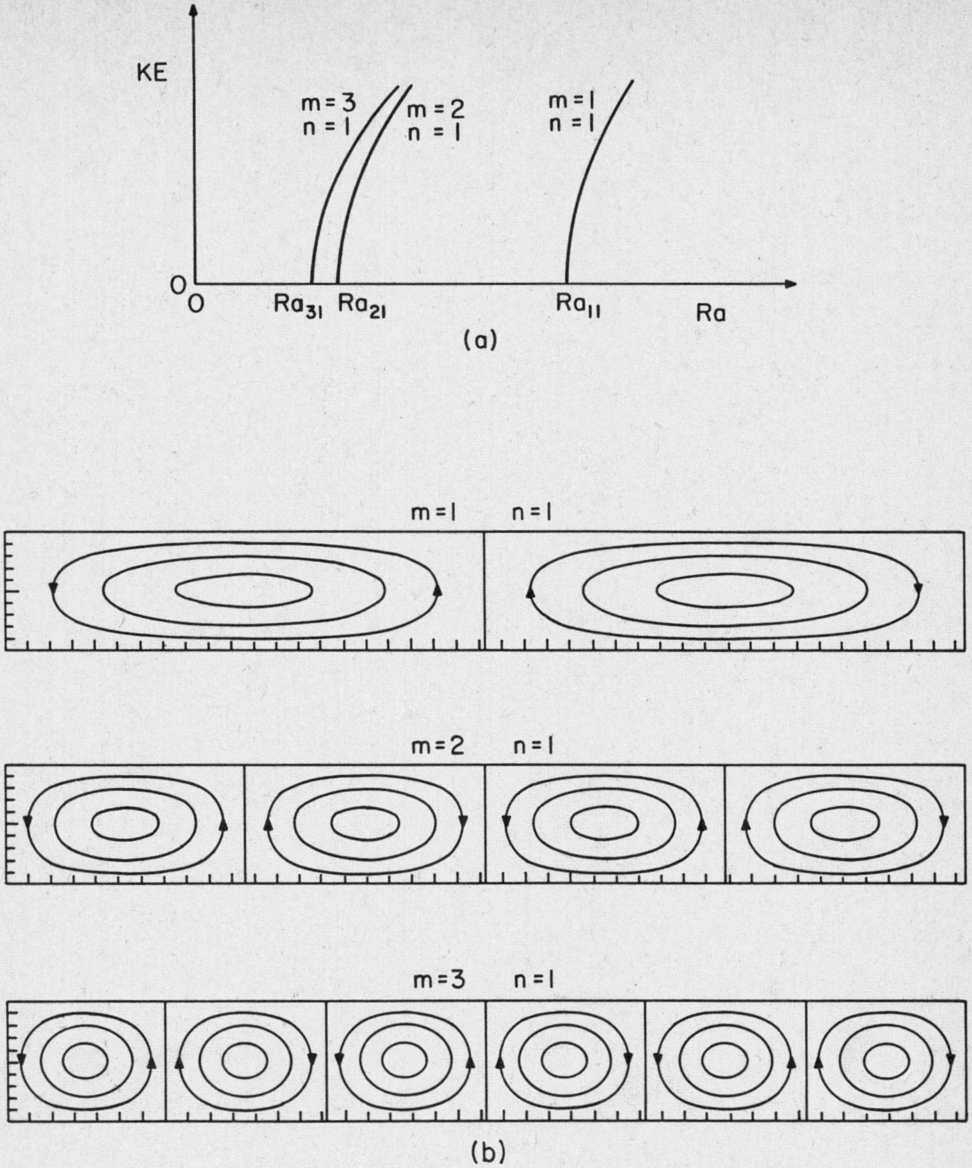

Fig. 2.3 The kinetic energies (a) and circulation patterns (b) for three of the convective solutions branching from the conductive one at $Ra_{mn}=Ra_c(m,n)$.

$$0 = \frac{Pm}{(m^2a^2+n^2)} T^s_{mn} - P(\frac{m^2a^2+n^2}{a}) \psi^s_{mn} \quad , \tag{2.97}$$

$$0 = mn\psi^s_{mn} T^s_{0,2n} + m\, Ra\, \psi^s_{mn} - (\frac{m^2a^2+n^2}{a})T^s_{mn} \quad , \tag{2.98}$$

$$0 = -\frac{1}{2}mn\psi^s_{mn} T^s_{mn} - \frac{4n^2}{a} T^s_{0,2n} \quad . \tag{2.99}$$

Although a straightforward method, the Lyapunov-Schmidt procedure, is available for finding the solutions to (2.97)-(2.99), we postpone discussion of it until Chapter 8. Here we obtain the stationary solutions by rewriting (2.97) to express T^s_{mn} as a function of ψ^s_{mn}, substituting the result into (2.99) to find $T^s_{0,2n}$ as a function of ψ^s_{mn}, and finally inserting these results into (2.98) to obtain a cubic polynomial equation. The nontrivial solutions of this equation are:

$$\psi^s_{mn} = \pm \frac{\sqrt{8}}{(m^2a^2+n^2)} (Ra-Ra_c)^{1/2} \quad , \tag{2.100}$$

$$T^s_{mn} = \pm \sqrt{8}\, (\frac{m^2a^2+n^2}{ma}) (Ra-Ra_c)^{1/2} \quad , \tag{2.101}$$

$$T^s_{0,2n} = -(Ra-Ra_c)/n \quad . \tag{2.102}$$

From (2.100)-(2.102) we see that the amplitude of the convective motion is proportional to $(Ra - Ra_c)^{1/2}$; moreover, if $Ra > Ra_c$, then $\psi_{mn}T_{mn} > 0$ and $T_{0,2n} < 0$ for all values of m and n--in particular $m = n = 1$. Thus, the convective solution has the correct form. In addition, the magnitude of each component of the convective solution approaches zero as $Ra \to Ra_c$ and so the convective solution is created smoothly at $Ra = Ra_c$ via a bifurcation. In Fig. 2.4 the curves for the conductive and convective solutions combine to create a form that resembles a pitchfork or a trident. Provided that the convective solution is stable, we conclude that the Lorenz system is able to model properly all the features of convection that we discussed in Section 2.1.

One result that we had not anticipated is that we have two nonlinear convective solutions rather than one. In order to determine which one is stable, we may again perform a linear analysis to see if deviations from $(\psi^s_{mn}, T^s_{mn}, T^s_{0,2n})$ decay or grow.

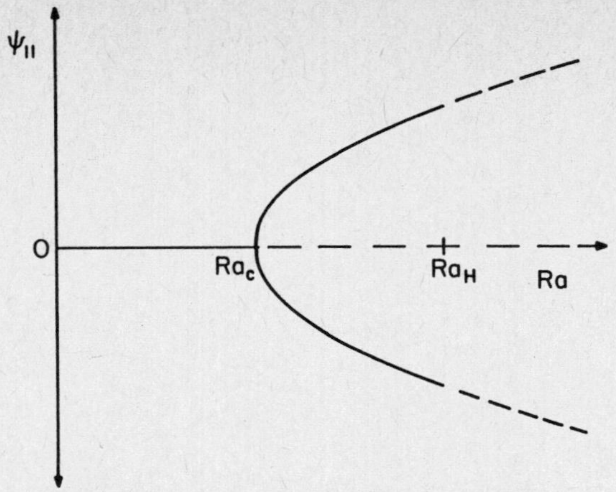

Fig 2.4 Bifurcation diagram for the solutions to the Lorenz model. Stable solutions are denoted by solid lines, unstable ones by dashed lines. The value for Ra_H is determined in Chapter 4 (see (4.44)).

The details of this calculation are given in Section 4.2.2. The results are that both stationary convective solutions are stable at least for a range of values of Ra for which $Ra_c < Ra < Ra_H$ (Fig. 2.4). We have reached the pleasing conclusion that the branching convective solutions to the Lorenz model are stable at least for a range of supercritical values of Ra, and so we conclude that they are observable. But we have encountered a dilemma: with two possible stable convective solutions appearing simultaneously, and both apparently observable, which one do we actually see? We postpone the answer until Chapter 8, but we note that here the difference between the two solutions is only in circulation sense. That is, when m = n = 1, for one solution ($\psi_{11}^s < 0$), we have fluid rising in the center of the domain, and for the other solution ($\psi_{11}^s > 0$), we have fluid sinking in the center (Fig. 2.5).

We have shown that a simple three-component model of a physical system can be effective as measured by the four fundamental modeling principles discussed in Chapter 1. The Lorenz model possesses sufficient complexity to represent correctly the nonlinear form of the first convective solution. The model reproduces the energetics of the original partial differential system by having the correct forms for both the kinetic and available potential energies, and the energy generation and dissipation rates. Because only three components are required to formulate the model, the dominant features are emphasized in the most efficient manner possible.

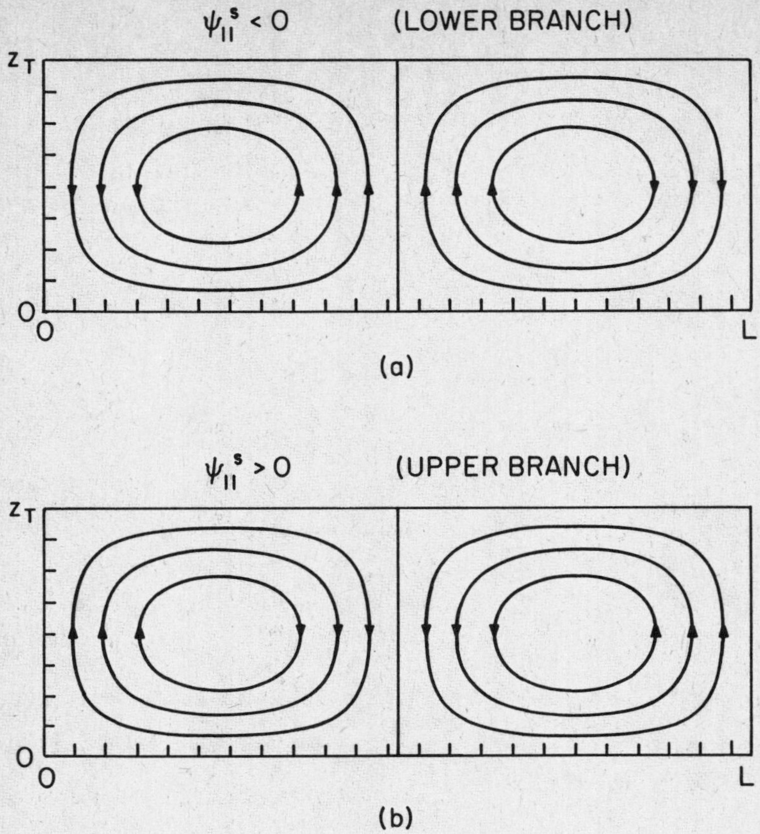

Fig. 2.5 Schematic representation of the circulation patterns for the two convective solutions to the Lorenz model for the case m=n=1.

We have not examined the three intermediate modeling principles that necessarily involve investigation of larger nonlinear models to see whether the Lorenz solutions can be identified in them and to determine whether the results depend either on the precise choice of dimensionless parameters or on the level of truncation used in the expansions of the dependent variables. We consider these questions in later chapters of the monograph, in which we discover that larger models are needed to represent more adequately the initial convective flows. First, though, we review some of the fundamental concepts of stability and bifurcation, ascertain some of the expected forms for the branching solutions, and outline how we determine the expected geometrical forms for the nonlinear solutions. We begin the review in the next chapter by discussing the procedure by which we create a spectral model.

CHAPTER 3

FROM THE EQUATIONS OF MOTION TO SPECTRAL MODELS

R. WAYNE HIGGINS

We identified in Chapter 2 a number of properties of the solutions to a partial differential system that we expected a low-order model to capture. Specifically, we developed and discussed the three-coefficient Lorenz (1963) model of classical Rayleigh-Bénard convection. However, to obtain the ordinary differential system, we implicitly utilized the Galerkin technique or spectral method, a method with which we may create an appropriate system of ordinary differential equations from the original partial differential system. This method involves the following four steps:

1) Choose, and simplify via appropriate scaling arguments, a system of partial differential equations.
2) Identify a suitable set of orthogonal functions, or eigenfunctions, to represent the spatial dependence of the variables in a Fourier series having temporally dependent coefficients.
3) Expand the dependent variables as sums of products of temporally dependent amplitude coefficients and spatially dependent eigenfunctions, and then truncate each series to one of a predetermined finite length.
4) Develop a system of n first-order ordinary differential equations relating the temporal variations of the amplitude coefficients to functions of the coefficients themselves.

This last step must itself be divided into four parts, as we discuss in Section 3.3.

In this monograph we, for the most part, assume that the first step has already been accomplished. (One exception to this is encountered in Chapter 8, in which we present an analysis whose goal is to flag the need to add representations of important physical effects to the original partial differential system.) The remaining steps are the topics of this chapter, and we illustrate them by rederiving the simple Lorenz (1963) model presented in Chapter 2. First, however, we review the reasons for utilizing highly truncated spectral models and then show how to interpret some of their solutions.

3.1 The Physical Relevance of Phase Space Trajectories

The usual equations of atmospheric motion--the Navier-Stokes equations and the First Law of Thermodynamics--involve substantial nonlinearity, and thus exact solutions to the full set of equations are difficult, if not impossible, to find. Here we are interested mainly in the study of the bifurcation and stability properties of the solutions to these equations, which is often a tractable problem because the bifurcation and stability theorems that apply to partial differential equations have forms applicable to an equivalent approximate system of ordinary differential equations.

There are a number of advantages for using low-order sets of ordinary differential equations (or highly truncated spectral models); some of the more obvious are:

1) Particular solutions of the low-order systems can often be found.
2) Applications of the bifurcation and stability theorems are often conceptually and technically much simpler for the ordinary differential systems.
3) Qualitative aspects of atmospheric flow that we are trying to represent can often be quantified by just a few carefully chosen harmonics in phase space, thereby making low-order models both useful and efficient.
4) Numerical simulation of solutions of partial differential equations is many times more expensive than numerical simulation of solutions of low-order models.
5) Many analytical calculations are feasible for low-order models that are not feasible for partial differential equations.
6) Study of the ordinary differential equations provides one means for proving the existence of solutions to the partial differential equations (see, for example, Section 15.2.4 of Dutton (1986)).

For these reasons, we choose to convert our set of partial differential equations into spectral form.

If we use a spectral model to study the evolution of a physical system, then the evolutionary behavior is revealed by trajectories in phase space. It is important to understand the connection between flows in <u>physical space</u>, in which fluid motions are represented by temporal variations of the scalar and vector quantities at fixed spatial positions, and those in phase space, in which fluid motions are represented by temporal variations of the amplitudes of specified waveforms. This connection is illustrated in this section by considering how simple waveforms appear in the two spaces. Specifically, four examples are considered; these are exponential decay, linear translation, amplitude vacillation, and wavenumber vacillation. These examples are relevant because they illustrate how specific aspects of waveforms are interpreted in phase space. Indeed, each of these phenomena has been isolated and studied extensively in such laboratory vessels as the externally forced rotating annulus (e.g., Fultz et al., 1959).

3.1.1 Exponential decay. Waves, such as lee waves, that are stationary in physical space would have amplitudes $\hat{A}$ and phases ϕ that are not varying in time; a prototypical form for such a wave is

$$f(x) = \hat{A} \sin(2m\pi x/L + \phi) \quad , \tag{3.1}$$

in which m is an integer, L is the length of the domain, and L/m is the wavelength of the wave. Such waves are represented simply by points in phase space; to see how, we rewrite (3.1) using a trigonometric identity as

$$f(x) = \hat{A} \cos(\phi) \sin(2m\pi x/L) + \hat{A} \sin(\phi) \cos(2m\pi x/L) \quad . \tag{3.2}$$

Upon defining

$$A_m = \hat{A} \cos(\phi) \quad , \tag{3.3}$$

$$B_m = \hat{A} \sin(\phi) \quad , \tag{3.4}$$

we have

$$f(x) = A_m \sin(2m\pi x/L) + B_m \cos(2m\pi x/L) \quad . \tag{3.5}$$

The points in phase space corresponding to (3.5) have coordinates (A_m, B_m) and lie on a circle of radius $\hat{A}$. In Fig. 3.1 such a point is labeled "$t = \infty$" and is called a fixed point or stationary point of the flow.

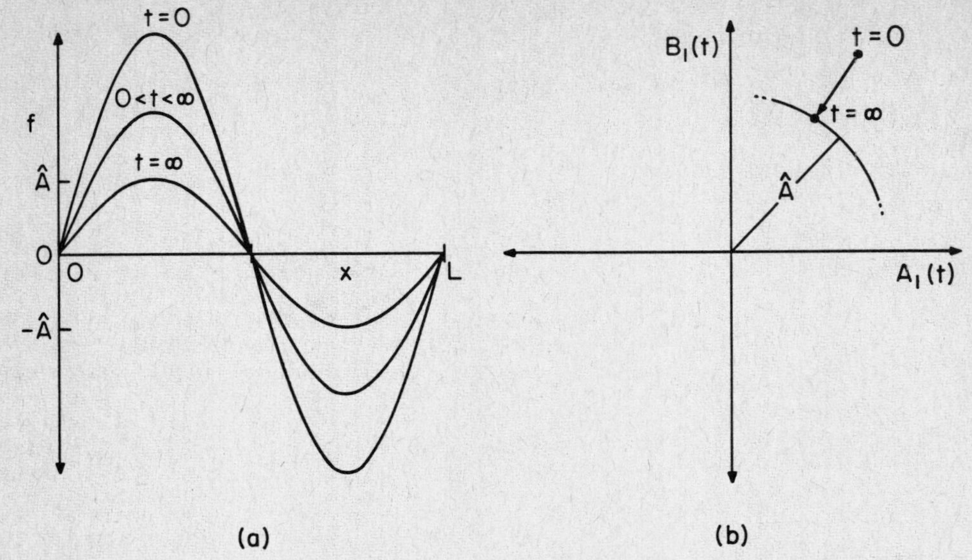

Fig. 3.1 A representation of exponential decay to a (phase-locked) stable stationary solution in physical space (a) and in phase space (b) for a value of ϕ satisfying $\pi/4<\phi<\pi/2$. The initial wave is denoted by "t=0" and the stationary solution by "t=∞".

If the initial amplitude is, say, greater than the amplitude $\hat{A}$ of a stable stationary solution, then the system may evolve toward the stable solution in several different ways (see Chapter 4). One way is via a pure decay of the amplitude to that of the stable solution while the spatial configuration remains unchanged. This evolution is displayed in Fig. 3.1, with the behavior in physical space shown in (a) and that in phase space shown in (b). The path in phase space is a radial line, but more general paths are possible if both the amplitude and the phase change as the solution decays toward the stable one.

3.1.2 Linear translation. If the waveform presented in the previous subsection is propagating spatially, then the crest of the wave is moving in some direction. In this case, the phase ϕ of the wave is changing at some rate, and so we rewrite (3.1) as

$$f(x,t) = \hat{A}\sin(2m\pi x/L - \omega t) \quad . \tag{3.6}$$

We include the minus sign in (3.6) to ensure that propagation is to the right when $\omega > 0$. Here ω is the frequency of the oscillation at any given point x, $\omega L/(2m\pi)$ is the speed of propagation, and $2\pi/\omega$ is the period T of the wave. As before, we introduce

$$A_m(t) = \hat{A}\cos(\omega t) \quad , \tag{3.7}$$

$$B_m(t) = -\hat{A}\sin(\omega t) \quad . \tag{3.8}$$

After utilizing a trigonometric identity and substituting (3.7)-(3.8) into the result, we obtain an expression for a linearly translating wave:

$$f(x,t) = A_m(t)\sin(2m\pi x/L) + B_m(t)\cos(2m\pi x/L) \quad . \tag{3.9}$$

Figure 3.2a is obtained from (3.6) by plotting f(x,t) versus x at various fixed values of t (for m=1). This figure shows that the wave maximum propagates downstream as the value of t increases (see dashed line in Fig. 3.2a), thereby simulating wave translation in physical space. To specify a trajectory in phase space that corresponds to this translation in physical space, we use the amplitude coefficients (3.7)-(3.8). Again, we increase the value of t and calculate the corresponding change in the values of $A_m(t)$ and $B_m(t)$. Figure 3.2b shows that wave translation in physical space corresponds, in this case, to a circular trajectory in phase space involving two coefficients that are associated with the same wavenumber, m. In general, wave translations result in elliptical phase space trajectories because $A_m(t)$ and $B_m(t)$ need not vary sinusoidally.

3.1.3 Amplitude vacillation. Another type of temporal solution occurs if the wave does not propagate, but the amplitude varies periodically. This behavior is known as amplitude vacillation, and at a fixed wavenumber m is illustrated by a wave solution of the form

$$f(x,t) = \hat{A}\sin(\omega t)\sin(2m\pi x/L) \quad , \tag{3.10}$$

in which the amplitude coefficient $A_m(t)$ is

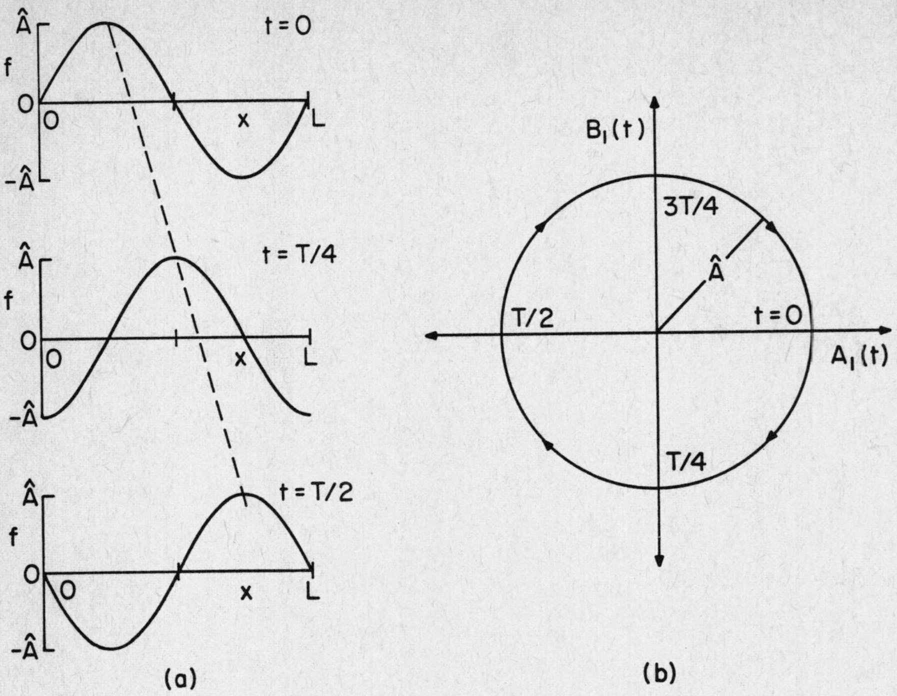

Fig. 3.2 A representation of linear wave translation in physical space (a) and the corresponding trajectory in phase space (b). In (b) the arrows point in the direction of increasing values of t.

$$A_m(t) = \hat{A} \sin(\omega t) \quad . \tag{3.11}$$

As before, we use (3.10) to construct Fig. 3.3 (for m=1). Figure 3.3a shows that as the value of t increases, f(x,t) amplifies and decays in a periodic manner (<u>without</u> the wave translating). Figure 3.3b shows that in this case, amplitude vacillation in physical space corresponds to oscillation along a line in phase space. We note that (3.6) and (3.10) could be combined to produce a wave that both translates and vacillates in amplitude at a fixed wavenumber m.

3.1.4 Wavenumber vacillation. Finally, suppose that we seek a phase space trajectory that represents a periodic change in the dominant wavenumber of a fluid flow. An obvious atmospheric example is the change in wavenumber we might observe over a period of time on a 500 mb chart. To represent this phenomenon crudely, let

$$f(x,t) = \hat{A} \cos(\omega t) \sin(2m\pi x/L) - \hat{A} \sin(\omega t) \sin(2n\pi x/L) \quad , \tag{3.12}$$

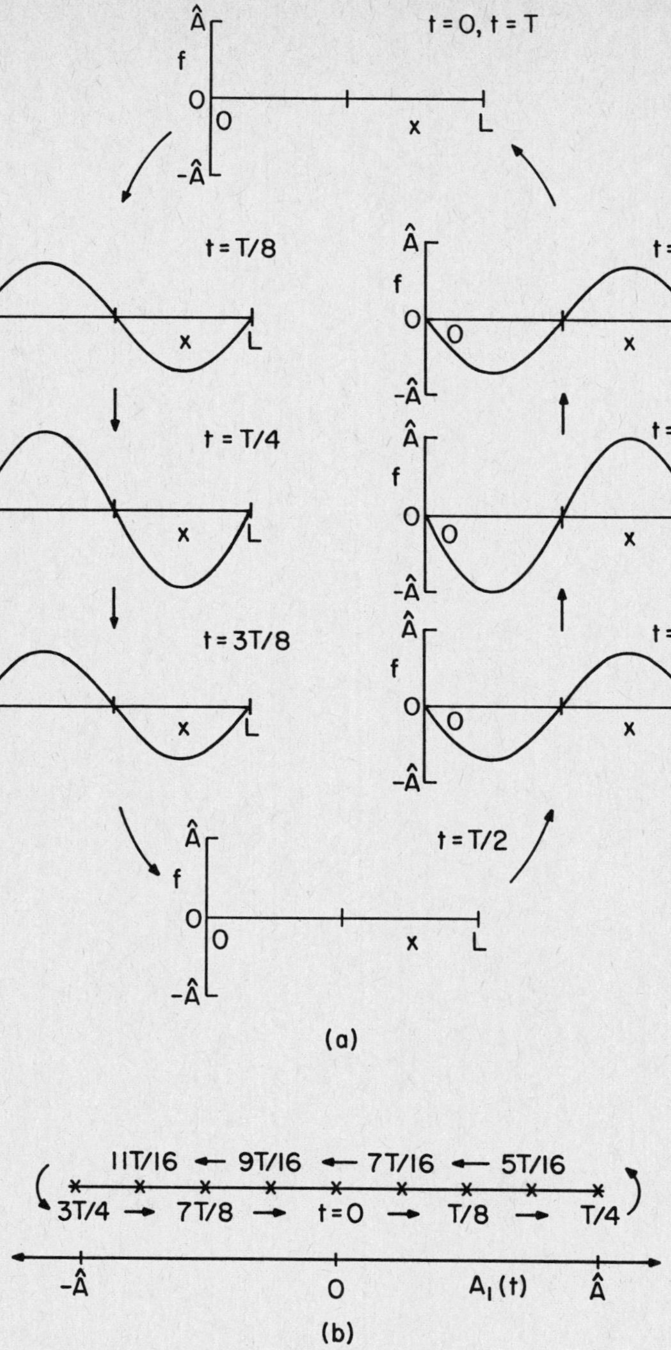

Fig. 3.3 A representation of wave amplitude vacillation in physical space (a) and the corresponding trajectory in phase space (b). In (a) and (b) the arrows point in the direction of increasing values of t.

in which $m \neq n$. We define the amplitudes now by

$$A_m(t) = \hat{A} \cos(\omega t) \quad , \tag{3.13}$$

$$A_n(t) = - \hat{A} \sin(\omega t) \quad . \tag{3.14}$$

Figure 3.4a shows that for $m = 1$ and $n = 2$, $f(x,t)$ undergoes a regular oscillation between waveforms having wavenumber 1 and wavenumber 2. In Fig. 3.4b, the trajectory given by (3.12) is a circular one involving two amplitude coefficients A_m and A_n.

It is important to note that the evolution of a given flow might involve any or all of the processes mentioned above. The net result is a flow that appears to be more complicated in the spectral domain than these examples might suggest. In addition, our choice of periodic amplitude coefficients is the simplest one; in general, we might expect their temporal variations to be aperiodic.

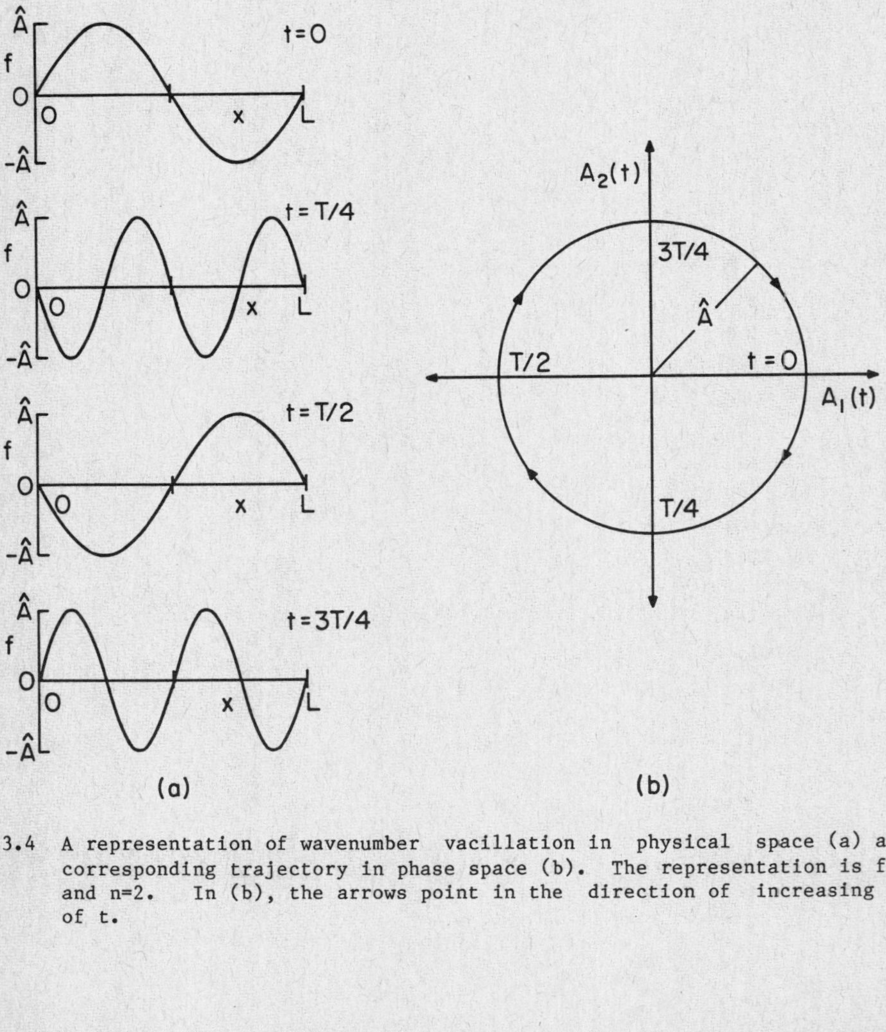

Fig. 3.4 A representation of wavenumber vacillation in physical space (a) and the corresponding trajectory in phase space (b). The representation is for m=1 and n=2. In (b), the arrows point in the direction of increasing values of t.

3.2 Finding Appropriate Basis Functions

The second step in producing a spectral model is to develop a set of mutually orthogonal functions that describe the spatial dependence of each dependent variable in the partial differential system. Using these basis functions, we write the dependent variables in expansions and then we use truncated versions of them to develop a finite-dimensional system via the Galerkin technique (see Section 3.3). Usually, we identify the basis functions from an analysis of a suitable eigenvalue problem that usually depends on the geometry of the periodic domain.

This boundary value problem can be specified in a number of ways, but each problem involves solving a system of linear partial differential equations subject to appropriate boundary conditions (for additional details, see, for example, Section 2.15 of Chandrasekhar, 1961). One of the simplest and most common procedures is to solve the Helmholtz problem

$$\nabla^2 F = -\sigma F \quad , \tag{3.15}$$

in the given two- or three-dimensional domain. In three-dimensional problems, it is more natural to use the Stokes problem in place of (3.15) because the resulting spectral evolutionary equations no longer depend on pressure. For example, when the flow is incompressible, this boundary value problem is given by (see Section 17.3.1)

$$-\frac{1}{\rho_o}\nabla p + \nu\nabla^2 \underset{\sim}{v} = -\gamma\nu\underset{\sim}{v} \quad ,$$

$$\nabla\cdot\underset{\sim}{v} = 0 \quad .$$

In shallow convection studies, the Helmholtz problem is a natural problem to use for specifying the functions in the expansions for the variables $\nabla^2\psi$ and T', because, owing to dissipative effects, the rates of change of these variables depend on their Laplacians (see (2.17)-(2.18)). To be able to obtain usable solutions to (3.15), we must specify boundary conditions, and so completely determine the eigenvalue problem. If a countable number of distinct functions $F_i(\underset{\sim}{x})$, $i=1,2,\ldots,\infty$, and their associated real numbers σ_i, $i=1,2,\ldots,\infty$, constitute the complete set of solutions to (3.15), then we refer to the $F_i(\underset{\sim}{x})$ as the (spatial) eigenfunctions and to the σ_i as the (spatial) eigenvalues. By convention we order the functions and eigenvalues so that $\sigma_1 < \sigma_2 < \cdots$.

The forms for the boundary conditions that we can consider are limited by introducing the requirement that the solutions $F_1(\tilde{x})$, $F_2(\tilde{x})$, ... to (3.15) be independent of each other in the sense that each function represents a portion of the spatial structure that no other function represents. Mathematically, this independence is specified for real functions $F_k(\tilde{x})$ by requiring that

$$\int_V F_i F_j \, dV = \begin{cases} 0 & i \neq j \\ K & i = j \end{cases} , \tag{3.16}$$

in which V represents the area or volume of the domain having two or three dimensions, and in which K is a normalization constant. (For complex functions we replace F_j in (3.16) by the complex conjugate of F_j). Functions that satisfy (3.16) are defined to be orthogonal, and if K = 1, orthonormal.

To see what types of boundary conditions are admissible, we suppose that we have two different solutions $F_m(\tilde{x})$, $F_n(\tilde{x})$ to (3.15), and so

$$\nabla^2 F_m = - \sigma_m F_m , \tag{3.17}$$

$$\nabla^2 F_n = - \sigma_n F_n . \tag{3.18}$$

We multiply (3.17) by F_n and (3.18) by F_m, and then we subtract the two resulting equations to obtain

$$F_n \nabla^2 F_m - F_m \nabla^2 F_n = (\sigma_n - \sigma_m) F_m F_n . \tag{3.19}$$

If the functions F_i are orthogonal and the values of σ_i are distinct, then the integral of the right side of (3.19) vanishes for all choices of m and n. In this case, we have that

$$\int_V [F_n \nabla^2 F_m - F_m \nabla^2 F_n] dV = 0 , \tag{3.20}$$

or that

$$\int_V \left[\nabla\cdot(F_n\nabla F_m) - \nabla F_n\cdot\nabla F_m - \nabla\cdot(F_m\nabla F_n) + \nabla F_m\cdot\nabla F_n\right]dV = 0 \quad . \tag{3.21}$$

The Divergence Theorem implies that (3.21) can be written as

$$\int_B \underset{\sim}{\eta}\cdot[F_n\nabla F_m - F_m\nabla F_n]dB = \int_B [F_n \frac{\partial F_m}{\partial\eta} - F_m \frac{\partial F_n}{\partial\eta}]dB = 0 \quad , \tag{3.22}$$

in which $\underset{\sim}{\eta}$ is the exterior unit vector normal to the boundary B. A general form for the boundary conditions that implies that the boundary integral (3.22) vanishes and hence leads to orthogonal functions $F_i(\underset{\sim}{x})$ as solutions to (3.15) is

$$C_1 F + C_2 \frac{\partial F}{\partial\eta} = 0 \qquad \text{on B} \quad , \tag{3.23}$$

in which C_1 and C_2 are arbitrary constants. The fact that (3.23) is an appropriate form for the boundary conditions can be seen by combining (3.22) and (3.23) to obtain

$$\int_B [F_n(-\frac{C_1}{C_2}F_m) - F_m(-\frac{C_1}{C_2}F_n)]dB = 0 \quad . \tag{3.24}$$

In many cases, however, we choose the simpler boundary conditions F = 0 on B or $\partial F/\partial\eta = 0$ on B.

To produce the basis functions for the spectral models that represent shallow convective flow confined to a rectangular domain $0 \leq x^* \leq 2\pi$, $0 \leq z^* \leq \pi$, we solve the version of the boundary value problem (3.15) and (3.23) given by

$$\tilde{\nabla}^2\Psi^* = -\sigma\Psi^* \quad , \tag{3.25}$$

$$\Psi^*(0,z^*) = \Psi^*(2\pi,z^*) = \Psi^*(x^*,0) = \Psi^*(x^*,\pi) = 0 \quad , \tag{3.26}$$

in which Ψ^* is a dimensionless variable and

$$\tilde{\nabla}^2 = a^2\frac{\partial^2}{\partial x^{*2}} + \frac{\partial^2}{\partial z^{*2}} \quad , \tag{3.27}$$

$$a = 2z_T/L \quad , \tag{3.28}$$

$$x^* = 2\pi x/L \quad , \tag{3.29}$$

$$z^* = \pi z/z_T \quad . \tag{3.30}$$

The above boundary conditions imply that only complete waves are possible in the horizontal, but that half and full waves are possible in the vertical. The task of finding the eigenfunctions is made simpler if we seek separable solutions for $\Psi^*(x^*,z^*)$ of the form

$$\Psi^*(x^*,z^*) = F(x^*)\ G(z^*) \quad . \tag{3.31}$$

In this case, a typical term in the spectral expansion for $\psi^*(x^*,z^*,t^*)$ would be

$$\psi^*(x^*,z^*,t^*) \sim \hat{\psi}(t^*)\Psi^*(x^*,z^*) = \hat{\psi}(t^*)\ F(x^*)\ G(z^*) \quad , \tag{3.32}$$

in which $\hat{\psi}(t^*)$ is an amplitude coefficient (see Section 3.3).

To find the functions $F(x^*)$ and $G(z^*)$, we substitute (3.31) into (3.25) and obtain

$$a^2\ G\ \frac{\partial^2 F}{\partial x^{*2}} + F\ \frac{\partial^2 G}{\partial z^{*2}} = -\ \sigma\ FG \quad . \tag{3.33}$$

Upon dividing (3.33) by the product FG, we find

$$\frac{a^2}{F}\frac{\partial^2 F}{\partial x^{*2}} + \frac{1}{G}\frac{\partial^2 G}{\partial z^{*2}} = -\ \sigma \quad . \tag{3.34}$$

The first term in (3.34) involves only functions of x^*, while the second only functions of z^*; yet, the two terms sum to a constant, $-\sigma$. The only way this can occur for all values of x^* and z^* is for the terms themselves to be constants that sum to $-\sigma$. Thus, we conclude that $F(x^*)$ and $G(z^*)$ are solutions to the separate equations

$$a^2\ \frac{\partial^2 F}{\partial x^{*2}} + \sigma_H\ F = 0 \quad , \tag{3.35}$$

and

$$\frac{\partial^2 G}{\partial z^{*2}} + (\sigma - \sigma_H)\ G = 0 \quad , \tag{3.36}$$

in which σ_H is the horizontal set, and $(\sigma - \sigma_H)$ the vertical set, of eigenvalues. In order to find the required basis functions $\Psi^*(x^*,z^*)$, we must solve (3.35) and (3.36) independently.

We begin by substituting a solution of the form

$$F(x^*) \sim \exp(sx^*) \quad , \tag{3.37}$$

into (3.35) and find that $s^2 = -\sigma_H/a^2$ must hold. Because $F(x^*)$ is a solution to the linear problem (3.35) and there are two admissible values of s, the general solution for $F(x^*)$ is

$$F(x^*) = A \exp[i\sqrt{\sigma_H}\, x^*/a] + B \exp[-i\sqrt{\sigma_H}\, x^*/a] \quad . \tag{3.38}$$

With Euler's identity, we may write (3.38) in the simpler form

$$F(x^*) = \tilde{A} \sin[\sqrt{\sigma_H}\, x^*/a] + \tilde{B} \cos[\sqrt{\sigma_H}\, x^*/a] \quad , \tag{3.39}$$

in which $\tilde{A} = i(A - B)$ and $\tilde{B} = (A + B)$. The boundary conditions (3.26) imply that $\tilde{B} = 0$ and that the argument of the sine function in (3.39) must be equal to mx^* with $m = \pm 1, \pm 2, \ldots$ in order for there to be only complete waves; consequently, the horizontal eigenvalues σ_H are

$$\sigma_H = a^2 m^2 \quad , \quad m = \pm 1, \pm 2, \ldots \quad . \tag{3.40}$$

The form for $F(x^*)$ is then reduced to

$$F(x^*) = \tilde{A} \sin(mx^*) \quad , \quad m = \pm 1, \pm 2, \ldots \quad . \tag{3.41}$$

The solution for $G(z^*)$, obtained in a similar manner, is

$$G(z^*) = \tilde{C} \sin(nz^*) \quad , \quad n = \pm 1, \pm 2, \ldots \quad , \tag{3.42}$$

in which the eigenvalue σ obeys

$$\sigma_{mn} = (ma)^2 + n^2 \quad , \quad m = \pm 1, \pm 2, \ldots \; ; \quad n = \pm 1, \pm 2, \ldots \quad . \tag{3.43}$$

We note that the expression in (3.43) appears quite commonly as coefficients in some terms of a spectral model; see for example (2.75)-(2.77).

Equations (3.41) and (3.42) may be combined to specify completely the spatial dependence of $\psi^*(x^*,z^*,t^*)$:

$$\psi^*(x^*,z^*,t^*) = \sum_m \sum_n \psi_{mn}(t^*) \sin(mx^*) \sin(nz^*) \quad , \tag{3.44}$$

in which $\Psi^*_{mn}(x^*,z^*) = \sin(mx^*) \sin(nz^*)$ are the appropriate basis functions. A comparison of (3.44) and (2.73) reveals that selection of the single harmonics m in x^* and n in z^* produces the expansion used in the Lorenz (1963) model.

To produce the Galerkin form of the equations, expansions of the type given in (3.44) are needed for each dependent variable in the set of original partial differential equations. Throughout most of this monograph, we limit discussions to flows in rigid or horizontally cyclic rectangular domains and to models created with eigenfunctions satisfying the Helmholtz problem (3.15). Consequently, we need only trigonometric functions to expand the variables. We are not required to adopt this approach, however, for we can use any linear problem to define the eigenfunctions. For example, as suggested by Ladyzhenskaya (1969), a better approach might be to incorporate dynamical information directly into the basis functions. This is accomplished by extracting linear eigenvalue problems directly from the model equations (see Dutton and Wells, 1984), and requires a more sophisticated analysis of the linear differential equations (see, for example, Kirchgässner, 1975). In any case, once we have developed suitable sets of basis functions for the variables, we create the spectral model, a task we describe in the next section.

3.3 Forming the Spectral Model

Now that we have forms for the Fourier expansion of each dependent variable, we have completed the first three steps in the outline given in the introduction to this chapter. The final step is to form the spectral model, and this procedure itself involves four steps. In order to form an ordinary differential equation for an amplitude coefficient $a_{mn}(t)$ we

4.1) Substitute the Fourier expansions for the variables into the appropriate partial differential equation,

4.2) Multiply the resulting equation by the particular eigenfunction that the coefficient $a_{mn}(t)$ multiplies in the expansion (for complex eigenfunctions, we must multiply by the complex conjugate of the eigenfunction),

4.3) Integrate the result over the spatial domain, using orthogonality of the eigenfunctions in the expansion,

4.4) Write only those terms that are nonzero; that is, retain only those terms that act to alter directly the values of $a_{mn}(t)$.

We note that the resulting solution $a_{mn}(t)$ is only an approximation to the complete solution since we have truncated the Fourier series. However, it is plausible and in some cases proved (Temam, 1983), that, if we have truncated the series wisely, then the approximation is a satisfactory one.

To illustrate the process of forming a spectral model, we consider classical Rayleigh-Bénard convection whose appropriate dimensional system of equations is (cf. (2.34)-(2.35))

$$\frac{\partial}{\partial t^*} \tilde{\nabla}^2 \psi^* = - J(\psi^*, \tilde{\nabla}^2 \psi^*) + P(1+a^2)^{-1} \tilde{\nabla}^4 \psi^* + P(1+a^2) \frac{\partial T^*}{\partial x^*} \quad , \tag{3.45}$$

$$\frac{\partial T^*}{\partial t^*} = - J(\psi^*, T^*) + r \frac{\partial \psi^*}{\partial x^*} + (1+a^2)^{-1} \tilde{\nabla}^2 T^* \quad , \tag{3.46}$$

in which the domain is given by $0 \le x^* \le 2\pi$ and $0 \le z^* \le \pi$. In addition, the normalized Rayleigh number r is defined in (2.36), the Prandtl number P in (2.29) and the aspect ratio a in (3.28); the dimensionless Laplacian $\tilde{\nabla}^2$ is given in (3.27), the operator $\tilde{\nabla}^4 \psi^* = \tilde{\nabla}^2(\tilde{\nabla}^2 \psi^*)$ and the Jacobian J for dimensionless variables f^* and g^* is

$$J(f^*, g^*) = \frac{\partial f^*}{\partial x^*} \frac{\partial g^*}{\partial z^*} - \frac{\partial f^*}{\partial z^*} \frac{\partial g^*}{\partial x^*} \quad . \tag{3.47}$$

The appropriate eigenvalue problem for the dependent variables ψ^* and T^* was solved for ψ^* in Section 3.2. We discovered that

$$\psi^*(x^*, z^*, t^*) = \sum_{m=1}^{\infty} \sum_{n=1}^{\infty} \psi_{mn}(t^*) \sin(mx^*) \sin(nz^*) \quad , \tag{3.48}$$

is an appropriate expansion for ψ^*; we may show easily that

$$T^*(x^*,z^*,t^*) = \sum_{m=0}^{\infty} \sum_{n=1}^{\infty} T_{mn}(t^*) \cos(mx^*) \sin(nz^*) \quad , \tag{3.49}$$

is the corresponding expansion for T^*.

Next, we truncate the series at an appropriate number of terms. With the arguments presented in Section 2.2, we arrive at the smallest effective truncation (2.78)-(2.79) able to produce a nonlinear model:

$$\psi^*(x^*,z^*,t^*) = \sqrt{2}\, X(t^*) \sin x^* \sin z^* \quad , \tag{3.50}$$

$$T^*(x^*,z^*,t^*) = \sqrt{2}\, Y(t^*) \cos x^* \sin z^* - Z(t^*) \sin 2z^* \quad , \tag{3.51}$$

in which $X = \psi_{11}$, $Y = T_{11}$ and $Z = - T_{02}$, and the $\sqrt{2}$ has been introduced so that the basis functions are orthonormal. Now we use the expansion (3.50)-(3.51) to convert (3.45)-(3.46) to a spectral form. Here, we illustrate the Galerkin technique in detail for only the temperature equation (3.46), because only the spectral temperature equations have nonlinear terms. The results for the momentum equation (3.45) follow by analogy.

We begin with Step 4.1 and substitute (3.50)-(3.51) into (3.46). After taking the appropriate derivatives, we obtain

$$\begin{aligned}
&\sqrt{2}\, \dot{Y} \cos x^* \sin z^* - \dot{Z} \sin 2z^* = \\
&\quad - \sqrt{2}\, X \cos x^* \sin z^* \left(\sqrt{2}\, Y \cos x^* \cos z^* - 2Z \cos 2z^*\right) \\
&\quad + \sqrt{2}\, X \sin x^* \cos z^* \left(- \sqrt{2}\, Y \sin x^* \sin z^*\right) \\
&\quad + r \sqrt{2}\, X \cos x^* \sin z^* \\
&\quad - (1+a^2)^{-1} \left(\sqrt{2}\, a^2\, Y \cos x^* \sin z^* + \sqrt{2}\, Y \cos x^* \sin z^*\right) \\
&\quad + 4(1+a^2)^{-1} Z \sin 2z^* \quad ,
\end{aligned} \tag{3.52}$$

in which the overdot denotes temporal differentiation. We note that the term involving a^2Y appears owing to the definition (3.27) of the dimensionless Laplacian operator. We now are ready to use the orthogonality properties of the basis functions to eliminate the spatial dependence in the equations. But before we carry out these calculations (Steps 4.2 and 4.3 above), we make several observations.

In general, we employ orthogonal functions in the expansions of the variables because these functions greatly simplify the calculations needed to form a spectral model. During these calculations, we must evaluate integrals that contain single, double, or triple products of the trigonometric functions. Integrals of a single sine or cosine function are easy to evaluate and depend on the range of integration. That is, we have

$$\int_0^{2\pi} \sin(mx^*)\, dx^* = 0 \quad , \tag{3.53}$$

$$\int_0^{2\pi} \cos(mx^*)\, dx^* = 0 \quad , \tag{3.54}$$

$$\int_0^{\pi} \sin(nz^*)\, dz^* = \begin{cases} 2/n & , \text{ n odd} \\ 0 & , \text{ n even} \end{cases} \quad . \tag{3.55}$$

Here, we evaluate the integrals of both $\sin(mx^*)$ and $\cos(mx^*)$ because we sometimes consider domains that are cyclic in x^*, but we evaluate the integral of only $\sin(nz^*)$ because $\cos(nz^*)$ does not appear in the expansions of the variables.

For double products, we find that

$$\int_0^{2\pi} \sin(\ell x^*)\, \sin(mx^*)\, dx^* = \begin{cases} 0, & \ell \neq m \\ \pi, & \ell = m \end{cases} \quad , \tag{3.56}$$

$$\int_0^{2\pi} \cos(\ell x^*)\, \cos(mx^*)\, dx^* = \begin{cases} 0, & \ell \neq m \\ \pi, & \ell = m \end{cases} \quad , \tag{3.57}$$

$$\int_0^{2\pi} \sin(\ell x^*)\, \cos(mx^*)\, dx^* = 0 \quad , \tag{3.58}$$

$$\int_0^{\pi} \sin(kz^*)\, \sin(nz^*)\, dz^* = \begin{cases} 0, & k \neq n \\ \pi/2, & k = n \end{cases} \quad . \tag{3.59}$$

In these cases, only integrals involving squares of functions are nonzero; this shows that these functions are orthogonal.

Equations similar to (3.56)-(3.59) exist for the triple products, but they are most easily evaluated using trigonometric identities to re-express them as sums of double products. For example,

$$\int_0^{2\pi} \sin(jx^*)\ \sin(\ell x^*)\ \cos(mx^*)\ dx^* =$$

$$\int_0^{2\pi} \frac{1}{2}\left[\cos(j-\ell)x^* - \cos(j+\ell)x^*\right]\cos(mx^*)\ dx^*$$

$$= \begin{cases} \pi/2 & , j-\ell=m \\ -\pi/2 & , j+\ell=m \\ 0 & , \text{otherwise} \end{cases} \quad , \qquad (3.60)$$

in which we have used (3.57) to evaluate the second integral. We note that this integral is nonzero only if either the sum or the difference of two wavenumbers equals the third. As triple products appear during the calculation of nonlinear terms, arising for example from the Jacobians, we see that three amplitude coefficients associated with the appropriate eigenfunctions having three wavenumbers j, ℓ, m are necessary for the inclusion of some nonlinear terms in a model. But not just any three values will do--they must be related by either $j - \ell = m$ or $j + \ell = m$; these conditions are known as selection rules, which must be satisfied for nonlinearity to appear. Actually, selection rules for the wavenumbers in both the x^*- and z^*-directions must be satisfied simultaneously for a particular nonlinear interaction to be modeled. Thus, spectral truncations must be chosen carefully in order for nonlinear effects to be represented adequately in the system.

We may picture how some of the above products integrate to zero, while others do not, by graphing the integrand and then noting whether or not the areas above and below the abscissa balance. Examples of linear, quadratic and cubic expressions are given in Fig. 3.5.

We now return to the process of creating a spectral model by performing Steps 4.2 and 4.3; that is, we multiply each term in (3.52) by the appropriate basis function and integrate over the domain $0 \leq x^* \leq 2\pi$, $0 \leq z^* \leq \pi$. Because there are two temporal derivatives of the temperature coefficients in (3.52), given by $\dot{Y}$ and $\dot{Z}$, we must perform these steps twice. When completed, we obtain two ordinary differential equations, one for $\dot{Y}$ and the other for $\dot{Z}$.

To obtain an equation for $\dot{Y}$, we multiply (3.52) by the eigenfunction for which Y is the coefficient--that is by ($\cos x^* \sin z^*$)--and then integrate, to find

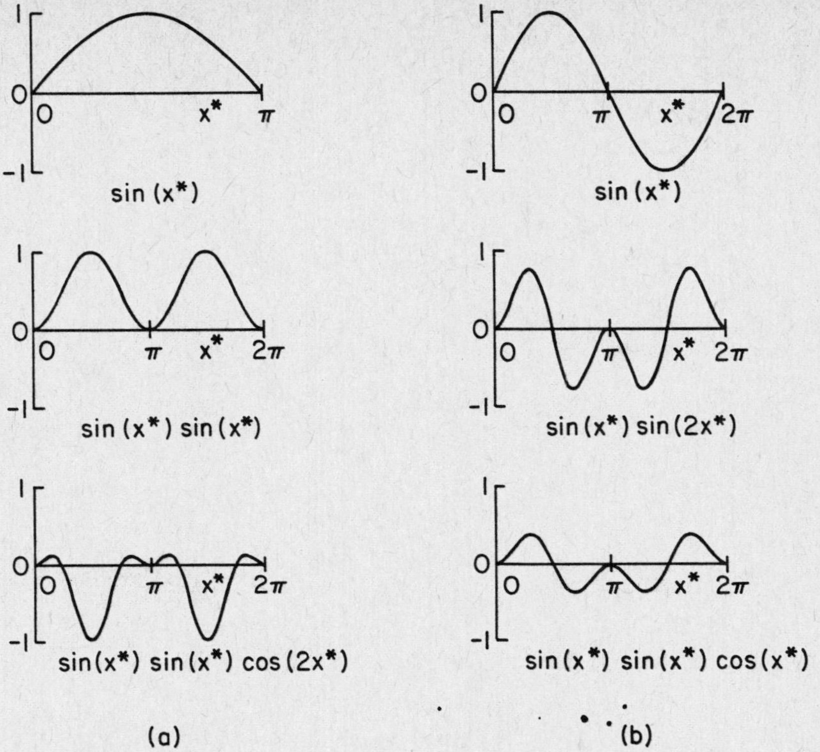

Fig. 3.5 Examples of integrands that do not vanish (a) and that do vanish (b).

$$
\begin{aligned}
&\sqrt{2}\,\dot{Y} \int_0^{2\pi} \cos x^* \cos x^*\, dx^* \int_0^{\pi} \sin z^* \sin z^*\, dz^* \\
&- \dot{Z} \int_0^{2\pi} \cos x^*\, dx^* \int_0^{\pi} \sin z^* \sin 2z^*\, dz^* = \\
&- 2\, X\, Y \int_0^{2\pi} \cos x^* \cos x^* \cos x^*\, dx^* \int_0^{\pi} \sin z^* \cos z^* \sin z^*\, dz^* \\
&+ 2\sqrt{2}\, X\, Z \int_0^{2\pi} \cos x^* \cos x^*\, dx^* \int_0^{\pi} \sin z^* \cos 2z^* \sin z^*\, dz^* \\
&- 2\, X\, Y \int_0^{2\pi} \sin x^* \sin x^* \cos x^*\, dx^* \int_0^{\pi} \cos z^* \sin z^* \sin z^*\, dz^* \\
&+ r\sqrt{2}\, X \int_0^{2\pi} \cos x^* \cos x^*\, dx^* \int_0^{\pi} \sin z^* \sin z^*\, dz^* \\
&- \sqrt{2}\, Y \int_0^{2\pi} \cos x^* \cos x^*\, dx^* \int_0^{\pi} \sin z^* \sin z^*\, dz^* \\
&+ 4(1+a^2)^{-1}\, Z \int_0^{2\pi} \cos x^*\, dx^* \int_0^{\pi} \sin z^* \sin 2z^*\, dz^* \quad , \qquad (3.61)
\end{aligned}
$$

in which we have first combined the two terms in (3.52) involving $-(1+a^2)^{-1}Y$. Step 4.3 involves evaluating the integrals in (3.61) using (3.56)-(3.59), and we observe immediately that several of the integrals are zero. Using some trigonometric identities, we evaluate the triple products that arise in the nonlinear terms as

$$\int_0^{2\pi} \cos x^* \cos x^* \cos x^* \, dx^* = \int_0^{2\pi} \cos x^* \frac{1}{2} (1+\cos 2x^*) \, dx^* = 0 \quad , \tag{3.62}$$

$$\int_0^{2\pi} \cos x^* \sin x^* \sin x^* \, dx^* = \int_0^{2\pi} \cos x^* \frac{1}{2} (1-\cos 2x^*) \, dx^* = 0 \quad , \tag{3.63}$$

$$\int_0^{\pi} \sin z^* \sin z^* \cos 2z^* \, dz^* = \int_0^{\pi} \frac{1}{2} (1-\cos 2z^*) \cos 2z^* \, dz^* = -\frac{\pi}{4} \quad . \tag{3.64}$$

To complete the process in Step 4.4, we combine all of the results to find that (3.61) becomes simply

$$\dot{Y} = - X Z + r X - Y \quad . \tag{3.65}$$

This is one of the three spectral equations we seek. The right side of (3.65) contains a nonlinear term, an energy generation (or buoyancy) term, and a dissipation term, respectively.

We obtain a similar equation for $\dot{Z}$ by analogy. After multiplying (3.52) by $\sin 2z^*$ and evaluating the integrals, we find that

$$\dot{Z} = X Y - b Z \quad , \tag{3.66}$$

in which $b = 4/(1+a^2)$. Notice that the right side of (3.66) consists only of a nonlinear term and a dissipation term.

Finally, to complete the model, we execute this procedure one more time by substituting the basis functions (3.50)-(3.51) into the vorticity equation (3.45), multiplying by $(\sin x^* \sin z^*)$ and integrating the result, to obtain

$$\dot{X} = P Y - P X \quad . \tag{3.67}$$

Notice that there is no nonlinear term in (3.67), but that energy generation and dissipation terms do appear. In order to include such nonlinear terms, we must consider a larger expansion for ψ^* (see Chapter 9). The ordinary differential equations (3.65)-(3.67) complete the spectral model of Lorenz (1963). For a complete discussion of all of the properties of the Boussinesq equations that this low-order model captures, as well as some of the bifurcation and stability properties of its stationary solutions, see Chapter 2.

Although the above calculations are straightforward, they are tedious when performed manually. Creation of low-order models having more than six equations becomes a process that is ripe for sign errors and missed terms. The redevelopment of the model that is necessary for purging the equations of these errors could be applied much better to analysis and interpretation of the resulting system of equations. Fortunately, in recent years computer software has been developed that is able to perform a wide variety of symbolic manipulations, ranging from simple substitutions of expressions to factoring, differentiating, or integrating polynomials. These algorithms can be used for the rapid and accurate development of low-order spectral models (Pyle, 1986). Examples of such a program and its symbolic output are shown in Tables 3.1 and 3.2 for the Lorenz model. The program MACSYMA was used and run on a SYMBOLICS 3670 computer; only 66 seconds were required for the program to generate the $\dot{X}_2 = \dot{Y}$ equation (3.65)! In Table 3.1, a portion of the program is shown, together with explanations of the particular manipulations being performed; in Table 3.2, a portion of the output is given, together with references to the corresponding equations in this chapter. As the application of low-order spectral modeling proceeds to more complicated physical problems, it is apparent that use of such symbolic manipulators is unavoidable if significant progress is to be made.

Now that we are able to create a low-order model, we are ready to begin studying its properties. Even though we are interested in the nonlinear character of the solutions, we find that the appropriate initial analysis is a linear one; it is the topic of the next chapter.

Table 3.1 Sample Symbolic Program to Calculate $\dot{Y}$ Equation

	Program	Explanation
(C1)	`del2(var1):=a**2*diff(var1,x,2)+diff(var1,z,2);`	Define $\tilde{\nabla}^2(\ )$
(C2)	`del4(var1):=a**4*diff(var1,x,4)+2*a**2*diff(var1,x,2,z,2)+diff(var1,z,4);`	Define $\tilde{\nabla}^4(\ )$
(C3)	`jacb(var1,var2):=diff(var1,x,1)*diff(var2,z,1)-diff(var2,x,1)*diff(var1,z,1);`	Define $J(f^*,g^*)$
(C4)	`s:sqrt(2)*x1*sin(x)*sin(z);`	Define ψ^* expansion
(C5)	`t:sqrt(2)*x2*cos(x)*sin(z)-x3*sin(2*z);`	Define T^* expansion
(C6)	`sg:a**2+1;`	Define σ_{11}
(C7)	`eq1:del2(s)=-jacb(s,del2(s))+(p/sg)*del4(s)+p*sg*diff(t,x,1);`	Calculate $\tilde{\nabla}^2\psi^*$ equation
(C8)	`eq2:t=-jacb(s,t)+r*diff(s,x,1)+(1/sg)*del2(t);`	Calculate T^* equation
(C9)	`ex2:eq2*cos(x)*sin(z);`	Isolate $\dot{X}_2 = \dot{Y}$ equation
(C10)	`ex2:integrate(ex2,x,0,2*%pi);`	Integrate with respect to x^*
(C11)	`ex2:integrate(ex2,z,0,%pi);`	Integrate with respect to z^*
(C12)	`ex2:ex2*(1/coeff(lhs(ex2),x2));`	Simplify $\dot{X}_2$ equation
(C13)	`ex2:factor(ex2);`	Final result

Table 3.2 Some Output from Program in Table 3.1

	Output	Equation in Text
(D1)	DEL2(VAR1) : = A^2 DIFF(VAR1, X, 2) + DIFF(VAR1, Z, 2)	(3.27)
(D2)	DEL4(VAR1) : = A^4 DIFF(VAR1, X, 4) + 2 A^2 DIFF(VAR1, X, 2, Z, 2) + DIFF(VAR1, Z, 4)	--
(D3)	JACB(VAR1, VAR2) : = DIFF(VAR1, X, 1) DIFF(VAR2, Z, 1) - DIFF(VAR2, X, 1) DIFF(VAR1, Z, 1)	(3.47)
(D4)	SQRT(2) SIN(X) X1 SIN(Z)	(3.50)
(D5)	SQRT(2) COS(X) X2 SIN(Z) - X3 SIN(2 Z)	(3.51)
(D6)	A^2 + 1	--
(D7)	- SQRT(2) A^2 SIN(X) X1 SIN(Z) - SQRT(2) SIN(X) X1 SIN(Z) =	
	$\frac{\text{P (SQRT(2) } A^4 \text{ SIN(X) X1 SIN(Z) + 2 SQRT(2) } A^2 \text{ SIN(X) X1 SIN(Z) + SQRT(2) SIN(X) X1 SIN(Z))}}{A^2 + 1}$	
	+ SQRT(2) SIN(X) X1 COS(Z) (-SQRT(2) A^2 COS(X) X1 SIN(Z) - SQRT(2) COS(X) X1 SIN(Z))	
	- SQRT(2) COS(X) X1 (-SQRT(2) A^2 SIN(X) X1 COS(Z) - SQRT(2) SIN(X) X1 COS(Z)) SIN(Z) - SQRT(2) (A^2 + 1) P SIN(X) X2 SIN(Z)	--
(D8)	SQRT(2) COS(X) X2 SIN(Z) - X3 SIN(2 Z) =	
	$\frac{\text{4 X3 SIN(2 Z) - SQRT(2) } A^2 \text{ COS(X) X2 SIN(Z) - SQRT(2) COS(X) X2 SIN(Z)}}{A^2 + 1}$ + SQRT(2) R COS(X) X1 SIN(Z)	
	- SQRT(2) COS(X) X1 SIN(Z) (SQRT(2) COS(X) X2 COS(Z) - 2 X3 COS(2 Z)) - 2 SIN^2(X) X1 X2 COS(Z) SIN(Z)	(3.52)
(D9)	COS(X) SIN(Z) (SQRT(2) COS(X) X2 SIN(Z) - X3 SIN(2 Z)) =	
	COS(X) SIN(Z) { $\frac{\text{4 X3 SIN(2 Z) - SQRT(2) } A^2 \text{ COS(X) X2 SIN(Z) - SQRT(2) COS(X) X2 SIN(Z)}}{A^2 + 1}$	
	- SQRT(2) COS(X) X1 SIN(Z) (SQRT(2) COS(X) X2 COS(Z) - 2 X3 COS(2 Z))	
	- 2 SIN^2(X) X1 X2 COS(Z) SIN(Z) + SQRT(2) R COS(X) X1 SIN(Z)}	(3.61)
(D10)	SQRT(2) %PI X2 SIN^2(Z) = SIN(Z) (2 SQRT(2) %PI X1 X3 SIN(Z) COS(2 Z) + (SQRT(2) %PI R X1 - SQRT(2) %PI X2) SIN(Z))	--
(D11)	$\frac{\text{SQRT(2) \%PI}^2 \text{ X2}}{2} = \frac{\text{- SQRT(2) \%PI}^2 \text{ X1 X3 - SQRT(2) \%PI}^2 \text{ X2 + SQRT(2) \%PI}^2 \text{ R X1}}{2}$	--
(D12)	X2 = $\frac{\text{- SQRT(2) \%PI}^2 \text{ X1 X3 - SQRT(2) \%PI}^2 \text{ X2 + SQRT(2) \%PI}^2 \text{ R X1}}{\text{SQRT(2) \%PI}^2}$	--
(D13)	X2 = - (X1 X3 + X2 - R X1)	(3.65)

CHAPTER 4

LINEAR STABILITY ANALYSIS

RONALD GELARO

Once we have created a low-order model using the methods discussed in Chapter 3, the next task is to analyze its properties. Because we study forced, dissipative systems, we find typically that for sufficiently weak forcing, dissipation damps flows to a single solution as time approaches infinity. Although we discuss this thoroughly in Chapters 6 and 17, we note here that this unique solution is often the (time-independent) trivial one in which all spectral components vanish. In classical Rayleigh-Bénard convection, for example, this trivial solution corresponds to pure conduction (see Chapter 2). When all small perturbations of a solution decay, then we say that such a solution is asymptotically stable.

For stronger forcing, the dissipation might no longer be large enough for the trivial solution to be stable. Indeed, in such a case the flow is likely to depart from the trivial solution and so at least some of the spectral components of the flow are nonzero. As we discuss in Chapters 5 and 11, the existence of an unstable solution suggests that a bifurcation has occurred at some critical value of the forcing. A critical value is one for which neither decay nor amplification occurs in some mode, and such a critical value is identified via a linear analysis of the equations.

Thus, the first step in the study of the nonlinear behavior of a system is to find a time-independent, or stationary, solution such as the trivial one and then to perform a linear analysis of it to determine its stability properties. In particular, we seek those values of the forcing for which the trivial solution is neither asymptotically stable nor unstable. In this chapter we show how to perform a stability analysis of stationary solutions, and then armed with knowledge of the critical values of the forcing, we proceed to a nonlinear analysis in later chapters.

4.1 The Concept of Stability

A mathematically stable solution corresponds to an "observable" state of a given system. This concept has a wide variety of applications. For example, many chemical reactions involving two or more compounds form a third that transforms into some other substance so rapidly that the intermediate compound is unobserved in the laboratory. This intermediate compound corresponds to an unstable solution of the equations that describe the evolution of the chemical system. We noted earlier that a system may often have several solutions. However, if a perturbation of a solution S grows to produce a vastly different solution, then S is not stable and therefore is not observable. Mathematically, an observable state is a solution to a system with the property that slight perturbations damp out to produce the original state.

Although we show in Chapter 5 that bifurcation is related to stability, stability does not arise from nonuniqueness in the system. A formal discussion of stability is given in Minorsky (1962), but the major points can be seen from a simple example. Consider the equation

$$\frac{dx}{dt} = \lambda x \quad , \tag{4.1}$$

which has the trivial solution as well as the time-dependent trajectory

$$x(t) = x(0)e^{\lambda t} \quad . \tag{4.2}$$

In the case $x(0) = 0$, we have $x(t) = 0$ for all t; thus an initial condition on that point causes the trajectory to remain there. When $x(0) \neq 0$, we have three possibilities for the stability of the trivial solution:

1) If $\lambda = 0$, then $x(t) = x(0)$, there is no growth or decay, and the trivial solution is (neutrally) stable.
2) If $\lambda < 0$, then $x(t) \to 0$ as $t \to \infty$ and we say that the trivial solution is asymptotically stable.
3) If $\lambda > 0$, then $x(t) \to \pm\infty$ as $t \to \infty$ and the trivial solution is unstable.

In the unstable case, infinitesimal perturbations (which in all physical systems are omnipresent) cause the trajectory to depart from the stationary point, and the trivial solution is not physically realizable. The above definitions of stability apply generally to stationary solutions; there are comparable definitions for temporally periodic solutions, but we present those in Chapter 14.

4.2 The Method for Stability Calculations

The determination of stability is begun commonly by rewriting the system as one that describes the evolution of a perturbation. As before, the linearized version of the perturbation equations suffices because it is a theorem that a nonlinear solution that is linearly stable is also nonlinearly stable to small perturbations (Hirsch and Smale, 1974). We call this property infinitesimal stability. Global stability requires that a solution be stable to an arbitrarily large perturbation, but global stability cannot be determined from the linearized equations.

To construct the perturbation or variational equations, we note that the original ordinary differential system has the general form

$$\dot{y}_k = f_k(y_1, \ldots, y_n, R, \xi_1, \ldots, \xi_p) \quad ; \quad k=1, \ldots, n \quad , \tag{4.3}$$

in which the y_k are spectral components and both R and ξ_j are dimensionless parameters. We have isolated R because it is the particular forcing or control parameter of interest; for classical Rayleigh-Bénard convection discussed in Chapter 2, R is the Rayleigh number Ra and the parameters ξ_j are the Prandtl number P and the aspect ratio a. In general, the f_k are real, analytic functions of all the variables; stationary solutions to (4.3) are those for which $f_1 = f_2 = \cdots = f_n = 0$.

We find a stationary solution $y_i(t) = y_i^s$ to (4.3) and then write general solutions to (4.3) in the form

$$y_i(t) = y_i^s + x_i(t) \quad ; \quad i=1, \ldots, n \quad . \tag{4.4}$$

The behavior of the deviations $x_i(t)$ from a known stationary solution y_i^s provides the desired information about the stability of y_i^s. Substituting (4.4) into (4.3), using Taylor's Theorem to expand about y_i^s and keeping only linear terms in $x_i(t)$, we arrive at the variational equations

$$\dot{x}_i = \sum_{j=1}^{n} \left(\frac{\partial f_i}{\partial y_j}\right)_s x_j = \sum_{j=1}^{n} a_{ij} x_j \quad ; \quad i = 1, \ldots, n \quad , \tag{4.5}$$

in which the subscript s denotes that the derivatives are evaluated at $y_i = y_i^s$. In general, (4.5) has n simple solutions

$$x_i^\ell(t) = c_i^\ell \exp[\lambda_\ell t] \quad ; \quad i=1, \ldots, n \quad ; \quad \ell = 1, \ldots, n \quad , \qquad (4.6)$$

that satisfy

$$\dot{x}_i^\ell = \lambda_\ell x_i^\ell \quad ; \quad i=1, \ldots, n \quad ; \quad \ell = 1, \ldots, n \quad . \qquad (4.7)$$

These solutions or <u>pure</u> <u>modes</u> form a <u>basis</u> that is the set of solutions of (4.5): Any solution of (4.5) is expressed uniquely as a <u>superposition</u> of the pure solutions, that is as a sum

$$x_i(t) = \sum_{\ell=1}^{n} b_\ell x_i^\ell(t) = \sum_{\ell=1}^{n} b_\ell c_i^\ell \exp[\lambda_\ell t] \quad ; \quad i=1, \ldots, n \quad . \qquad (4.8)$$

Before proceeding, we summarize the reasons for deriving (4.5). Recall that we wish to determine whether or not the stationary solution y_i^s is a stable solution of (4.3). Thus, we need to know whether a nearby time-dependent solution $y_i(t) \to y_i^s$ as $t \to \infty$. Because this behavior corresponds to that of the time-dependent perturbation $x_i(t)$ in (4.4), we seek solutions to (4.5). For example, if $x_i(t) \to 0$ as $t \to \infty$, then $y_i(t) \to y_i^s$ and the stationary solution is asymptotically stable.

To determine the solutions $x_i(t)$ we need to know the n numbers λ_ℓ in (4.6). Toward this end, we set $\lambda = \lambda_\ell$ and substitute (4.6) into (4.5) to obtain

$$\lambda c_i^\ell e^{\lambda t} = \sum_{j=1}^{n} a_{ij} c_j^\ell e^{\lambda t} \quad ; \quad i=1, \ldots, n \quad . \qquad (4.9)$$

If we cancel $e^{\lambda t}$, then (4.9) has solutions provided that λ, c_1^ℓ , ..., c_n^ℓ satisfy

$$\lambda c_i^\ell = \sum_{j=1}^{n} a_{ij} c_j^\ell \quad ; \quad i=1,\ldots, n \quad . \qquad (4.10)$$

Rewriting (4.10) in the form

$$\sum_{j=1}^{n} a_{ij} c_j^\ell - \lambda c_i^\ell = \sum_{j=1}^{n} (a_{ij} - \lambda \delta_{ij}) c_j^\ell = 0 \quad ; \quad i=1, \ldots, n \quad , \qquad (4.11)$$

and carrying out the summation on the left side of (4.11), we produce the system

$$\left.\begin{aligned} (a_{11} - \lambda)c_1^\ell + a_{12}c_2^\ell + \cdots + a_{1n}c_n^\ell &= 0 \\ a_{21}c_1^\ell + (a_{22} - \lambda)c_2^\ell + \cdots + a_{2n}c_n^\ell &= 0 \\ &\vdots \\ a_{n1}c_1^\ell + a_{n2}c_2^\ell + \cdots + (a_{nn} - \lambda)c_n^\ell &= 0 \end{aligned}\right\} \quad . \tag{4.12}$$

For $x_i^\ell(t)$ to be a member of the basis, (4.12) must have a nontrivial solution. Because (4.12) is a linear, homogeneous system, the determinant of the constant coefficients c_i^ℓ must vanish:

$$\begin{vmatrix} a_{11} - \lambda & a_{12} & \cdots & a_{1n} \\ a_{21} & a_{22} - \lambda & \cdots & a_{2n} \\ \vdots & \vdots & \vdots & \vdots \\ a_{n1} & a_{n2} & \cdots & a_{nn} - \lambda \end{vmatrix} = 0 \quad , \tag{4.13}$$

which, when expanded, yields an nth-degree polynomial equation in λ of the form

$$\lambda^n + e_1\lambda^{n-1} + \cdots + e_{n-1}\lambda + e_n = 0 \quad . \tag{4.14}$$

Equation (4.14) is called the <u>characteristic equation</u> whose n roots $\lambda_1, \ldots, \lambda_n$ are the <u>characteristic exponents</u> of (4.5) and are the eigenvalues of the matrix (a_{ij}). As λ takes on the n values λ_ℓ, we obtain the eigenvectors (c_i^ℓ) and therefore the pure modes $x_i^\ell(t)$ that form the basis. Now any solution $x_i(t)$ to the variational equations (4.5) can be written as a linear combination (4.8) of the n members of the basis.

Because of the exponential form of the solution (4.8), the perturbations $x_i(t) \to 0$ only if each λ_ℓ has a negative real part. Recalling that the solution to (4.3) is of the form $y_i(t) = y_i^s + x_i(t)$, we see that three cases must be considered.

1) If $Re\{\lambda_\ell\} < 0$ for <u>every</u> λ_ℓ, then $|\exp(\lambda_\ell t)| \to 0$ as $t \to \infty$ and $x_i(t) \to 0$. Thus, $y_i(t) \to y_i^s$ and we conclude that y_i^s is an asymptotically stable stationary solution.

2) If $\mathrm{Re}\{\lambda_\ell\} > 0$ for <u>some</u> λ_ℓ, then $|\exp(\lambda_\ell t)| \to \infty$ as $t \to \infty$ and $x_i(t) \to \infty$. Thus, $y_i(t)$ cannot tend to y_i^s and we conclude that y_i^s is an unstable stationary solution.

The above results can be stated formally as

> <u>Theorem</u>. If all the characteristic exponents of the variational equation (4.5) based on the stationary solution $y_i(t) = y_i^s$ of an autonomous system have negative real parts, then y_i^s is asymptotically stable. If at least one characteristic exponent has a positive real part, then y_i^s is unstable.

3) If $\mathrm{Re}\{\lambda_\ell\} = 0$ for <u>some</u> λ_ℓ with $\mathrm{Re}\{\lambda_\ell\} < 0$ for all other λ_ℓ, then we have a critical point at which stability changes. There are two important cases for these critical points: one for which

$$\mathrm{Re}(\lambda_\ell) = 0 \text{ and } \mathrm{Im}(\lambda_\ell) \neq 0 \quad , \tag{4.15}$$

and the other for which $\mathrm{Re}(\lambda_\ell) = 0$ and $\mathrm{Im}(\lambda_\ell) = 0$ so that

$$\lambda_\ell = 0 \quad . \tag{4.16}$$

<u>4.2.1 Stability of the conductive solution to the Lorenz model.</u> Using the above results, we can obtain the stability portrait for the stationary solutions of the Lorenz model. We recall that this model can be written as (cf. (2.80)-(2.82)):

$$\dot{X} = -PX + PY \quad , \tag{4.17}$$

$$\dot{Y} = -XZ + rX - Y \quad , \tag{4.18}$$

$$\dot{Z} = XY - bZ \quad , \tag{4.19}$$

in which r is the forcing parameter of interest. In Section 2.2.2 we calculated the stability of only the trivial solution $X = Y = Z = 0$; here we adopt a more general approach that applies to all stationary solutions (X^s, Y^s, Z^s). Thus, we write the solutions to (4.17)-(4.19) in the form (4.4) as

$$X(t) = X^s + X'(t) \quad , \tag{4.20}$$

$$Y(t) = Y^s + Y'(t) \quad , \tag{4.21}$$

$$Z(t) = Z^s + Z'(t) \quad , \tag{4.22}$$

and then substitute them into (4.17)-(4.19). We neglect products of primed terms to form the linearized version of the equations given by

$$\dot{X}' = - PX' + PY' \quad , \tag{4.23}$$

$$\dot{Y}' = - Z^sX' - X^sZ' + rX' - Y' \quad , \tag{4.24}$$

$$\dot{Z}' = Y^sX' + X^sY' - bZ' \quad . \tag{4.25}$$

Solutions of (4.23)-(4.25) have the form (4.6):

$$X'(t) = \hat{X}e^{\lambda t} \quad , \tag{4.26}$$

$$Y'(t) = \hat{Y}e^{\lambda t} \quad , \tag{4.27}$$

$$Z'(t) = \hat{Z}e^{\lambda t} \quad . \tag{4.28}$$

Substituting (4.26)-(4.28) into the linearized equations (4.23)-(4.25), we obtain the variational equations for the Lorenz system

$$- (P + \lambda)\hat{X} + P\hat{Y} = 0 \quad , \tag{4.29}$$

$$- Z^s\hat{X} + r\hat{X} - X^s\hat{Z} - (1 + \lambda)\hat{Y} = 0 \quad , \tag{4.30}$$

$$Y^s\hat{X} + X^s\hat{Y} - (b + \lambda)\hat{Z} = 0 \quad , \tag{4.31}$$

in which the terms involving λ originate from the derivatives on the left sides of (4.23)-(4.25). As before in (4.13), the determinant of coefficients of (4.29)-(4.31) must vanish for the variational equations to have a nontrivial solution, and thus we obtain the general form for the characteristic equation

$$(b + \lambda)\left[(P + \lambda)(1 + \lambda) + P(Z^s - r)\right] + X^sY^sP + (X^s)^2(P + \lambda) = 0 \quad . \tag{4.32}$$

To determine the stability of the conductive solution, we substitute $X^s = Y^s = Z^s = 0$ into (4.32) and obtain

$$(b + \lambda)[\lambda^2 + (P + 1)\lambda - P(r - 1)] = 0 \quad , \tag{4.33}$$

whose characteristic exponents are

$$\lambda_{1,2} = -\frac{1}{2}(P + 1) \pm \frac{1}{2}\left[(P + 1)^2 + 4P(r - 1)\right]^{1/2} \quad , \tag{4.34}$$

$$\lambda_3 = -b \quad . \tag{4.35}$$

Because each of r, P, and b is positive, we see that λ_2 and λ_3 are always negative. However, λ_1 can change sign depending on the value of r; for $r < 1$, $\lambda_1 < 0$ and for $r > 1$, $\lambda_1 > 0$. Thus, the basic solution is asymptotically stable for $r < 1$ and unstable for $r > 1$. The characteristic exponent $\lambda_1 = 0$ occurs at $r = r_c = 1$, where the basic solution loses its stability; we may recall from Chapter 2 that this value coincides with the value (2.67) of the primary bifurcation point on the basic solution computed in Section 2.1.4.

4.2.2 Stability of the convective solutions. In Section 2.2.3 we determined the convective solutions of the generalized form of the Lorenz model. These solutions (2.100)-(2.102) correspond here to

$$X^s = Y^s = \pm [b(r - 1)]^{1/2} \quad , \tag{4.36}$$

$$Z^s = r - 1 \quad . \tag{4.37}$$

To calculate the stability of these solutions, we substitute either one into the general form (4.32) of the characteristic equation to obtain

$$\lambda^3 + (b + P + 1)\lambda^2 + b(P + r)\lambda + 2Pb(r - 1) = 0 \quad . \tag{4.38}$$

Setting $\lambda = 0$ in (4.38), we obtain the equation

$$2Pb(r - 1) = 0 \quad . \tag{4.39}$$

Thus, the only exchange of stability between the convective branch and another stationary solution occurs at the bifurcation point $r = r_c = 1$; of course, this other solution is simply the conductive one. However, because (4.38) cannot be factored easily, the roots λ are difficult to find analytically. But to examine stability, we need only know the signs of the real parts of the characteristic exponents.

We can use the Hurwitz Theorem (see Appendix A) to determine whether $\mathrm{Re}(\lambda) < 0$ for each λ (Chetayev, 1961). To use this theorem, we must calculate a sequence of determinants Δ_i that are constructed from various combinations of the coefficients of (4.38). Stable solutions occur exactly when $\Delta_i < 0$ for every i and loss of stability is signaled by a change of sign of at least one of the Δ_i.

In the present case, we must calculate the three minors Δ_i (A.7)-(A.9); because (4.38) is a cubic polynomial equation, these minors are

$$\Delta_1 = (b + P + 1) \quad , \tag{4.40}$$

$$\Delta_2 = (b + P + 1)\, b(P + r) - 2Pb(r - 1) \quad , \tag{4.41}$$

$$\Delta_3 = 2bP(r - 1)\Delta_2 \quad . \tag{4.42}$$

The convective solution is stable if $\Delta_1 > 0$, $\Delta_2 > 0$, and $\Delta_3 > 0$. Notice that $\Delta_1 > 0$ for all values of r, and so we have two cases to consider. When $\Delta_3 = 0$ but $\Delta_2 \neq 0$, we find that $r = r_c = 1$, which, as we noted above, is where both the conductive and convective solutions meet. The other case is given by $\Delta_2 = 0$ and $\Delta_3 \neq 0$. The convective solutions are stable as long as $r > 1$ and $\Delta_2 > 0$, which we see from (4.41) corresponds to

$$r(b - P + 1) > - P(P + b + 3) \quad , \tag{4.43}$$

in which $P > 0$ and $b > 0$. If $P < b + 1$, then (4.43) is satisfied and all the roots of (4.38) have negative real parts. In this case, the convective solution is always stable and the only stability exchange occurs between the conductive and convective solutions. However, when $P > b + 1$, (4.43) is exactly equivalent to

$$r < \frac{P(P + b + 3)}{P - b - 1} = r_H \quad , \tag{4.44}$$

and thus $\Delta_2 = 0$ when $r = r_H$. Because $r_H > 1$ whenever $P > b + 1$, we see that

$Re(\lambda) < 0$ for a certain range $1 < r < r_H$ of r. Thus, convective solutions are not always stable because at least one root λ has a positive real part when $r > r_H$. We find in Chapter 11 that $r = r_H$ is a Hopf bifurcation point at which a temporally periodic solution emanates from the stationary one (4.36)-(4.37). When $r > r_H$, numerical solutions to (4.17)-(4.19) exhibit surprising behavior as discussed in Section 15.3.2.

4.3 Stable and Unstable Manifolds.

The concept of stable and unstable manifolds, which are special, possibly higher dimensional surfaces in phase space, helps us to understand the stability of (stationary) solutions y_i^s. This concept links the linear notion of stability and exponential growth or decay with the nonlinear notions of bifurcation and the existence of multiple solutions. Now we examine the behavior of the perturbations $x_i(t)$ early in their evolution, in contrast to our previous concern with the evolution as time approached infinity. The necessary ideas are developed in Dutton and Wells (1984) and Sections 17.3.4 and 17.3.5; here we briefly summarize the main points. For simplicity we assume that all characteristic exponents λ are real.

An unstable stationary solution or equilibrium point is represented in Fig. 4.1 as the origin of a real two-dimensional phase space (Chapter 3) and is shown as the point 0. For this point, there is one negative exponent λ_-, hence one attracting direction, and one positive exponent λ_+, hence one repelling direction. Thus a perturbation decays to zero along the attracting x_2-axis but grows along the repelling x_1-axis. The x_2-axis is tangent to a manifold called the stable manifold S and the x_1-axis is tangent to the unstable manifold U. These manifolds can be specified as follows. All trajectories beginning on the stable manifold S remain on S and approach the unstable fixed point 0 as $t \to +\infty$. The direction of approach is parallel to the x_2-axis very near 0. Similarly, all trajectories beginning on the unstable manifold U remain on U and approach the unstable fixed point 0 as $t \to -\infty$; as $t \to +\infty$ these trajectories approach some other attractors that could be a stable stationary solution, a temporally periodic solution, or something more complicated (see Section 15.3). The latter conclusion follows from the fact that the solutions must be finite and so the perturbations must be bounded.

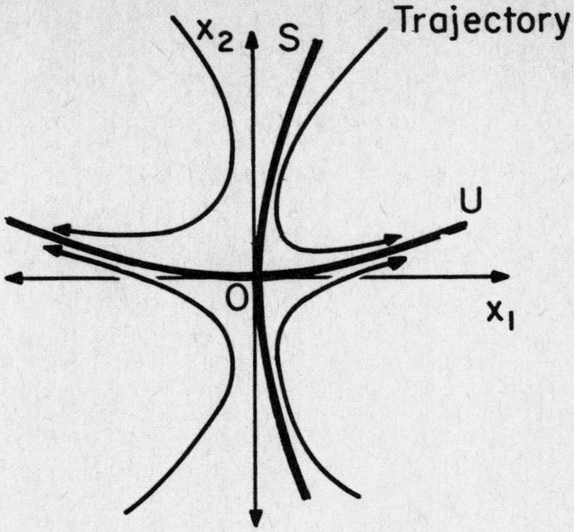

Fig. 4.1 Stable and unstable manifolds S and U of an unstable fixed point at the origin 0 in two dimensions. Trajectories approach 0 in the direction asymptotically parallel to the x_2-axis but depart from 0 in the direction asymptotically parallel to the x_1-axis.

The direction of departure is parallel to the x_1-axis very near 0. The collection of points composing either S or U is curved generally, but forms lines tangent to the x_2- and x_1-axes as shown in Fig. 4.1. It should be noted that S divides the two-dimensional space locally into two separate parts, so that information from one side cannot be communicated to the other. That is, trajectories beginning on the right of S remain on the right and those on the left remain on the left, at least for short times.

In three dimensions, the stable manifold could be a plane and the unstable manifold a line if there are two contracting and one expanding directions -- that is, if there are two negative exponents and one positive one. This is shown schematically in Fig. 4.2 where S and U are depicted and the unstable fixed point is the origin 0. Again it can be seen that near the origin the stable manifold divides the three-dimensional space into two separate parts. These concepts also make sense in the infinite-dimensional case, but in models relevant to viscous fluid dynamics, the unstable manifold is always finite-dimensional; significantly all the attractors are finite-dimensional as well (Constantin et al., 1985).

One way to see why these attractors ought to be finite-dimensional is illustrated in Fig. 4.3, in which typical trajectories are shown departing from the stationary solution 0 and approaching toward the attractors C_1 and C_2. These attractors apparently lie in a finite-dimensional extension of the finite-dimensional unstable manifold U. These considerations may be formalized to study such attractors (Wells and Dutton, 1986); here we are interested primarily in the general fact that we expect attractors to lie in well-behaved extensions of the unstable manifolds of unstable stationary solutions.

Further examination of Fig. 4.3 reveals that all trajectories not initially on the stable manifold S eventually approach either C_1 or C_2. In contrast, all trajectories that are initially on S eventually approach the unstable stationary solution 0. As in the two-dimensional case, the stable manifold provides the boundary separating two attractor basins (Fig. 4.3); the <u>attractor basin</u> is the set of initial conditions whose trajectories all approach a particular attractor.

The above discussion leads to several important conclusions. Suppose that the stationary point 0 has just lost stability in a single direction. Then, far away from the newly unstable solution 0, it still appears stable. There are two reasons for this phenomenon. First, there are usually a large number of attracting

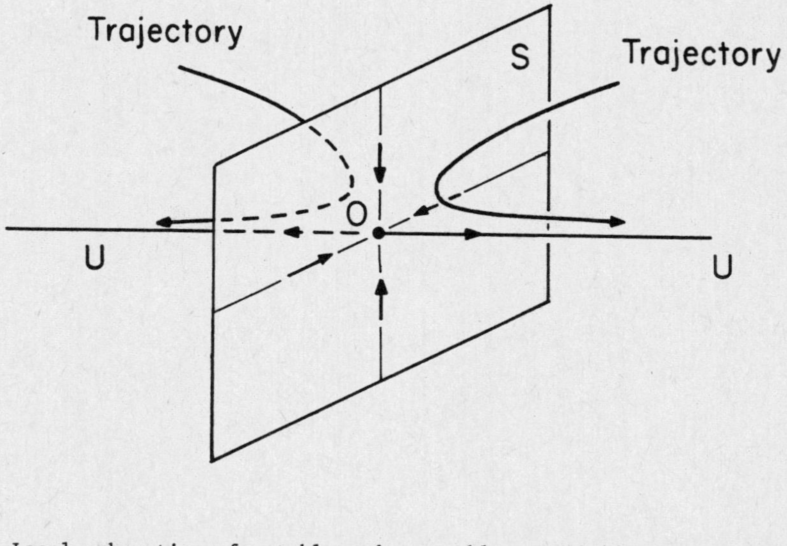

Fig. 4.2 Local schematic of stable and unstable manifolds S and U of an unstable fixed point 0 in three dimensions. Note that near 0, S divides the three-dimensional space into two subvolumes or attractor basins.

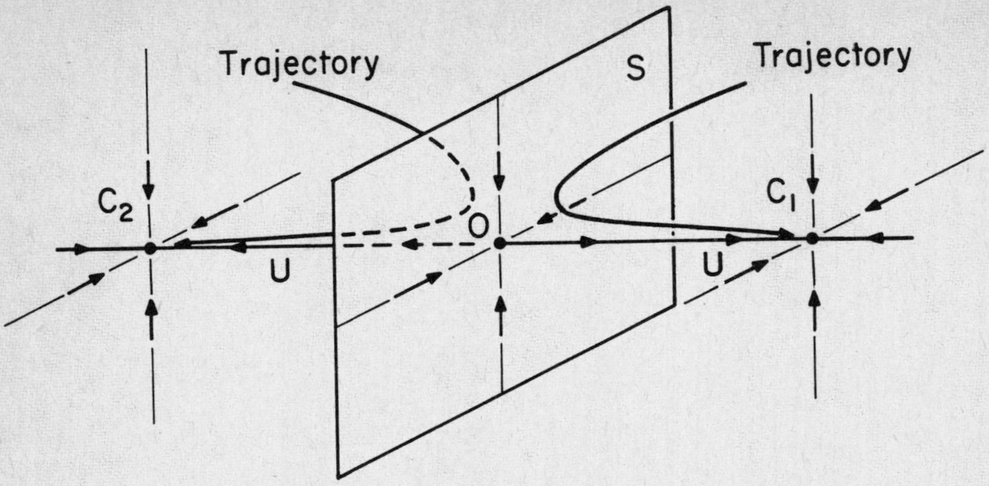

Fig. 4.3 Semi-local schematic of stable and unstable manifolds S and U for an unstable fixed point 0 in three dimensions. Trajectories initially approach 0 but eventually approach one of two stable fixed points C_1 and C_2 on an extension of the unstable manifold U. The two subvolumes created by S are the attractor basins for the two fixed points.

directions whose corresponding characteristic exponents have large negative real parts. Second, the exponent corresponding to the repelling direction has a small positive part. A trajectory therefore begins to approach the unstable solution until it becomes close enough for expansion to take over. Only then does the trajectory head towards a new stable solution. This behavior is shown in Fig. 4.3.

If a hierarchy of unstable equilibria exists, then the trajectory may approach a series of unstable equilibrium points, one after the other, until a final stable solution is obtained. An example of this behavior was discussed by Shirer (1984), who examined some solutions to a six-coefficient model. There are nine stationary solutions residing in a six-dimensional phase space, and the planar projections of these solutions and the repelling and attracting directions near them are shown in Fig. 4.4. These directions are linked to one another and produce several paths along which trajectories might evolve. These paths divide near the five unstable solutions, which are denoted by the symbols "•" and "o" in Fig. 4.4, and end on one of four stable solutions, which are denoted by the symbols "x", "+", "–" and "*". Because the unstable solution at the center is the most strongly attracting, the

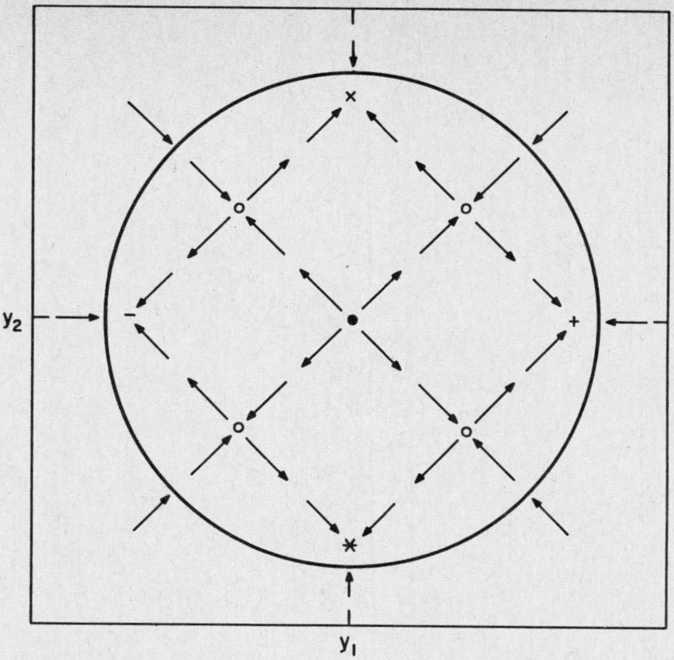

Fig. 4.4 Planar projections of the nine fixed points that reside in a six-dimensional phase space and the attracting and repelling directions near them. Here there are five unstable fixed points (denoted by "•" and "o") and four stable fixed points (denoted by "+", "x", "-", "*"). Typical trajectories approach the unstable point "•", then one of four unstable points "o", and finally one of the stable points "+", "x", "-", or "*" (after Shirer, 1984).

planar projection of a typical six-dimensional trajectory could be the following: A trajectory approaches from above the unstable solution labeled "•" at the origin, and then expands in one of four directions. Along each of these directions, the trajectory would approach another unstable solution labeled "o", and then depart in one of two directions near o toward one of the stable solutions "x", "+", "-", or "*". From this point of view, we expect that unstable solutions would be observable for a finite time that may be physically relevant; as a consequence, identifying unobservable states with unstable solutions may be an over-simplification. Moreover, as a trajectory approaches each unstable fixed point in Fig. 4.4, there are at least two possible directions along which the trajectory could expand. Thus, unstable equilibria represent critical points for a trajectory at which the trajectory must "decide" in which direction to head; moreover, this decision occurs very near the unstable fixed points. Near these points, then, the trajectories must be known very accurately if a correct prediction of the final evolution is sought; in this sense predictability problems are expected primarily when the trajectories are near unstable points (Shirer, 1984; see also Section 15.3.2).

From a modeling viewpoint the above ideas have an important implication. In the infinite-dimensional case, the stable fixed points and other attractors are on extensions of finite-dimensional unstable manifolds. This observation implies that an infinite-dimensional system is squeezed into a finite-dimensional one (Temam, 1983). More specifically, if the attractor in a given truncated model is strong enough, then the infinite-dimensional model contains a nearby attractor of the same shape (for example, the shape of a stationary solution is a point; the shape of a periodic solution is a circle; and the shape of the Lorenz attractor (Section 15.3.2) is a figure 8) (Wells and Dutton, 1986). And if the truncated model is sufficiently large, then any bifurcating attractor in the infinite-dimensional system may be approximated as closely as desired in both shape and location. As a consequence, this property indicates that the spectral modeling approach discussed in this monograph is formally correct and provides the motivation for the argument that suitable finite-dimensional spectral models are able to provide good approximations of the complete solutions.

We can use these ideas to see how to construct a realistic low-order model. First, the eigenfunctions representing the unstable manifold must be in the low-order model of the system. But these are not the only ones. As is shown in Fig. 4.3, some eigenfunctions representing the stable manifold S initially dominate the evolution and hence control the approach of the trajectory toward the unstable manifold U. In addition, some are surely crucial for determining the direction of eventual expansion away from the unstable solution toward either C_1 or C_2. As mentioned earlier, S locally provides the boundary separating the attractor basins of C_1 and C_2, and predictability problems always occur when the trajectories approach the intersection of S and U. No low-order model is able to represent correctly the evolution of all initial points; but as more components of S are included in the model, the evolution from more initial points can be represented correctly. Enough components of S must be included in order that the number of incorrectly modeled trajectories is sufficiently small.

The early evolution must therefore be known accurately and a minimum model should include the proper components from the stable manifold in order to represent transient solutions properly. Clearly, which of the stable manifold terms that should be kept is a difficult question. Certainly, these terms are important for specification of the ultimate evolution of the system. But also, it is even possible that during the time scales of interest, the trajectory remains within the vicinity of the unstable equilibrium point (see Section 15.3). In this situation the terms from the stable manifold play a crucial role in the physical interpretation of the solution of interest. This problem remains an interesting but complicated one of current research; in Section 17.4.1, we discuss a possible means for creating finite models that uses coordinates based on stable and unstable manifolds of the points in phase space.

We have noted here that the existence of unstable solutions implies the existence of other attractors in a model having bounded solutions. In the simplest cases, these attractors may be either stationary or temporally periodic solutions. We might guess that the distance between the attractors on the unstable manifold and the unstable solution at the origin would be related to the magnitude $|\lambda_+|$ of the positive characteristic exponent. Moreover, we would expect that as $\lambda_+ \to 0$ the attractors would collapse onto the origin; that is, the stable solutions would bifurcate from the unstable one when $\lambda_+ = 0$. In many cases, this phenomenon occurs, and so we suspect that stability loss and bifurcation are linked concepts. We show that this relation holds for branching stationary solutions in Chapter 5 and for branching periodic solutions in Chapter 11.

CHAPTER 5

BIFURCATION ANALYSIS OF STATIONARY SOLUTIONS

RONALD GELARO

In Chapter 1, we outlined seven modeling principles that summarized the essential properties to be included in any mathematical model representing a physical system. The principles that a model contain adequate complexity imply strongly that mathematical models of hydrodynamic flows preserve the nonlinearity inherent in the original equations. In this chapter, we examine some implications of nonlinearity and show how we can use mathematical theorems to provide insight into how flows might evolve as the values of certain crucial parameters are varied. As discussed in previous chapters, these parameters may describe the system in terms of the characteristic spatial or temporal scales or in terms of the rates of forcing or dissipation.

Because of nonlinearity, these models have solutions whose qualitative characters can change dramatically with small changes in the rates of forcing. In Chapter 1 we noted that laboratory versions of convective flows demonstrate that as a viscous fluid is increasingly heated from below, the conductive state is replaced first by two-dimensional time-independent convective rolls, then by three-dimensional steady cells, and eventually by time-dependent flows that become turbulent for large heating rates (Krishnamurti, 1970a, 1970b). If a system has a solution for all values of the various parameters, then it is a candidate for the study of bifurcating, or branching, solutions; such behavior can describe mathematically the transitions observed in laboratory experiments. As we noted in Chapter 4, a study of the stability properties of the branching solutions is necessary, because the stable ones correspond to physically realizable states. Fortunately, as we began to see in Chapter 4, the analysis of such <u>nonlinear</u> behavior can be performed simply by studying the <u>linearized</u> forms of these systems.

5.1 Uniqueness of Solutions and the Implicit Function Theorem

A system of spectral equations such as the Lorenz (1963) model comprises a set of nonlinear, ordinary differential equations. This type of system can be written in the general form

$$\dot{y}_k = f_k(y_1, \ldots, y_n, R, \xi_1, \ldots, \xi_p) \qquad (5.1)$$

$$; \qquad k=1, \ldots, n \quad ,$$

$$f_k(0, \ldots, 0, R, \xi_1, \ldots, \xi_p) = 0 \qquad (5.2)$$

in which R and ξ_i are dimensionless parameters and f_k are real, analytic functions of all the variables. As in Chapter 4, we isolate the parameter R because it changes value as the forcing rate varies; thus R controls bifurcation. Stationary solutions y_j^s to (5.1) are those for which $f_1 = f_2 = \cdots = f_n = 0$. A stationary solution that exists for _all_ values of the parameters R and ξ_i is called a _basic solution_. We assume that (5.1) has a basic solution (5.2) at the origin, that is one for which $y_j^s(t) \equiv 0$ for all j and t, and we assume that this basic solution loses stability at R_c as the value of R _increases_ past that of R_c.

To determine whether a particular stationary solution to (5.1) is unique, we locate on that solution a bifurcation point R_c whose value depends on those of the remaining parameters ξ_i. Bifurcation points on the basic solution are called _primary bifurcation points_; these are R_1 and R_2 in Fig. 5.1. The solutions emanating from the basic one are called _primary branches_. If they branch toward smaller values of R, then they are called _subcritical primary branches_ (P_1 in Fig. 5.1), and if they branch toward larger values, then they are called _supercritical primary branches_ (P_2 in Fig. 5.1) (see Section 5.3). Bifurcation points on the primary branches are called _secondary bifurcation points_ (R_3 in Fig. 5.1) and the emanating solutions are called _secondary branches_ (S_3 in Fig. 5.1).

Because (5.1) possesses the trivial solution, we begin by looking for possible bifurcation points on this solution. Normally, we look first for points at which other stationary solutions meet the known one, and that is the only case we consider in this chapter. Accordingly, we replace (5.1) by the corresponding time-independent system

$$f_k(y_1, \ldots, y_n, R, \xi_1, \ldots, \xi_p) = 0 \quad ; \quad k=1, \ldots, n \quad . \qquad (5.3)$$

Obviously, we must provide a means for determining if and where a bifurcation point exists on the trivial solution. In other words, because the trivial solution to

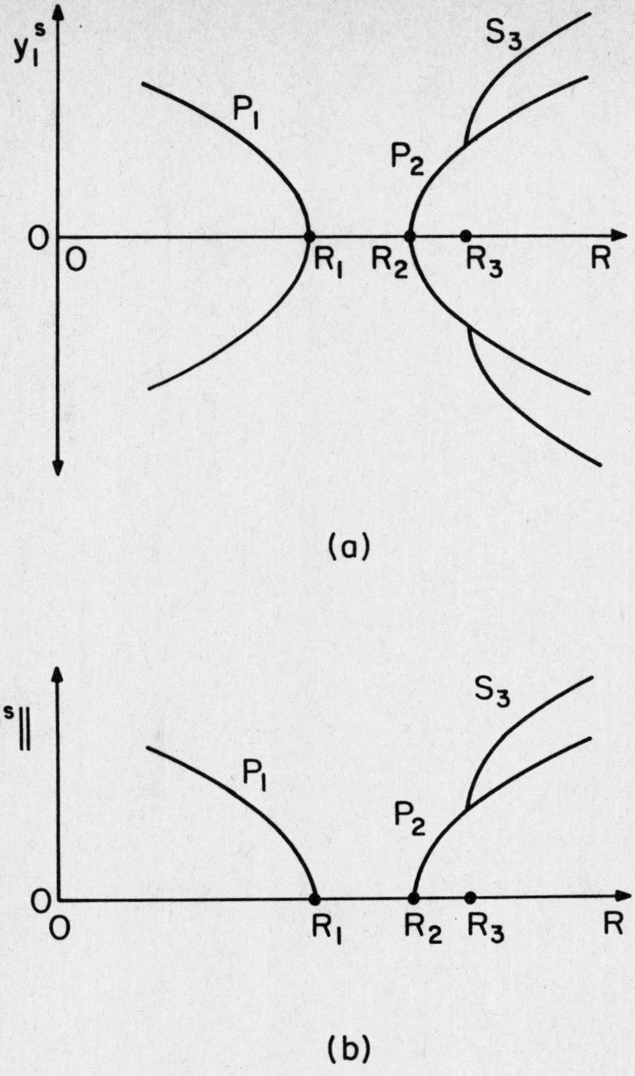

Fig. 5.1 Schematic diagram of the solutions to (5.1) plotted as a function of the parameter R; in (a) the ordinate is one component y_1^s of the solution y^s and in (b) the ordinate is a norm of y^s. The primary bifurcation points R_1 and R_2 and the secondary bifurcation point R_3 are shown. Primary branch P_1 is a subcritical one and P_2 is a supercritical one; S_3 is a supercritical secondary branch (after Shirer, 1978).

(5.3) exists for all values of the parameters R and ξ_i, we need to determine whether or not this solution is locally unique for all values of these parameters. To make such a determination, we use the <u>Implicit Function Theorem</u> (I.F.T.), which gives the necessary conditions for (5.3) to have a unique solution in the neighborhood of a known one. In this case, the known solution is the trivial one

$$y_1^s = y_2^s = \cdots = y_n^s = 0 \quad . \tag{5.4}$$

Because (5.4) is a solution to (5.3) for all values R^o and ξ_i^o of R and ξ_i, there can be no nearby stationary solutions bifurcating from (5.4) provided the conditions of the I.F.T. are satisfied. Thus, for there to be a bifurcation point on the trivial solution, one of the necessary conditions of the I.F.T. must be violated.

The classical form of the I.F.T., as well as an informative explanation of the theorem, appears in Shirer (1978). To state the I.F.T., we consider a system of equations such as (5.3) in which the functions $f_1, \ldots, f_n$ have continuous first derivatives.

1. Suppose that there is a single point $(R^o, \xi_i^o; y_j^s)$ such that $f_1(R^o, \xi_i^o; y_j^s) = \cdots = f_n(R^o, \xi_i^o; y_j^s) = 0$. Here R^o is a value of R, ξ_i^o is a value of ξ_i, where $i = 1, \ldots, p$, and y_j^s is a value of y_j, where $j = 1, \ldots, n$.
2. Let the determinant D of the matrix of partial derivatives of the functions f_k with respect to the variables $y_1, \ldots, y_n$ evaluated at (R, ξ_i) be given by

$$D(R,\xi_i;y_j) = \det\left[\frac{\partial f_k}{\partial y_j}(R,\xi_i;y_j)\right] \quad ; \quad \left\{\begin{array}{l} i=1, \ldots, p \\ j=1, \ldots, n \\ k=1, \ldots, n \end{array}\right. \quad . \tag{5.5}$$

3. Suppose that $D(R^o, \xi_i^o; y_j^s) \neq 0$. Then there exists a neighborhood of the point $(R^o, \xi_i^o; y_j^s)$ in which the value of (R, ξ_i) uniquely determines that of y_j.

In Fig. 5.2, a graphical representation of the result of the I.F.T. is given near the fixed values (R^o, ξ_i^o) of the parameters (R, ξ_i). In this figure, because $D(R^o, \xi_i^o; y_j^s) \neq 0$, there is no other solution in the rectangular neighborhood enclosed by the dashed lines. Moreover, we note that even if $D(R_c, \xi_i^o; y_j^s) = 0$ at a point $(R_c, \xi_i^o; y_j^s)$ very close to $(R^o, \xi_i^o; y_j^s)$, then we can still define a neighborhood around $(R^o, \xi_i^o; y_j^s)$ in which $D \neq 0$, showing that the solution y_j^s is unique.

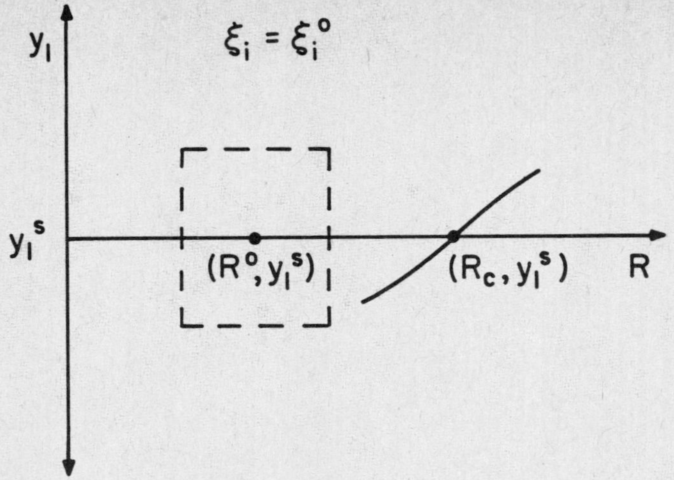

Fig. 5.2 The projection of a point $(R^o, \xi_i^o; y_j^s)$ onto the R - y_1 plane; near this point the projection y_1^s of the solution y_j^s is locally unique, that is within the dashed box. At the point $(R_c, \xi_i^o; y_j^s)$ the solution y_j^s is no longer unique and we expect a bifurcation to be depicted in the projection as shown near (R_c, y_1^s) (after Shirer, 1978).

5.2 Locating the Bifurcation Point: When Uniqueness Fails

A natural extension of the results in Section 5.1 is that the point $(R_c, \xi_i^o; y_j^s)$ at which D = 0 is precisely the point in whose vicinity the solution (5.4) may be nonunique. Thus, if a bifurcation point exists, then it must be given by the point $(R_c, \xi_i^o; y_j^s)$. The equation

$$D(R_c,\xi_i^o;y_j^s) = \det\left[\frac{\partial f_k}{\partial y_j}(R_c,\xi_i^o;y_j^s)\right] = 0 \quad ; \quad \begin{cases} i=1, \ldots, p \\ j=1, \ldots, n \\ k=1, \ldots, n \end{cases} , \tag{5.6}$$

when solved for $R_c(\xi_i^o; y_j^s)$ gives the location of a potential bifurcation point. Equation (5.6) is called the <u>bifurcation equation</u> for the stationary solution $y_j = y_j^s$ to (5.3).

However, as mentioned in the introduction to this chapter, much can be learned about bifurcation from the linearized forms of the original system of equations. Toward this end, we can use an alternative argument to obtain (5.6). For a fixed value (R_c, ξ_i^o) of the parameters, (5.3) becomes a system of equations in n variables that may be written as

$$f_k(y_1, \ldots, y_n, R_c, \xi_1^o, \ldots, \xi_p^o) = 0 \quad ; \quad k=1, \ldots, n \quad . \tag{5.7}$$

We can use Taylor's Theorem to expand the functions f_k about any solution $y_j = y_j^s$ such that

$$f_k(R_c,\xi_i^o; y_j) = f_k(R_c,\xi_i^o;y_j^s) + \frac{\partial f_k}{\partial y_1}(R_c,\xi_i^o;y_j^s)(y_1 - y_1^s) + \cdots$$

$$+ \frac{\partial f_k}{\partial y_n}(R_c,\xi_i^o;y_j^s)(y_n - y_n^s) + O(y^2) \quad ; \quad \begin{cases} i=1, \ldots, p \\ j=1, \ldots, n \\ k=1, \ldots, n \end{cases} , \tag{5.8}$$

in which $O(y^2)$ denotes the terms of quadratic and higher order. Using the fact that $y_j = y_j^s$ is a solution to (5.3) for $(R,\xi_i) = (R_c,\xi_i^o)$, we obtain

$$f_1(R_c,\xi_i^o;y_j^s) = \cdots = f_n(R_c,\xi_i^o;y_j^s) = 0 \quad ; \quad \begin{cases} i=1, \ldots, p \\ j=1, \ldots, n \end{cases} . \tag{5.9}$$

Applying (5.9) and neglecting the $O(y^2)$ terms, we can use (5.8) to rewrite the system of equations (5.7) in the form

$$\frac{\partial f_k}{\partial y_1}(R_c,\xi_i^o;y_j^s)(y_1 - y_1^s) + \cdots + \frac{\partial f_k}{\partial y_n}(R_c,\xi_i^o;y_j^s)(y_n - y_n^s) = 0 \quad ; \quad \begin{cases} i=1, \ldots, p \\ j=1, \ldots, n \\ k=1, \ldots, n \end{cases} . \tag{5.10}$$

Equation (5.10) is a linear, homogeneous version of the original model (5.7). Thus, (5.10) has a <u>unique</u> <u>trivial</u> solution at $(R^o,\xi_i^o;y_j^s)$ if and only if the condition $D \neq 0$ holds at $R_c = R^o$. For there to be a <u>nontrivial</u> solution at the point $(R_c,\xi_i^o;y_j^s)$, the determinant of the coefficients of (5.10) must vanish; that is

$$D(R_c,\xi_i^o;y_j^s) = \det\left[\frac{\partial f_k}{\partial y_j}(R_c,\xi_i^o;y_j^s)\right] = 0 \quad ; \quad \begin{cases} i=1, \ldots, p \\ j=1, \ldots, n \\ k=1, \ldots, n \end{cases} . \tag{5.11}$$

We see that (5.11) is precisely the bifurcation equation (5.6). Thus, we arrive at the result that <u>a necessary condition that the nonlinear equations have nonunique</u>

<u>solutions at a point is identical to the condition that the corresponding linear equations have a nontrivial solution</u>.

The only points at which uniqueness can be lost in linear or nonlinear systems are those at which D = 0; the only points at which stability can change are those at which D = 0. Thus, we conclude that there is a strong connection between change of stability and loss of uniqueness -- that is, between stability exchange and bifurcation. To specify this connection we recall that in Chapter 4 we defined the coefficients in the variational equations (4.5) to be

$$a_{kj} = \frac{\partial f_k}{\partial y_j}(R^o, \xi_i^o; y_j^s) = \left(\frac{\partial f_k}{\partial y_j}\right)_s \quad ; \quad \begin{cases} i=1, \ldots, p \\ j=1, \ldots, n \\ k=1, \ldots, n \end{cases} \quad . \tag{5.12}$$

We note that in the present context, the bifurcation equation (5.6) or (5.11) corresponds to

$$\det\{a_{kj}\} = 0 \quad ; \quad \begin{cases} j=1, \ldots, n \\ k=1, \ldots, n \end{cases} \quad . \tag{5.13}$$

Thus we see that (5.13) corresponds to the case $\lambda = 0$ in the determinant (4.13), or the case $e_n = 0$ in the characteristic equation (4.14); but $\lambda = 0$ is the condition (4.16) for stability change. At least for stationary solutions, then, we conclude that bifurcation and stability exchange are linked because <u>both</u> the possible non-uniqueness of the one and the stability change of the other are identified by the vanishing of the <u>same</u> determinant. Thus, from the analysis in Chapter 4 we see immediately that the point r_c on the stationary conductive and convective solutions to the Lorenz model is a bifurcation point at which stability is exchanged. However, in the above discussion we have linked only one type of stability exchange to bifurcation; we consider the other type (Hopf bifurcation) in Chapter 11.

5.3 Expected Stabilities of Typical Branching Stationary Solutions

We can form a general picture of the expected stability exchange between bifurcating stationary solutions by applying bifurcation and stability theory to some simple examples of systems that exhibit branching solutions. In general, there are three types of bifurcation that we classify according to the ranges of the critical parameter (in this case, R) for which the branching solutions exist. We caution that these general results apply only to the case of single bifurcation points at which only one characteristic exponent vanishes; other stability results are possible if the bifurcation points are double (see, for example, Section 9.1). Also, we recall that we assume that the basic solution is stable for $R < R_c$ and unstable for $R > R_c$.

5.3.1 Supercritical branching. A supercritical bifurcation is one in which the branching solution exists locally for $R \geq R_c$ (P_2 in Fig. 5.1), and this is the type of branching exhibited by the Lorenz (1963) model. Here, we examine a one-dimensional example that is simpler than the Lorenz model, but that exhibits similar branching behavior.

Consider the equation

$$\frac{dy}{dt} = - y[y^2 - (R - R_c)] \quad , \tag{5.14}$$

which has the stationary solutions

$$y_s = 0 \quad , \tag{5.15}$$

$$y_s = \pm \sqrt{R - R_c} \quad , \tag{5.16}$$

and the bifurcation point $R = R_c$ as shown in Fig. 5.3. To determine the stability

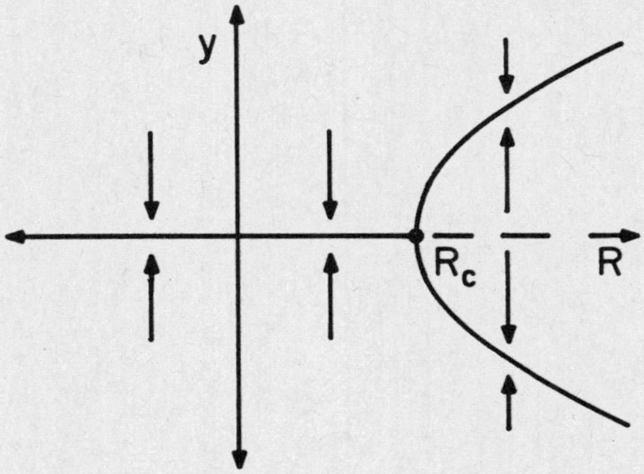

Fig. 5.3 Supercritical branching solutions. The vertical arrows indicate the temporal behavior of small perturbations about the solutions. The primary branches for $R>R_c$ are stable.

of either (5.15) or (5.16), we assume $y = y_s + y'$. When $y_s = 0$, the linearized equation is

$$\lambda y' = \frac{dy'}{dt} = (R - R_c)y' \quad , \tag{5.17}$$

which has solutions of the form

$$y' = \hat{y} \exp[\lambda t] = \hat{y} \exp[(R - R_c)t] \quad . \tag{5.18}$$

By simple inspection of (5.18), we can ascertain the three possibilities for the sign of the exponent λ:

A. If $R < R_c$, then $\lambda < 0$ and the basic solution is stable.

B. If $R = R_c$, then $\lambda = 0$ and we discover the bifurcation point.

C. If $R > R_c$; then $\lambda > 0$ and the basic solution is unstable.

The three cases above are summarized in Fig. 5.3. Note that the stability of the solutions is indicated by the types of lines: stable solutions are denoted by solid lines, unstable solutions by dashed lines.

To determine the stability of (5.16), we write (5.14) in the form

$$\frac{dy}{dt} = \frac{d}{dt}(y_s + y') = -(y_s + y')[(y_s + y')^2 - (R - R_c)] \quad . \tag{5.19}$$

Keeping only linear terms in the perturbation y' and using (5.16) to find that the constant terms sum to zero, we have the linearized version of (5.19)

$$\lambda y' = \frac{dy'}{dt} = -3y'y_s^2 + (R - R_c)y' = -2(R - R_c)y' \quad . \tag{5.20}$$

Because y_s in (5.16) is supercritical, it exists only for $R \geq R_c$. Thus we need to consider only two cases:

A. If $R = R_c$, then $\lambda = 0$ and again we obtain the bifurcation point.

B. If $R > R_c$, then $\lambda < 0$ and the primary branch is stable.

As depicted in Fig. 5.3, the general stability picture for supercritical branching reveals that the basic solution is stable for $R < R_c$. At the point $R = R_c$, the basic solution exchanges stability (smoothly) with the primary branch, which in this example is stable for all $R > R_c$.

5.3.2 Subcritical branching. A subcritical bifurcation is one in which the branching solution exists locally for $R \leq R_c$ (P_1 in Fig. 5.1). In this case the branching solution is unstable and we do not see a smooth transition to a different regime as the value of R is increased past the critical point $R = R_c$. A simple system that exhibits subcritical branching is obtained by altering the signs in (5.14) so that the new system becomes

$$\frac{dy}{dt} = y\,[y^2 + (R - R_c)] \quad . \tag{5.21}$$

In this case, the stationary solutions to (5.21) are (cf. (5.16))

$$y_s = 0 \quad , \tag{5.22}$$

$$y_s = \pm\sqrt{R_c - R} \quad , \tag{5.23}$$

and they are depicted in Fig. 5.4. The linearized form of (5.21) for the basic solution is identical to that of (5.17). Thus the stability portrait for the basic olution in the subcritical case is the same as that for the supercritical case: the solution is stable for $R < R_c$ (Fig. 5.4).

For the primary branches (5.23), the linearized version of (5.21) becomes (cf. (5.20))

$$\lambda y' = \frac{dy'}{dt} = 2y'y_s^2 = 2(R_c - R)y' \quad . \tag{5.24}$$

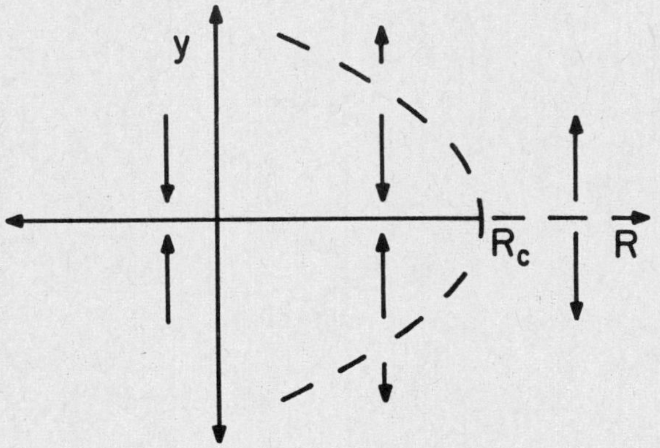

Fig. 5.4 Subcritical branching solutions. The vertical arrows indicate the temporal behavior of small perturbations about the solutions. The primary branches exist for $R<R_c$; thus, no exchange of stability occurs with the basic solution and the primary branches are unstable.

Because the branching solution is subcritical, we have the two cases:

A. If $R < R_c$, then $\lambda > 0$ and the primary branch is unstable.

B. If $R = R_c$, then $\lambda = 0$ and we have the bifurcation point.

Although the basic solution is again stable for $R < R_c$, the primary branch does not exist for $R > R_c$ and there is no stability exchange at the primary bifurcation point. In general, subcritical branches are unstable and trajectories in phase space approach some other solution once R is increased past R_c.

In the above case (5.21), the subcritical branch (5.23) extends to $-\infty$, but in some cases, a subcritical branch may curve back and exist for $R > R_n$; as we see in Section 6.2, this can occur if the stationary solutions are controlled by a a quintic or a higher degree odd polynomial equation. These branches can be stable for $R > R_n$ and form an example of <u>snap-through bifurcation</u> (Fig. 5.5). Here a sufficiently large perturbation of a stable solution may approach another stable solution, "skipping" the intermediate unstable branch. In this case the perturbation must be large enough to depart from an asymptotically stable solution and we say that

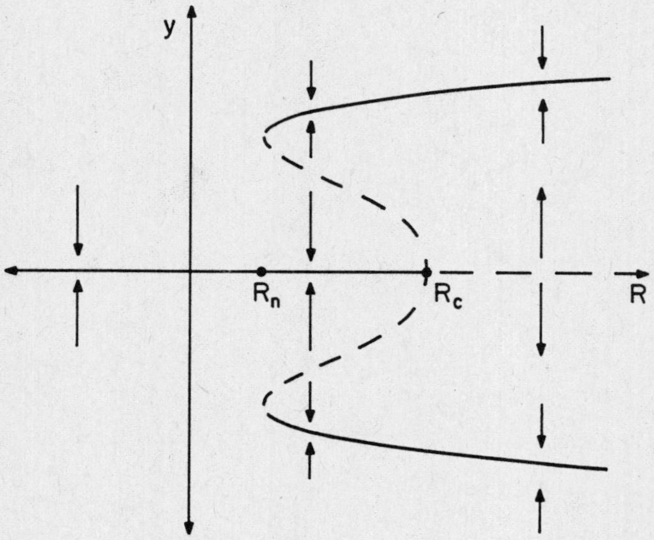

Fig. 5.5 Subcritical branching solutions with a snap-through bifurcation. The vertical arrows indicate the temporal behavior of small perturbations about the solutions. Here, the primary branches curve back and exist for $R > R_n$. Thus, the solutions may display finite-amplitude instability, and the possibility of observing hysteresis is introduced.

the model solutions exhibit finite-amplitude instability. When a subcritical branch exists together with a snap-through bifurcation, the possibility of hysteresis is introduced. In this case the discontinuous jump occurs at different values of the parameter depending on whether its value is being increased or decreased. For example, in Fig. 5.5, we might expect a discontinuous jump from the basic solution to the snap-through branch as R is increased past R_c. However, as we decrease R along the snap-through branch, a discontinuous jump back down to the basic solution might not occur until R is decreased below R_n. Hysteresis also is discussed in Section 6.3.2.

5.3.3 Transcritical branching. A slightly more complicated stability profile exists when a primary branch intersects the basic solution asymmetrically. In this case we have a transcritical bifurcation (Fig. 5.6). Transcritical branching is exhibited by the system

$$\frac{dy}{dt} = - y[y^2 - 2y - (R - R_c)] \quad , \tag{5.25}$$

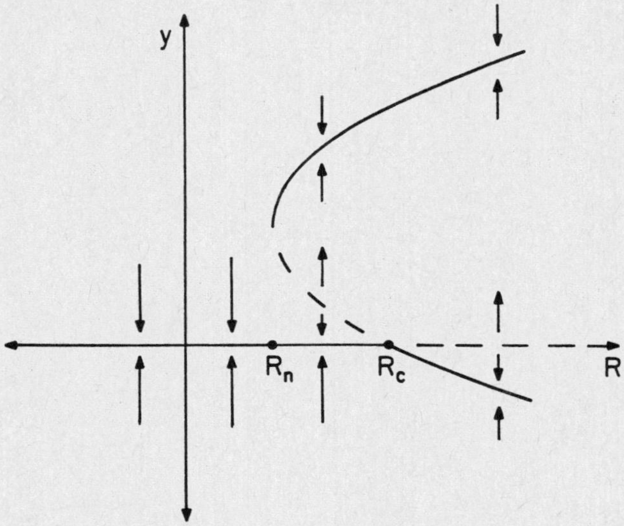

Fig. 5.6 Transcritical branching solutions. The vertical arrows indicate the temporal behavior of small perturbations about the solutions. Here, the trident shown in Fig. 5.4 is no longer symmetric about the abscissa. As a result, stability characteristics are present that are typical for both supercritical and subcritical branches.

which has stationary solutions

$$y_s = 0 \quad , \tag{5.26}$$

$$y_s = 1 \pm \sqrt{1 + (R - R_c)} \quad . \tag{5.27}$$

The stability profile for (5.26) is the typical one for a basic solution; that is, the solution is stable for $R < R_c$. For the primary branches, we consider the positive and negative roots in (5.27) separately. For both roots, however, the linearized version of (5.25) is

$$\frac{dy'}{dt} = - y_s(y_s - 1)\ 2y' \quad . \tag{5.28}$$

Substituting the positive root into (5.28), we obtain

$$\frac{dy'}{dt} = - \{[1 + [1 + (R - R_c)]^{1/2}][[1 + (R - R_c)]^{1/2}]\}\ 2y'$$

$$= - [[1 + (R - R_c)]^{1/2} + [1 + (R - R_c)]]\ 2y' \quad . \tag{5.29}$$

If we now use the substitution $x = [1 + (R - R_c)]$, then (5.29) becomes

$$\lambda y' = \frac{dy'}{dt} = -2(\sqrt{x} + x)\ y' \quad . \tag{5.30}$$

From Fig. 5.6, we note that the positive root exists for $R > R_n$, in which $R_n = R_c - 1$. Thus we need to consider two cases.

A. $R = R_n = R_c - 1$:

Thus, $x = [1 + (R - R_c)]$

$= [1 + (-1)] = 0.$

From (5.30), we see $x = 0$ implies $\lambda = 0$. The stationary point $y_s = 1$ and $R = R_n$, which is not a bifurcation point, is called a <u>regular turning point</u>; a different label R_n is used for this special value of R because no new solution splits from another one, but an existing one simply turns away from its earlier values.

B. $R > R_n = R_c - 1$:

Thus, $x = [1 + (R - R_c)]$

$= [1 + d]$, where $d > -1$, so $x > 0$.

In this case $\lambda = -2e$, where $e > 0$, so $\lambda < 0$ and the solution is stable for $R > R_n$ (Fig. 5.6).

Finally, we need to consider the negative root in (5.27). Again using the substitution $x = [1 + (R - R_c)]$, we obtain the linearized form

$$\lambda y' = \frac{dy'}{dt} = 2(\sqrt{x} - x)\, y' \quad . \tag{5.31}$$

Here, we need to consider four cases.

A. $R = R_n = R_c - 1$:

Thus, $x = [1 + (R - R_c)]$

$= [1 + (-1)] = 0$.

Again, $x = 0$ implies $\lambda = 0$ and $R = R_n$ is the value of R at a regular turning point.

B. $R_n < R < R_c$:

Thus, $x = [1 + (R - R_c)]$

$= [1 + f]$, where $-1 < f < 0$, so $0 < x < 1$.

In this case $\lambda = 2(\sqrt{x} - x) > 0$, which implies that the negative root is unstable for $R_n < R < R_c$.

C. $R = R_c$:

Thus, $x = [1 + (R - R_c)] = 1$, which from (5.31) implies that $\lambda = 0$ and that $R = R_c$ is a bifurcation point.

D. $R > R_c$:

Thus $x = [1 + (R - R_c)]$

$= [1 + g]$, where $g > 0$, so $x > 1$.

In this case $\lambda = 2(\sqrt{x} - x) < 0$, which from (5.31) implies that the negative root is stable for $R > R_c$.

The stability profile for the negative root is shown in Fig. 5.6. As R is increased along the basic solution, the flow may evolve in one of two ways. For infinitesimal perturbations, we observe a smooth transition from the basic solution to negative values of y as R is increased past R_c, implying a supercritical bifurcation has occurred. However, in the presence of finite amplitude perturbations, we may observe a discontinuous jump from the basic solution to the positive root for values of $R_n < R < R_c$. In this case, hysteresis is also possible, as we found in the snap-through case discussed in Section 5.3.2.

5.4 Some General Comments on Stability Properties

In subsequent chapters of this monograph, we consider the stability of stationary solutions to systems of ordinary differential equations. In general, the exchanges of stability between branching solutions follow the general rules outlined in the previous section: solutions emanating supercritically from stable ones are in turn stable and those branching subcritically are unstable. But in larger N-equation systems, there are N characteristic exponents associated with each solution, and some of them may have positive real parts. Thus, we might wonder what the stability behavior would be for the solutions branching from these unstable solutions. To investigate this question, we use a conservation principle involving the signs of the characteristic exponents; in more complicated branching cases, application of this principle provides a very useful technique for checking whether the correct stability behavior has been deduced (see Chapters 7 and 9 for examples).

The bookkeeping operation we use to track the changes in signs of the characteristic exponents involves calculating the degree of the stationary solutions (Milnor, 1965). The <u>degree</u> $d(\underset{\sim}{y}^s,R)$ of the stationary solution $\underset{\sim}{y}^s$ is defined to be

$$d(\underset{\sim}{y}^s,R) = \mathrm{sgn}[D(\underset{\sim}{y}^s,R)] = \mathrm{sgn}[\lambda_1\lambda_2\cdots\lambda_N] \quad , \tag{5.32}$$

in which $\underset{\sim}{y}^s = (y_1^s, \ldots, y_N^s)$, D is the determinant (5.5) of the matrix of partial derivatives of f_k, $\lambda_1, \ldots, \lambda_N$ are the characteristic exponents, and $\mathrm{sgn}(\phi)$ is given by

$$\mathrm{sgn}(\phi) = \begin{cases} 1 & \text{for } \phi > 0 \\ -1 & \text{for } \phi < 0 \\ \text{undefined} & \text{for } \phi = 0 \end{cases} \quad . \tag{5.33}$$

Because a characteristic exponent vanishes only at $R = R_c$, $d(\underset{\sim}{y}^s,R)$ is defined only when $R = R_c$; thus, $d(\underset{\sim}{y}^s, R) = \pm 1$ whenever $R \neq R_c$. In practice the value of $d(\underset{\sim}{y}^s,R)$ is obtained by using the first equality in (5.32). However, from the second equality we can derive a general rule for determining the stabilities of stationary solutions by tracking the signs of the characteristic exponents through even a complicated hierarchy of transitions (see Chapters 7 and 9).

This general rule rests ultimately on a conservation principle originating from the conclusion in the Index Theorem (Milnor, 1965). The quantity that is conserved is the index $I(R)$ of a system of ordinary differential equations having a finite number of stationary solutions, each of which having a nonzero $D(\underset{\sim}{y}^s,R)$. For such a system, the index $I(R)$ is defined to be

$$I(R) = \sum_{\underset{\sim}{y}^s} d(\underset{\sim}{y}^s,R) \quad . \tag{5.34}$$

The theorem can be stated as the following:

> Index Theorem. Consider the system $\dot{\underset{\sim}{y}} = \underset{\sim}{f}(\underset{\sim}{y},R)$ where $\underset{\sim}{y} = (y_1, \ldots, y_N)$, R is the bifurcation parameter, and for clarity the remaining parameters $(\xi_1, \ldots, \xi_p)$ have been suppressed. Suppose that the system has only a finite number of stationary solutions $\underset{\sim}{y}_s$ for all values of R, and that for $R \neq R_c$ each solution is characterized by $D(\underset{\sim}{y}^s,R) \neq 0$. Then we have
>
> $$I(R) = I(R') \text{ for } R < R_c < R' \quad . \tag{5.35}$$

For applications of the Index Theorem to tracking the behavior of the characteristic exponents, we make the following two observations. The first is that the value of I is conserved as the value of R is varied past that of R_c. The second is that, more generally, even if there are $m = 1,2,\ldots,M$ critical values $R_m = R_{c_m}$ of R at which $D(\underset{\sim}{y}^s,R) = 0$ occurs, the index I remains constant as the value of R is varied successively past each value of R_m. In N-component forced dissipative systems, it follows that $I(R) = (-1)^N$, because there is normally a range $-\infty < R < R_u$ of parameter values for which the stationary solution is unique and globally stable so that all N characteristic exponents have negative real parts (see Section 6.1). The implication of the above observations is that, even after a sequence of bifurcations has occurred, the sum of the indices is $(-1)^N$, as we illustrate below.

Suppose we have a (basic) solution $\tilde{y}^s = 0$ having n exponents with negative real parts and N-n exponents with positive real parts (Fig. 5.7a). At a critical value R_c of R, one of the exponents must vanish; from the preceding results for stationary solutions, we expect that a negative exponent would change sign as the value of R is increased past that of R_c. (Certainly this need not always be the case, as we discover in Section 7.2.5.) Thus there are n-1 exponents having negative real parts and the degree $d(0,R) = d_0(R)$ of the basic solution is

$$d_0(R) = \begin{cases} (-1)^n = I(R) & , \quad R < R_c \\ (-1)^{n-1} & , \quad R > R_c \end{cases} \quad . \tag{5.36}$$

For each branching nontrivial solution, there must be either n-1 or n exponents having negative real parts, because n-1 of them have strictly negative real parts at $R = R_c$. But since the sum of the degrees must be $(-1)^n$ for all $R \neq R_c$, we see below that $d(\tilde{y}^s,R) = (-1)^n$ for each nontrivial solution, and we conclude that each nontrivial solution must have n exponents with negative real parts. To see this fact, let $d_1(R) = \pm 1$ and $d_2(R) = \pm 1$ be the degrees of the two nontrivial stationary solutions. Then the conclusion of the Index Theorem tells us that for $R < R_c < R'$ we have

$$\begin{aligned} (-1)^n &= I(R) \\ &= I(R') = d_0(R') + d_1(R') + d_2(R') \\ &= (-1)^{n-1} + d_1(R') + d_2(R') \quad . \end{aligned} \tag{5.37}$$

Since $d_1(R') = \pm 1$ and $d_2(R') = \pm 1$, it follows immediately that $d_1(R') = d_2(R') = (-1)^n$. (For example, if we suppose that $d_1(R') = d_2(R') = (-1)^{n-1}$, then $I(R') = 3(-1)^{n-1} \neq (-1)^n$, which is unacceptable.)

If we had a different type of stability exchange at R_c so that the basic solution gained an $(n+1)^{st}$ exponent with negative real part, then we still are able

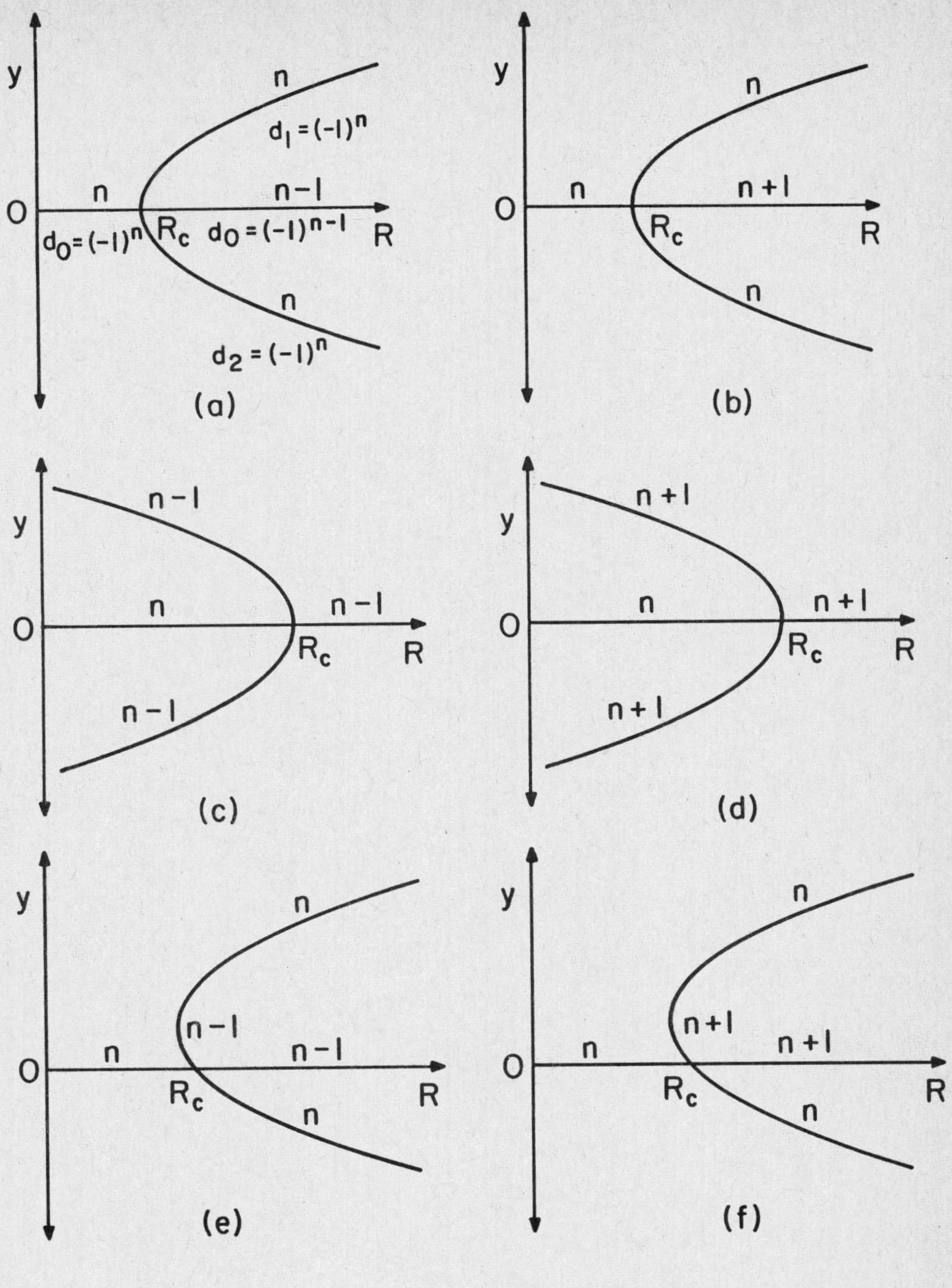

Fig. 5.7 Examples of branching cases showing the number (n-1, n, or n+1) of characteristic exponents having negative real parts; for each solution, the associated degree values d_0, d_1, and d_2 are (-1) raised to this number, as shown explicitly in (a). Supercritical branching is considered in (a), (b), subcritical branching in (c), (d) and transcritical branching in (e), (f).

to conclude that the supercritically branching nontrivial solution has n exponents with negative real parts (Fig. 5.7b). As before we have

$$d_0(R) = \begin{cases} (-1)^n = I(R) & , \quad R < R_c \\ (-1)^{n+1} & , \quad R > R_c \end{cases} \quad ; \tag{5.38}$$

if $d_1(R') = d_2(R') = (-1)^n$, then for $R > R_c$ we find that

$$I(R') = d_0(R') + d_1(R') + d_2(R') = (-1)^{n+1} + (-1)^n + (-1)^n = (-1)^n = I(R) \quad . \tag{5.39}$$

The important conclusion we reach is that: when a stationary solution branches supercritically from another stationary solution at $R = R_c$ via the vanishing of a single characteristic exponent, then the stability properties are transferred from the subcritical portion of one solution to the supercritical portion of the other.

A similar analysis can be used for the subcritically branching case to show that, whether the basic solution gains or loses an exponent with negative real part, the number of exponents having negative real parts on the nontrivial solution for $R < R_c$ is the same as the number on the basic solution for $R > R_c$ (Fig. 5.7c,d). When we combine the results for supercritical and subcritical branching, we see that in general, the stability properties are transferred from one solution to another as we vary the parameter value in the direction of the branching solution.

Even in the transcritically branching case, the above general statement holds (Fig. 5.7e,f). If the solution branches toward larger values of R, then the new solution must have n exponents with negative real parts provided that the conductive solution had n; also the number of exponents having negative real parts associated with the subcritical branch when $R < R_c$ is the same as the number associated with the basic solution when $R > R_c$. On the basis of the conservation of index alone we cannot deduce the number of exponents with negative real parts that would be associated with the nontrivial solution once it turns back toward larger values of R. All we know is that zero is the sum of the degrees of the two branches emanating from a regular turning point. But if transcritical branching is a perturbation of either supercritical or subcritical branching, (see Section 6.3.1), then we may conclude that the degree of the upper branch must be the same as that of the lower one, as displayed in Fig. 5.7e,f.

As we have seen, we may learn quite a bit about the expected stability properties by carefully tracking the signs of the characteristic exponents. We exploit these ideas further in Chapters 7 and 9 to verify that the stability results we obtain are consistent.

In Section 5.3, we discussed three canonical types of bifurcation using an ordinary differential equation whose right side f(y) was a cubic polynomial function. This choice for f(y) was made deliberately, because in general we find that the stationary solutions to low-order hydrodynamic models are governed by odd-degree polynomial equations. Some motivations for this conclusion are given in the next chapter, in which we also consider other types of branching forms for the stationary solutions.

CHAPTER 6

TYPICAL BRANCHING FORMS: STATIONARY SOLUTIONS

PAUL A. HIRSCHBERG

Well-posed hydrodynamic problems are represented mathematically by differential equations known as <u>forced dissipative systems</u>. Any circulation determined by such a problem corresponds to the solution of an initial/boundary value problem associated with the differential equations. These circulations are driven by external or internal forcing and are retarded by viscous effects. Indeed, as we noted in Section 2.1.4, it is the balancing of these effects that creates steady states.

It is significant that in the absence of forcing, dissipative effects cause perturbations of any size to decay to zero. This sets even weakly viscous flows apart from inviscid ones, for in the unforced case, the presence of even a small amount of viscosity ensures the existence of a unique long-term stationary solution to the equivalent initial/boundary value problem. It seems plausible that unique solutions still exist for viscous systems when the forcing is present, but very weak. We prove this result rigorously in Section 17.2.3, but discuss it informally below. For now, we note that although many hydrodynamic flows are nearly inviscid, it is fundamentally important to recognize that viscous effects do ensure that there are unique solutions in some range of parameter values, and so a nonlinear analysis of the equations can begin in this region of parameter space. In a sense, then, the presence of viscosity allows us to organize our study of the problem.

As we see in this chapter, the fact that a unique stationary solution exists in a range of parameter values places constraints on the forms of the branching solutions and hence on the forms of the polynomial equations governing them. We must be aware of these acceptable forms so that we may judge whether a particular model is producing qualitatively reasonable results. In this chapter, we discuss some of the admissible forms and then note how they can be altered as we add other kinds of parameters representing different types of forcing. This discussion sets the stage for the analysis in Chapter 8, in which we identify the fundamentally different types of parameters that exist in a particular problem.

6.1 Properties of Forced Dissipative Systems

To determine whether a unique stationary solution S to a system of equations exists, we normally use energy methods (Joseph, 1981); that is, we form an energy rate equation for the perturbations of S and then use various inequalities to rewrite the equation in a form that has exponential solutions. The energies of these solutions can be seen to be bounded by a function that decays with time when the parameter values are in certain ranges, and so the perturbations must damp to zero. For example, the (eddy) viscosity ν and the (eddy) thermometric conductivity κ may need to exceed certain critical values that depend, in part, on the extreme values of the shear terms in the flow itself. Although numerical estimates for these extreme values are difficult to determine, their existence is sufficient to guarantee that all perturbations decay to zero, thereby proving the existence of a unique, long-term, stationary solution S (see Joseph, 1981 and Section 17.2.3).

In this section, we use a less formal approach to motivate the above results. We consider Rayleigh-Bénard convection, whose associated partial differential equations are (2.25)-(2.26); for convenience we restate them here:

$$\frac{\partial}{\partial t^*}(\tilde{\nabla}^2\psi^*) + J(\psi^*,\tilde{\nabla}^2\psi^*) - P\frac{\partial T^*}{\partial x^*} - \frac{P}{a}\tilde{\nabla}^4\psi^* = 0 \quad , \tag{6.1}$$

$$\frac{\partial T^*}{\partial t^*} + J(\psi^*,T^*) - Ra\frac{\partial \psi^*}{\partial x^*} - \frac{1}{a}\tilde{\nabla}^2 T^* = 0 \quad , \tag{6.2}$$

in which the dimensional stream function ψ is defined in (2.13)-(2.14), the Laplacian $\tilde{\nabla}^2$ and the Jacobian J operators are defined in (2.27) and (2.19), the Prandtl number P is given in (2.29) and the aspect ratio a is specified in (2.30). Here the Rayleigh number Ra is

$$Ra = \frac{g\Delta_z T z_T^3}{\nu\kappa T_{oo}\pi^4} \quad , \tag{6.3}$$

in which, by convention, the vertical temperature difference $\Delta_z T > 0$ when the basic state temperature decreases with height.

In Chapter 2, we considered the convective case of $\Delta_z T > 0$ with $Ra > Ra_c > 0$. But (6.1)-(6.2) are valid for the statically stable case of $\Delta_z T < 0$ with $Ra < 0$. In this case we may use (2.46) to define the kinetic energy KE by

$$KE = \frac{1}{2}\int_0^{2\pi}\int_0^{\pi} |\tilde{\nabla}\psi^*|^2 \, dz^* dx^* \quad . \tag{6.4}$$

Here, however, the available potential energy AE' has a different form than AE (2.47), and we define

$$AE' = \frac{1}{2}\int_0^{2\pi}\int_0^{\pi} \frac{P}{-Ra} T^{*2} \, dz^* dx^* \quad . \tag{6.5}$$

In the present case $Ra < 0$ so that $AE' > 0$, and hence AE' is an allowable energy form. For this situation, the rate of change of total energy E = KE + AE' is

$$\frac{\partial E}{\partial t^*} = -\int_0^{2\pi}\int_0^{\pi} [\frac{P}{a}(|\tilde{\nabla}^2\psi^*|^2 - \frac{1}{Ra}|\tilde{\nabla}T^*|^2)] \, dz^* dx^* \quad . \tag{6.6}$$

The energy generation term GA (2.51) that serves as an energy source in the convective case is no longer present, but has now taken the form of an energy conversion term C(AE',KE) by which available potential energy is converted to kinetic energy (see Dutton, 1976). Here C(AE',KE) has the equivalent forms

$$C(AE',KE) = \int_0^{2\pi}\int_0^{\pi} P\, T^* \frac{\partial\psi^*}{\partial x^*} \, dz^* dx^* = \int_0^{2\pi}\int_0^{\pi} P\, T^* w^* \, dz^* dx^*$$

$$= -\int_0^{2\pi}\int_0^{\pi} P\, \psi^* \frac{\partial T^*}{\partial x^*} \, dz^* dx^* \quad . \tag{6.7}$$

These two expressions are shown to be equal by integrating one by parts to produce the other, subject to the usual boundary conditions of cyclic continuity in the x^*-direction. Here $C(AE',KE) > 0$ means energy is transferred from AE' to KE and, in this case, we see that kinetic energy is gained if relatively warm fluid ($T^* > 0$) is rising ($w^* > 0$) or cold fluid is sinking.

Examination of (6.6) reveals that when $Ra < 0$, the term on the right is normally negative. In this case, because the energies are also positive quantities, we expect that their values would decrease monotonically to vanish as time approaches infinity. Thus, we expect that perturbations of <u>any</u> size would decay to zero, so that, at least in the parameter range $Ra < 0$, the conductive basic state $\psi^* = T^* = 0$ is unique and globally stable.

We may extend the parameter range of unique solutions to positive values of Ra by following Busse (1981) and noting that when Ra > 0, we have the energy equations

$$\frac{\partial}{\partial t^*} KE = \int_0^{2\pi} \int_0^{\pi} P \frac{\partial \psi^*}{\partial x^*} T^* \, dz^* dx^* - \int_0^{2\pi} \int_0^{\pi} \frac{P}{a} |\tilde{\nabla}^2 \psi^*|^2 \, dz^* dx^* \quad , \tag{6.8}$$

$$\frac{\partial}{\partial t^*} AE = Ra \int_0^{2\pi} \int_0^{\pi} P \frac{\partial \psi^*}{\partial x^*} T^* \, dz^* dx^* - \int_0^{2\pi} \int_0^{\pi} \frac{P}{a} |\tilde{\nabla} T^*|^2 \, dz^* dx^* \quad . \tag{6.9}$$

Here the kinetic energy KE is given by (6.4), but now the available potential energy AE is the same as (2.47) used in Chapter 2:

$$AE = \frac{1}{2} \int_0^{2\pi} \int_0^{\pi} P T^{*2} \, dz^* dx^* \quad . \tag{6.10}$$

As the magnitude of Ra is increased, we might expect that at some value Ra_b, damping would be balanced by amplification, and an energetically steady state would be possible; in this case (6.8)-(6.9) become

$$\int_0^{2\pi} \int_0^{\pi} \frac{\partial \psi^*}{\partial x^*} T^* \, dz^* dx^* = \int_0^{2\pi} \int_0^{\pi} \frac{1}{a} |\tilde{\nabla}^2 \psi^*|^2 \, dz^* dx^* \quad , \tag{6.11}$$

$$Ra_b \int_0^{2\pi} \int_0^{\pi} \frac{\partial \psi^*}{\partial x^*} T^* \, dz^* dx^* = \int_0^{2\pi} \int_0^{\pi} \frac{1}{a} |\tilde{\nabla} T^*|^2 \, dz^* dx^* \quad . \tag{6.12}$$

Upon multiplying (6.11) and (6.12) together and then solving the result for Ra_b, we have

$$Ra_b = \frac{\int_0^{2\pi} \int_0^{\pi} |\tilde{\nabla}^2 \psi^*|^2 \, dz^* dx^* \int_0^{2\pi} \int_0^{\pi} |\tilde{\nabla} T^*|^2 \, dz^* dx^*}{\{\int_0^{2\pi} \int_0^{\pi} a \frac{\partial \psi^*}{\partial x^*} T^* \, dz^* dx^*\}^2} \quad . \tag{6.13}$$

Now we see that the Rayleigh number Ra_b represents a ratio of dissipation to vertical heat flux. In addition, the expression on the right can be minimized subject to the boundary conditions and (6.1)-(6.2) with temporal derivatives set to zero (Busse, 1981). Thus, we expect that convective flows could exist only when $Ra > Ra_u = \min(Ra_b) > 0$. This behavior is shown rigorously using variational methods applied to the linearized form of (6.1)-(6.2) (see Sections 2.13-2.14 of Chandrasekhar, 1961). Moreover, we note that for all values of $Ra < Ra_u$, only a unique, globally stable conductive solution exists. With further analysis (see Sorokin, 1953), it can be shown that $Ra_u = Ra_c$, the critical value (2.65) at which a convective solution bifurcates from the conductive one; then, in this case, we have that $Ra_b \to Ra_c$ as $\psi^* \to 0$ and $T^* \to 0$. More generally, when a forcing parameter R is also the bifurcation parameter, the region of parameter space for which a globally stable, unique basic solution exists is given by $-\infty < R < R_u \leq R_c$. Furthermore, the basic solution exchanges stability with a branching solution at some value of $R_c \geq R_u$ (Fig. 6.1) (Joseph, 1976); in most cases $R_c > R_u$, in contrast to the situation in classical Rayleigh-Bénard convection.

To see how to interpret physically the meaning of (6.13), we use (2.20)-(2.21), (2.23)-(2.24), (2.27)-(2.30) and (2.45) to write (6.13) in the dimensional form

$$(\Delta_z T)_b = \frac{z_T \nu\kappa T_{oo}}{g} \frac{\int_0^L \int_0^{z_T} |\nabla^2\psi|^2 \, dz \, dx \int_0^L \int_0^{z_T} |\nabla T'|^2 \, dz \, dx}{\{\int_0^L \int_0^{z_T} \frac{\partial\psi}{\partial x} T' \, dz \, dx\}^2} , \qquad (6.14)$$

in which $(\Delta_z T)_b$ is the vertical temperature difference associated with Ra_b; steady convection is possible when $\Delta_z T \geq (\Delta_z T)_b$. From (6.14) we see that if the diffusion

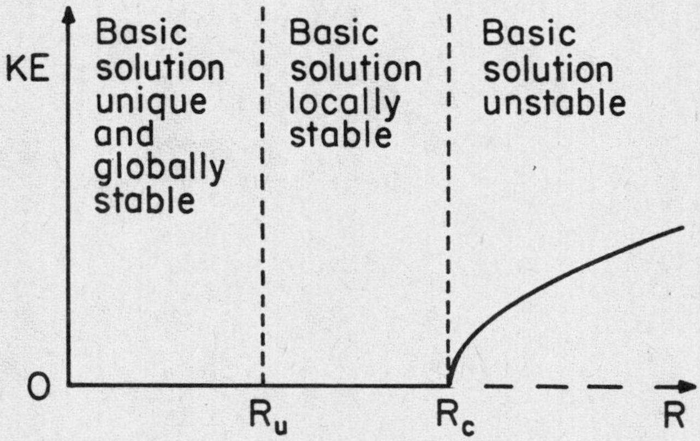

Fig. 6.1 Typical results of an analysis of the trivial basic state of a forced dissipative system using energy methods. The basic solution is globally stable and unique when $R<R_u$, locally stable for $R_u<R<R_c$, and unstable for $R>R_c$. For Rayleigh-Bénard convection R=Ra and $Ra_u=Ra_c$ (after Joseph, 1976).

terms in the numerator are relatively large in magnitude compared with the square of the vertical heat flux term in the denominator, then a relatively large vertical temperature difference $\Delta_z T$ would be needed in order for convection to occur. In contrast, there may be fluid configurations in which the flow can transport heat upward efficiently and thus produce a relatively large heat flux term. Then the ratio of dissipation terms to heat flux terms would be smaller than in the first case above, and the value of $(\Delta_z T)_b$ would be smaller. If we suppose that the fluid contains enough random perturbations for the most efficient configuration to be excited, then we may conclude that convection would be expected to occur at the smallest possible value $(\Delta_z T)_u$ of $(\Delta_z T)_b$. Thus, we arrive at the physical interpretation of Chandrasekhar (1961, p. 34) for the onset of convection:

"Instability occurs at the minimum temperature gradient at which a balance can be steadily maintained between the kinetic energy dissipated by viscosity and the internal energy released by the buoyancy force."

We apply this principle in Chapter 7 to find the minimum, or preferred, value of $Ra_c = Ra_u$. In this case as $Ra_b \to Ra_c$, we have that $\psi \to 0$ and $T' \to 0$ and for free boundary conditions that $\min(Ra_c) = 27/4$ when $a^2 = 1/2$; then we may rewrite (6.14) as

$$\lim_{\substack{\psi \to 0 \\ T' \to 0}} \frac{\int_0^L \int_0^{z_T} |\nabla^2\psi|^2 \, dz \, dx \int_0^L \int_0^{z_T} |\nabla T'|^2 \, dz \, dx}{\left\{\int_0^L \int_0^{z_T} \frac{\partial\psi}{\partial x} T' \, dz \, dx\right\}^2} = \frac{27\pi^4}{4z_T^4} , \qquad (6.15)$$

in which ψ and T' are the dimensional stationary solutions to the boundary value problem associated with (6.1)-(6.2). Equation (6.15) should give the observed limiting ratio of the dissipation to the vertical heat flux in the convecting flow that develops as the value of $\Delta_z T$, or Ra, is increased past its critical value $(\Delta_z T)_c$, or Ra_c.

The existence of a region in parameter space for which a forced, dissipative system has unique, globally stable solutions leads to important implications for the allowable forms for the branching nonlinear solutions. Since in many cases these branches can be obtained by solving polynomial equations in a single spectral component, the restrictions on the branching forms are reflected in the acceptable forms for these polynomial functions. We discuss these limitations in the next section.

6.2 Stationary Solutions: Odd-Degree Polynomial Equations

In Chapters 2 and 4 we listed the convective solutions to the Lorenz model without showing the intermediate steps in the calculation. We give them here, because they show how the form of the polynomial equation governing the stationary solutions is determined. We recall from (2.75)-(2.77) that the Lorenz model is (for m = n = 1)

$$\dot{\psi}_{11} = \frac{P}{(a^2+1)} T_{11} - P\left(\frac{a^2+1}{a}\right) \psi_{11} \quad , \tag{6.16}$$

$$\dot{T}_{11} = \psi_{11} T_{02} + \mathrm{Ra}\, \psi_{11} - \left(\frac{a^2+1}{a}\right) T_{11} \quad , \tag{6.17}$$

$$\dot{T}_{02} = -\frac{1}{2} \psi_{11} T_{11} - \frac{4}{a} T_{02} \quad . \tag{6.18}$$

We obtain the stationary solutions of (6.16)-(6.18) by setting the time derivatives to zero and then solving (6.16) and (6.18) to express T^s_{11} and T^s_{02} as functions of ψ^s_{11}:

$$T^s_{11} = \frac{(a^2+1)^2}{a} \psi^s_{11} \quad , \tag{6.19}$$

$$T^s_{02} = -\frac{(a^2+1)^2}{8} (\psi^s_{11})^2 \quad . \tag{6.20}$$

Substitution of (6.19)-(6.20) into (6.17) (with $\dot{T}_{11} = 0$) yields the cubic equation

$$(\psi^s_{11})^3 - \left[\frac{8}{(a^2+1)^2} (\mathrm{Ra} - \mathrm{Ra}_c)\right]\psi^s_{11} = 0 \quad , \tag{6.21}$$

in which

$$\mathrm{Ra}_c = \frac{(a^2+1)^3}{a^2} \quad . \tag{6.22}$$

Solutions to (6.21) are given in Fig. 6.2; inspection of Figs. 6.1 and 6.2 shows that indeed the conductive solution is the only stationary one when $\mathrm{Ra} < \mathrm{Ra}_c$, as expected. We may verify that (6.19)-(6.21), or (2.100)-(2.102) obey (6.13) when we interpret Ra_b as Ra and then insert the expansions (2.73)-(2.74) into (6.13) to find

$$Ra = \frac{\int_0^{2\pi}\int_0^{\pi} (a^2+1)^2\, \psi_{11}^2\, \sin^2 x^*\, \sin^2 z^*\, dz^* dx^*}{[\int_0^{2\pi}\int_0^{\pi} a\psi_{11}T_{11}\, \cos^2 x^*\, \sin^2 z^*\, dz^* dx^*]^2} \times$$

$$\int_0^{2\pi}\int_0^{\pi} [a^2 T_{11}^2\, \sin^2 x^*\, \sin^2 z^* + T_{11}^2\, \cos^2 x^*\, \cos^2 z^* + 4T_{02}^2\, \cos^2(2z^*)] dz^* dx^* \quad . \tag{6.23}$$

In (6.23) we have only written the contributions involving squares of the basis functions, because these are the only ones that do not vanish upon integration. Because (6.23) is valid only for stationary solutions to (6.16)-(6.18), we must have

$$Ra = \frac{(a^2+1)^3}{a^2} + \frac{8(T_{02}^s)^2(a^2+1)^2}{(T_{11}^s)^2 a^2} \quad . \tag{6.24}$$

First we note from (6.24) that $Ra_u = \min(Ra_b) = \min(Ra) = (a^2+1)^3/a^2 = Ra_c$, a result consistent with the fact that the solutions are unique for $Ra < Ra_u = Ra_c$ in the complete Rayleigh-Bénard problem. Next we observe that the expressions for T_{11}^s and T_{02}^s in (6.19)-(6.20) obey (6.24), provided that

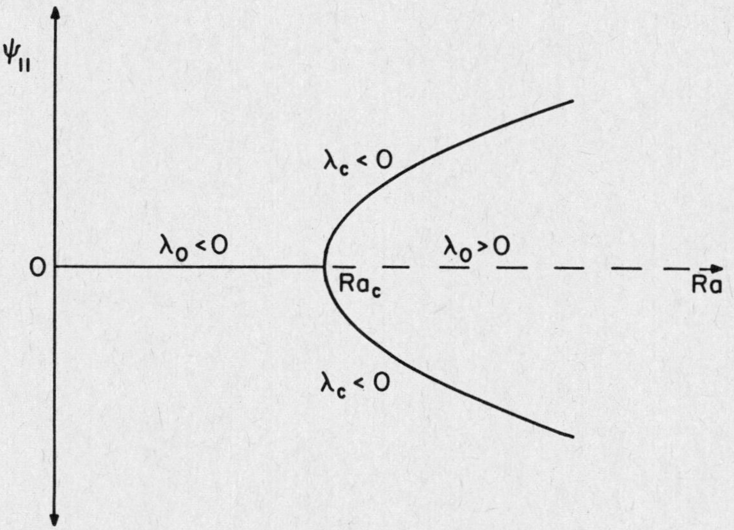

Fig. 6.2 Bifurcation and stability diagram for the Lorenz model showing the amplitudes of the stationary solutions as functions of Ra. Stable solutions are denoted by solid lines, unstable ones by dashed lines. The characteristic exponents for the conductive solution are denoted by λ_o, the ones for the convective solutions by λ_c. When $\lambda<0$ a solution is stable, and when $\lambda>0$ it is unstable.

$$(\psi_{11}^{s})^2 = \frac{8(Ra - Ra_c)}{(a^2+1)^2} \quad , \tag{6.25}$$

which is the expression for ψ_{11}^{s} given in (2.100). Finally, because

$$\frac{(T_{02}^{s})^2}{(T_{11}^{s})^2} \propto (\psi_{11}^{s})^2 \quad , \tag{6.26}$$

we see from (6.24) and (6.25) that $Ra \to Ra_c$ as $\psi_{11}^{s} \to 0$, as we would expect when a bifurcation occurs at $Ra = Ra_c$.

What allows the Lorenz model to produce qualitatively correct branching results is the fact that the governing polynomial equation (6.21) is a cubic one in the amplitude s of the form

$$s[s^2 - (R - R_c)] = 0 \quad , \tag{6.27}$$

in which R is a general bifurcation parameter. This equation has a basic solution $s = 0$ for all values of the parameter R, as well as two more solutions that exist only for $R > R_c$. Thus, solutions to (6.27) have the qualitative behavior shown in Fig. 6.2. We might ask what other forms of polynomial equations produce acceptable branching results; in the remainder of this section, we consider special cases of the general n^{th}-degree polynomial equation

$$s^n + C_{n-1}(R;\xi_j)s^{n-1} + C_{n-2}(R;\xi_j)s^{n-2} + \cdots + C_0(R;\xi_j) = 0, \qquad j = 1,\ldots,p \quad . \tag{6.28}$$

For the present purposes, we restrict the discussion to those cases in which a real solution exists for all values of the parameters R and ξ_j, and for convenience it is the trivial solution $s = 0$. From inspection of (6.28) we see that $s = 0$ for all values of R and ξ_j whenever $C_0 = 0$. Of course, the basic state need not be a trivial one. For instance, there could be a nonzero basic flow present (Fig. 6.3) as in the case of quasi-geostrophic flow in a channel (Vickroy and Dutton, 1979).

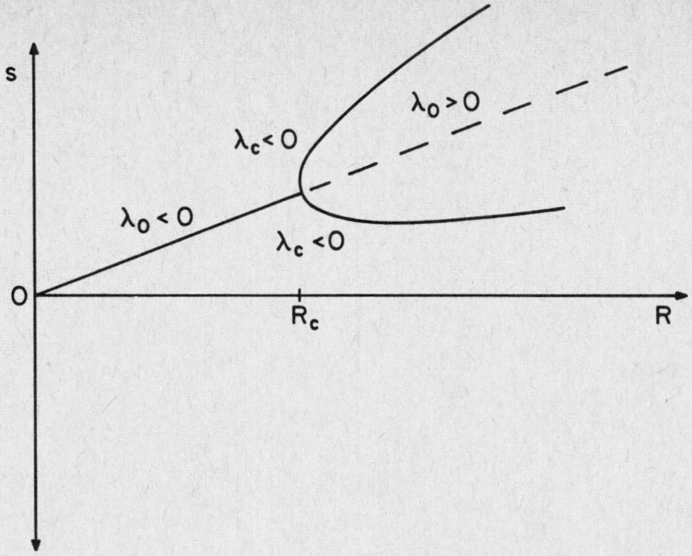

Fig. 6.3 Hypothetical bifurcation and stability diagram illustrating a nonzero basic state. Here s and R are the amplitude and the parameter; stable and unstable solutions are denoted as in Fig. 6.2.

We begin testing arbitrary polynomial equations by first considering the quadratic case. As an example, let the stationary solutions be governed by

$$s^2 + C_1(R)s = 0 \quad , \tag{6.29}$$

or

$$s\left[s + C_1(R)\right] = 0 \quad , \tag{6.30}$$

in which for simplicity we have not written explicitly the other parameters ξ_j. This even-degree polynomial equation has two roots, one being the trivial (s = 0) solution, and the other, the nontrivial solution

$$s = - C_1(R) \quad . \tag{6.31}$$

If $C_1(R) = -(R - R_c)$, then we find that the amplitude of the nontrivial solution is a linear function of R (Fig. 6.4). But because there is no range of values of

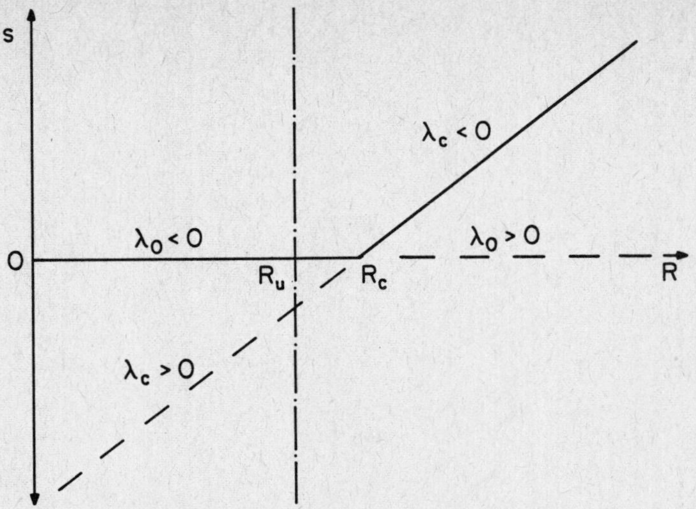

Fig. 6.4 Bifurcation and stability diagram for the solutions (6.31) and s=0 to the quadratic polynomial equation (6.29). This case does not produce an acceptable solution form. Here s and R represent the amplitude and the parameter, R_c is the critical value of R, and stable and unstable solutions are denoted as in Fig. 6.2. Values of $R<R_u$ represent the range in which the trivial solution should be globally stable and unique.

R such that $-\infty < R < R_u \leq R_c$ for which the trivial solution is unique, this case does not comply with the required form given in Fig. 6.1.

As noted above, the stationary solutions to the Lorenz model obey a cubic equation that meets the requirements for acceptable solution forms (Fig. 6.2). We can imagine a different cubic equation, however, for which this is not so. If

$$s = \pm (R_c - R)^{1/2} \quad , \tag{6.32}$$

is the nontrivial solution to this equation, then we find that these solutions branch subcritically into the forbidden zone, as illustrated in Fig. 6.5.

As another example of a governing even-degree polynomial equation, we examine a quartic one. From (6.28) the general form of this equation is given by

$$s^4 + C_3(R)s^3 + C_2(R)s^2 + C_1(R)s + C_0(R) = 0 \quad . \tag{6.33}$$

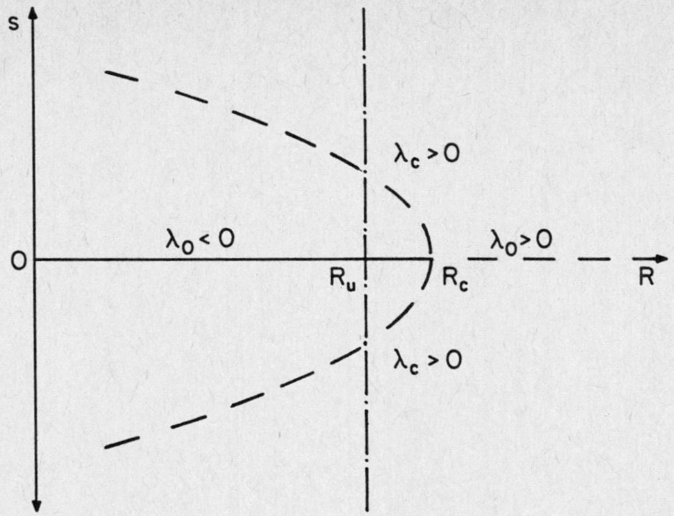

Fig. 6.5 Bifurcation and stability diagram showing the solutions (6.32) and s = 0 to a cubic polynomial equation whose form is not acceptable. Description of the diagram as in Fig. 6.4.

Since we are demanding that the trivial solution s = 0 exists, we must find one or three nontrivial real roots. Thus, a general solution form for this case might be as shown in Fig. 6.6. As can be seen in this figure, such a form also must be discarded since it inevitably curves back into the forbidden region $R < R_u$.

As one last case, we consider an odd-degree, quintic equation of the form

$$s^5 + C_4(R)s^4 + C_3(R)s^3 + C_2(R)s^2 + C_1(R)s + C_0(R) = 0 \quad . \tag{6.34}$$

A possible depiction of the solutions to this equation is shown in Fig. 6.7. Even though there are solutions that branch subcritically, we see that the form of the branches is acceptable. At a regular turning point, whose value of R is $R_n \geq R_u$, the solution turns toward larger values of R. For values of R in the range $R_n < R < R_c$, three asymptotically stable solutions exist, creating a representation of finite-amplitude instability and snap-through bifurcation (see Section 5.3.2). Certainly, as for the cubic case, we could find instances of quintic equations that are not allowed. But we note that the quintic equation is the lowest order one that models subcritical branches adequately, as illustrated in Fig. 6.7. We encounter a system exhibiting this behavior when we study rotating convection in Section 7.2.

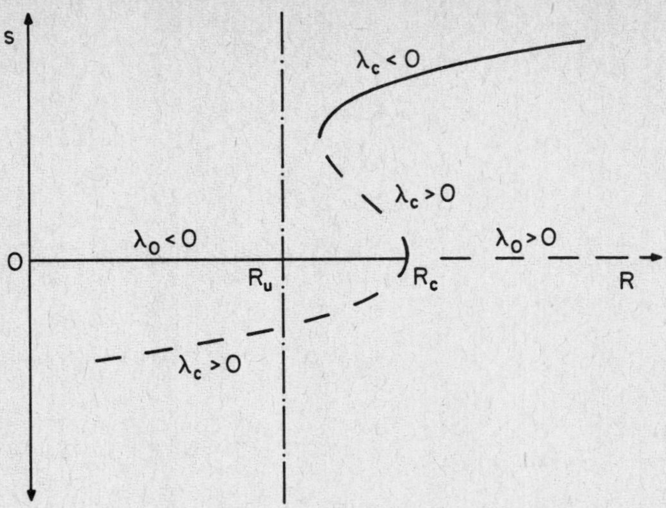

Fig. 6.6 Bifurcation and stability diagram for typical solutions to the quartic equation (6.33). This case does not produce an acceptable solution form. Description of the diagram as in Fig. 6.4.

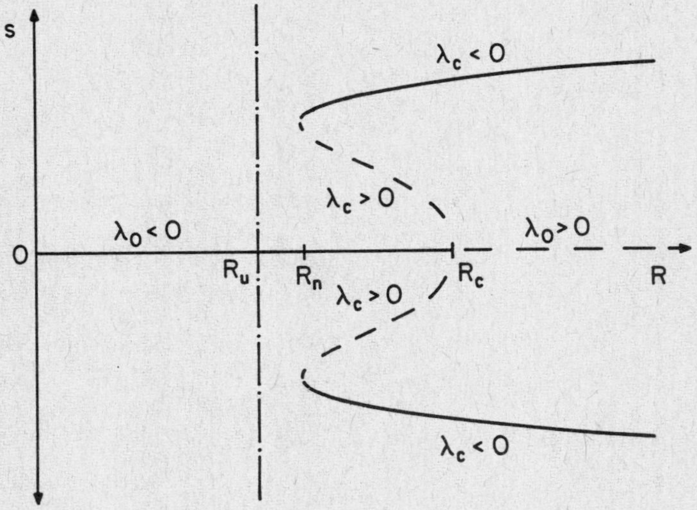

Fig. 6.7 Bifurcation and stability diagram for typical solutions to the quintic equation (6.34). This case produces an acceptable solution form. Here R_n is the value of R at a regular turning point; otherwise, description of the diagram as in Fig. 6.4.

6.3 Parameters and Transition Types

The above examples show that only odd-degree polynomial equations produce acceptable forms for stationary solutions. With this information in mind, we concentrate on cubic equations and explore their possible solutions and graphical representations. First, however, we examine the trident in Fig. 6.2 more closely.

In the Boussinesq equations governing Rayleigh-Bénard convection, there are three dimensionless parameters: the Rayleigh number Ra, the Prandtl number P, and the aspect ratio a, in which P and a are examples of the parameters ξ_j in (6.28). Also, we recall from (6.22) that the critical value Ra_c of the Rayleigh number is a function only of the aspect ratio. Figures 6.8a-c illustrate this relationship schematically. As the value of a increases, that is, as the domain height z_T becomes a larger fraction of the length L, the magnitude of Ra_c increases. In other words, a stable conductive solution exists for larger values of Ra. This result is valid as long as we stay within the scaling limits of the Boussinesq approximation. The fact that Ra_c attains a minimum value $Ra_c = 27/4$ is used in Chapter 7 to specify a preferred value of a.

Often, the solutions to nonlinear problems are functions of many parameters. To facilitate the analysis of these solutions, we find it useful to depict them graphically in three dimensions. The stationary solutions to the Lorenz model can be displayed in this way. We notice from (6.21) that the stationary solutions are not dependent on the Prandtl number, P. So, if we plot these solutions as functions of both Ra and P (Fig. 6.9), then we find that the trident does not change shape. It simply extends in the P-direction, forming a solution surface that is shaped as a snow plow. We can view the trident in Fig. 6.2 as being only a two-dimensional cross section of this three-dimensional plot, and conveniently this cross section is valid for <u>any</u> value of P. Thus, P does not introduce any qualitative changes into the branching behavior.

6.3.1 Shifting the trident.

The physical effects incorporated in the Lorenz model of Rayleigh-Bénard convection are fairly simple. The forcing is only a linear

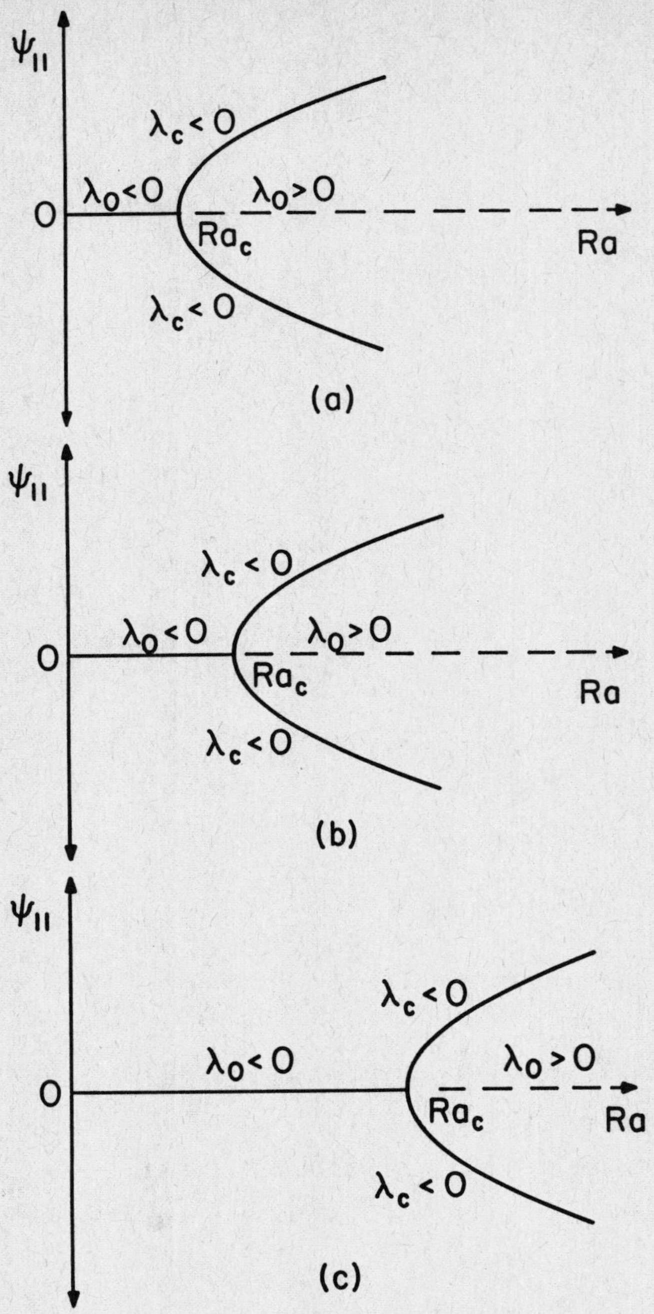

Fig. 6.8 Bifurcation and stability diagrams illustrating the effect of aspect ratio, a, on the value of Ra_c. In a) a=0.5, b) a=1, and c) a=2. Stable and unstable solutions are denoted as in Fig. 6.2.

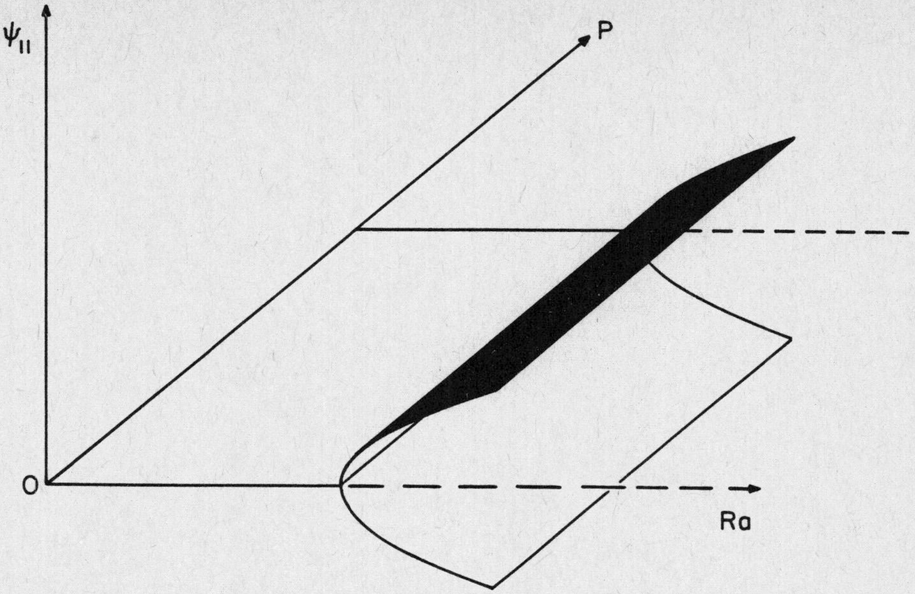

Fig. 6.9 Depiction of the stationary solutions to the Lorenz model as functions of Ra and the Prandtl number P. Stable and unstable solutions denoted as in Fig. 6.2.

function of height. Therefore, the mathematical structure of the model is not very complex, and the stationary solutions obey the cubic polynomial equation of the form

$$s^3 + C_1(R;\xi_j)s = 0 \quad , \quad j = 1,\ldots,p \quad . \tag{6.35}$$

In this expression, $C_1(R;\xi_j)$ is proportional to the vertical forcing rate given by R. The cubic polynomial equations for models having more representations $R_1,\ldots,R_q$ of the physical effects might be more complicated than (6.35). From (6.28) we find that the general form of a third-degree polynomial equation is

$$s^3 + C_2(R_i;\xi_j)s^2 + C_1(R_i;\xi_j)s + C_0(R_i;\xi_j) = 0 \quad \begin{cases} i=1,\ldots,q \\ j=1,\ldots,p \end{cases} \quad . \tag{6.36}$$

For example, there could be a physical system with two forcing parameters R_1 and R_2 appearing in only the s^2 and s coefficients. Physically these parameters might correspond to the vertical heating rate R_1 and the latent heating rate R_2 (Huang and Källén, 1986). If we suppress the parameters ξ_j, then we might have the simpler form

$$s^3 + C_2(R_2)s^2 + C_1(R_1)s = 0 \quad , \tag{6.37}$$

which contains the trivial solution s = 0 as well as the nontrivial ones

$$s = -\frac{C_2(R_2)}{2} \pm \frac{[C_2^2(R_2) - 4C_1(R_1)]^{1/2}}{2} \quad . \tag{6.38}$$

It is evident that the addition of the forcing term $C_2(R_2)$ into the cubic equation shifts the trident either up or down, depending on the sign of $C_2(R_2)$. In fact, the equations for the regular turning point on the new solution are given by

$$s = -\frac{C_2(R_2)}{2} \quad \text{and} \quad C_2^2(R_2) = 4C_1(R_1) \quad . \tag{6.39}$$

As illustrated in Fig. 6.10a-c, if $C_2(R_2) > 0$, then the trident is shifted down, and if $C_2(R_2) < 0$, then the trident is shifted up. Finally, if $C_2(R_2) = 0$, then the trident centers on the trivial solution. For this last case we cannot label one of the two convective states as more likely to appear at $R_1 = R_{1c}$. Both solutions are stable, and both appear simultaneously at $R_1 = R_{1c}$. As a consequence, the sense of the roll circulations cannot be predicted without more information (see Section 6.3.2). Notice, however, that in cases in which $C_2(R_2) \neq 0$, there are preferred routes by which stability is exchanged. At $R_1 = R_{1c}$ one solution branches subcritically, hence being unstable, and the other branches supercritically, hence being stable. When $C_2(R_2) < 0$, the trivial solution is replaced smoothly by the lower branch as the value of R_1 is increased. In contrast, when $C_2(R_2) > 0$, the trivial solution exhanges stability with the positive solution. In both cases the only way to reach the other solution is through a large perturbation or a finite-amplitude instability as discussed in Section 5.3.3. In this instance, we can also see examples of hysteresis.

<u>6.3.2 Splitting the trident</u>. The stationary solutions of a two-dimensional model of convection forced by a vertical heating rate R_1 and a horizontal heating rate R_3 are governed by the form

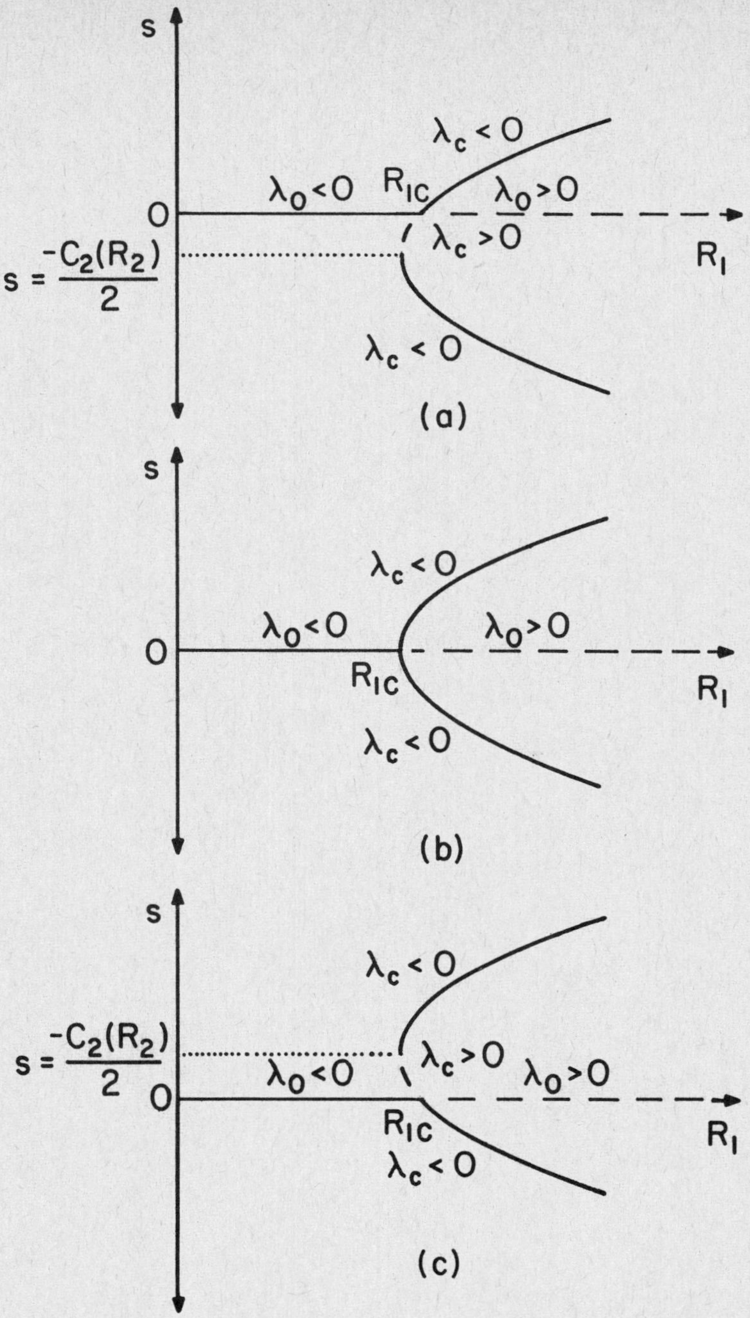

Fig. 6.10 Bifurcation and stability diagrams illustrating the effect of forcing in the quadratic term of a cubic polynomial equation (6.37). Here three values of the second forcing term R_2 are chosen so that $C_2(R_2)>0$ (a), $C_2(R_2)=0$ (b), and $C_2(R_2)<0$ (c). The magnitudes (6.39) of the solutions at the regular turning points are indicated by dotted lines. Stable and unstable solutions are denoted as in Fig. 6.2.

$$s^3 + C_2(R_3)s^2 + C_1(R_1)s + C_0(R_3) = 0 \quad , \tag{6.40}$$

in which again we have not explicitly shown the other parameters ξ_j. Models having stationary solutions controlled by polynomial equations of the form (6.40) were studied by Yost and Shirer (1982) and Shirer and Wells (1982); these models are discussed further in Chapter 8. Here we note how the solution form depends on the values of R_1 and R_3.

With the substitution

$$\hat{s} = s + C_2(R_3)/3 \quad , \tag{6.41}$$

we may rewrite (6.40) in the form

$$\hat{s}^3 - C_4(R_1,R_3)\hat{s} - C_5(R_1,R_3) = 0 \quad , \tag{6.42}$$

in which

$$C_4(R_1,R_3) = C_2^2(R_3)/3 - C_1(R_1) \quad , \tag{6.43}$$

$$C_5(R_1,R_3) = -\,2C_2^3(R_3)/27 + C_1(R_1)C_2(R_3)/3 - C_0(R_3) \quad . \tag{6.44}$$

The problem is now reduced to one in which we consider how $\hat{s}$ depends on C_4 and C_5, which are functions of the physically derived parameters R_1 and R_3.

In studying the problem in its present form (6.42), we normally ask such questions as

1) How does the number of stationary solutions change as the values of C_4 and C_5 are varied?
2) At which values of C_4 and C_5 does this number change?
3) Does varying only C_4 lead to a different type of transition than does varying only C_5?

For a given polynomial equation such as (6.42), we can divide parameter space into separate regions, each characterized by a fixed number of stationary solutions. Once this division is done, we may try to describe the spatial arrangement of each region.

However, it is important to determine the way in which one stationary solution is replaced by another, because such a transition between stationary solutions can occur in either a smooth or a sudden manner.

In order to understand when these different types of transitions occur and how the parameters are related to them, we consider (6.42) in more detail. The transition from three simple real roots to a single one occurs at values of (C_4,C_5) for which (6.42) has a pair of double roots. The condition for a root x_o of a polynomial equation $f(x) = 0$ to be a double root is for x_o also to be a root of $f'(x_o) = 0$. Applying this criterion to (6.42), we find that $\hat{s}$ also must be a root of

$$3\hat{s}^2 - C_4 = 0 \quad . \tag{6.45}$$

In the Lorenz model (6.16)-(6.18) this transition occurs at $Ra = Ra_c$, which is given in (6.22). After eliminating $\hat{s}$ from (6.42) and (6.45) (by, say, the Euclidean Algorithm in Appendix B), we find that the transition values of (C_4,C_5) are the ones satisfying

$$F_p = C_4^3/27 - C_5^2/4 = 0 \quad , \tag{6.46}$$

whose locus is the cusp shown in Fig. 6.11.

For magnitudes of (C_4,C_5) within the cusp, (6.42) has three simple real roots. For values of (C_4,C_5) outside of the cusp, (6.42) has one simple real root. At the origin $C_4 = C_5 = 0$, (6.42) has a triple real root, and this bifurcation point is called a <u>cusp point</u>. For values of (C_4,C_5) on the rest of the cusp, (6.42) has both a simple real root and a double one. These points are called <u>fold points</u> or <u>regular turning points</u> (see Section 5.3.3). Because the points that compose the cusp are points at which two or more solutions of (6.42) meet, we call them <u>singular points</u> (see Chapter 8), and they are specified by values of (C_4,C_5) satisfying (6.46).

We can better understand the behavior by plotting in $(\hat{s},C_4,C_5)$ space the locus of roots of (6.42). The resulting surface is called a <u>cusp surface</u> and is shown in Fig. 6.12. When $C_4 > 0$ and $C_5 = 0$, the three roots $\hat{s}_o$ of (6.42) are

$$\hat{s}_o = \begin{cases} \sqrt{C_4} \\ 0 \\ -\sqrt{C_4} \end{cases} \quad . \tag{6.47}$$

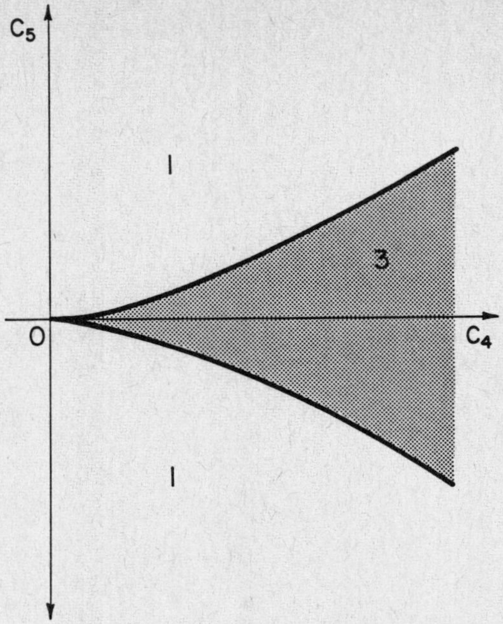

Fig. 6.11 Fold points $F_p=0$ at which two or more stationary solutions of (6.42) meet; the locus of points is given by (6.46) and forms a cusp. For values of C_4 inside the cusp ($F_p>0$), three real equilibria exist, and for values outside the cusp ($F_p<0$), only one exists (after Shirer and Wells, 1983).

If this result is represented graphically (Fig. 6.13b), then we obtain the familiar trident (Fig. 6.8). Plausible stabilities of the solutions $\hat{s}_o$ in (6.47) can be obtained by supposing that (6.42) is the right side of a simple differential equation

$$\dot{\hat{s}} = - \hat{s}^3 + C_4\hat{s} + C_5 \quad . \tag{6.48}$$

Then upon writing

$$\hat{s} = s' + \hat{s}_o \quad , \tag{6.49}$$

substituting (6.49) into (6.48), and neglecting the s'^2 and s'^3 terms, we obtain

$$\dot{s}' = - (3\hat{s}_o^2 - C_4)s' \quad . \tag{6.50}$$

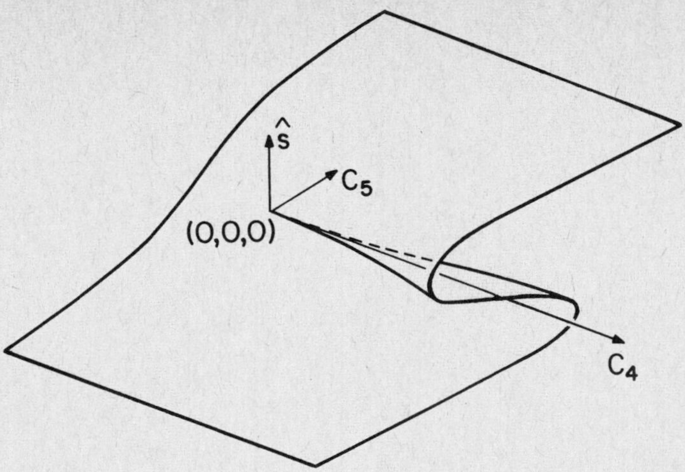

Fig. 6.12 The magnitude $\hat{s}$ of the stationary solutions of (6.42) as functions of the parameters C_4 and C_5; the resulting surface is called a cusp surface (after Shirer and Wells, 1983).

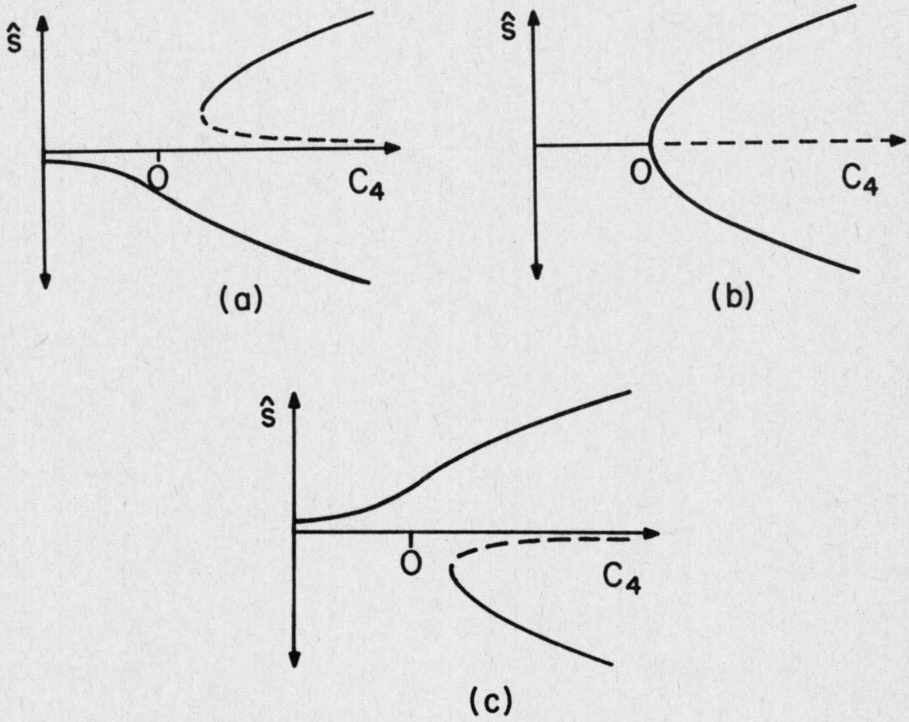

Fig. 6.13 Cross sections through Fig. 6.12 for $C_5<0$ (a), $C_5=0$ (b), and $C_5>0$ (c) (after Shirer and Wells, 1983).

The solution to (6.50) is

$$s' = \tilde{s}\exp(\lambda t) \quad , \tag{6.51}$$

in which

$$\lambda = -(3\hat{s}_o^2 - C_4) \quad . \tag{6.52}$$

If $\lambda > 0$, then s' grows and the stationary solution $\hat{s}_o$ is unstable. If $\lambda < 0$, then s' decays and $\hat{s}_o$ is stable. We find the stable and unstable solutions in (6.47) by substituting them into (6.52) to obtain

$$\lambda = \begin{cases} -2C_4 \\ C_4 \\ -2C_4 \end{cases} \quad . \tag{6.53}$$

Thus, $\hat{s}_o = -\sqrt{C_4}$ and $\hat{s}_o = \sqrt{C_4}$ are stable stationary solutions of (6.48) while $\hat{s}_o = 0$ is an unstable one. Because $\lambda = -3\hat{s}_o^2 + C_4$ vanishes on the cusp surface in Fig. 6.12 along the two curves separating the middle pleat from the others, we conclude that the middle pleat consists of unstable stationary points while the upper and lower pleats consist of stable stationary points (cf. Fig. 6.13).

Finally, when $C_4 = C_5 = 0$, which is a singular or bifurcation point of cusp type, the three solutions of (6.42) meet at $\hat{s}_o = 0$. We note that $\lambda = 0$ at this point, and so, as expected, the existence of singular points and the exchange of stability are strongly related (see Chapters 4 and 5).

Now we determine how transitions between the stationary solutions of (6.48) are affected when the values of C_4 and C_5 are varied. If a cross section of the cusp surface in Fig. 6.12 is taken when $C_5 = 0$, then we find that the stationary solutions form a trident. As we follow the single branch of the trident by increasing the value of C_4 in Fig. 6.13b, we can see that the motionless solution $\hat{s} = 0$ is replaced by a nontrivial one as the value of C_4 passes zero. Although a small change in the value of C_4 in the neighborhood of the bifurcation point ($C_4 = C_5 = 0$) causes a rapid transition from one stationary solution to another, the transition is a smooth one.

When $C_5 \neq 0$, the slopes of the curves decrease and a gradual evolution from a nearly motionless solution to a nontrivial one takes place. As a result, the smooth transition between two of the stationary solutions that occurs when $C_5 = 0$ is replaced by annihilation of these two solutions at a regular turning point. When $C_5 < 0$ (Fig. 6.13a), the stationary solution follows a curve originating from the lower branch of the trident and the regular turning point separates the upper and middle pleats of the cusp surface. In contrast, when $C_5 > 0$ (Fig. 6.13c) the stationary solution follows a curve originating from the upper branch, and the regular turning point separates the middle and lower pleats.

By adding C_5 to the differential equation, we make the physical applicability of the solutions of the cubic equation (6.42) more apparent. When the trident form describes the stationary behavior, C_5 must equal zero. If any slight error in knowing the value of C_5 occurs, then the bifurcation point disappears and the stationary solution follows a curve originating from one of the branches of the trident. Thus, the model is too sensitive when only one parameter (C_4) is included in it. By adding C_5 we make the model results insensitive to the small errors that might occur when we measure the values of C_4 and C_5. We exploit this fact in Chapter 8 when we identify the qualitatively crucial parameters of a problem.

When C_5 is nonzero and its sign is allowed to vary as the value of C_4 is held constant, then the exchange of stability from one stationary solution to another may or may not occur in a sudden manner. If we start at point A in Fig. 6.14b and perturb the stationary solution slightly by increasing the value of C_5, then the magnitude of $\hat{s}$ decreases by a small amount. However, if we increase the value of C_5 slightly beyond that of point B, then we observe a sudden, catastrophic jump to point C in the magnitude of the stationary solution. Now if we perturb the stationary solution slightly by decreasing the value of C_5, then the value of $\hat{s}$ also decreases a little. As we decrease the value of C_5 slightly past that of point D, we observe a large jump in the magnitude of the stationary solution back to point A. This behavior is an example of a <u>hysteresis loop</u>, where points B and D are regular turning points on the cusp surface. A hysteresis loop occurs for all values of $C_4 > 0$. However, as the value of C_4 decreases, the distance between B and D shrinks until at

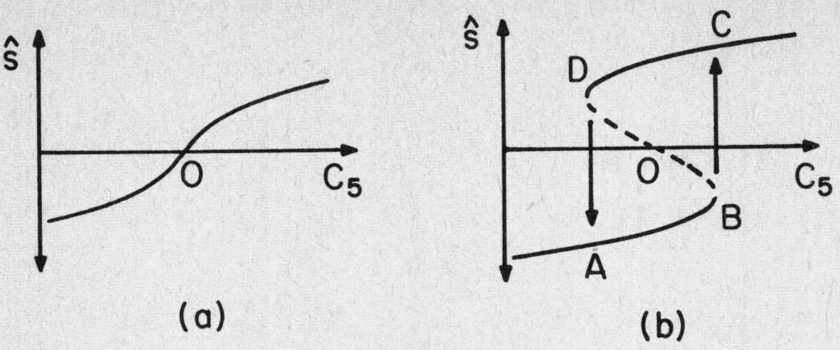

Fig. 6.14 Cross sections through Fig. 6.12 for $C_4<0$ (a), and $C_4>0$ (b). A hysteresis loop is shown in part (b) (see text); sudden transitions are denoted by vertical arrows (Shirer and Wells, 1983).

$C_4 = 0$ it vanishes. Finally, for all negative values of C_4 and for all values of C_5 we see only smooth variations among the stable stationary solutions (Fig. 6.14a).

We have seen in Fig. 6.13 that fixing the value of C_5 and varying the value of C_4 always leads to smooth transitions, but we have found in Fig. 6.14b that fixing the value of C_4 and varying the value of C_5 sometimes leads to sudden transitions. Thus, these two parameters are of different types because they are associated with different types of branching behavior. An important part of completing the analysis is to discover how many parameters there are in the differential equation or family of differential equations that could describe different types of transitions. For the above example we have two, and we discuss the other cases in Chapter 8.

We are now able to ascertain whether a model is a plausible candidate for describing a physical system by observing whether its solutions have one of the acceptable forms described in this chapter. Once a model survives this first screening, we still must analyze it thoroughly. Because there are still an infinite number of solutions available to a fluid, and clearly only one is seen in a given experiment, we must find a way to discover which solution would be expected. We noted in the last part of this chapter that some of the problem involves including those parameters that control the different possible transition types. But given a certain transition type, we must find a mechanism that determines which of the possible solutions occurs. Such a mechanism has been proposed and is commonly used, and we examine it in detail in the following chapter.

CHAPTER 7

THE EXPECTED BRANCHING SOLUTION: PREFERRED WAVELENGTHS

MARK J. LAUFERSWEILER

In the previous chapters, we have noted that exchanges of stability from one solution to another typically occur at critical values of the forcing parameter. We have seen that these critical values are determined by the other parameters of the problem. For example, in classical Rayleigh-Bénard convection, the critical Rayleigh number Ra_c depends upon the aspect ratio a, and as a result, some nonlinear solutions can appear at smaller values of the Rayleigh number--or vertical temperature difference--than other solutions (see Fig. 6.8). Consequently, a critical value of the forcing, regarded as a function of the other parameters, may take on a minimum value. In such a case, there is then a minimum critical value of the forcing at which a new solution branches. As noted in Section 6.1, this property is typical of a forced, dissipative system, in which instability occurs at the minimum value of the forcing for which a balance can be maintained between energy gain and energy loss.

If the minimum critical value of the forcing depends on parameters whose values may be altered by fluid configurations, then a favored response is possible. Usually this response depends on geometry because it involves the wavelengths of the flow. In an analysis of a problem, then, we must distinguish between two types of parameters--forcing or <u>control parameters</u> that govern bifurcations and stability exchanges between solutions, and free or <u>response parameters</u> that are subject to fluid behavior. The expected configuration of the flow is found by minimizing, with respect to the response parameters, the values of the control parameters. For a fixed value of the control parameter R that is greater than the critical value R_c, we show here that this approach is equivalent in many cases to looking for the wavelength of the fastest growing wave.

In this chapter we illustrate this equivalence by studying classical Rayleigh-Bénard convection, which has only one bifurcation point Ra_c on the conductive solution. In addition, we examine rotating Rayleigh-Bénard convection to see how the minimization process is affected when there are two bifurcation points to consider.

7.1 Classical Rayleigh-Bénard Convection

We begin by reviewing the generalized form of the Lorenz system developed in Chapter 2. Because the analysis presented here applies to bifurcation points rather than regular turning points, we only include one forcing parameter (see Chapter 6). We discuss the fact that Rayleigh-Bénard convection depends on a second control parameter in Chapter 8.

7.1.1 A generalized Lorenz system. In Chapter 2, we used the following expansions for the stream function ψ^* and the temperature perturbation T^*:

$$\psi^*(x^*,z^*,t^*) = \psi_{mn}(t^*)\sin(mx^*)\sin(nz^*) \quad , \tag{7.1}$$

$$T^*(x^*,z^*,t^*) = T_{mn}(t^*)\cos(mx^*)\sin(nz^*) + T_{0,2n}(t^*)\sin(2nz^*) \quad , \tag{7.2}$$

where m and n are the horizontal and vertical integral wavenumbers, respectively. We must restrict the choices of m and n to integers in order that the functions remain cyclic in the domain $0 \leq x \leq L$, or vanish at $z = 0, z_T$.

The spectral system is (cf. (2.75)-(2.77))

$$\dot{\psi}_{mn} = \frac{mP}{\sigma_{mn}} T_{mn} - \frac{\sigma_{mn}P}{a}\psi_{mn} \quad , \tag{7.3}$$

$$\dot{T}_{mn} = mn\,\psi_{mn}T_{0,2n} + m\,Ra\,\psi_{mn} - \frac{\sigma_{mn}}{a}T_{mn} \quad , \tag{7.4}$$

$$\dot{T}_{0,2n} = -\frac{mn}{2}\psi_{mn}T_{mn} - \frac{4n^2}{a}T_{0,2n} \quad , \tag{7.5}$$

in which

$$P = \nu/\kappa \quad , \tag{7.6}$$

$$a = 2z_T/L \quad , \tag{7.7}$$

$$Ra = g\,\Delta_z T\, z_T^3/\nu\kappa T_{oo}\pi^4 \quad , \tag{7.8}$$

are the Prandtl number, aspect ratio, and the Rayleigh number respectively, and

$$\sigma_{mn} = m^2a^2 + n^2 \quad . \tag{7.9}$$

7.1.2 Minimizing the critical Rayleigh number. A stability analysis of the conductive solution to (7.3)-(7.5) produces the critical value Ra_c of the control parameter Ra:

$$Ra_c = \frac{\sigma_{mn}^3}{m^2 a^2} = \frac{(m^2a^2+n^2)^3}{m^2a^2} \quad . \tag{7.10}$$

In order to determine the appropriate response parameter, we plot in Fig. 7.1 the values of Ra_c as functions of aspect ratio a for various values of the wavenumbers m and n. Because each curve attains an absolute minimum, we refer to the curve as a well and to the collection of curves as a well diagram. The points a_{mj} are discussed in Chapter 9 and the values for them are given in Table 9.1. In Fig. 7.1a each curve represents solutions to (7.10) for a specific horizontal wavenumber m when n = 1. Note that each curve has its own respective minimum and each minimum occurs at the same value of Ra_c, yet each minimum occurs at a different value of a. In Fig. 7.1b where n = 2, the same qualitative result occurs. The only differences between the two figures are that the values of Ra_c and a at which the minima occur are different; both Ra_c and a are larger in value, causing a slight shift to the right and a major shift up in each of the curves.

As noted in the introduction to the chapter, the existence of a minimum in Ra_c is indicative of the expected behavior in an actual fluid: there exist motions by which the instabilities can be relieved most easily. By minimizing the value of Ra_c, physically we are finding the smallest possible vertical temperature gradient that could support convection (see Section 6.1 here and Section 2.14 of Chandrasekhar, 1961). Thus, the fluid selects a cellular motion having an aspect ratio a that produces a value of Ra_c as close to the minimum value as possible.

But now we seem to have a problem--there are apparently an infinite number of pairs of values of m and a for which the minimum value of Ra_c is the same. How can we determine the one the fluid would choose? To resolve this problem, we note that m and a always appear together in (7.10); plotting Ra_c as a function of α = ma produces a single curve for each value of n (Fig. 7.2). Thus, the appropriate aspect ratio is not the domain aspect ratio a, but rather the cell aspect ratio α, given by

$$\alpha = ma = 2z_T m/L = 2z_T/\ell_m \quad , \tag{7.11}$$

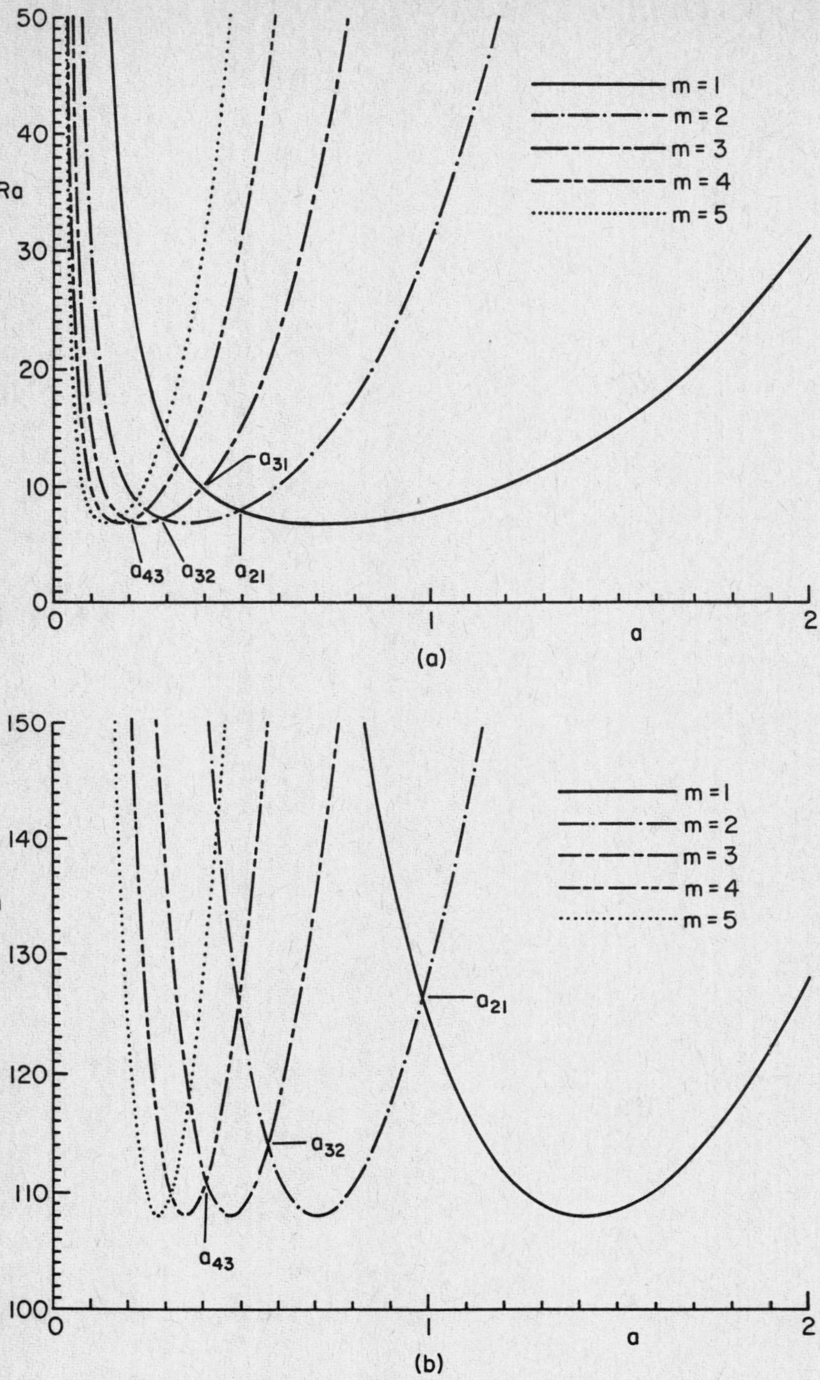

Fig. 7.1 Well diagram for the critical Rayleigh number Ra_c as a function of the domain aspect ratio a for various wavenumbers. The minimum value of Ra_c is the same for each m, but the corresponding value of a is not. In (a) the case n=1 is shown and in (b) the case n=2 is shown. Values of the points a_{mj} are given in Table 9.1.

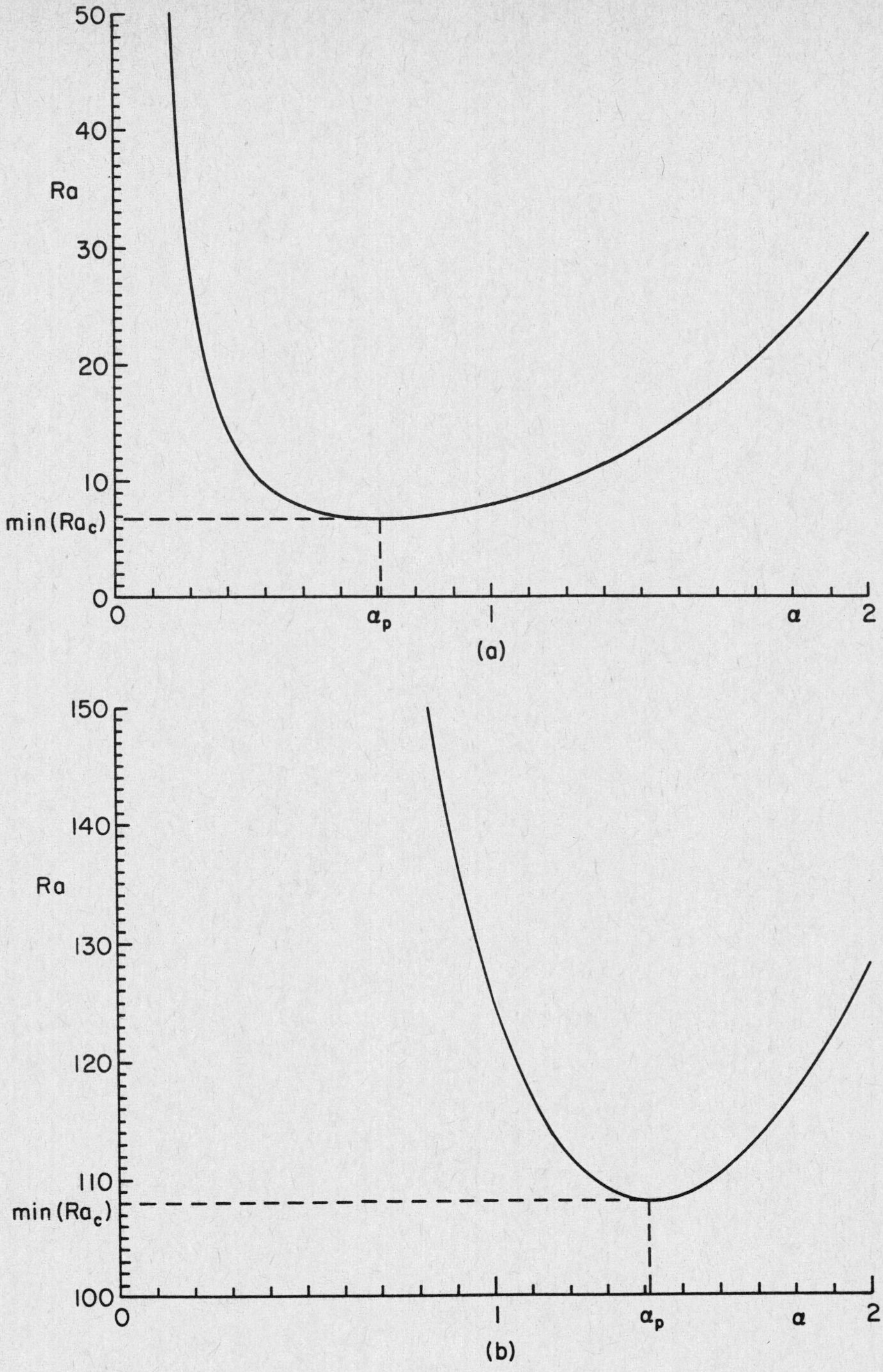

Fig. 7.2 The critical Rayleigh number Ra_c as a function of cell aspect ratio α = ma for n=1 (a) and n=2 (b). There is a single curve in each case, showing that a unique cell structure is preferred, branching at Ra=min(Ra_c) and having cell aspect ratio α_p.

in which $\ell_m = L/m$ is the horizontal wavelength of the cell and the domain contains m cells (see Fig. 2.3b). For each n there is a value of α associated with the minimum value of Ra_c. Clearly the smallest value of Ra_c is given by $n = 1$; since normally the domain top z_T is fixed at some value, this corresponds to a single cell in the vertical. But because the magnitude of z_T is usually known, the value α_p of α associated with the minimum value of Ra_c immediately gives a preferred value of the cell wavelength ℓ_m. This value of α depends on n and can be found by first differentiating (7.10) with respect to $\alpha = ma$, or by the more convenient combination $\alpha^2 = m^2a^2$, to obtain

$$\frac{\partial Ra_c}{\partial(m^2a^2)} = \frac{3(m^2a^2 + n^2)^2}{m^2a^2} - \frac{(m^2a^2 + n^2)^3}{(m^2a^2)^2} \quad , \tag{7.12}$$

and then setting this result to zero, to find

$$\alpha_p^2 = m^2a^2 = n^2/2 \quad . \tag{7.13}$$

As noted above, we find that the smallest possible value for Ra_c occurs when $n = 1$, and so we may write (7.13) as

$$\alpha_p^2 = m^2a^2 = \frac{(2z_T)^2}{\ell_m^2} = 1/2 \quad . \tag{7.14}$$

Substituting this result into (7.10), we find that

$$Ra_c = \frac{27}{4} = 6.75 \quad , \tag{7.15}$$

which is the absolute minimum value for Ra_c. Referring to Figs. 7.1a and 7.2a, we see that (7.15) is the value at which all the minima occur.

Thus, from the point of view of the flow, there is a single preferred wavelength,

$$\ell = 2\sqrt{2}\, z_T \quad , \tag{7.16}$$

for the branching cell. Introduction of the domain aspect ratio a is somewhat arbitrary but provides a convenient means for setting up the problem. The interpretation of Fig. 7.1, then, is that as the wavelength L of the container is increased, the number m of cells that would be expected to be found in the container increases in such a way that ℓ remains the same (Fig. 7.3).

Normally when we pose problems, we should take care to choose domain wavelengths L to be large enough for us to subsequently find the natural wavelength ℓ for the flow in the fluid. In the present problem, for example, choosing $L < 2\sqrt{2}\, z_T$ would produce aphysical results, while choosing $L = 20\sqrt{2}\, z_T = 10\ell$ would yield a preferred value $\alpha^2 = 1/2$ for the cell of wavenumber 10. After performing the above analysis, we might wish to rescale the problem by setting m = 1 and using ℓ_m rather than L in the dimensionless forms; this is what Lorenz (1963) did when he developed his model (see Chapter 2). But, as we discuss in Chapter 9, using the gravest mode m = 1 in the scaling may mask physically important secondary

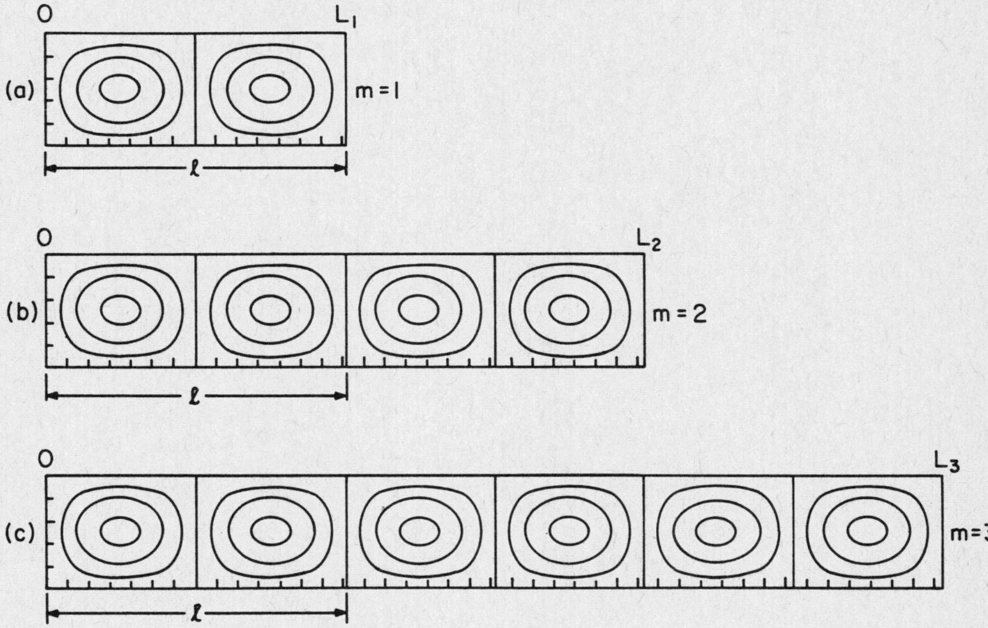

Fig. 7.3 Examples of three containers having distinct domain aspect ratios but for which the cell aspect ratio α is the same, and at its preferred value α_p. In each case $\alpha=\sqrt{2}/2$ and $\ell=2\sqrt{2}z_T$ but in (a) $L_1=2\sqrt{2}z_T$, $a=\sqrt{2}/2$ and m=1; in (b) $L_2=4\sqrt{2}z_T$, $a=\sqrt{2}/4$ and m=2; and in (c) $L_3=6\sqrt{2}z_T$, $a=\sqrt{2}/6$ and m=3.

branching behavior involving transitions to cells of larger wavelengths. A safer approach is to choose L so that $m > 1$ is the preferred wavenumber of the developing cell.

7.1.3 The fastest growing wave. A standard approach in many stability analyses of a flow is to determine which of the available wavelengths amplifies most rapidly. Presumably, this fastest growing wave dominates the response of the fluid and is the one most likely to be observed. Typically, the value of a control parameter such as the Rayleigh number is fixed and the wavelength, or aspect ratio, is varied until the maximum value of the real part of the (largest) positive characteristic exponent λ is found. This gives the wavelength of the expected wave as well as its growth rate; if the growth rates are realistic, then the wave is regarded as observable. In this subsection we determine when the procedure of finding the cell aspect ratio associated with the minimum value of Ra_c is equivalent to the procedure of finding the cell aspect ratio producing the largest growth rate.

To see this equivalence, we recall from (2.95) that, for each m and n, the positive exponent that signals bifurcation is given by

$$\lambda_{mn} = -\frac{(m^2a^2+n^2)(P+1)}{2a} + \frac{1}{2a}\left[(P-1)^2(m^2a^2+n^2)^2 + 4Pm^2a^2Ra/(m^2a^2+n^2)\right]^{1/2} . \quad (7.17)$$

These exponents are real, so we may determine the growth rates from (7.17). If we choose $P = 1$, $n = 1$ and $a = \sqrt{2}/2$, so that $m = 1$ is the wavenumber of the cell that first appears at $Ra_c = 27/4$, then we may plot λ_{m1} as a function of Ra for various values of m. We do this in Fig. 7.4 for the cases $m = 1,2,3$; the wavelengths ℓ_m of these cells are $\ell_1 = 2\sqrt{2}\, z_T$, which is the preferred wavelength ℓ in (7.16), $\ell_2 = \sqrt{2}\, z_T < \ell_1$ and $\ell_3 = 2\sqrt{2}\, z_T/3 < \ell_2$. We see from Fig. 7.4 that the $m = 1$ solution does indeed branch at the smallest value of Ra_c and that its exponent λ_{11} is the the largest one whenever $Ra_c = 27/4 < Ra < 40$. Thus for values of Ra in this range, the fastest growing wave has the same wavelength, $2\sqrt{2}\, z_T$, as the one that minimizes the value of Ra_c. But if we choose $Ra > 40$, then we would deduce from Fig. 7.4 that the $m = 2$ wave, which has the wavelength $\sqrt{2}\, z_T$, would be the fastest growing one. However, because stability would be transferred from the conductive to the $m = 1$ convective solution when Ra exceeds 27/4, we have no reason to believe that the $m = 2$

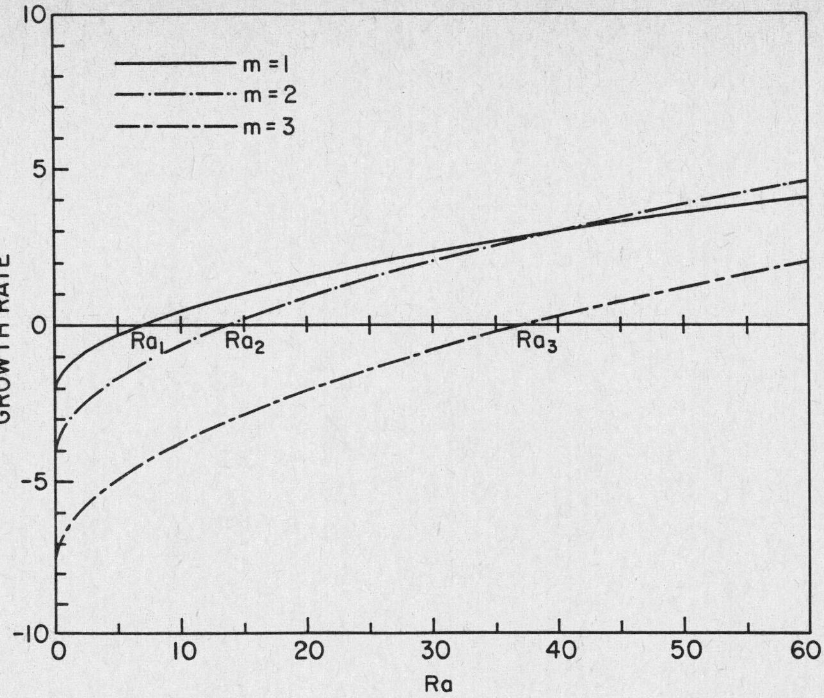

Fig. 7.4 The dependence of the growth rates or characteristic exponents λ_{m1} on the Rayleigh number Ra for $n=\underline{1}$, $m=1,2,\underline{3}$, $a=\sqrt{2}/2$, and $P=1$; the wavelengths for the three cells are $\ell_1=2\sqrt{2}z_T$, $\ell_2=\sqrt{2}z_T$, and $\ell_3=2\sqrt{2}z_T/3$. Note that λ_{11} crosses the axis at $Ra_1=27/4$, λ_{21} crosses at $Ra_2=27/2$, and λ_{31} crosses at $Ra_3=1331/36$.

solution could be stable and observable when Ra > 40. Thus, the two approaches are equivalent, and the determination of the wavelength of the fastest growing wave is physically relevant, only when the value of Ra is relatively near that of Ra_c.

In Fig. 7.4, we consider only waves having wavelengths ℓ_m that are smaller than the optimal one $\ell = 2\sqrt{2}\ z_T$; in order to complete the analysis we must also consider wavelengths that are greater than ℓ. To do this, we must choose a different value of a, which we are perfectly free to do, so that a cell having wavenumber m > 1 occurs first. In Fig. 7.5 we consider the case $a = \sqrt{2}/6$, for which the $m = 3$ cell has the preferred wavelength $\ell_3 = \ell = 2\sqrt{2}\ z_T$. Now the choices $m = 1$ and $m = 2$ correspond to waves having larger wavelengths than ℓ: $\ell_1 = 6\sqrt{2}\ z_T$ and $\ell_2 = 3\sqrt{2}\ z_T$. We see from Fig. 7.5 that these longer waves also grow at slower rates than the one having wavelength $2\sqrt{2}\ z_T$, and so we conclude that indeed the optimal, physically expected wavelength is the one given by minimizing the value of Ra_c.

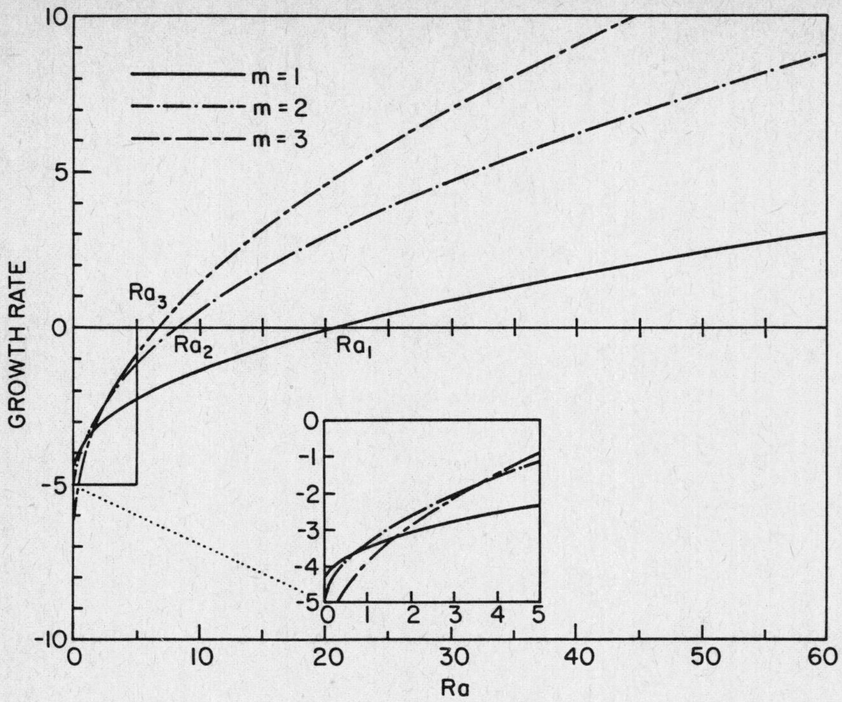

Fig. 7.5 Same as in Fig. 7.4 except $a = \sqrt{2}/6$. Now λ_{31} crosses at Ra=27/4, and the wavelengths of the branching cells are $\ell_1=6\sqrt{2}z_T$, $\ell_2=3\sqrt{2}z_T$ and $\ell_3=\ell=2\sqrt{2}z_T$. Here λ_{31} crosses the axis at $Ra_3=27/4$, λ_{21} at $Ra_2=1331/162$, and λ_{11} at $Ra_1=6859/324$.

7.2 Rotating Rayleigh-Bénard Convection

In this section and in the remainder of the chapter, we discuss the effects on the preferred wavelengths of the branching solutions when rotation is included in the problem of Rayleigh-Bénard convection. First, we develop a five-coefficient model similar to that of Veronis (1966). Then, we use the methods discussed in Section 7.1 for studying the stability of the conductive solution and for minimizing the critical value of the forcing parameter. We find that including rotation in the Rayleigh-Bénard problem greatly increases the complexity of the analysis.

7.2.1 A generalized Veronis model. Although the problem remains two-dimensional, we must include the roll-parallel v-component of the flow in order to model the effects of rotation. We introduce the dimensionless Coriolis parameter, which is proportional to the square root of the Taylor number, as

$$f^* = fz_T^2/\pi^2\nu \quad , \tag{7.18}$$

in which f is the Coriolis parameter. Then using the definitions (7.6)-(7.8) and (7.18), we can write the dimensionless system of partial differential equations as

$$\frac{\partial u^*}{\partial t^*} + u^* \frac{\partial u^*}{\partial x^*} + w^* \frac{\partial u^*}{\partial z^*} - \frac{f^*P}{a} v^* + \frac{\partial p^*}{\partial x^*} - \frac{P}{a} \tilde{\nabla}^2 u^* = 0 \quad , \tag{7.19}$$

$$\frac{\partial w^*}{\partial t^*} + u^* \frac{\partial w^*}{\partial x^*} + w^* \frac{\partial w^*}{\partial z^*} + \frac{1}{a^2} \frac{\partial p^*}{\partial z^*} - \frac{P}{a^2} T^* - \frac{P}{a} \tilde{\nabla}^2 w^* = 0 \quad , \tag{7.20}$$

$$\frac{\partial v^*}{\partial t^*} + u^* \frac{\partial v^*}{\partial x^*} + w^* \frac{\partial v^*}{\partial z^*} + \frac{f^*P}{a} u^* - \frac{P}{a} \tilde{\nabla}^2 v^* = 0 \quad , \tag{7.21}$$

$$\frac{\partial T^*}{\partial t^*} + u^* \frac{\partial T^*}{\partial x^*} + w^* \frac{\partial T^*}{\partial z^*} - \mathrm{Ra}\, w^* - \frac{1}{a} \tilde{\nabla}^2 T^* = 0 \quad . \tag{7.22}$$

We next form an equation for the horizontal vorticity $-\eta^*$ (cf. (2.16) and (2.27)) by operating on (7.19) with $-\partial(\ )/\partial z^*$ and on (7.20) with $a^2\partial(\ )/\partial x^*$. Thus, we rewrite (7.19)-(7.22) as:

$$\frac{\partial}{\partial t^*} \tilde{\nabla}^2\psi^* + J(\psi^*,\tilde{\nabla}^2\psi^*) + \frac{f^*P}{a} \frac{\partial v^*}{\partial z^*} - P \frac{\partial T^*}{\partial x^*} - \frac{P}{a} \tilde{\nabla}^4\psi^* = 0 \quad , \tag{7.23}$$

$$\frac{\partial v^*}{\partial t^*} + J(\psi^*,v^*) - \frac{f^*P}{a} \frac{\partial \psi^*}{\partial z^*} - \frac{P}{a} \tilde{\nabla}^2 v^* = 0 \quad , \tag{7.24}$$

$$\frac{\partial T^*}{\partial t^*} + J(\psi^*,T^*) - \mathrm{Ra} \frac{\partial \psi^*}{\partial x^*} - \frac{1}{a} \tilde{\nabla}^2 T^* = 0 \quad . \tag{7.25}$$

For the spectral expansion, we are not as general as we were in the Lorenz system (Section 7.1), and we specify wavenumber n = 1 in the vertical. We use the following expansions for the stream function ψ^*, the temperature perturbation T^*, and the y-component of velocity v^*:

$$\psi^*(x^*,z^*,t^*) = \psi_{m1}(t^*) \sin(mx^*) \sin(z^*) \quad , \tag{7.26}$$

$$T^*(x^*,z^*,t^*) = T_{m1}(t^*) \cos(mx^*) \sin(z^*) + T_{02}(t^*) \sin(2z^*) \quad , \tag{7.27}$$

$$v^*(x^*,z^*,t^*) = v_{m1}(t^*) \sin(mx^*) \cos(z^*) + v_{2m,0}(t^*) \sin(2mx^*) \quad , \tag{7.28}$$

where as before, m is the horizontal integral wavenumber. As in the Lorenz model, the T_{02} term in (7.27) measures the effects of the convective perturbations that can alter the background temperature profile (see Fig. 2.1b). The $v_{2m,0}$ term in (7.28) is required in order to represent variations in the velocity field that are independent of height. Significantly, the expansion (7.26)-(7.28) is the same as that produced by a power series analysis about a critical value Ra_c of Ra (see Veronis, 1959; Kloeden and Wells, 1983; Kloeden, 1986a). The boundary conditions for the domain $0 \leq x^* \leq 2\pi$ and $0 \leq z^* \leq \pi$ are cyclic continuity in the horizontal and the conditions (see Section 2.1.3)

$$\psi^* = 0; \quad \frac{\partial^2\psi^*}{\partial z^{*2}} = 0; \quad T^* = 0; \quad \frac{\partial v^*}{\partial z^*} = 0 \quad \text{at } z^* = 0, \pi \quad . \tag{7.29}$$

Now using the Galerkin technique from Chapter 3, we obtain the following spectral system

$$\dot{\psi}_{ml} = \frac{-f^*P}{a\sigma_{ml}} v_{ml} + \frac{mP}{\sigma_{ml}} T_{ml} - \frac{P\sigma_{ml}}{a} \psi_{ml} \quad , \tag{7.30}$$

$$\dot{T}_{ml} = m\,\psi_{ml}\,T_{02} + m\,Ra\,\psi_{ml} - \frac{\sigma_{ml}}{a} T_{ml} \quad , \tag{7.31}$$

$$\dot{T}_{02} = -\frac{m}{2}\psi_{ml}\,T_{ml} - \frac{4}{a} T_{02} \quad , \tag{7.32}$$

$$\dot{v}_{ml} = -m\,\psi_{ml}\,v_{2m,0} + \frac{f^*P}{a}\psi_{ml} - \frac{P\sigma_{ml}}{a} v_{ml} \quad , \tag{7.33}$$

$$\dot{v}_{2m,0} = \frac{m}{2}\psi_{ml}\,v_{ml} - 4Pm^2a\,v_{2m,0} \quad , \tag{7.34}$$

where σ_{ml} is defined in (7.9).

By including rotation, we have introduced a new parameter into the problem, the dimensionless Coriolis parameter f^*. In laboratory experiments, for example, this parameter would be equivalent to the rate Ω at which the vessel spins about its axis. Of importance here is that this parameter affects the critical value Ra_c of Ra.

7.2.2 Linear stability of the conductive solution. We proceed in the same manner as in Chapter 4, and note that the solutions to the linearized system obtained from (7.30)-(7.34) are nontrivial provided that

$$\begin{vmatrix} -P\sigma_{ml}/a - \lambda & mP/\sigma_{ml} & -f^*P/a\sigma_{ml} & 0 & 0 \\ m\,Ra & -\sigma_{ml}/a - \lambda & 0 & 0 & 0 \\ f^*P/a & 0 & -P\sigma_{ml}/a - \lambda & 0 & 0 \\ 0 & 0 & 0 & -4/a - \lambda & 0 \\ 0 & 0 & 0 & 0 & -4m^2aP - \lambda \end{vmatrix} = 0 \quad . \tag{7.35}$$

From (7.35), we have the characteristic equation

$$\{\lambda^3 + \frac{\sigma_{ml}}{a}(2P + 1)\lambda^2 + [\frac{\sigma_{ml}^2}{a^2}(P^2 + 2P) + \frac{f^{*2}P^2}{a^2\sigma_{ml}} - \frac{m^2PRa}{\sigma_{ml}}]\lambda + P^2\sigma_{ml}^3/a^3 + f^{*2}P^2/a^3 - \frac{m^2P^2Ra}{a}\}[(\lambda + 4/a)(\lambda + 4m^2aP)] = 0 \quad . \tag{7.36}$$

The critical Rayleigh number Ra_c is then found from $\lambda = 0$ to be

$$Ra_c = \frac{\sigma_{ml}^3}{m^2a^2} + \frac{f^{*2}}{m^2a^2} = \frac{(m^2a^2 + 1)^3}{m^2a^2} + \frac{f^{*2}}{m^2a^2} = \frac{(\alpha^2 + 1)^3}{\alpha^2} + \frac{f^{*2}}{\alpha^2} \quad . \tag{7.37}$$

Equation (7.37) has the same form as that found in the original partial differential equations (Veronis, 1966). Thus, the system (7.30)-(7.34) obeys one of the modeling principles that we use to ensure that low-order models accurately represent fluid flow (see Section 1.3). As for the Lorenz system discussed in Section 2.2, this fact helps justify the truncation used to form the spectral model. Also, the first term on the right side of (7.37) is the typical form (7.10) of Ra_c found previously for $n = 1$. As we can see, the second term in (7.37) depends on rotation and acts to stabilize the flow because it creates larger values of Ra_c.

Proceeding with the analysis, we calculate $\partial Ra_c/\partial(m^2a^2) = 0$ to find that the minimum value of Ra_c occurs when f^* and ma are related by

$$f^{*2} = (2m^2a^2 - 1)(m^2a^2 + 1)^2 = (2\alpha^2 - 1)(\alpha^2 + 1)^2 \quad , \tag{7.38}$$

which results in

$$\alpha^2 = m^2a^2 \geq 1/2 \quad . \tag{7.39}$$

The inequality (7.39) replaces the equality (7.14) for the preferred cell aspect ratio α. Therefore, rotation affects both the minimum value of Ra_c and the value of $\alpha = ma$ at which the minimum occurs. In Fig. 7.6, we use (7.38) to illustrate how the expected value of α varies with f^{*2}. In order to find specific values of Ra_c, we choose a fixed value of f^* and then obtain the corresponding value of α. As a final check, we note that when $f^* = 0$, we have that $\alpha = \sqrt{2}/2$, which corresponds to the result (7.14) for the nonrotating Lorenz system. Thus, we conclude that rotation affects the preferred wavelengths. Since we now have values for α^2 that are greater than 1/2, we discover that the preferred wavelengths in rotating convection are less than those $\ell = 2\sqrt{2}\ z_T$ in nonrotating convection.

7.2.3 The Hopf bifurcation. The addition of rotation also creates the possibility for temporally periodic solutions to bifurcate from the trivial solution (see Chapter 11); these Hopf bifurcation points are identified by having $Re(\lambda) = 0$ and $Im(\lambda) \neq 0$ as roots to the characteristic equation (7.36). These points also give values of the control parameter at which stability is exchanged with a nonzero

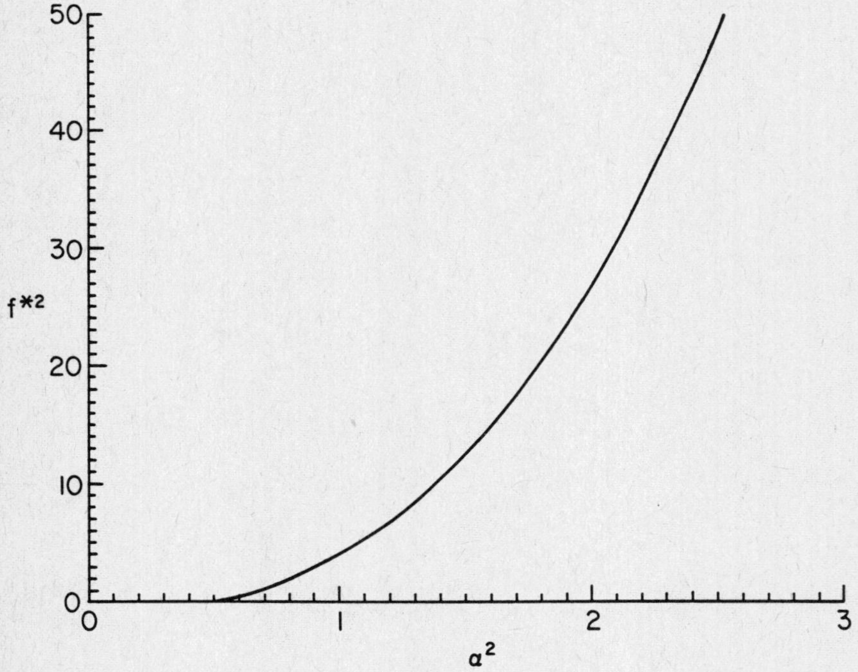

Fig. 7.6 The functional dependence of the squared dimensionless Coriolis parameter f^{*2} on the squared cell aspect ratio α^2 for the branching stationary solutions.

solution and so their minimum values can also be associated with expected cell aspect ratios.

Significantly, the Hopf bifurcation points obey the same formulas in the ordinary differential system as in the partial differential system (Kloeden, 1986), and again this is consistent with the modeling philosophy discussed in Chapters 1 and 2. Therefore, we conclude that the Hopf bifurcation in the five-coefficient model is physically relevant and is not an artifact of the severe truncation (but see Section 15.3.3).

For convenience, we define the coefficients in the bracketed portion of the characteristic equation (7.36) as

$$e_1 = \frac{\sigma_{ml}}{a}(1 + 2P) \quad , \tag{7.40}$$

$$e_2 = \frac{2P\sigma_{ml}^2}{a^2} + \frac{m^2P^2}{\sigma_{ml}}(Ra_c - Ra/P) \quad , \tag{7.41}$$

$$e_3 = \frac{m^2P^2}{a}(Ra_c - Ra) \quad , \tag{7.42}$$

in which we have introduced Ra_c via (7.37). The Hurwitz Theorem discussed in Appendix A states that the roots of a cubic polynomial equation $\lambda^3 + e_1\lambda^2 + e_2\lambda + e_3 = 0$ all have negative real parts if and only if the inequalities $e_1 > 0$, $e_1e_2 - e_3 > 0$, and $e_3 > 0$ are satisfied (see (A.7)-(A.9)). Applying these criteria to (7.36), we obtain the following consequences:

1) From (7.40) that $e_1 > 0$ for all values of Ra.
2) From (7.42) that $e_3 > 0$ if and only if $Ra < Ra_c$.
3) Finally, that $e_1e_2 - e_3 > 0$ may not occur for all values of Ra. In particular, $e_1e_2 - e_3 > 0$ only when

$$Ra < Ra_H = \frac{2(1+P)\sigma_{ml}^3}{\alpha^2} + \frac{2P^2}{(1+P)}\frac{f^{*2}}{\alpha^2} \quad . \tag{7.43}$$

In order for a bifurcation to occur, we need to have failure of one of the inequalities $e_3 > 0$ or $e_1e_2 - e_3 > 0$. That is, as the magnitude of Ra is increased from very small values, one of the inequalities $Ra < Ra_c$ or $Ra < Ra_H$ fails first, according to whether $Ra_c < Ra_H$ or $Ra_H < Ra_c$. If $Ra_c < Ra_H$ is found, then we expect a stationary solution to bifurcate from the conductive one.

In contrast, if $Ra_H < Ra_c$ is found, then we expect a more subtle bifurcation to occur. This type of bifurcation is discussed in detail in Chapter 11 and is called a Hopf bifurcation. Furthermore, the inequality $Ra_H < Ra_c$ can hold only if $P < 1$. To see this fact, we combine (7.37), (7.43), and $Ra_H < Ra_c$ to produce the inequality

$$(1-P)f^{*2} > (1+P)\sigma_{m1}^3 \quad . \tag{7.44}$$

Since the right side is positive, we see that $P < 1$ is required. In this case, the Hopf Bifurcation Theorem gives the limiting frequency ω_o of the branching solution that is temporally periodic (see Section 11.1). This frequency ω_o is given by the imaginary part of λ; it is easy to show that $\omega_o^2 = e_2$ when $e_1e_2 = e_3$. Thus, when $Ra = Ra_H$ we have that

$$\omega_o^2 = \frac{P^2}{a^2}\left[\frac{f^{*2}(1-P)}{\sigma_{m1}(1+P)} - \sigma_{m1}^2\right] \quad . \tag{7.45}$$

Combination of (7.44) and (7.45) shows that $\omega_o^2 > 0$ precisely when $Ra_H < Ra_c$ ensuring that a Hopf bifurcation occurs whenever (7.44) is satisfied. Moreover, the limiting period T of the solution is $T = 2\pi/\omega_o$, but T is not the physically relevant period for an individual wave of wavelength $\ell_m = L/m$. To find this cell period τ, we note from (2.22) that the dimensionless time that depends <u>only</u> on the cell dimensions ℓ_m and z_T is $mt^* = 2\pi^2\kappa t/(\ell_m z_T)$. Hence it follows that the cell period τ is related to T by $\tau = mT$ and that the cell frequency ω_m is given by $\omega_m = 2\pi/\tau = \omega_o/m$. Thus, we can rewrite (7.45) in terms of cell aspect ratio $\alpha = ma$ and cell frequency ω_m as

$$\omega_m^2 = \frac{P^2[f^{*2}(1-P)-(\alpha^2+1)^3(1+P)]}{\alpha^2(\alpha^2+1)(1+P)} \quad . \tag{7.46}$$

To deduce whether we expect to observe steady or temporal flows, we begin by identifying in P-f^{*2} space where the inequality $Ra_H < Ra_c$ is satisfied. From (7.44) we see that $0 < P < 1$ and $f^{*2} > 0$, but that the region depends on α^2. To determine the dependence on α^2 of the boundaries of the region, we replace (7.44) with the equality

$$f^{*2} = \frac{(1+P)}{(1-P)} \sigma_{m1}^3 , \tag{7.47}$$

and for each value of α^2, plot f^{*2} as a function of P. These curves are shown in Fig. 7.7. It is clear from the figure that these regions enlarge monotonically as $\alpha^2 \to 0$ to determine the boundary given by setting $\alpha^2 = 0$ in (7.47), which is

$$f^{*2} = \frac{(1+P)}{(1-P)} . \tag{7.48}$$

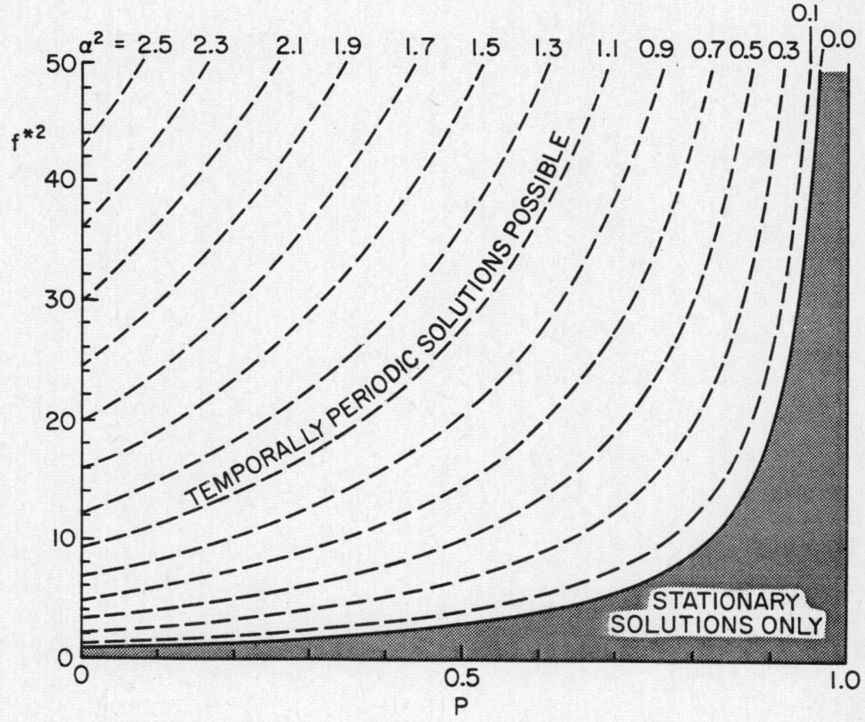

Fig. 7.7 The regions in P-f^{*2} space in which $Ra_H < Ra_c$ and temporally periodic solutions branch first from the conductive solution. These regions are bounded by P = 0 and curves that depend on α^2 (dashed lines). Above and to the left of a dashed line labeled α_o^2, only periodic solutions for which $\alpha^2 \geq \alpha_o^2$ are possible. In the shaded area, $Ra_c < Ra_H$ and only branching stationary solutions exist.

This curve is labeled 0.0 in Fig. 7.7; the shaded region to the right of this curve is the region in which only branching stationary solutions are possible. Moreover, it is clear from the figure that $f^{*2} > 1$ is necessary for Hopf bifurcation to occur, showing that rotation is necessary for temporally periodic flows to branch from the conductive state.

The next step is to determine the preferred values of α^2 associated with the two bifurcating solutions. Already, we have performed the minimization of Ra_c and have shown the dependence of α^2 on f^{*2} in Fig. 7.6. In P-f^{*2} space, the lines for fixed $\alpha^2 > 1/2$ would be parallel to the P-axis. Now we must determine the minimum value of Ra_H. Differentiation with respect to α^2 of the equality in (7.43) yields the relationship

$$f^{*2} = \frac{(1 + P)^2}{P^2} (2\alpha^2 - 1)(\alpha^2 + 1)^2 \quad , \tag{7.49}$$

which again results in $\alpha^2 > 1/2$. When f^{*2} and α^2 are related by (7.49), we may rewrite (7.43) and (7.46) as

$$\min(Ra_H) = 6(\alpha^2 + 1)^2(P + 1) \quad , \tag{7.50}$$

and

$$\omega_m^2 = \frac{(2\alpha^2 - 3\alpha^2 P^2 - 1)(\alpha^2 + 1)}{\alpha^2} \quad . \tag{7.51}$$

From (7.51) we see that $\alpha^2 > 1/2$ and $0 < P^2 < 2/3$ must hold, which is consistent with (7.39) and (7.49).

In contrast to the preferred values of α^2 in the stationary case, the preferred values of α^2 in the temporally periodic case depend on the Prandtl number P, and this adds a degree of complication to the problem. But a very tricky aspect of using the results of (7.49)-(7.51) is that, while (7.49) may hold, (7.44) may fail. Thus, it is possible to solve (7.49)-(7.51) to obtain values of Ra_H that are not in fact Hopf bifurcation points.

Instead of attempting to find for fixed values of f^{*2} and P the preferred values of α^2 associated with a Hopf bifurcation, in Fig. 7.8 we plot, for a fixed value of α^2, the values of f^{*2} and P for which that α^2 is the preferred value. These curves are the ones having negative slope in Fig. 7.8. They are obtained by using (7.49) whenever (7.44) is satisfied. When (7.44) fails, we alter the procedure and use the bounding curve (7.47) at which $Ra_H = Ra_c$. These curves were shown in Fig. 7.7 and are the ones having positive slope in Fig. 7.8. To obtain the line at which the slope changes in Fig. 7.8, we eliminate α^2 between (7.47) and (7.49) to find

$$f^{*2} = \frac{27(1+P)^4(1-P)^2}{(2-3P^2)^3} \quad . \tag{7.52}$$

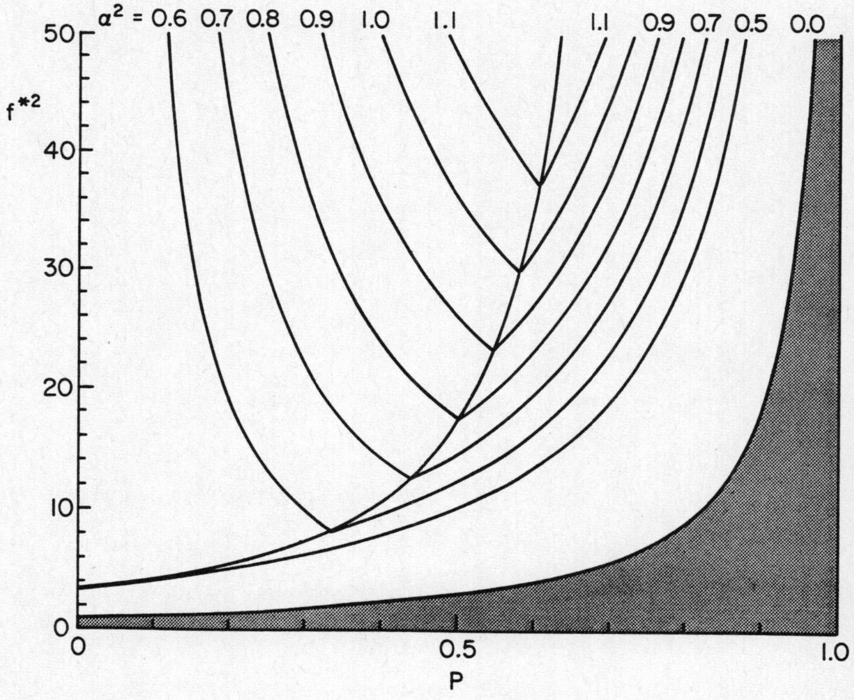

Fig. 7.8 The preferred values of the squared cell aspect ratio α^2 as functions of both f^{*2} and P for the bifurcating time-dependent solutions. The curve at which the contours change slope is given by (7.52). In the shaded area only stationary solutions exist.

To complete the determination of whether we expect to see branching stationary or periodic solutions, we must combine the results given in Figs. 7.6 and 7.8. This combination is not straightforward, however, as we discuss in the next subsection.

7.2.4 Stationary or periodic solution: which is preferred? To see how to discover which of the two possible solutions would be expected, we recall the physical setting of the problem. Given a vessel containing a fluid specified by P and rotating at a rate given by f^{*2}, we increase the vertical temperature difference given by Ra until the fluid responds by creating a circulation pattern having a certain value of cell aspect ratio α. In the previous two subsections, we studied the separate cases of branching stationary and branching periodic solutions, and we determined the preferred value of α^2 for each. Here, in the complete problem, we combine the results to give both the first expected solution type and the associated value of α^2.

We begin by noting that both Ra_c and Ra_H are functions of f^{*2} and P. Yet their minimum values for specific values of f^{*2} and P are not the same, and each may occur at a different value of α. We illustrate in Fig. 7.9 how the values of Ra_c and Ra_H depend on α and P; here we have chosen $f^{*2} = 20$. In Fig. 7.9, the solid curve denotes Ra_c (7.37), which is independent of P, while the dashed curves show Ra_H (7.43) for various values of P. Because $Ra_H < Ra_c$ must hold for a fixed value of α^2, we do not plot all values given by (7.43). From Fig. 7.9 we see that when P = 0.2, the minimum value of Ra_H, which occurs at $\alpha = 0.78$, is smaller than the minimum value of Ra_c, which occurs at $\alpha = 1.34$. Thus when P = 0.2, as the value of Ra is increased, we expect that a temporally periodic solution having cell aspect ratio $\alpha = 0.78$ (or wavelength $\ell_m = 2.56\ z_T$) would branch once $Ra > Ra_H$; such a cell is illustrated in Fig. 7.10a, in which the stream function field at a fixed time is shown. For reference, we have chosen a value of L so that in the case $f^* = 0$ of Rayleigh-Bénard convection, the m = 1 cell would fill the domain (cf. Fig. 2.1a). When P = 0.4, however, the well in Fig. 7.9 for Ra_H has been raised and shifted to the right so that now the preferred value of $\alpha = 0.87$. However, now the minimum value of Ra_c is less than the minimum value of Ra_H. Thus, we expect that a stationary solution would branch first as the value of Ra is increased and that the preferred cell aspect ratio $\alpha = 1.34$, or $\ell_m = 1.49\ z_T$ (Fig. 7.10b). As the value

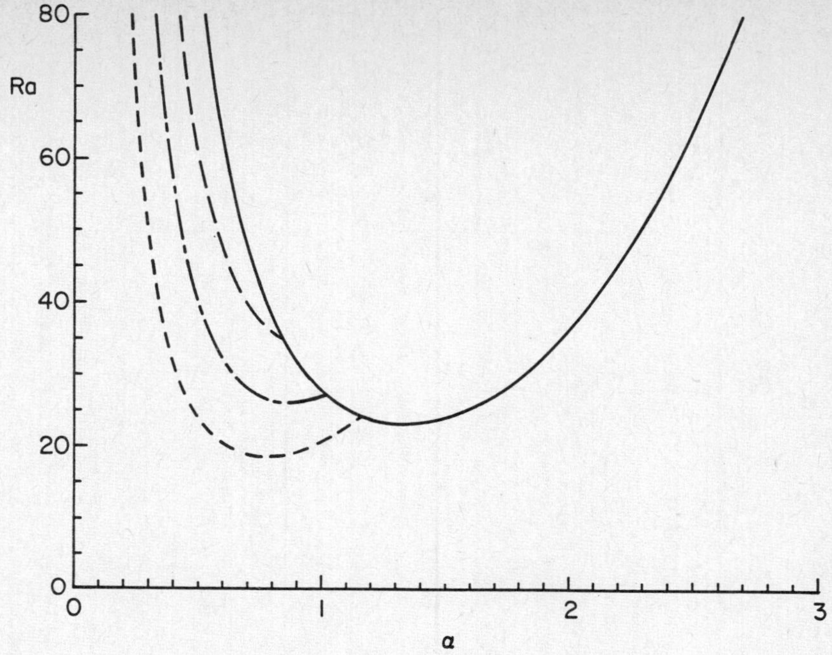

Fig. 7.9 The well diagrams for the bifurcation points Ra_c (solid line) and Ra_H (dashed lines) for values of P when $f^{*2}=20$: P=0.2 (short dash), P=0.4 (double dash), and P=0.6 (long dash). Note that Ra_c is independent of P, and that, for fixed values of α, the bifurcation points obey $Ra_H < Ra_c$.

of P increases, the well for Ra_H retreats past the one for Ra_c and we expect an abrupt change in the fluid response, from a temporally varying cell having a relatively long horizontal wavelength to a steady cell having a relatively short wavelength.

As the value of P increases further, the wells for Ra_H shift upward even more. When P = 0.6, the curve meets the one for Ra_c before it attains its minimum value. The crossing of the Ra_c curve by the minima in the Ra_H curves is reflected in Fig. 7.8 by the corners in the α^2 contours; the lines having positive slope are now seen to correspond to the values of α^2 for which $Ra_H = Ra_c$ (cf. Fig. 7.9).

When we vary the value of f^{*2}, the relative positions of the wells for Ra_H and Ra_c change. To determine the values of f^{*2} and P at which the change in positions takes place, we must equate the minimum values of Ra_H and Ra_c. We recall from (7.38) that, for given values of f^{*2} and P, Ra_c takes on its minimum value at $\alpha = \alpha_c$ when

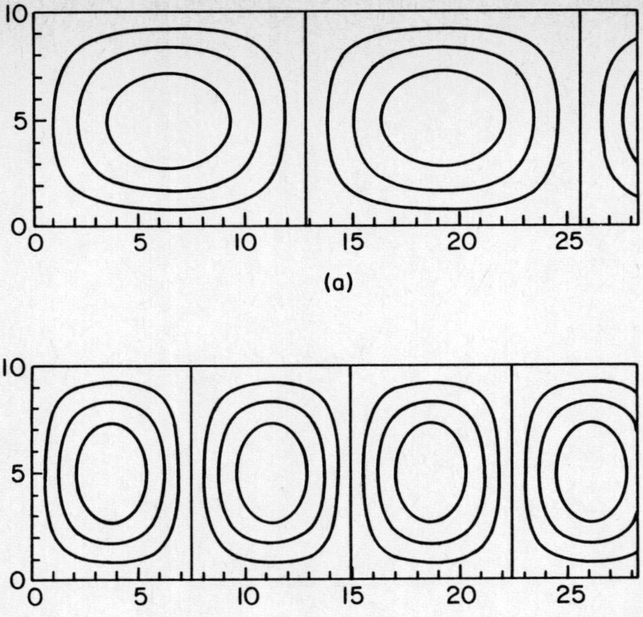

(b)

Fig. 7.10 The stream function diagrams for $\alpha^2=0.61$ and $P=0.2$ for a temporal solution (a) and $\alpha^2=1.79$ and $P=0.4$ for a stationary solution (b) when $f^{*2}=20$. We note that the stationary case in (b) applies to all values of $P>0.33$ (see Fig. 7.11). The domain aspect ratio is chosen to be $a=\sqrt{2}/2$, which is the preferred cell aspect ratio obtained in classical Rayleigh-Bénard convection for the case m=1 (cf. Fig. 2.1a). The units in the x^*- and z^*-directions are arbitrary.

$$f^{*2} = (2\alpha_c^2 - 1)(\alpha_c^2 + 1)^2 \quad . \tag{7.53}$$

Furthermore, Ra_H takes on its minimum value at $\alpha = \alpha_H$, given by (7.49), when

$$f^{*2} = \frac{(1+P)^2}{P^2}(2\alpha_H^2 - 1)(\alpha_H^2 + 1)^2 \quad . \tag{7.54}$$

Upon setting $\alpha = \alpha_c$ in (7.37), we obtain the minimum value $\min(Ra_c)$ of Ra_c; similarly setting $\alpha = \alpha_H$ in (7.43), we obtain $\min(Ra_H)$ of Ra_H in (7.50). Then a change in relative well position occurs in P-f^{*2} space if and only if $\min(Ra_H) = \min(Ra_c)$, which is given by

$$6(\alpha_H^2 + 1)^2(P+1) = 3(\alpha_c^2 + 1)^2 \quad . \tag{7.55}$$

Now α_c^2 and α_H^2 may be eliminated from (7.53)-(7.55) by first equating the right sides of (7.53) and (7.54) and then appropriately dividing the result by (7.55). This quotient expresses α_c^2 as a linear function of α_H^2. This function is substituted into the right side of (7.55) to obtain an equation relating α_H^2 and P:

$$4(1+P)(8P^4-P-1)(\alpha_H^2+1)^2 - 12(1+P)(2P^2-P-1)(\alpha_H^2+1)$$
$$- 9(2P^2-P-1)^2 = 0 \quad . \qquad (7.56)$$

Equation (7.56) may be solved for α_H^2 as a function of P. Once these values of α_H^2 are substituted into (7.54), we discover f^{*2} as a function of P via α_H^2.

We summarize the above results in Fig. 7.11, in which the dashed lines depict the region of temporal solutions, the dashed-dotted lines depict the region of stationary solutions, and the solid line separates the two regions; the appropriate values of α^2 are shown next to each curve. The drastic difference between the two regions is in the values of the squared aspect ratio. For values of f^{*2} in the range 20 to 50, the values of α^2 for the stationary region are more than twice those for the periodic region.

<u>7.2.5 The stationary solution and branching direction</u>. Until now, we have not considered whether the stationary or temporal solutions branch subcritically or supercritically. We discover in Chapters 5 and 11 that supercritically branching solutions, which exist for $Ra > Ra_c$ or $Ra > Ra_H$, are stable. In this case it is clear that finding preferred cell aspect ratios by minimizing the value of Ra_c or Ra_H makes sense because the stable solutions emanate from the unstable one. But how do we interpret the results when the solution branches subcritically? We investigate this question in this subsection.

Although Kloeden and Wells (1983) determined that the branching periodic solution was subcritical and therefore unstable, Pyle (1986) discovered errors in their algebra; in fact, the periodic solution is supercritical and stable. But the stationary solutions can branch subcritically, and so we focus attention on them here. The following analysis follows the one performed by Veronis (1966) and applies for $Ra < Ra_c$.

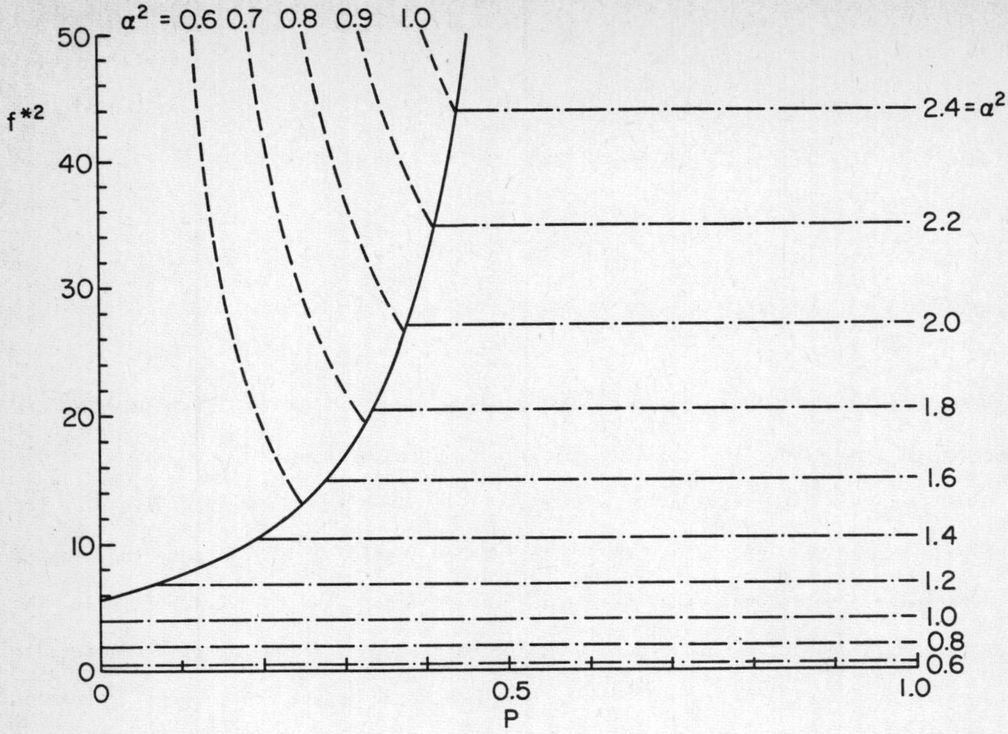

Fig. 7.11 The lines of constant values of α^2 that produce the absolute minimum value of the critical Rayleigh number Ra_c or Ra_H. Note that there are two regions, one for the stationary solutions (dashed-dotted lines) and the other for the temporal solutions (dashed lines). The case $\alpha^2=1/2$ occurs when $f^{*2}=0$.

Setting the right sides of (7.30)-(7.34) equal to zero, we can solve for the stationary solutions by reducing the problem to a quintic polynomial equation in ψ_{m1}:

$$\psi_{m1}\left[\frac{\sigma_{m1}^2}{P^2}\alpha^2\left(\frac{\psi_{m1}^2}{8}\right)^2+\left(\frac{\sigma_{m1}^3}{P^2}+\alpha^4\,Ra_c-\frac{\alpha^2}{P^2}Ra\right)\frac{\psi_{m1}^2}{8}+\sigma_{m1}\alpha^2\,(Ra_c-Ra)\right]=0 \quad ,(7.57)$$

in which we have used (7.37) and $\alpha^2 = m^2a^2$. This polynomial equation has the solution $\psi_{m1} = 0$, representing the conductive state, and the solutions

$$\frac{\psi_{m1}^2}{8}=\left[\frac{\alpha^2}{P^2}(Ra-Ra_c)-\alpha^4\,Ra_c+\frac{f^{*2}}{P^2}\pm\left\{\left(\frac{\alpha^2}{P^2}(Ra-Ra_c)-\alpha^4\,Ra_c+\frac{f^{*2}}{P^2}\right)^2+\frac{4\alpha^4}{P^2}(\alpha^2\,Ra_c-f^{*2})(Ra-Ra_c)\right\}^{1/2}\right]\Big/\left[\frac{2\sigma_{m1}^2}{P^2}\alpha^2\right] \quad . \quad (7.58)$$

In Chapter 6, we found that quintic polynomial equations, such as (7.57), have solutions fitting one of three cases: 1) one real and four complex solutions, 2) three real and two complex solutions, and 3) five real solutions. When a quintic polynomial equation has five real solutions, we obtained subcritical branching at $Ra = Ra_c$ with a regular turning point at $Ra = Ra_n$ to supercritical branching (Fig. 6.7). Here when $Ra < Ra_c$ and the radical in (7.58) is small enough, it is possible for $\psi_{ml}^2 > 0$ to occur for both choices of positive and negative signs in front of the radical. This allows the existence of five real solutions for ψ_{ml} and we can expect subcritical branching with a regular turning point occurring at $Ra = Ra_n$ in this case.

Therefore, we consider the case in which nontrivial real solutions exist for $Ra < Ra_c$. A regular turning point occurs when the radical in (7.58) vanishes and the resulting value of ψ_{ml}^2 is positive. The first condition is given by

$$Ra_n = [\{\sigma_{ml}^3(\alpha^{-2} - P^2)\}^{1/2} + f^*P]^2 < Ra_c \quad , \tag{7.59}$$

and the second condition is given by

$$f^{*2} > P^2\sigma_{ml}^3\alpha^2/(1 - \alpha^2P^2) \quad . \tag{7.60}$$

Finally, (7.59) and (7.60) are valid only if

$$P^2 < 1/\alpha^2 \quad . \tag{7.61}$$

From here, Veronis minimized the values of Ra_n at the regular turning point. However, we believe that minimization of Ra_n is not physically relevant. To support this contention, we suppose that we have a larger model containing two primary branches of the Veronis form. In Chapter 9 we show that this is typical behavior when considering larger models. Fig. 7.12 is the expected bifurcation diagram for this larger model, and with it we can investigate the stability of one primary branch (denoted by solid and dashed lines) emanating from the minimum value of Ra_c when it coexists with another primary branch (denoted by dotted lines) for which the value of Ra_n is minimized.

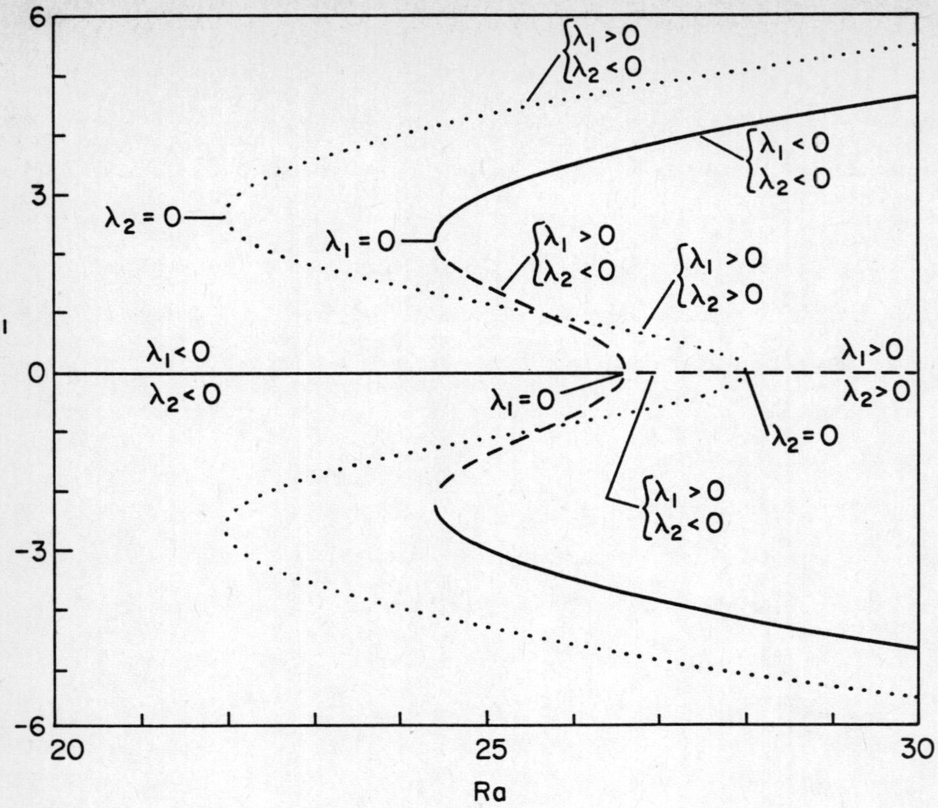

Fig. 7.12 The expected bifurcation diagram for a hypothetical larger model that contains two primary branches of the Veronis type; also shown are the characteristic exponents and their signs. The solid lines denote the stable portions of the first primary branch, while the dashed lines denote the unstable portions of the first branch. Dotted lines denote the second primary branch that is entirely unstable.

The minimized values of Ra_c and Ra_H are the ones controlling both the response parameter α^2 and the value of Ra_n in this problem. This control originates from the fact that the subcritical branch links stability exchange at Ra_n to stability exchange at Ra_c; that is, loss of stability at Ra_c is equivalent to gain of stability at Ra_n. This link occurs because the characteristic exponent λ that vanishes at $Ra = Ra_c$ is positive along the subcritical branch, vanishes again at $Ra = Ra_n$, and then becomes negative once the solution turns back toward larger values of Ra (see Fig. 6.7). In Fig. 7.12 this exponent λ is denoted by λ_1 for the solid and dashed curves, and by λ_2 for the dotted curve. The value of α that gives the minimum value of Ra_n produces a value of Ra_c at which stability is not lost (Fig. 7.12). Since the conductive solution is expected to lose stability at the smallest value of Ra_c, the minimized value of Ra_c determines the appropriate value of $Ra_n > \min(Ra_n)$. This value is the appropriate one because it gives rise to an observable stable stationary solution at the regular turning point.

To visualize this phenomenon, we trace the signs of the characteristic exponents in Fig. 7.12 and determine the stability of the two primary branches; as discussed in Section 5.4 this method is based on the fact that the index of the system is conserved. As we follow the trivial solution, λ_1 changes sign first from negative to positive signaling the loss of stability of the trivial solution. This is followed by λ_2 changing sign to positive. Moving up the dotted branch emanating from the point where $\lambda_2 = 0$, we see that λ_2 changes back to negative at a regular turning point while λ_1 still remains positive. This branch, which has the smaller value of Ra_n, is unstable since one exponent is still positive. However, moving up the branch emanating from the point where $\lambda_1 = 0$, we see that λ_1 is positive while λ_2 is negative until we reach the regular turning point where λ_1 changes from positive to negative. This branch, which is associated with the smallest value of Ra_c, becomes stable since all the exponents are negative on the upper portion beyond the regular turning point. We note that the index is conserved in this branching picture (see Section 5.4), and so the stability results are consistent. Thus, we conclude that the minimization of Ra_n in a larger model would not produce a physically relevant result since that branch is unstable and thus unobservable.

In the previous subsection, we found the regions of $P\text{-}f^{*2}$ space for which temporally periodic solutions were expected and those for which stationary solutions were expected. However, these solutions may branch either subcritically or supercritically and hence correspond to observable states either at finite amplitude or at infinitesimal amplitude. Now we further subdivide the $P\text{-}f^{*2}$ region accordingly. Earlier in this subsection we noted that the temporal solutions always branch supercritically, and so no further subdivision of this region is needed.

Thus, we consider the region in which stationary solutions are expected. To divide this region into the subcritical and supercritical portions, we observe that $Ra_n = Ra_c$ occurs at the boundary. This boundary is given by replacing strict inequality in (7.60) with equality to yield

$$f^{*2} = P^2\sigma_{m1}^3\alpha^2/(1 - \alpha^2P^2) \quad . \tag{7.62}$$

We combine this equation with the one (7.38) producing the minimum value of Ra_c to obtain a function relating P and α^2:

$$P^2 = (2\alpha^2-1)/(3\alpha^4) \quad . \tag{7.63}$$

To obtain the boundary shown in Fig. 7.13, we choose a value of α^2, determine the value of P from (7.63) and find the value of f^{*2} from (7.38). For values of f^{*2} and

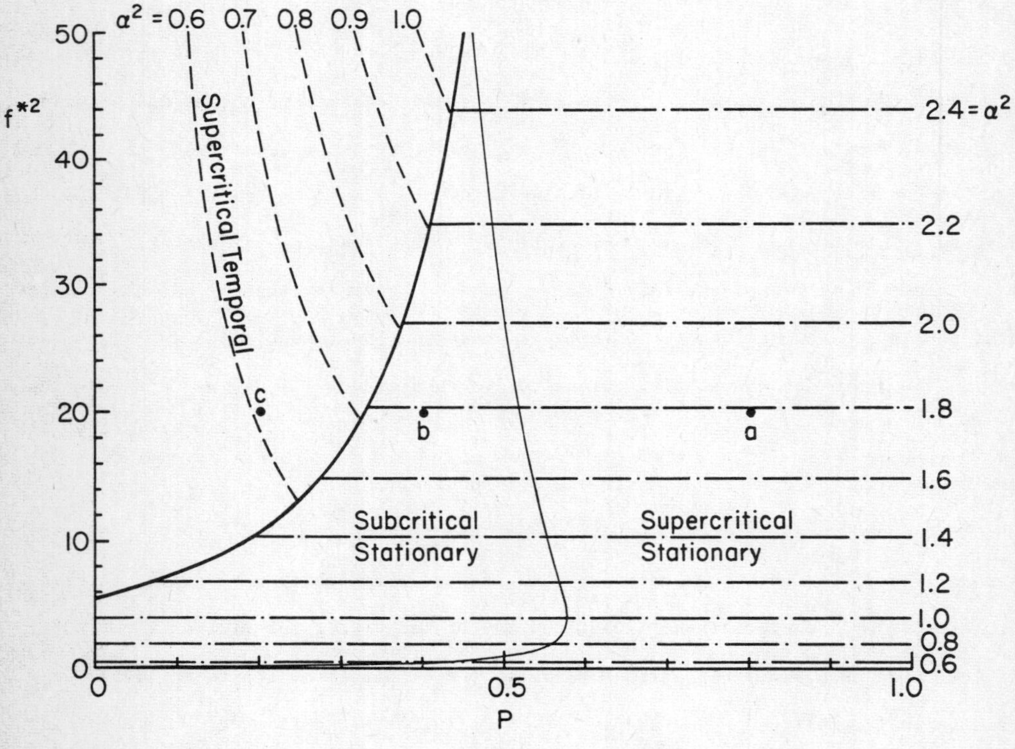

Fig. 7.13 Same as Fig. 7.11 except that the stationary solution region is now divided into regions of subcriticality and supercriticality; subcritical stationary solutions are to the left and supercritical ones are to the right of the line in the dashed-dotted region. As before, the contours are labeled using values of $\alpha^2 = m^2a^2$. The points a,b,c denote the values used in Fig. 7.14a,b,c.

P to the left of the curve, the stationary solutions emanating from Ra_c are subcritical and turn supercritical at Ra_n. Even though the Hopf bifurcation points occur in the region in which subcritical stationary branching occurs, we find below that once the solution has turned supercritical, it is stable. For values to the right of the curve, the branch from Ra_c is supercritical and hence immediately stable.

To illustrate the above statements, in Fig. 7.14 we examine for a constant value of $f^{*2} = 20$ the bifurcation diagrams for three values of P, one value for each of the

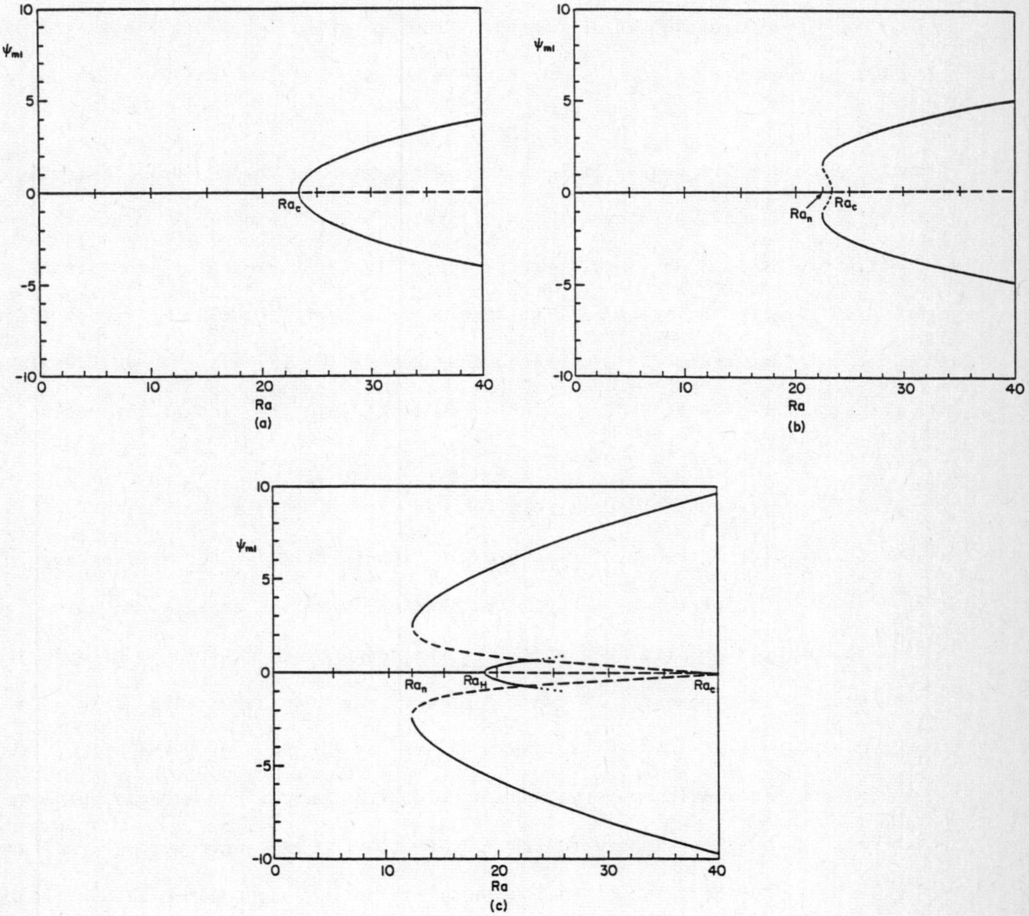

Fig. 7.14 The bifurcation diagrams for the five-coefficient Veronis model for f^{*2}=20 and P=0.8 (a), P=0.4 (b), and P=0.2 (c), in which the solid lines represent stable branches and the dashed lines denote unstable branches. The maximum values of $\psi_{m1}(t^*)$ were used for the periodic solution, the stable portion of which was obtained numerically; the dots indicate the probable existence of an unstable periodic solution.

three regions shown in Fig. 7.13. These points are labeled a,b,c in Fig. 7.13 to correspond to the cases shown in Fig. 7.14a,b,c. All stable solutions are indicated by solid lines and all unstable solutions are indicated by dashed lines. In each figure, we used the value of α^2 that produced the appropriate minimum value of Ra_c or Ra_H.

In Fig. 7.14a (P = 0.8), we show an example of supercritical branching, in which the convective solution immediately acquires stability from the conductive solution. When the value of P is decreased so that the narrow line on Fig. 7.13 is crossed (Fig. 7.14b, P = 0.4), we find that the stationary solution branches subcritically, but that no Hopf bifurcation is expected. The branching convective solution is unstable, but becomes stable once it curves back at $Ra = Ra_n$ toward larger values of Ra.

Finally, when P = 0.2 and we have entered the region in which Hopf bifurcations are expected (Fig. 7.14c), we discover that a stable periodic solution branches from the conductive one at $Ra = Ra_H$, and, perhaps surprisingly, that the upper stationary, supercritically directed solution is also stable. The periodic solution was obtained through numerical integration of the Veronis system (7.30)-(7.34); the dotted lines indicate the fact that the periodic solution does not join the subcritical solution but is nevertheless apparently unstable.

The stability of the stationary solution was determined via calculation of the characteristic exponents given by the cubic equation in (7.36). For a wide range of values of α, P and f^{*2} for which a Hopf bifurcation yields the expected solution, we found the following stability behavior for the conductive solution: A conjugate pair of characteristic exponents, λ_1 and λ_2, crosses the imaginary axis at $Ra = Ra_H$, and the third exponent $\lambda_3 < 0$. For a range of values of $Ra > Ra_H$, the first two exponents have nonzero imaginary parts and positive real parts, but at some value Ra_r of Ra near Ra_c, the imaginary parts vanish so that the two exponents become real and equal (Fig. 7.15). As the value of Ra increases further, λ_2 approaches zero while λ_1 increases in value. The stationary bifurcation is signaled by λ_2 crossing the origin from positive to negative values, which is behavior opposite to that encountered previously in Chapter 4 for steady bifurcation! For $Ra > Ra_c$, there is only one positive exponent λ_1, as we typically find in simple bifurcation (see Fig. 6.7).

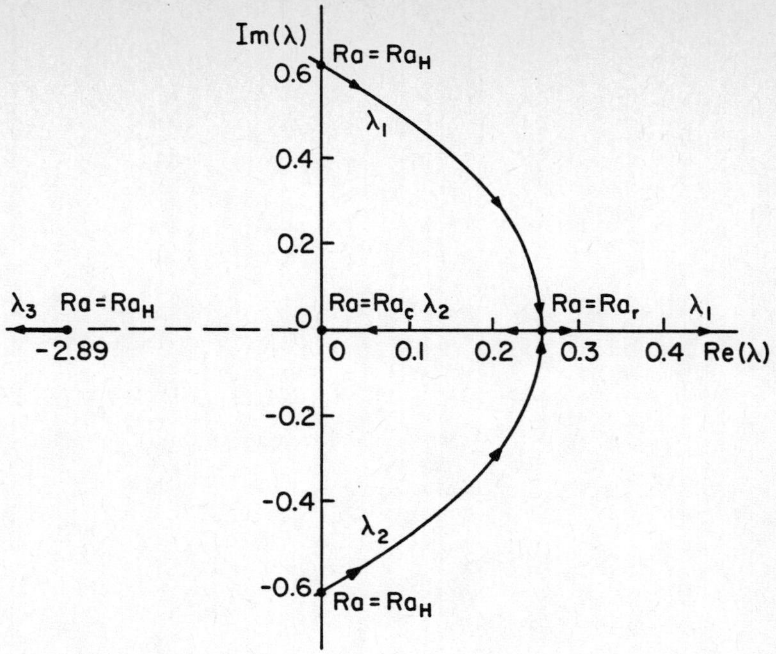

Fig. 7.15 Values of the three characteristic exponents $\lambda_1,\lambda_2,\lambda_3$ that are the roots to the bracketed portion of the characteristic equation (7.36) governing the stability of the conductive solution; here P=0.2, α^2=0.61, and f^{*2}=20, which is the case given in Fig. 7.14c. As the value of Ra increases, the values of the exponents change as indicated by the arrows.

Thus, there is one positive exponent λ_1 associated with the subcritically branching solution. This exponent vanishes at Ra = Ra_n and becomes negative on the upper convective solution, and so it is stable (Fig. 6.7). Intriguingly, we find that the stability properties of the convective solution are the same whether or not there is a Hopf bifurcation point on the conductive solution.

The above results are a bit surprising, because we at first might expect that the occurrence of both Hopf and stationary bifurcation points on the conductive solution would lead to three characteristic exponents having positive real parts when Ra > Ra_c; instead we discovered that only one was positive. But a careful examination of the characteristic equation (7.36) shows that in many situations governed by cubic equations, the above exponent behavior is the expected one.

We begin by noting that the existence of both bifurcation points is determined by the same cubic equation and so they are not independent of one another. By the

Fundamental Theorem of Algebra, any n^{th}-degree polynomial equation of the form

$$f(\lambda) = \lambda^n + e_1\lambda^{n-1} + \cdots + e_n = 0 \quad , \tag{7.64}$$

can be written as

$$f(\lambda) = (\lambda-\lambda_1)(\lambda-\lambda_2)\cdots(\lambda-\lambda_n) = 0 \quad , \tag{7.65}$$

in which, of course, the $\lambda_1,\lambda_2,\ldots,\lambda_n$ are the roots of (7.64) and (7.65). Comparison of (7.64) and (7.65) shows that the sum of the n roots $\lambda_1,\ldots,\lambda_n$ is equal to $-e_1$, and that the product is equal to $(-1)^n e_n$. From the characteristic equation (7.36) and its coefficients (7.40)-(7.42), we conclude that

$$\lambda_1 + \lambda_2 + \lambda_3 = -\sigma_{m1}(2P+1)/a < 0 \quad , \tag{7.66}$$

and

$$\lambda_1\lambda_2\lambda_3 = (Ra - Ra_c)m^2P^2/a \quad . \tag{7.67}$$

Thus, when $Ra < Ra_c$ at least one root is negative, the other two roots are both positive, both negative, or complex, and the sum of the values of the roots is independent of Ra. Generally, the characteristic equations that we encounter have roots that sum to a negative number, because their coefficients e_1 usually depend only on the dissipative terms in the system (see Section 17.3 for further discussion of the implications of this fact). Here we conclude that we cannot have both $Re(\lambda_1) = Re(\lambda_2) > 0$ implying a previous Hopf bifurcation and $\lambda_3 = 0$ signaling a stationary bifurcation, because, as noted above, we must always have a negative exponent $\lambda_3 < 0$. At $Ra = Ra_H$, we have $\lambda_3 = -\sigma_{m1}(2P+1)/a$, and for $Ra > Ra_H$, we see that λ_3 must take on a negative value having a larger magnitude. Thus, the stationary bifurcation must be produced by the vanishing of either λ_2 or λ_1, and so both λ_1 and λ_2 must be real when $Ra = Ra_c$. The only way this can happen is for $Im(\lambda_1) \to 0$ and $Im(\lambda_2) \to 0$ as $Ra \to Ra_r$, where $Ra_H < Ra_r < Ra_c$; at $Ra = Ra_r$, $\lambda_1 = \lambda_2 > 0$ must hold because no stability exchange has occurred yet (Fig. 7.15). Since the sum of the exponents is independent of Ra, further increases in the value of Ra lead to λ_2 decreasing to zero, causing the bifurcation of a stationary solution. Because one exponent is still positive when $Ra > Ra_c$ and because a subcritically bifurcating solution carries the stability properties of the conductive solution when $Ra > Ra_c$ (see Section 5.4), a consistent branching picture is the one given in Fig. 7.14c. We conclude that if the stability of a solution is controlled entirely by a cubic characteristic equation, then the stability properties of a subcritically branching stationary solution are completely unaffected by the occurrence of a Hopf bifurcation point on the conductive solution. Only with characteristic polynomial equations of higher order would it be possible to find more varied stability behavior.

As we have seen in this section, the method for determining the preferred horizontal wavelengths varies very little from that which was discussed in Section 7.1.2. Now, however, we must choose the value of the dimensionless Coriolis parameter f^* before we can determine the cell aspect ratio that minimizes the value of Ra_c for the stationary solution. Moreover, when determining the cell aspect ratio for the time-dependent solution, we must choose the value of the Prandtl number P since Ra_H depends on P.

Once these parameters are set, either (7.38) for Ra_c or (7.49) for Ra_H gives the preferred cell aspect ratio α, depending on which regime is selected for study. From here, the method is the same. We assume a value for the domain height z_T, and from (7.11), we can then calculate the preferred wavelength ℓ_m for the first convective mode.

Thus, we have seen how the effects of rotation can complicate the analysis by introducing Hopf bifurcation points into the Rayleigh-Bénard problem. A change in the ordering of the Hopf and stationary bifurcation points can lead to a discontinuous jump in the preferred value of α^2. The inequalities deduced from using the Hurwitz Theorem can also limit the analysis, showing that we cannot blindly use the derivative method in determining the minimum value of the forcing parameter.

So far, identification of the preferred wavelengths has been accomplished via analysis of the bifurcation points linked to trident branching forms. However, as noted in Chapter 6, only a restricted class of control parameters leads to such symmetric branching forms, and more generally, we must identify all classes of parameters in order to specify fully a physical problem. Locating and interpreting these parameters are the topics of the following chapter.

CHAPTER 8

IDENTIFYING CRUCIAL PARAMETERS WITH CONTACT CATASTROPHE THEORY

R. WAYNE HIGGINS AND ARTHUR N. SAMEL

We noted in Chapter 2 that the adequacy of a low-order model may be judged by comparing the behavior of its solutions with observations, or by comparing the properties of its solutions with those of the complete system. To expedite this evaluation, we use the seven modeling principles introduced in Section 1.3. The first four guide the development of the smallest effective model; the other three guide the comparison of this model with nearby ones. Here two nearby models are ones whose differential equations have functional forms that differ by a small amount from each other. The sense of this comparison is given in Principle Six, which says that a model should preserve overall structure under sufficiently small perturbations; this behavior is known as structural stability (see Introduction to Abraham and Marsden, 1967).

To illustrate what is meant by the expressions "nearby functional forms", "structural stability", and "small perturbations of functional forms", we recall that in Section 5.3 we discussed the stability properties of the solutions to the model described by the single differential equation (5.14), which is

$$\frac{dy}{dt} = -y[y^2 - (R - R_c)] \quad . \tag{8.1}$$

We wish to compare the behavior of this model with that of a nearby one described by

$$\frac{dy}{dt} = -y[y^2 - (R - R_c)] - \varepsilon \quad , \tag{8.2}$$

where the value of ε is small and nonzero. The two functional forms in (8.1) and (8.2) are near each other because they differ by only a small perturbation ε. However, as we encountered in Section 6.3.2, the branching behavior of the stationary solutions to (8.1) is qualitatively different from the behavior of those to (8.2). This is seen easily in Fig. 8.1, in which the stationary solutions to (8.1) form a trident, but those to (8.2) do not. Consequently, the perturbation ε has drastically altered the structure of the branching stationary solutions and so of the model (8.1). We conclude that the model (8.1) violates Principle Six and is not structurally stable. However, we have not seen that (8.2) violates this principle,

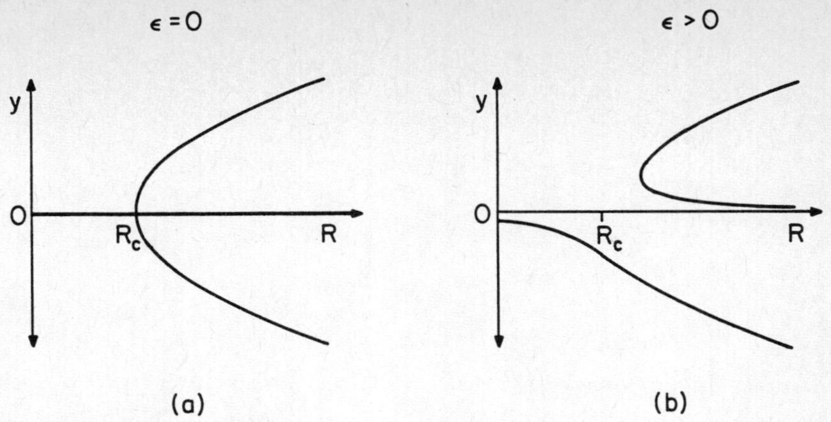

Fig. 8.1 The branching behavior of two nearby cubic forms. In (a) the stationary solutions to (8.1) are shown and in (b) the stationary solutions to (8.2) are shown for $\varepsilon>0$; note that R_c in (b) is only a point of reference, not a bifurcation point.

and in fact we discuss below in what sense it does not. Moreover, by setting $\varepsilon = 0$ in (8.2), which observationally is an occurrence having zero probability, we can see that model (8.1) also violates Principle Five, which states that a model should represent situations that occur with finite probability.

We may resolve the above difficulties with (8.1) if we extend (8.1) to (8.2) by adding a control parameter ε to the right side of (8.1). Although it is difficult to prove, the new system (8.2), which contains two control parameters R and ε, has the same branching behavior as that of any small perturbation of (8.2). That is, any such small perturbation would contain both branching forms in Fig. 8.1. Thus, relative to Principles Five and Six, the model (8.2) is judged to be adequate. Since the behavior of the stationary solutions to both (8.1) and the Lorenz model is similar, we surmise that, although we have shown in Chapter 2 that the Lorenz model is adequate relative to Principles One to Four, it is inadequate relative to Principles Five and Six.

In this chapter, we show that this supposition is correct by demonstrating how to apply a formal theory known as contact catastrophe theory to complete models by adding control parameters to them. This application involves two major efforts, as discussed by Shirer and Wells (1983). The first is to identify the missing control parameters in a simplified system such as (8.1) related to that of a low-order model such as the Lorenz model. The second is to interpret the new parameters by identifying them with physical effects represented by terms in the original partial differential equations. Outlining these efforts is the topic of this chapter, which follows closely the discussion of contact catastrophe theory in Shirer and Wells (1983). We begin by developing a general procedure for creating the appropriate simplified system.

8.1 The Lyapunov-Schmidt Splitting Procedure

The spectral models that we develop from a set of partial differential equations generally have the form

$$\dot{y}_k = f_k(y_1,\ldots,y_n;\ R_1,\ldots,R_m;\ \xi_1,\ldots,\xi_p) \qquad ;\ k = 1,\ldots,n \quad , \tag{8.3}$$

in which the n variables y_k are the amplitudes or spectral coefficients of the solutions, R_i are the control parameters such as the Rayleigh number that qualitatively affect the branching behavior, and ξ_j are other parameters such as the Prandtl number that could alter the critical values of the control parameters. In general we assume that the f_k are C^∞ functions for which all partial derivatives are defined and are continuous. A familiar example of (8.3) is the Lorenz system (2.80)-(2.82):

$$\dot{X} = -PX + PY \quad , \tag{8.4}$$

$$\dot{Y} = -XZ + rX - Y \quad , \tag{8.5}$$

$$\dot{Z} = XY - bZ \quad . \tag{8.6}$$

Here (X,Y,Z) are the spectral components y_k, r is a control parameter R_1, and P and b are passive parameters ξ_1 and ξ_2.

In this chapter, we are not interested in the preferred values of the control parameters, but only in how many we must include in the model. We focus attention on the critical values of the control parameters because these are the values at which transitions occur. Before we may begin, however, we must express (8.3) in perturbation form by finding a stationary solution $y_k = y_k^s$ and then defining

$$x_k = y_k - y_k^s \quad . \tag{8.7}$$

If (8.3) is rewritten using (8.7), then the stationary solution $y_k = y_k^s$ is given by the trivial solution $x_k = 0$. A stability analysis of this solution produces a critical value $\tilde{R} = (R_{1c},\ldots,R_{mc}) = \tilde{R}_c$; for notational simplicity we may define

$$\rho_i = R_i - R_{ic} \qquad ; \qquad i = 1,\ldots,m \quad , \tag{8.8}$$

so that the critical values of the control parameters are given by $\rho_i = 0$. Thus, with the use of (8.7)-(8.8), we have shifted the origin of the phase space to the region of interest, and we re-express (8.3) as

$$\dot{x}_k = f_k(x_1,\ldots,x_n;\ \rho_1,\ldots,\rho_m;\ \xi_1,\ldots,\xi_p) \qquad ; \qquad k = 1,\ldots,n \quad . \tag{8.9}$$

8.1.1 Development of the procedure. The Lyapunov-Schmidt Splitting Lemma provides an objective means by which we can transform the n (quadratic) polynomial equations on the right side of (8.9) into a new set of equations in which the nonlinear behavior is controlled by a small number c of (higher degree) polynomial equations. To accomplish this transformation, we first separate the variables x_k into two groups

$$g_i = x_i \qquad ; \qquad i = 1,\ldots,n-c \quad , \tag{8.10}$$

$$h_j = x_{n-c+j} \qquad ; \qquad j = 1,\ldots,c \quad , \tag{8.11}$$

in which we may have first re-ordered the x_k before assigning them to groups g_i and h_j. Now we have the transformation

$$\tilde{f}(\tilde{x}) \rightarrow \tilde{f}(\tilde{g},\tilde{h}) \quad . \tag{8.12}$$

For clarity we have written (8.12) using vector form so that, for example, $\tilde{f} = (f_1,\ldots,f_n)$; in this chapter we often adopt this notational convention, but drop the tildas. Now we wish to find a transformation of f into a new system that has the same number of stationary solutions, but has a more amenable form. We seek to replace the problem of solving n equations $f_k(x) = 0$ in n unknowns x_k with the reduced problem of solving $c < n$ equations in c unknowns h_j. That is, symbolically we seek the following equivalence:

$$\left.\begin{array}{lcl} f_1(\underset{\sim}{x}) = 0 & & g_1 = 0 \\ f_2(\underset{\sim}{x}) = 0 & & g_2 = 0 \\ \cdot & & \cdot \\ \cdot & & \cdot \\ \cdot & & \cdot \\ f_{n-c}(\underset{\sim}{x}) = 0 & \Longleftrightarrow & g_{n-c} = 0 \\ f_{n-c+1}(\underset{\sim}{x}) = 0 & & p_1(h_1,\ldots,h_c) = 0 \\ \cdot & & \cdot \\ \cdot & & \cdot \\ \cdot & & \cdot \\ f_n(\underset{\sim}{x}) = 0 & & p_c(h_1,\ldots,h_c) = 0 \end{array}\right\} . \tag{8.13}$$

The improvement in the problem comes from the fact that, in the right side of (8.13), g_i and h_j are the only arguments. We notice that the first n-c equations on the right are solved by simply setting the n-c arguments g_i to zero and that the last c equations only involve the arguments h_j.

We begin by writing f(g,h) in the form

$$f(g,h) = \left[\begin{array}{c|c} A(g,h) & B(g,h) \\ \hline C(g,h) & D(g,h) \end{array}\right] \begin{bmatrix} g \\ h \end{bmatrix} = \left[\Gamma(g,h)\right] \begin{bmatrix} g \\ h \end{bmatrix} , \tag{8.14}$$

where n-c is the rank of the matrix Df of partial derivatives $\partial f_i/\partial x_j$ evaluated at the origin x = 0 and where the re-ordering implicit in (8.10)-(8.11) has been carried out so that A is an (n-c) × (n-c) matrix that is invertible near the origin g = h = 0. We observe that the rank of Df at the origin is the same as the rank of Γ at the origin. The Lyapunov-Schmidt Splitting Lemma states that there exists a transformation, called a contact transformation, so that (8.14) can be changed into a contact equivalent system of the form we seek. We use the symbol "~" to denote contact equivalence and note then that the lemma allows us to write

$$\left[\begin{array}{c|c} A(g,h) & B(g,h) \\ \hline C(g,h) & D(g,h) \end{array}\right] \begin{bmatrix} g \\ h \end{bmatrix} \sim \begin{bmatrix} g \\ p(h) \end{bmatrix} \quad , \tag{8.15}$$

for some c-component function p(h).

Two systems are said to be contact equivalent if we can recover one from the other first by multiplying the right side of (8.14) by an invertible matrix M and then performing a nonlinear change of variables. Contact equivalent functions possess the same stationary solutions as the original system; the process used to determine a contact equivalent function is called a contact transformation. Unfortunately, the stability of the stationary solutions in two contact equivalent systems can change, but more refined transformations that preserve both the stationary solutions and their stabilities are possible (see Chapter 6 of Shirer and Wells, 1983).

It is useful to proceed with a sketch of the proof of the Lyapunov-Schmidt Splitting Lemma because we use key portions of it later, when we apply a contact transformation to the Lorenz system. Because part of a contact transformation allows multiplication of the original matrix by some invertible one, we may multiply (8.14) by

$$M = \begin{bmatrix} A(g,h)^{-1} & 0 \\ -C(g,h)A(g,h)^{-1} & I_c \end{bmatrix} \quad , \tag{8.16}$$

in which I_c is the c × c identity matrix, to obtain

$$f(g,h) \sim \begin{bmatrix} I_{n-c} & A^{-1}B \\ 0 & D-CA^{-1}B \end{bmatrix} \begin{bmatrix} g \\ h \end{bmatrix} \quad . \tag{8.17}$$

From this result, we can define

$$\Delta(g,h) = D(g,h) - C(g,h)A(g,h)^{-1}B(g,h) \quad , \tag{8.18}$$

which is a c × c matrix equation. Because the upper left block in (8.17) is the (n−c) × (n−c) identity matrix I_{n-c}, and the rank of $\Gamma(0,0)$ in (8.14) is (n−c), we must have

$$\Delta(0,0) = 0 \quad . \tag{8.19}$$

Alternatively, we say that corank(f) = c and in practice we use (8.18) and (8.19) to verify that we have made the correct choices for the matrices A, B, C, and D.

We perform the second step of the contact transformation by defining the coordinate transformation

$$\overline{g} = g + A(g,h)^{-1}B(g,h)h \quad , \tag{8.20}$$

$$\overline{h} = h \quad . \tag{8.21}$$

After substituting (8.20)-(8.21) into (8.17), we may rewrite f(g,h) as

$$f(g,h) \sim \begin{bmatrix} I_{n-c} & 0 \\ 0 & \Delta(g,h) \end{bmatrix} \begin{bmatrix} \overline{g} \\ \overline{h} \end{bmatrix} \quad , \tag{8.22}$$

or simply as

$$f(g,h) \sim \begin{bmatrix} \overline{g} \\ \Delta(g,h)\overline{h} \end{bmatrix} \quad . \tag{8.23}$$

Although this result is similar to that of the Lyapunov-Schmidt Splitting Lemma, we must express the right side of (8.23) in terms of the original variables g and h only. To begin, we use Taylor's Theorem to write

$$\Delta(g,h) = S(\overline{h}) + \sum_{i=1}^{c} \overline{g}_i \, \Xi_i(\overline{g},\overline{h}) \quad , \tag{8.24}$$

in which $S(\overline{h})$ and $\Xi_i(g,h)$ are smooth $c \times c$ matrices. After applying (8.20)-(8.21) to (8.23) (Shirer and Wells, 1983), we arrive at the equivalence

$$f(g,h) \sim \begin{bmatrix} g \\ S(h)h \end{bmatrix} \quad , \tag{8.25}$$

where $S(h)$ is the first term in the Taylor expansion (8.24). Some of the manipulations necessary for obtaining (8.25) are very involved, but the equality $S(h) = S(\overline{h})$ is immediate from (8.21). To complete the proof, we set

$$p(h) = S(h)h \quad . \tag{8.26}$$

From (8.24) we see that

$$\Delta(g,h) = S(h) \quad , \tag{8.27}$$

when

$$\overline{g} = 0 \text{ and } \overline{h} = h \quad . \tag{8.28}$$

From (8.20) we note that $\overline{g} = 0$ when

$$g + A(g,h)^{-1}B(g,h)h = 0 \quad . \tag{8.29}$$

Thus, if (8.29) holds, then $p(h)$ is given by

$$p(h) = S(h)h = \Delta(g,h)h \quad . \tag{8.30}$$

Reversing this argument, we arrive at an algorithm called the <u>Lyapunov-Schmidt Splitting Procedure</u>:

(i) Let $g = \Sigma(h)$ be a solution to (8.29). Then,

$$\Sigma(h) + A(\Sigma(h),h)^{-1}B(\Sigma(h),h)h = 0 \quad . \tag{8.31}$$

We notice that a unique solution $g = \Sigma(h)$ exists by the Implicit Function Theorem (see Section 5.1), and that $\Sigma(0) = 0$.

(ii) Then we have from (8.18) and (8.30) that

$$p(h) = \left[D(\Sigma(h),h) - C(\Sigma(h),h)A(\Sigma(h),h)^{-1}B(\Sigma(h),h)\right]h \quad , \tag{8.32}$$

or that

$$p(h) = D(\Sigma(h),h)h + C(\Sigma(h),h)\Sigma(h) \quad . \tag{8.33}$$

8.1.2 Application to the Lorenz model. We illustrate the above procedure by applying it to the Lorenz system, which is given by (8.4)-(8.6). This system already admits the trivial solution and so no change of variables (8.7) must be performed. However, we recall that the singular or bifurcation point is given by $r_c = 1$, and so we set $\rho_1 = r - r_c = r - 1$ and choose $\rho_1 = 0$ by setting $r = 1$. To specify g and h, we set

$$[X,Y,Z] = [g_1,h,g_2] \quad . \tag{8.34}$$

In practice, definitions such as (8.34) are obtained by trial and error, and verified as adequate by checking that A is invertible and that $\Delta(0,0) = 0$. Now the form of (8.4)-(8.6) at the singular point $\rho_1 = 0$ is given by

$$\dot{g}_1 = - Pg_1 + Ph = 0 \quad , \tag{8.35}$$

$$\dot{g}_2 = g_1h - bg_2 = 0 \quad , \tag{8.36}$$

$$\dot{h} = - g_1g_2 + g_1 - h = 0 \quad . \tag{8.37}$$

In order to apply a contact transformation to the Lorenz system, we put (8.35)-(8.37) into the form of (8.14)

$$f(g,h) = \begin{bmatrix} -P & 0 & P \\ 0 & -b & g_1 \\ 1 & -g_1 & -1 \end{bmatrix} \begin{bmatrix} g_1 \\ g_2 \\ h \end{bmatrix} = 0 \quad , \tag{8.38}$$

where

$$A(g,h) = \begin{bmatrix} -P & 0 \\ 0 & -b \end{bmatrix} \quad , \qquad (8.39)$$

$$B(g,h) = \begin{bmatrix} P \\ g_1 \end{bmatrix} \quad , \qquad (8.40)$$

$$C(g,h) = [1,-g_1] \quad , \qquad (8.41)$$

$$D(g,h) = [-1] \quad . \qquad (8.42)$$

Note that $P > 0$ and $b > 0$ so that A is invertible as required. To verify that we have made the correct choices for A to D, we substitute (8.39)-(8.42) evaluated at $[g_1,g_2,h] = [0,0,0]$ into (8.18) to obtain

$$\Delta(0,0) = -1 - [1,0] \begin{bmatrix} -P^{-1} & 0 \\ 0 & -b^{-1} \end{bmatrix} \begin{bmatrix} P \\ 0 \end{bmatrix} = -1+1 = 0 \quad . \qquad (8.43)$$

Because A is a nonsingular 2×2 matrix and $\Delta(0,0) = 0$, the corank c of f is one. The corank is important for determining both the class of the singularity and the number of parameters that must be added to unfold it fully (see Section 8.2).

Next, we calculate the solutions $g = \Sigma(h)$ of (8.31). The g_i are given by

$$\begin{bmatrix} g_1 \\ g_2 \end{bmatrix} + \begin{bmatrix} -P^{-1} & 0 \\ 0 & -b^{-1} \end{bmatrix} \begin{bmatrix} P \\ g_1 \end{bmatrix} h = 0 \quad , \qquad (8.44)$$

or by

$$g_1 = h \quad , \qquad (8.45)$$

and

$$g_2 = h^2/b \quad . \tag{8.46}$$

The function p(h) is then found by substituting (8.45)-(8.46) into (8.41) and the result into (8.33). When this substitution is completed, we obtain

$$p(h) = -h^3/b \quad , \tag{8.47}$$

and conclude that the stationary solutions of (8.4)-(8.6) are the same as those of the transformed system

$$F(g,h,0) = \begin{bmatrix} g_1 \\ g_2 \\ -h^3/b \end{bmatrix} \quad . \tag{8.48}$$

We again note that the corank of this singularity is one since the number c of components in the function p(h) is one.

8.2 Identifying Crucial Parameters

We saw in Chapter 6 that the addition of two parameters to a cubic equation is necessary to describe fully the stationary behavior in the neighborhood of a singular point. But how many parameters would have to be added to a quartic or a quintic one? We could guess that, as in the cubic case, the next-to highest order term is eliminated while all other terms in descending order to the constant term are multiplied by parameters. As shown by application of a theorem of Mather (1968), this guess is correct, and this application produces what is called an unfolding of a singularity.

To motivate the procedure, we notice that adding two coefficients to (8.47) generates a new function given by

$$\Theta(h,c_1,c_2) = -h^3/b + c_1 h + c_2 \quad . \tag{8.49}$$

This function is an _unfolding_ of $p(h) = -h^3/b$, and c_1 and c_2 are the _unfolding_

<u>parameters</u>. More generally, the function $V(x,\beta_1,\ldots,\beta_q)$ is an <u>unfolding</u> and $\beta_1,\ldots,\beta_q$ are the unfolding parameters of $f(x)$, if simply

$$V(x,0) = f(x) \quad . \tag{8.50}$$

We obtain a new unfolding of $f(x)$ by applying a process analogous to a contact transformation. Instead of a straightforward coordinate change,

$$x = x(y) \quad , \tag{8.51}$$

we need a more involved coordinate change

$$x = x(y,\alpha) \quad , \tag{8.52}$$

parameterized by $\alpha = (\alpha_1,\ldots,\alpha_p)$. Notice that the number q of indices of β is not necessarily equal to the number p of α. We constrain this coordinate transformation to be the identity when $\alpha = 0$, and so

$$y = x(y,0) \quad . \tag{8.53}$$

Also, we need the parameters β to be functions of the new parameters α,

$$\beta = \beta(\alpha) \quad , \tag{8.54}$$

and for these functions to be constrained by the condition $\beta(0) = 0$. Finally, if we regard $M(y,\alpha)$ as an $n \times n$ smooth invertible matrix having the property that $M(y,0) = I_n$, in which I_n is the $n \times n$ identity matrix, then we may define a new function $E(y,\alpha)$ by setting

$$E(y,\alpha) = M(y,\alpha)\, V\big(x(y,\alpha),\, \beta(\alpha)\big) \quad . \tag{8.55}$$

Here $E(y,\alpha)$ is an unfolding of $f(y)$ because of the above constraints; we see this fact by combining $M(y,0) = I_n$, (8.50), (8.53), and (8.55), to write

$$\begin{aligned} E(y,0) &= M(y,0)\, V\big(x(y,0),\, \beta(0)\big) \\ &= I_n f(x(y,0)) \\ &= f(y) \quad . \end{aligned} \tag{8.56}$$

Here we say that the unfolding $E(y,\alpha)$ is a <u>pull-back</u> of $V(x,\beta)$, a pull-back by the functions $x(y,\alpha)$, $\beta(\alpha)$, and $M(y,\alpha)$.

As illustrated in Fig. 8.2, a pull-back operation can result in either loss of clarity or loss of information. As can be easily verified, for a fixed value of α, the correspondence $x = x(y,\alpha)$ precisely identifies the stationary points of E with

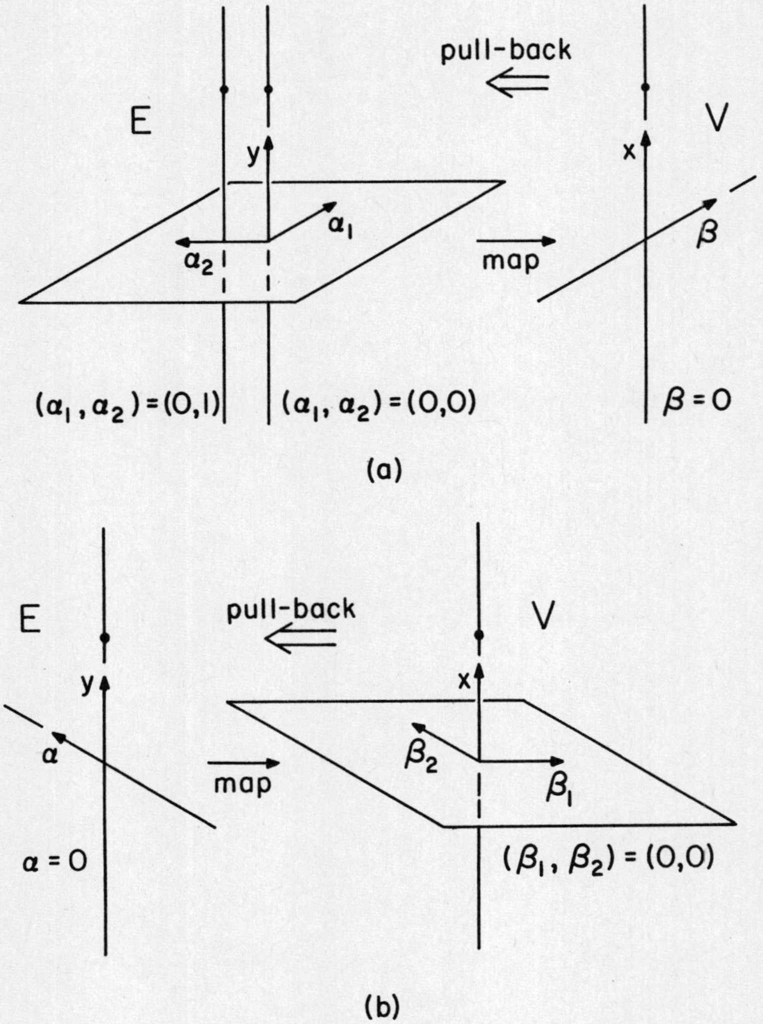

Fig. 8.2 Two examples of a pull-back operation. In (a), the map $(y,\alpha) \rightarrow [x(y,\alpha), \beta(\alpha)]$ is given by $x(y,\alpha) = y$ and $\beta(\alpha_1, \alpha_2) = \alpha_1$, and the pull-back operation leads to a loss of clarity. In (b), the map is given by $x(y,\alpha) = y$, $\beta(\alpha) = (0,\alpha)$ and the pull-back operation leads to a loss of information.

those of V. In each part of Fig. 8.2, therefore, the configuration of stationary points in a vertical line in the left diagram is identical to that in the corresponding vertical line in the right diagram. Thus, there is no loss of either information or clarity for a fixed value of α and a corresponding value of β. However, in the pull-back operation in Fig. 8.2a, many values of α correspond to a single value of β. Consequently, information in a single vertical in the right diagram is duplicated unnecessarily, leading to a loss of clarity. In Fig. 8.2b, a unique value of α corresponds to a single value of β, but there exist many values of β for which there exists no corresponding value of α. Thus, information about stationary points contained in a vertical defined by these values of β in the right diagram is not represented in any vertical of the left diagram, leading to a loss of information. We emphasize that pulling back is a very general procedure that preserves the configuration of the stationary points for any fixed values of the parameters.

The notions of unfolding and pull-back may seem entirely tautologous at first glance. Initial motivation for introducing them is given by the following observation: We wish to extend governing polynomials such as (8.47) by introducing into them new parameters to represent some new physical controls. That is, we would like to unfold expressions such as (8.47) to obtain expressions such as (8.49). Having extended the governing polynomials, we wish to transform them in such a way as to preserve their zeros, that is, their stationary points. The class of contact transformations is simply the largest manageable class of transformations that preserve stationary points. The pull-back operation is simply a fairly obvious generalization of a contact transformation. Thus we have some motivation, in general and rather vague philosophical terms, for introducing unfoldings, contact transformations, and pull-backs.

The overriding motivation, however, arises from a startling theorem of Mather (Mather, 1968). It states that for almost any function f(x), there exists an unfolding $V(x,\beta)$ that is "universal" in the sense that any other unfolding $E(y,\alpha)$ is a pull-back of $V(x,\beta)$. Thus, the configuration of stationary points of $E(y,\alpha)$ is determined by finitely many control parameters $\beta_1(\alpha),\ldots,\beta_q(\alpha)$; usually, in fact, q = 1, 2, 3, or 4. To emphasize the surprising content of this conclusion, we

Table 8.1 Corank 1 unfoldings. (After Shirer and Wells, 1983).

Form	Type	Codimension q of Singularity	Unfolding
x^2	Fold	1	$x^2 - \beta_1$
x^3	Cusp	2	$x^3 - \beta_2 x - \beta_1$
x^4	Swallowtail	3	$x^4 - \beta_3 x^2 - \beta_2 x - \beta_1$
x^5	Butterfly	4	$x^5 - \beta_4 x^3 - \beta_3 x^2 - \beta_2 x - \beta_1$

paraphrase the above information as follows: The location of the stationary points of $E(y,\alpha)$ is determined by, say, three numbers $\beta_1(\alpha)$, $\beta_2(\alpha)$, $\beta_3(\alpha)$ even if $\alpha = \alpha_1,\ldots,\alpha_p$ with $p \ggg 1$. In this way, a great deal of information is filtered out as irrelevant to the configuration of the stationary points.

Even more surprising is the fact that the theory of Mather enables us, fairly easily, to characterize these "universal" unfoldings and even to construct them from $f(x)$ alone. The one fly in the ointment is that a universal unfolding is not unique. Therefore the standard terminology is to drop the prefix "uni" from "universal" to reflect this fact, and thus to arrive at the term versal unfolding.

8.2.1 Mather's Theorem and versal unfoldings. As noted above, the primary purpose of applying Mather's Theorem is to construct new, extended systems from old ones. The goal is that the new system be a versal unfolding of the old one. By means of fairly routine calculations, Mather's Theorem also allows us to identify the crucial parameters that need to be added to a singular homogeneous polynomial function such as x^ℓ. A few of these results are given in Table 8.1. As we see in Section 8.3, the forms given in Table 8.1 provide only an initial unfolding that must be altered to become physically relevant.

In order to use Mather's Theorem, we must first introduce the differential matrix $Df(x)$ of some smooth function $f(x)$, where

$$Df(x) = \left[\partial f_i/\partial x_j(x)\right] \quad , \quad \begin{cases} i = 1,\ldots,n \\ j = 1,\ldots,n \end{cases} \quad , \tag{8.57}$$

and we number rows with index i and columns with j. We also introduce a smooth $q \times n$ matrix $N(x)$ depending smoothly on x and a condition called the Transversality Condition relating $N(x)$ and $f(x)$. The matrix $N(x)$ satisfies the Transversality Condition with respect to $f(x)$ near $x = 0$ if and only if every smooth n-vector function $Y(x)$ may be written near $x = 0$ as

$$Y(x) = Df(x) \cdot G(x) + H(x) \cdot f(x) + \gamma_1 N_1(x) + \cdots + \gamma_q N_q(x) \quad . \tag{8.58}$$

Here $G(x)$ is a suitable smooth n-vector function, $H(x)$ is a suitable smooth $n \times n$ matrix function, and γ is a suitable constant q-vector; in addition, $G(x)$, $H(x)$ and γ all depend on $Y(x)$. As it turns out, all but a finite number of the terms that describe $Y(x)$ can be included in the first two terms of (8.58), and so $N(x)$ involves the remaining terms that must be added to describe $Y(x)$ fully.

It may appear impossible to verify (8.58) for every possible smooth vector function $Y(x)$ near the origin; however, it may be verified easily for the Lorenz system. The primary application of the Transversality Condition is for finding a suitable new matrix $N'(x)$ from the known one $N(x)$. Now we may state the theorem:

Mather's Theorem. The n-component unfolding $V(x,\beta)$ with $\beta = (\beta_1,\ldots,\beta_q)$ of the n-component function $f(x)$ is versal if and only if the $q \times n$ matrix

$$N(x) = \left[\frac{\partial V_i}{\partial \beta_j}(x,0) \right]^T \quad ; \quad \begin{cases} i = 1,\ldots,n \\ j = 1,\ldots,q \end{cases} \quad , \tag{8.59}$$

satisfies the Transversality Condition with respect to $f(x)$.

Note that in practice, $N(x)$ gives us all of the necessary terms in (8.58) for an unfolding of $f(x)$. We summarize this fact in the following corollary:

Corollary. If the matrix $N(x)$ satisfies the Transversality Condition with respect to $f(x)$, then

$$V(x,\beta) = f(x) + \beta \cdot N(x) \quad , \tag{8.60}$$

is a versal unfolding of $f(x)$.

We regard as invisible any function that may be written as (8.58) with $\gamma = 0$.

Functions that we cannot write in this way are classified by the terms $\gamma \cdot N(x)$, which are obtained by erasing the invisible portion $Df(x) \cdot G(x) + H(x) \cdot f(x)$ in (8.58). Thus, we refer to $N(x)$ as the unfolding matrix of (8.60) and its columns as the unfolding functions of (8.60). It is this corollary that is used to find the versal unfoldings shown in Table 8.1.

We now return to the Lorenz system (8.35)-(8.37) and determine a versal unfolding of it. We recall that the nonlinear function is a cubic one of the form

$$p(h) = - h^3/b \quad . \tag{8.61}$$

If we expand some function $Y(h)$ using Taylor's Theorem, then we have

$$Y(h) = Y(0) + Y'(0)h + Y''(0)h^2/2 + z(h)h^3 \quad , \tag{8.62}$$

which we may rewrite in the form of the Transversality Condition as

$$Y(h) = - Dp(h)\left(\frac{b}{6} Y''(0)\right) - \left(bz(h)\right)p(h) + Y(0) + Y'(0)h \quad , \tag{8.63}$$

where

$$- (b/6)Y''(0) = G(h) \quad , \tag{8.64}$$

$$- bz(h) = H(h) \quad , \tag{8.65}$$

$$\begin{bmatrix} 1 \\ h \end{bmatrix} = N(h) \quad , \tag{8.66}$$

and

$$\left[Y(0), Y'(0)\right] = \gamma \quad . \tag{8.67}$$

Because $Y(h)$ is arbitrary, $N(h)$ in (8.66) satisfies the Transversality Condition and we may use the Corollary to Mather's Theorem with $\beta_1 = Y(0)$ and $\beta_2 = Y'(0)$, to conclude that

$$V(h,\beta) = - h^3/b + \beta_2 h + \beta_1 \quad , \tag{8.68}$$

is a versal unfolding of the polynomial function p(h) about $\beta_2 = \beta_1 = 0$. With the above procedure, we may use Mather's Theorem to verify the unfoldings given in Table 8.1. However, for (8.68) to apply to the Lorenz system, we must consider the final step of placing the new terms in the original system. The means for carrying out this operation is the topic of the next subsection.

8.2.2 The Lyapunov-Schmidt Reducing Lemma. Now that we have described the method by which we can determine the polynomial equation that governs the stationary behavior of a nonlinear system of n differential equations, we need to identify the location of the parameters in an unfolding of the original n-coefficient system. The Lyapunov-Schmidt Reducing Lemma provides a method for performing this identification. To use the Reducing Lemma, we assume that f(g,h) and p(h) are written in the forms (8.14) and (8.30) and that

$$V(h,\beta) = p(h) + \beta_1 N_1(h) + \cdots + \beta_q N_q(h) \quad , \tag{8.69}$$

is a versal unfolding of p(h). Then, it follows from Mather's Theorem that

$$F(g,h,\beta) = f(g,h) + \begin{bmatrix} 0 \\ \\ \beta_1 N_1(h) + \cdots + \beta_q N_q(h) \end{bmatrix} , \tag{8.70}$$

is a versal unfolding of the system f(g,h) about $\beta = 0$. That is, we add the terms of the unfolding only to the equation for the variable h.

If we apply the Lyapunov-Schmidt Reducing Lemma to the Lorenz system, then we find that

$$F(g,h,\beta) = \begin{bmatrix} -P & 0 & P \\ 0 & -b & g_1 \\ 1 & -g_1 & -1 \end{bmatrix} \begin{bmatrix} g_1 \\ g_2 \\ h \end{bmatrix} + \begin{bmatrix} 0 \\ 0 \\ \beta_1 + \beta_2 h \end{bmatrix} , \tag{8.71}$$

or that

$$F(g,h,\beta) = \begin{bmatrix} -Pg_1 + Ph \\ g_1h - bg_2 \\ -g_1g_2 + g_1 - h + \beta_1 + \beta_2 h \end{bmatrix}, \tag{8.72}$$

is a versal unfolding of (8.35)-(8.37) about $\beta_1 = \beta_2 = 0$. After using (8.34) to rewrite (8.72) in the original variables, we see that

$$F(X,Y,Z,\beta) = \begin{bmatrix} PY - PX \\ -XZ + X - Y + \beta_1 + \beta_2 Y \\ -bZ + XY \end{bmatrix}, \tag{8.73}$$

is a versal unfolding of (8.4)-(8.6). Although there are many contact equivalent forms of the versal unfolding of (8.4)-(8.6), very few of the systems are physically equivalent. For instance, by comparing (8.4)-(8.6) with (8.73) we see that neither of the parameters β_1 or β_2 in (8.73) can represent the normalized Rayleigh number r. Thus, even though (8.73) is a versal unfolding of (8.4)-(8.6), the two systems are not physically equivalent because changes in the value of r cannot be represented by variations in β_1 or β_2. This conclusion leads us in the next section to ask how we can alter (8.73) to a new form in which β_1 and β_2 would be related to r.

8.3 Physically Interpreting the Parameters

Unfortunately, the Lyapunov-Schmidt technique discussed above often leads to a physically unrealizable versal unfolding. Hence, we might find it necessary to alter an unfolding to a more suitable form. To obtain this new form, a number of relevant questions must be answered:

1. How do we know if we have an unsuitable versal unfolding in the first place?
2. How do we find alternative locations for the model parameters? What is the methodology?
3. How do we accept or reject parameter locations on a physical basis?

4. How do we associate important physical effects with the proper model parameters?

In the rest of this chapter we show how to answer these questions.

8.3.1 The motivation for altering an unfolding. If the unfolding (8.70) or (8.73) is to make sense, then β_1 and β_2 must be associated with actual physical effects. Fig. 8.3 shows the stationary points of (8.68) for three different values of β_1. The case $\beta_1 = 0$ (Fig. 8.3b) corresponds to that of the Lorenz model (the

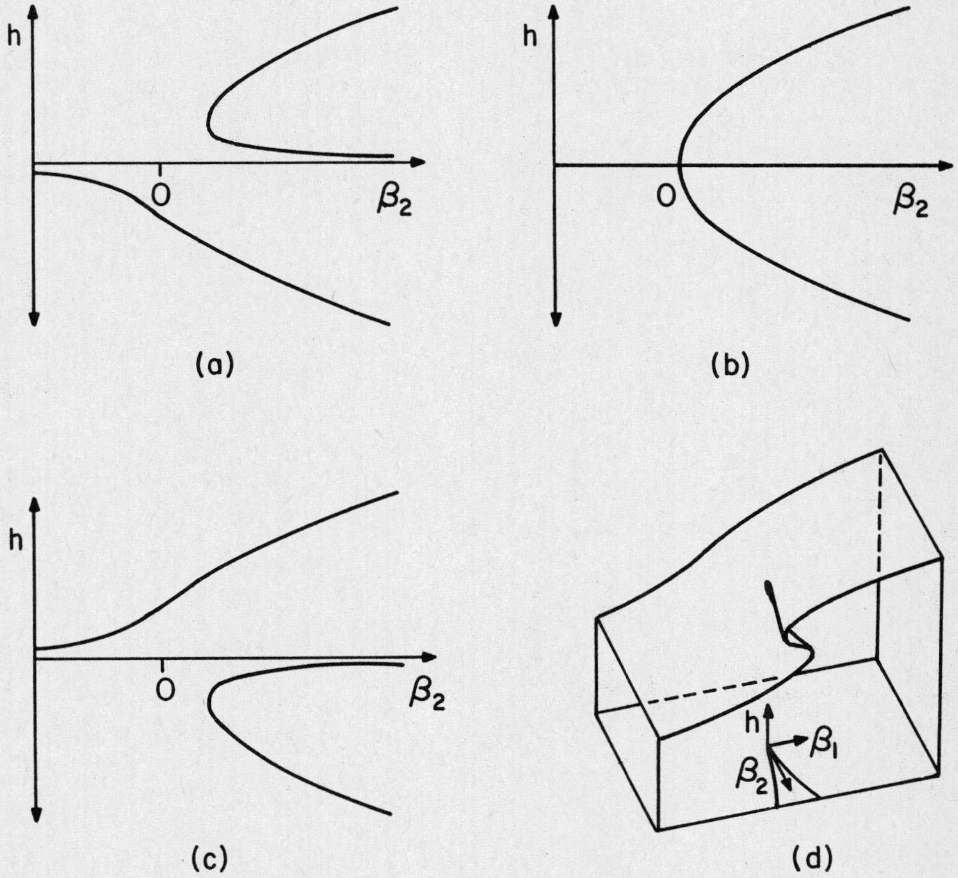

Fig. 8.3 Several ways in which the real-valued solutions of the cubic polynomial equation (8.68) can be displayed. The magnitude of the solution as a function of the linear coefficient β_2 is shown for the constant term $\beta_1<0$ (a), $\beta_1=0$ (b), and $\beta_1>0$ (c). In (d) the solution surface, which is the standard cusp surface, is shown as a function of both coefficients β_1 and β_2 (after Shirer and Wells, 1983).

familiar trident form) with the normalized Rayleigh number r evidently playing the role of β_2. But we require a physical interpretation of the new parameter β_1; identifying this physical interpretation is important for modeling properly the smooth development of a convective flow.

In addition to a determination of the number of independent parameters needed to describe branching behavior in a low-order model, we must guarantee that the locations of the new parameters -- given by the contact catastrophe theory -- are obtainable via insertion of a physically appropriate term into the original partial differential equations. Indeed, we have already noted that the use of the Lyapunov-Schmidt technique can lead to an unsuitable versal unfolding. In these cases, we must find locations for the new parameters that are amenable to physical interpretation.

In the original variables, an unfolding of the Lorenz model (8.4)-(8.6) is (8.73). Evidently the new parameter β_1 in the middle row of (8.73) represents a diabatic term in the thermodynamic equation $\dot{Y}$. However, β_2 cannot represent the normalized Rayleigh number r because it multiplies Y and so is in a dissipation term; there is no corresponding physical analog to this term in the original partial differential equation. Thus, we prefer another form of F that is still a versal unfolding. In the following subsection we discuss the method, which is based on the Transversality Condition, that is necessary to obtain a suitable alteration of (8.73). First, however, we must review the manner by which the physical system is forced; in general, the forcing used is either external or internal.

In a model, external forcing (or heating) is imposed on the boundaries of the domain under consideration. To develop the Lorenz model, for example, an external vertical temperature distribution was included in the temperature expansion (see Section 2.1.2), so that

$$T(x,z,t) = T_{oo} - \Delta_z T\left(\frac{z}{z_T}\right) + T'(x,z,t) \quad . \tag{8.74}$$

This expansion leads to a linear term in the Boussinesq version of the thermodynamic equation (2.35) that contains the normalized Rayleigh number r:

$$\frac{\partial T^*}{\partial t^*} = \cdots + r\,\frac{\partial \psi^*}{\partial x^*} + \cdots \quad . \tag{8.75}$$

Moreover, as we saw in deriving the Lorenz model in Section 2.2, r appears in an energy conversion term of one of the thermodynamic equations (cf. (8.5)):

$$\dot{Y} = \cdots + rX + \cdots \quad . \tag{8.76}$$

Thus, an externally imposed vertical temperature difference leads to a suitable location for the Rayleigh number in the final spectral model.

Internal forcing would include heating the fluid from within. Although there is no internal forcing in the Lorenz model (8.4)-(8.6), we could include the forcing by writing the thermodynamic equation (2.35) in the form

$$\frac{\partial T^*}{\partial t^*} = - J(\psi^*,T^*) + r \frac{\partial \psi^*}{\partial x^*} + (1+a^2)^{-1} \tilde{\nabla}^2 T^* + Q(x^*,z^*) \quad , \tag{8.77}$$

in which Q represents rates of latent, radiant and sensible heating. If we substitute the Fourier expansions (2.78)-(2.79), and an appropriate expansion for Q, into (8.77), then the result is a thermodynamic spectral equation of the form

$$\dot{Y} = \cdots + \beta_1 \quad , \tag{8.78}$$

in which β_1 is an inhomogeneous term that may be interpreted as a Fourier coefficient of the internally imposed heating rate Q.

<u>8.3.2 Altering versal unfoldings: The Lorenz model</u>. In Section 8.2.2 we obtained a versal unfolding of the Lorenz model given by (8.73). In this unfolding, we found that β_1 could be interpreted as a diabatic heating term but that β_2 could not be interpreted as a Rayleigh number because it appeared in a dissipation term. Thus, we must seek an alternative unfolding of the Lorenz model that provides a correct physical interpretation for both parameters. Our search is guided by the Transversality Condition (8.58).

Since r usually appears in an energy conversion term, we suspect that it might be possible to move β_2 from a product with Y to a product with X. In fact, this alteration can be accomplished if the Transversality Condition is satisfied. To apply the condition, we make the change of notation

$$[x_1,x_2,x_3] = [X,Y,Z] \quad . \tag{8.79}$$

Combining the unfolding (8.73), which is

$$\begin{bmatrix} F_1 \\ F_2 \\ F_3 \end{bmatrix} = \begin{bmatrix} -Px_1 + Px_2 \\ -x_1x_3 + x_1 - x_2 \\ x_1x_2 - bx_3 \end{bmatrix} + \beta_2 \begin{bmatrix} 0 \\ x_2 \\ 0 \end{bmatrix} + \beta_1 \begin{bmatrix} 0 \\ 1 \\ 0 \end{bmatrix} , \tag{8.80}$$

with (8.58), we obtain

$$\begin{bmatrix} Y_1 \\ Y_2 \\ Y_3 \end{bmatrix} = \begin{bmatrix} -P & P & 0 \\ -x_3+1 & -1 & -x_1 \\ x_2 & x_1 & -b \end{bmatrix} \begin{bmatrix} G_1(x) \\ G_2(x) \\ G_3(x) \end{bmatrix} + \begin{bmatrix} H_{11}(x) & H_{12}(x) & H_{13}(x) \\ H_{21}(x) & H_{22}(x) & H_{23}(x) \\ H_{31}(x) & H_{32}(x) & H_{33}(x) \end{bmatrix} \begin{bmatrix} -Px_1 + Px_2 \\ -x_1x_3 + x_1 - x_2 \\ x_1x_2 - bx_3 \end{bmatrix}$$

$$+ \gamma_2 \begin{bmatrix} 0 \\ x_2 \\ 0 \end{bmatrix} + \gamma_1 \begin{bmatrix} 0 \\ 1 \\ 0 \end{bmatrix} , \tag{8.81}$$

in which $G_i(x)$, $H_{ij}(x)$ and γ_i, which depend on $Y(x)$, must be specified, and the invisible portion $Df(x) \cdot G(x) + H(x) \cdot f(x)$ of $Y(x)$ is highlighted by the dashed lines. Thus, we are mainly interested in relating the solid column on the left to the sum of the two solid columns on the right of (8.81).

As a rule, to obtain a suitable alteration of an unfolding using the Transversality Condition, we first determine using some physical considerations those columns of $N(x)$ that fail to represent physical effects. In the Lorenz model, we have only one column to replace. Then we

- Select for deletion columns $N_i(x)$, $i=1,\dots,s$ on the right of (8.58), including some of those identified above as unsuitable.
- Select s suitable replacement columns $N_i'(x)$ for those identified above for replacement.
- Express the replacement columns $N_i'(x)$ in terms of $Df(x)$, $f(x)$, and $N(x)$ as in (8.58):

$$\left.\begin{array}{l} N_1'(x) = \left[\;\;\right] + \sum_{i=1}^{s} \gamma_{i1} N_i(x) \\ \quad\vdots \qquad\qquad \vdots \\ N_s'(x) = \left[\;\;\right] + \sum_{i=1}^{s} \gamma_{is} N_i(x) \end{array}\right\} . \tag{8.82}$$

- In (8.82), the dashed brackets enclose terms of the form $Df(x) \cdot G(x) + H(x) \cdot f(x)$.
- If the determinant D_γ of the matrix $[\gamma_{ij}]$ is nonzero, then we may replace the s columns $N_i(x)$ with the s columns $N_i'(x)$ to obtain a new versal unfolding

$$V'(x,\beta) = f(x) + \sum_{i=1}^{s} \beta_i N_i'(x) + \sum_{i=s+1}^{q} \beta_i N_i(x) \quad . \tag{8.83}$$

We call the process outlined above a <u>simple alteration</u> of a versal unfolding. Any linear versal unfolding of f(x) with q control parameters may be transformed into any other linear versal unfolding of f(x) with q control parameters by carrying out a finite sequence of simple alterations. In fact, the final versal unfolding may be obtained with one simple alteration involving all the columns of N(x). Unfortunately, experience with three low-order models indicates that finding the new unfolding in one step is impractical (Shirer and Wells, 1983). In a few cases, a simple alteration is accomplished with s = 1, an alteration we refer to as a <u>minimal alteration</u>. In the illustration below using the Lorenz model, minimal alterations suffice. More generally, however, several consecutive nonminimal alterations (s > 1) are necessary (see Chapters 4 and 5 of Shirer and Wells, 1983).

For the Lorenz model, the aim is to move β_2 from a product with x_2 to a product with x_1. Hence, we wish to eliminate the unfolding function

$$N_2 = \begin{bmatrix} 0 \\ x_2 \\ 0 \end{bmatrix} , \tag{8.84}$$

which appears on the right side of (8.81), and to replace it with

$$N_2' = \begin{bmatrix} 0 \\ x_1 \\ 0 \end{bmatrix} . \tag{8.85}$$

Therefore, we choose the function Y(x) to be the unfolding function N_2' we seek; that is we write

$$\begin{bmatrix} Y_1 \\ Y_2 \\ Y_3 \end{bmatrix} = \begin{bmatrix} 0 \\ x_1 \\ 0 \end{bmatrix} . \tag{8.86}$$

If (8.81) can be satisfied with this choice of Y(x) and with suitable choices for $G_i(x)$, $H_{ij}(x)$ and γ_i, then according to Mather's Theorem the column vectors may be switched as desired.

Via judicious guessing, we find that (8.81) holds if $\gamma_1 = G_1 = G_2 = G_3 = 0$, if the nonzero value for H_{ij} is $H_{21}(x) = -P^{-1}$, and if $\gamma_2 = 1$. Thus (8.81) becomes

$$\begin{bmatrix} 0 \\ x_1 \\ 0 \end{bmatrix} = \begin{bmatrix} 0 & 0 & 0 \\ -P^{-1} & 0 & 0 \\ 0 & 0 & 0 \end{bmatrix} \begin{bmatrix} -Px_1 + Px_2 \\ -x_1x_3 + x_1 - x_2 \\ x_1x_2 - bx_3 \end{bmatrix} + \begin{bmatrix} 0 \\ x_2 \\ 0 \end{bmatrix} . \tag{8.87}$$

From the conclusions of Mather's theory, we know that (8.73) may be replaced with the equivalent form

$$F_1 = -Px_1 + Px_2 \quad , \tag{8.88}$$

$$F_2 = -x_1x_3 + (\beta_2 + 1)\,x_1 - x_2 + \beta_1 \quad , \tag{8.89}$$

$$F_3 = x_1x_2 - bx_3 \quad . \tag{8.90}$$

Now, the parameter β_1 may be interpreted as a diabatic heating rate in (8.89). In addition, the parameter β_2 appears in the energy conversion term; it is proportional to the Rayleigh number r (actually $r = \beta_2 + 1$ so that $\beta_2 = \rho_1$ in (8.8)). The stationary solutions of a spectral model with either (8.73) or (8.88)-(8.90) as right sides are governed by a cusp surface (Fig. 8.3d).

Thus, we conclude that the external heating rate β_2 and the internal heating rate β_1 (that varies spatially in at least the horizontal) are independent effects. Both β_2 and β_1 are crucial parameters in (8.88)-(8.90) because their contributions to the branching solutions are manifested by different terms in the unfolding.

If we do not wish to interpret β_1 as a diabatic heating term, then we must find an alternative unfolding function for β_1. By comparing Fig. 8.3b with Figs. 8.3a and 8.3c, we see that β_1 serves to eliminate the trivial solution from the unfoldings. Thus, we suspect that adding an inhomogeneous term to either F_1 or F_3 would be a reasonable solution.

As a test of this hypothesis, we attempt to replace the unfolding function

$$N_1 = \begin{bmatrix} 0 \\ 1 \\ 0 \end{bmatrix} , \tag{8.91}$$

with

$$N_1' = \begin{bmatrix} 1 \\ 0 \\ 0 \end{bmatrix} , \tag{8.92}$$

in (8.88)-(8.90) by using the Transversality Condition. Suitable choices for $G_i(x)$, $H_{ij}(x)$ and γ_i imply that

$$\begin{bmatrix} 0 \\ 1 \\ 0 \end{bmatrix} = \begin{bmatrix} -P & P & 0 \\ 1-x_3 & -1 & -x_1 \\ x_2 & x_1 & -b \end{bmatrix} \begin{bmatrix} 1/3 \\ -2/3 \\ -x_2(3b)^{-1} \end{bmatrix} \tag{8.93}$$

$$+ \begin{bmatrix} 0 & 0 & 0 \\ 0 & 0 & -(3b)^{-1} \\ -2(3P)^{-1} & 0 & 0 \end{bmatrix} \begin{bmatrix} -Px_1+Px_2 \\ -x_1x_3+x_1-x_2 \\ x_1x_2-bx_3 \end{bmatrix} + P \begin{bmatrix} 1 \\ 0 \\ 0 \end{bmatrix} .$$

In (8.93), we interchanged the form of the Transversality Condition (for convenience) so that the solid column on the left could be replaced by the solid column on the right in (8.88)-(8.90).

Because (8.93) holds, we may rewrite (8.88)-(8.90) in the equivalent form

$$F_1 = -Px_1 + Px_2 + \beta_1 P \quad , \tag{8.94}$$

$$F_2 = -x_1 x_3 + (\beta_2 + 1)x_1 - x_2 \quad , \tag{8.95}$$

$$F_3 = x_1 x_2 - bx_3 \quad . \tag{8.96}$$

In this unfolding, β_1 has a different physical interpretation because it appears in an inhomogenous term in a momentum equation $\dot{x}_1$. Nevertheless, the stationary solutions in (8.94)-(8.96) are also governed by a cusp surface (Fig. 8.3d).

When $\beta_1 \neq 0$, we observe from (8.94)-(8.96) that x_1 cannot vanish. Because x_1 is a Fourier coefficient for the intensity of the fluid circulation, motion must occur even in the conductive case, if $\beta_1 \neq 0$. Since there is no acceleration in the steady case, we know from Jeffreys' Theorem (Dutton, 1976) that motion must occur whenever horizontal temperature gradients exist on a level surface. Thus we suspect that β_1 might be interpreted as an externally imposed horizontal temperature difference.

This conclusion is supported by the results of Yost and Shirer (1982), and Shirer and Wells (1982) who included an externally imposed horizontal temperature difference $\Delta_x T$ in their temperature expansion so that

$$T(x,z,t) = T_{oo} - \Delta_z T\left(\frac{z}{z_T}\right) + \Delta_x T\left(a\frac{x}{z_T}\right) \quad . \tag{8.97}$$

Using (8.97), they obtained a Boussinesq version of the momentum equation:

$$\frac{\partial}{\partial t^*}\tilde{\nabla}^2\psi^* = -J(\psi^*,\tilde{\nabla}^2\psi^*) + P(1+a^2)^{-1}\tilde{\nabla}^4\psi^* + P(1+a^2)\frac{\partial T^*}{\partial x^*} + P(1+a^2)\,Ha \quad . \tag{8.98}$$

We note that (8.98) contains an inhomogeneous term given by $P(1+a^2)Ha$; this term was not present in the previous momentum equation (2.34). In this term the dimensionless horizontal heating parameter is the Hadley number Ha, which is defined as

$$Ha = \frac{\Delta_x T}{\Delta_z T}\, r \quad . \tag{8.99}$$

Finally, the inhomogeneous term survives in the momentum equation of the Shirer and Wells (1982) model, which takes the form

$$\dot{x}_1 = - Px_1 + Px_2 - 8\sqrt{2}\ P\ Ha/\pi^2 \quad . \tag{8.100}$$

In Section 8.3.3, we give the complete Shirer and Wells (1982) model. After comparing (8.94) with (8.100), we might conclude that Ha and β_1 are related by

$$\beta_1 = - 8\sqrt{2}\ Ha/\pi^2 \quad . \tag{8.101}$$

Moreover, the system (8.94)-(8.96) is a better versal unfolding because we can accept each term in it on a physical basis. That is, each term in the unfolding follows directly from an appropriate term in the original partial differential equations.

Finally, it appears that shallow convection is properly viewed as being forced externally in both the horizontal and the vertical. Thus β_2 and β_1 represent independent physical effects in this interpretation. These results suggest that the Lorenz model is deficient because its stationary behavior can be described completely only when both r and Ha are present.

8.3.3 More complicated alterations of unfoldings. To acquire the unfolding (8.94)-(8.96), we determined a minimal alteration of the previous unfolding (8.88)-(8.90). Via the Transversality Condition, we replaced one column in the old unfolding with another column, to obtain the new unfolding. However, the alteration may not always be obtained in such a straightforward manner, as we illustrate next.

To obtain the spectral model discussed by Shirer and Wells (1982), whose model is a version of the Lorenz (1963) model, we consider the domain

$$0 \leq x^* \leq \pi \quad , \quad 0 \leq z^* \leq \pi \quad , \tag{8.102}$$

and the basis functions (2.78)-(2.79), or

$$\psi^*(x^*,z^*,t^*) = \sqrt{2}\ \ x_1 \sin x^* \sin z^* \quad , \tag{8.103}$$

$$T^*(x^*,z^*,t^*) = \sqrt{2}\ x_2 \cos x^* \sin z^* - x_3 \sin(2z^*) \quad . \tag{8.104}$$

These functions are the same ones used by Lorenz (1963). We substitute (8.103)-(8.104) into (8.98) and the thermodynamic equation

$$\frac{\partial T^*}{\partial t^*} = - J(\psi^*,T^*) + r \frac{\partial \psi^*}{\partial x^*} + Ha \frac{\partial \psi^*}{\partial z^*} + (1+a^2)^{-1} \tilde{\nabla}^2 T^* \quad , \tag{8.105}$$

and apply the Galerkin technique to obtain the Shirer and Wells (1982) model

$$\dot{x}_1 = - Px_1 + Px_2 - \underbrace{8\sqrt{2}\ P\ Ha/\pi^2}_{I} \quad , \tag{8.106}$$

$$\dot{x}_2 = - x_1 x_3 + rx_1 - x_2 \quad , \tag{8.107}$$

$$\dot{x}_3 = x_1 x_2 - bx_3 - \underbrace{\frac{16\sqrt{2}\ Ha}{3\pi^2} x_1}_{II} \quad . \tag{8.108}$$

Terms I and II, which did not appear in the original Lorenz (1963) model, arise from the modified basic state temperature expansion (8.97). After comparing (8.106)-(8.108) with the unfolding (8.94)-(8.96), we conclude that I is represented by $\beta_1 P$ in (8.94), but II is not present. It is important to remember, however, that (8.94)-(8.96) was obtained via a minimal alteration of the previous unfolding (8.88)-(8.90). We also recall that the Transversality Condition is essentially Taylor's Theorem with integral remainder. Hence, there is nothing to prevent us from replacing

$$N_1 = \begin{bmatrix} 0 \\ 1 \\ 0 \end{bmatrix} \quad , \tag{8.109}$$

in (8.88)-(8.90) with a column having more than one nonzero element, provided that the Transversality Condition still holds. In practice, changes of this type would be suggested by conversion of the modified partial differential equation into a low-order model. Here, the aim is to create an alteration that simultaneously accounts for both terms I and II in (8.106)-(8.108).

In fact, after applying the Transversality Condition, we find

$$\begin{bmatrix} 0 \\ 1 \\ 0 \end{bmatrix} = \begin{bmatrix} -P & P & 0 \\ 1-x_3 & -1 & -x_1 \\ x_2 & x_1 & -b \end{bmatrix} \begin{bmatrix} 1/9 \\ -8/9 \\ -x_2(9b)^{-1} \end{bmatrix} \tag{8.110}$$

$$+ \begin{bmatrix} 0 & 0 & 0 \\ 0 & 0 & -(9b)^{-1} \\ -2(9P)^{-1} & 0 & 0 \end{bmatrix} \begin{bmatrix} -Px_1 + Px_2 \\ -x_1x_3 + x_1 - x_2 \\ x_1x_2 - bx_3 \end{bmatrix} + \begin{bmatrix} P \\ 0 \\ \frac{2}{3}x_1 \end{bmatrix} .$$

Again, we replace the solid column on the left with the solid column on the right in (8.88)-(8.90). Finally the system may be written as

$$F_1 = -Px_1 + Px_2 + \beta_1 P \quad , \tag{8.111}$$

$$F_2 = -x_1x_3 + (\beta_2+1)x_1 - x_2 \quad , \tag{8.112}$$

$$F_3 = x_1x_2 - bx_3 + \frac{2}{3}\beta_1 x_1 \quad , \tag{8.113}$$

which is precisely the form of the right side of the Shirer and Wells (1982) model.

The unfolding (8.111)-(8.113) is the best yet because both crucial parameters β_1 and β_2 appear in the proper locations and they have the correct physical bases. It is fortuitous that the correct relationship between Ha and β_1 was obtained before term II of the Shirer and Wells (1982) model was included in (8.113); this result is not a general one. In more complicated situations, all of the appropriate terms may need to be present in the unfolding before such relationships can be deduced correctly.

8.3.4 Other applications of the unfolding technique. Shirer and Wells (1983) applied the theory discussed in this chapter to two other low-order models. For each unfolded physical system, they determined the number and type of crucial parameters necessary to unfold completely the stationary solutions. Their hypothesis was that these parameters represented a subset of the total number possible. Hence, with the proper subset they were one step closer to the goal of representing properly all of the transitions from laminar to turbulent flow in each low-order model.

In each unfolding, the original parameters and any new parameters that are necessary to complete the unfolding must be interpreted physically. But, the parameter locations in each unfolding must be obtainable via appropriate insertion of new terms into the original partial differential equations.

In Table 8.2 (from Shirer and Wells, 1982), the results for the unfolded versions of the Lorenz (1963) model of Rayleigh-Bénard convection, the Vickroy and Dutton (1979) model of quasi-geostrophic flow in a channel, and the Veronis (1966) model of rotating convection are presented. In each case, the original critical parameters and their physical effects are indicated. In addition, the highest order singularity, the number of parameters necessary in the unfolding, the parameters added, and their physical effects, are also specified for each case. We note that an error in Shirer and Wells (1982) concerning the interchangeability of two of the parameters in the unfolded Veronis model has been corrected in the table.

The Lorenz (1963) model, which we have discussed extensively, is a three-coefficient model whose stationary solutions are governed by a cubic polynomial equation. From Table 8.1, we might expect that the highest order singularity available would be a cusp point. Indeed, the cubic equation has three real-valued solutions, and so the bifurcation point is a cusp point. Moreover, we may use directly the local contact catastrophe procedure discussed in this chapter to determine the number and types of crucial parameters and their locations without first modifying the initial model.

But what about a low-order model that is not initially as general as possible? For example, the Vickroy and Dutton (1979) model is a three-coefficient model that has a governing quintic polynomial equation for the stationary solutions. Thus, from Table 8.1, we might expect that the highest order singularity would be a butterfly point. However, we find that this model has as many as five stationary solutions, but has no butterfly points. In fact, the highest order singularity is a cusp point (Shirer and Wells, 1983), and the Newtonian heating coefficients H_1 and H_2 are the only required unfolding parameters.

In such a situation, we cannot use the local contact catastrophe procedure to find a possible butterfly point because such a point is not present in the original model. Rather, we must return to the original system and deduce (mostly by physical

Table 8.2 Unfolded Physical Systems (from Shirer and Wells, 1982).

Physical System	Spectral Model (governing polynomial)	Original Critical Parameters	Original Physical Effects	Singularity Type	Number of Parameters in Unfolding	New Parameters in Unfolding	New Physical Effects
Rayleigh-Bénard Convection	Lorenz (1963) (cubic)	Rayleigh number Ra	Vertical heating rate	Cusp	2	Hadley number Ha	Horizontal heating rate
Quasi-Geostrophic Flow	Vickroy and Dutton (1979) (quintic)	H_1 H_2	Components of Newtonian heating rate at smallest and middle wavenumbers.	Butterfly	4	H_3	Component of Newtonian heating rate at largest wavenumber.
						$\|U\|$ or h_o	Magnitude of zonal flow or Amplitude of bottom topography.
Rotating Convection	Veronis (1966) (quintic)	Rayleigh number Ra	Vertical heating rate	Butterfly	4	Hadley number Ha or Tilt angle ε	Horizontal heating rate or Inclination of domain with respect to gravity
		Coriolis parameter f	Rotation rate			Q	Diabatic heating rate

intuition) those parameters that, once added to the model, might lead to a butterfly point. In the Vickroy and Dutton (1979) model, we find that adding the heating component H_1 and either a mean latitudinally varying horizontal wind profile or a varying terrain height produces a butterfly point that is far from the previously obtained cusp point (see Table 8.2). Therefore, to obtain the highest order singularity in this case, we require a more general model. This application represents a global use of the contact catastrophe method.

In the discussion above, we found that the Lorenz (1963) model had the correct initial structure, but that the Vickroy and Dutton (1979) model had a physically unsuitable structure and required modification. It is easy to imagine a low-order model whose structure is more complex than either of these models. Hence, when unfolding such a complicated model, we must be aware of the fact that either type of situation described above could arise. Moreover, in the corank one case, the order of the governing polynomial equation places a limit on the maximum codimension q of the singularity (see Table 8.1).

CHAPTER 9

HIERARCHIES OF TRANSITIONS: SECONDARY BRANCHING

PAUL A. HIRSCHBERG

To construct a truncated spectral model, first we must select a set of expansion functions. Applying the Galerkin technique outlined in Chapter 3, we obtain the particular associated system of ordinary differential equations. If we wish to extend this model to a larger one, then we must enlarge the set of expansion functions. But this selection of a second set of functions cannot be performed in an ad hoc manner, for Modeling Principle Seven leads us to require that the structure of the solutions to the smaller model be preserved in the larger. In this chapter we illustrate how to evaluate a larger model of classical Rayleigh-Bénard convection by considering an extension of the the three-coefficient model of Lorenz (1963) to the seven-coefficient model of Chang and Shirer (1984).

To obtain a plausible extension of the simple Lorenz model, we recall that it contains only one stream function component to describe the developing nonlinear flow. This stream function component is characterized by the single wavenumbers m in the horizontal and n=1 in the vertical. These components are the ones first seen in convective cells that develop once the Rayleigh number Ra exceeds its critical value Ra_c. As noted by Malkus and Veronis (1958), the convective planforms deduced from the linear and nonlinear problems are the same in the case of slightly supercritical convection (see also Chapter 2).

In the Lorenz model, the wavelengths of the flow must remain at the one first excited as the value of Ra is changed. However, in laboratory experiments (Krishnamurti, 1970a; Busse and Whitehead, 1971; Willis et al., 1972), in numerical simulations (Deardorff and Willis, 1965; Lipps and Somerville, 1971), and in the atmosphere (Atlas et al., 1983), the horizontal wavelengths of shallow convective cells are observed to increase as the value of Ra increases. In order to represent this phenomenon of cell broadening, we must include more spectral components for the stream function. Because the first-developing primary solution has only wavenumber m, changes in the dominant wavelength of the flow can occur only via an exchange of stability from the primary to a secondary solution that involves components of the flow having other wavenumbers.

Thus, we need a physical mechanism by which energy can be transferred from components having one wavenumber to components having different wavenumbers. It is representation of this mechanism that leads us to a plausible extension of the Lorenz model. As noted by Clever and Busse (1974) and by Dutton (1976, Chapter 11), this process of energy transfer involves terms originating from $\underset{\sim}{v}\cdot\nabla\underset{\sim}{v}$ in the equation of motion (2.10) or $J(\psi,\nabla^2\psi)$ in the vorticity equation (2.17). To include such nonlinear terms, we saw in Section 3.3 that the correct combination of three wavenumbers must be included in order that selection rules such as (3.60) can be satisfied.

A low-order model designed with the above concerns in mind was developed by Chang and Shirer (1984) to study the changes of wavenumber in two-dimensional Rayleigh-Bénard convection. Their model, based on one introduced by Saltzman (1962) and reviewed in detail in this chapter, is capable of representing all the nonlinear terms in the original partial differential equations (2.25)-(2.26). As anticipated above, we find that increases in the wavelengths of the cells can occur and are associated with secondary transitions between primary branches that each represent simple cells of different horizontal wavelengths. Because the model is cast in general form, it can be interpreted as being a family of low-order models. Under this interpretation, repeated applications of the model lead to a consistent hierarchy of transitions that otherwise could be obtained only by study of a much larger model. Physically, this sequence of bifurcations continues the process of cell broadening into Rayleigh number ranges well beyond that near the critical Rayleigh number. First, however, we argue using some general results of Bauer et al. (1975) that such hierarchies of secondary branching are fundamental to Rayleigh-Bénard convection.

9.1 Diagnosing Possible Secondary Branching

Perhaps surprisingly, it is sometimes possible to deduce, using an analysis of the stability of the trivial solution to the partial differential equations, whether secondary transitions might occur. Already we have seen that primary branches emanate from bifurcation points on the conductive solution, and we have noted in Chapter 2 that a suitably designed low-order model is able to represent accurately both the location of these points and the general character of their branching solutions. But how are we able to infer, from an analysis of the trivial solution, the existence of secondary solutions bifurcating from the primary ones?

We begin by recalling that a stability analysis of the partial differential equations (2.25)-(2.26) for Rayleigh-Bénard convection shows that a convective solution of horizontal wavenumber m bifurcates from the conductive solution at the value of the critical Rayleigh number Ra_c given by

$$Ra_c = (m^2a^2+1)^3/(m^2a^2) \quad . \tag{9.1}$$

It is important to realize that this expression actually represents an infinite number of critical Rayleigh numbers--for a fixed domain aspect ratio $a = 2z_T/L$, we obtain a bifurcation point for each value of m. For example, when $a = \sqrt{2}/6$, we obtain $Ra_c = 6.75$ when m = 3 and $Ra_c \cong 8.22$ when m = 2; emanating from each point we expect to find a supercritically branching solution. The bifurcation diagrams for these primary branches are shown in Fig. 9.1a,b and the corresponding stream function patterns are given in Fig. 9.2a,c. The solution labeled P_3 in Fig. 9.1a clearly yields a wavenumber-three pattern in Fig. 9.2a; similarly, P_2 yields a wavenumber-two pattern in Fig. 9.2c. Either solution is obtained separately from the Lorenz model by simply varying the value of m in (2.73)-(2.77). In this sense, then, the Lorenz model is actually a family of models representing the entire collection of primary convective branches. But, because the Lorenz model is only able to represent flows having a single horizontal wavenumber m, we can model only one convective solution at a time. Consequently, as shown in Fig. 9.1, the solution appears to be stable relative to perturbations having the same wavenumber. For each solution in Fig. 9.1, λ_m denotes the characteristic exponent that vanishes at the corresponding critical Rayleigh number Ra_m. Of course, each exponent has a value relative to the conductive solution that is different from what it has relative to the convective solution. However, the two exponents have the same limit of zero at $Ra = Ra_m$, and so the notation promotes a convenient analysis of how stability is lost or gained.

Now let us suppose that we have a larger spectral model, one that contains the spectral components for at least two wavenumbers, m and j. We require that it produce both critical Rayleigh numbers Ra_m and Ra_j for the two expected primary

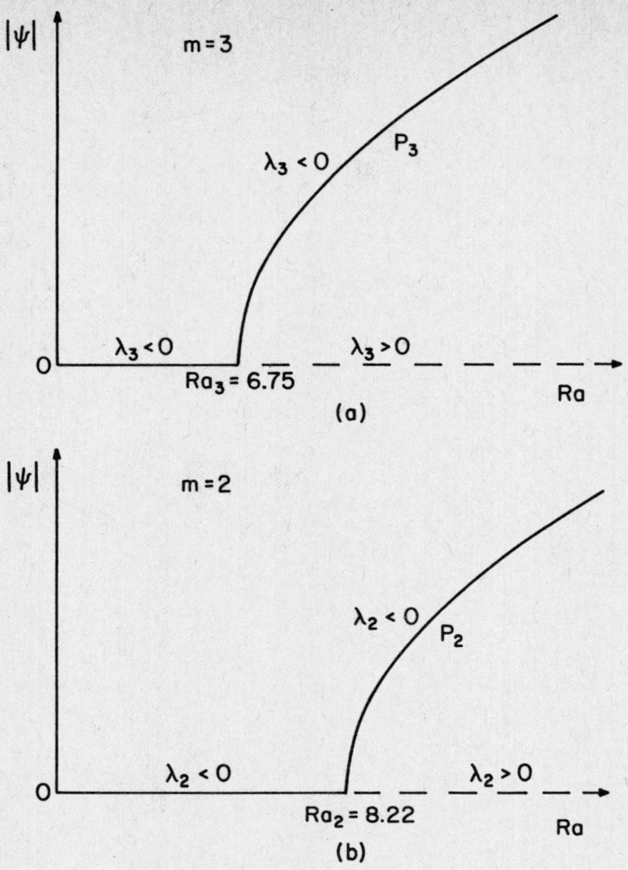

Fig. 9.1 Schematic bifurcation and stability diagrams illustrating the primary convective solutions P_m for the two wavenumbers m=3 (a) and m=2 (b). The magnitudes of the stationary solutions are plotted as functions of Ra. Stable solutions are denoted by solid lines, unstable solutions by dashed lines. In both diagrams, $a=\sqrt{2}/6$.

branches representing cells of wavenumbers m and j, respectively (Fig. 9.2a,c). These two bifurcation points on the conductive solution to the spectral model are

$$Ra_m = \frac{(m^2a^2+1)^3}{m^2a^2} , \quad (9.2)$$

$$Ra_j = \frac{(j^2a^2+1)^3}{j^2a^2} . \quad (9.3)$$

For systems of ordinary differential equations, Bauer et al. (1975) noted that a signal for the existence of secondary branches is that two or more primary bifurcation points attain the same value. A double value of the bifurcation points

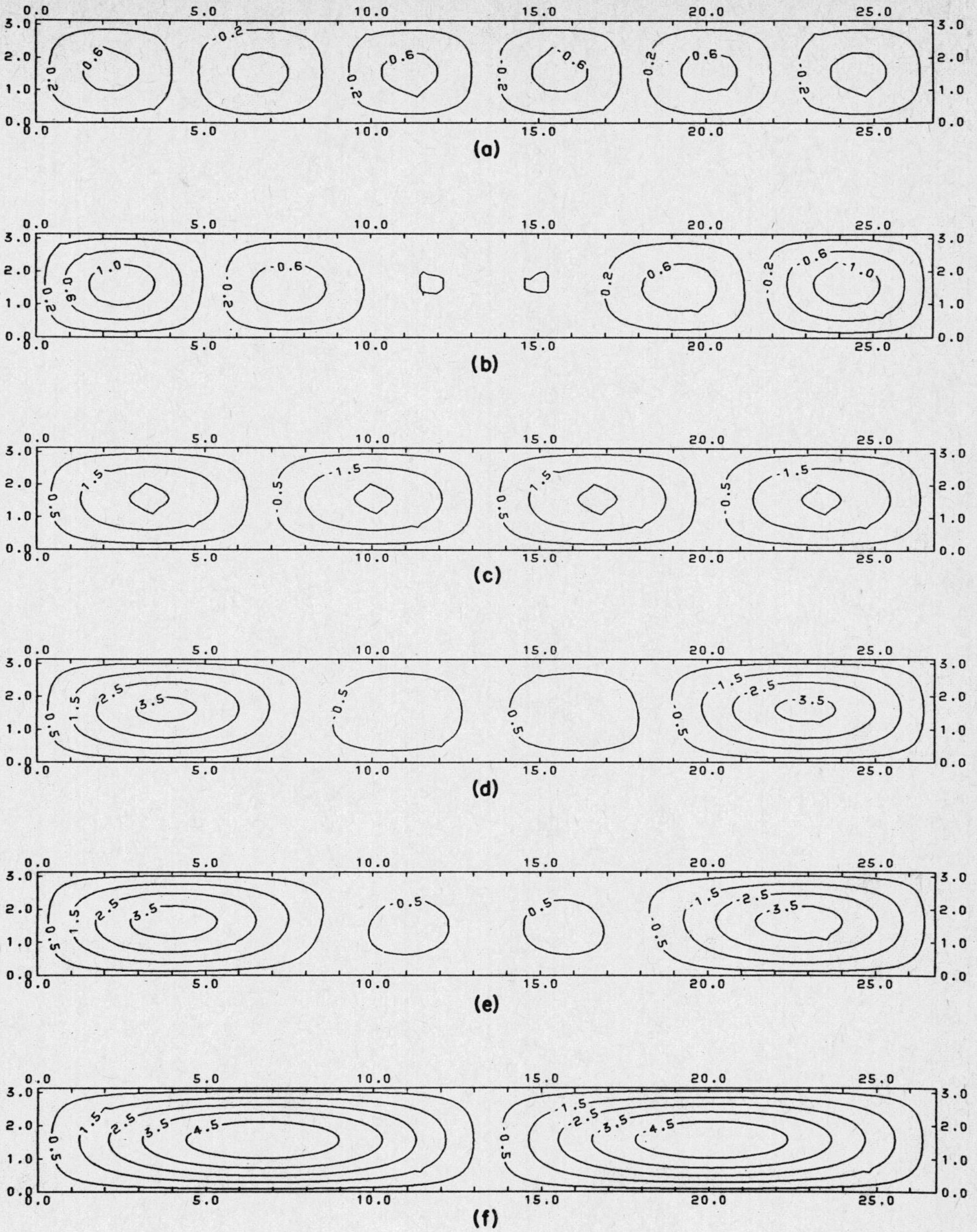

Fig. 9.2 Stream function diagram for some stationary solutions to the Chang and Shirer model. Here $a=\sqrt{2}/6$, P=0.1 and Ra=6.9 (a), Ra=7.5 (b), Ra=9.5 (c), Ra=12 (d), Ra=14 (e), and Ra=25 (f). Clearly, as the value of Ra increases, the wavelengths of the cells increase (from Chang and Shirer, 1984).

can occur here, but no triple values are possible (see Fig. 7.1); thus the highest multiplicity of the bifurcation point is two. A double value is obtained when $Ra_m = Ra_j$ or when the domain aspect ratio $a = a_{mj} = a_{jm}$ is given by (see Fig. 7.1)

$$a_{mj}^2 = \frac{m^{2/3} - j^{2/3}}{j^{2/3}m^2 - m^{2/3}j^2} \quad . \tag{9.4}$$

Note that the right side of (9.4) remains unchanged when m and j are interchanged, and so $a_{mj} = a_{jm}$. Some solutions to (9.4) are given in Table 9.1.

For example, if $a \cong 0.2874$, then two modes (m = 3, j = 2) appear simultaneously when the value of Ra is increased past the critical value, $Ra_c \cong 7.1275$. If we look at the bifurcation and stability diagram for this case, then we find that the two primary convective solutions (m = 3 and j = 2) emanate from the same point (Fig. 9.3). The fact that one solution is stable while the other is unstable follows immediately from the fact that the index I(Ra) of the system is conserved (see Section 5.4). If we base the calculation of the degree of a stable solution on the signs of only the controlling exponents λ_2 and λ_3, then we have $d(\underset{\sim}{y}^s, Ra) = \mathrm{sgn}(\lambda_2\lambda_3)$. Clearly, then, the degree of a stable solution is 1, that of an unstable solution having one positive exponent is -1, and that of an unstable solution having two positive exponents is 1. Thus, when $Ra < Ra_c$ and the conductive solution is unique

Table 9.1 Values of $a=a_{mj}=a_{jm}$ and Ra_c when $Ra_m=Ra_j$.

m	j	$a_{mj}=a_{jm}$	Ra_c
5	4	0.1579	6.8627
4	3	0.2037	6.9381
3	2	0.2874	7.1275
5	3	0.1813	7.3563
2	1	0.4934	7.8969
4	2	0.2467	7.8969
5	2	0.2185	8.8446
3	1	0.3951	9.8994
4	1	0.3358	12.2204
5	1	0.2952	14.7430

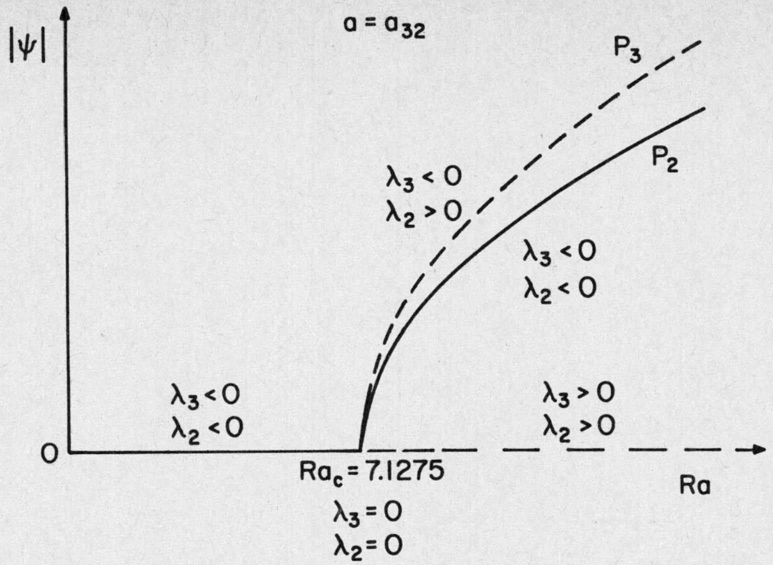

Fig. 9.3 Schematic bifurcation and stability diagram illustrating the case when two solutions having different wavenumbers m=3 and j=2 bifurcate from the conductive solution at the same value of Ra_c. The magnitudes of the stationary solutions are plotted as functions of Ra. Here $a=a_{32}\cong 0.2874$. Stable and unstable solutions are denoted by solid and dashed lines, respectively. The fact that P_2 is stable but P_3 is unstable determines the possible behavior of the connecting secondary branches (cf. Fig. 9.4).

and globally stable, we have that I(Ra) = d(0,Ra) = 1. If both primary branches P_2 and P_3 were stable, then we would sum the degrees of the three solutions to obtain I(Ra) = 3 when Ra > Ra_c, an occurrence that is impossible. Only the case of one stable and one unstable solution yields the required value I(Ra) = 1 when Ra > Ra_c. However, the choice of P_3 as unstable and P_2 as stable is not a result general to all models, but is restricted to the convective case studied below. Of note here is that the rule discussed in Section 5.3 that supercritical branching is correlated with stable bifurcating solutions works only when the bifurcation point is single-valued.

The hypothetical example discussed above is theoretically sound, but constructing a vessel having an aspect ratio $a = a_{mj}$ would prove to be practically impossible. However, we can imagine a vessel having dimensions for which the aspect ratio a is near a critical value, a_{mj}, and then we can seek the expected transitional behavior within the fluid. To develop the likely picture, first we suppose that the bifurcation diagram for the case $a = a_{mj}$ is the same as that given in Fig. 9.3, with P_m being the unstable solution and P_j being the stable one. Next we suppose that the value of a is varied slightly from that of a_{mj} so that the bifurcation points are no longer double.

To see how the bifurcation diagram might change, we consider the case $a < a_{mj}$ for which the branch P_m bifurcates first at $Ra_m < Ra_j$. Then for values of Ra greater than, but still very near, that of Ra_m, we expect that the single supercritical branch P_m would be stable. In contrast, for values of $Ra \gg Ra_m$, we would not expect that P_m would be stable. The only way to reconcile these two observations is to conclude that a secondary bifurcation point Ra_{mj} must have appeared on P_m at a value of Ra very near that of Ra_m (see Fig. 9.4a). Furthermore, as the value of a approaches that of a_{mj}, the bifurcation points Ra_{mj} and Ra_m coalesce. Thus, we conclude that perturbing a system in such a way that a double primary bifurcation point splits into two individual ones might lead to the emergence of a secondary bifurcation point that would travel up the primary branch as the magnitude of the perturbation increases (Bauer et al., 1975). Similarly, P_j cannot be stable for values of Ra greater than, but very near to, that of Ra_j, but is nevertheless stable for values of $Ra \gg Ra_j$. Therefore, we conclude that there must be a secondary bifurcation point Ra_{jm} on P_j that emerges from Ra_j.

Branching from each secondary bifurcation point we expect to find a secondary solution, and the simplest possiblity is for a single branch S_{mj} to link P_m and P_j (Fig. 9.4a). In this case, as the value of Ra increases, stability is transferred from one solution P_m having a dominant wavenumber m to another P_j having a smaller wavenumber j through a state S_{mj} necessarily involving both wavenumbers m and j. As noted by Bauer et al. (1975), we see that the existence of double primary points, an occurrence having zero probability, signals that secondary branching might occur in the nearby case of single primary bifurcation points, an occurrence having nonzero probability.

But as also noted by Bauer et al. (1975), secondary points need not emerge as the primary bifurcation points separate. Again under the assumption that when $a = a_{mj}$ the branch P_m is unstable and the branch P_j is stable, we consider the case $a > a_{mj}$. Then the supercritical branch P_j bifurcates first at $Ra_j < Ra_m$ and so P_j is

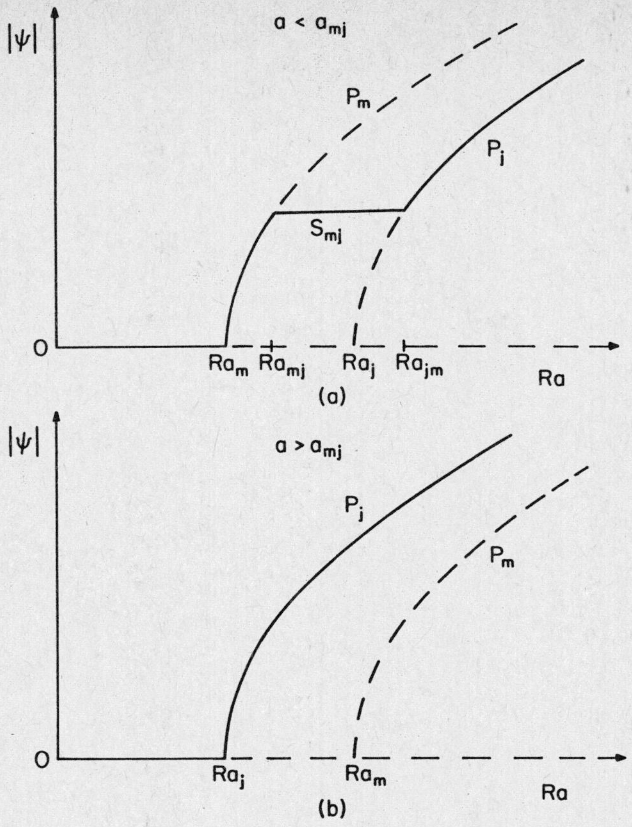

Fig. 9.4 Schematic bifurcation and stability diagram illustrating the branching behavior for values of a near its critical aspect ratio a_{mj}. The magnitudes of the stationary solutions are plotted as functions of Ra. Here P_m is the primary solution for wavenumber m, P_j is the primary solution for wavenumber j, Ra_m and Ra_j are the primary bifurcation points, Ra_{mj} and Ra_{jm} are the secondary bifurcation points, and S_{mj} is the connecting secondary solution. Stable and unstable solutions are denoted by solid and dashed lines, respectively. In (a), $a<a_{mj}$, P_m branches first and transfers stability to P_j via a secondary branch S_{mj}; in (b), $a>a_{mj}$, P_j branches first and no connecting secondary branch is possible.

expected to be stable. However, P_j already is stable in the limiting case $a = a_{mj}$, and so the emergence of a single secondary bifurcation point from the double primary bifurcation point cannot occur if we are to find the expected stability behavior. Also, the unstable branch P_m would remain unstable and no secondary bifurcation point would be expected on P_m. Consequently, we arrive at the bifurcation diagram given in Fig. 9.4b, in which no connecting secondary branch exists to transfer stability from a solution dominated by one wavenumber to a solution dominated by another one. From the above arguments, we see that the association between the sign of the difference $(a-a_{mj})$ and the existence of connecting secondary branches derives entirely from the fact that only one of the two branches P_m and P_j can be stable when they branch simultaneously from a double primary bifurcation point (Fig. 9.3). In Section 9.2.2, we reverse the argument to deduce what alternative branching diagram would need to exist when $a = a_{mj}$ if connecting secondary solutions appear in both the cases $a < a_{mj}$ and $a > a_{mj}$.

As we find in the next section, the above branching behavior occurs in a seven-component low-order model of classical Rayleigh-Bénard convection. Moreover, the existence of secondary branching for only the case $a < a_{mj}$ leads to a simple explanation of the observed lateral expansion of the cells as the value of Ra is increased.

9.2 The Chang and Shirer Model

Chang and Shirer (1984) extended the Lorenz model to simulate wavenumber interactions within the flow. Via the nonlinear term $J(\psi^*,\tilde{\nabla}^2\psi^*)$ in the vorticity equation, these interactions cause transfers of energy between wavenumbers. From the discussion in Section 9.1, this is the expected role that secondary branching plays in the development of the flow. Chang and Shirer found that to represent adequately the Jacobian term in the vorticity equation, a seven-coefficient spectral expansion is necessary. Their model follows that of Saltzman (1962), who used three harmonics in the stream function ψ^*, and four harmonics in the perturbation temperature field T^*. Using the dimensionless forms of Chapter 2, we express their expansions as

$$\psi^*(x^*,z^*,t^*) = \psi_{m1}(t^*)\sin(mx^*)\sin z^* + \psi_{j1}(t^*)\sin(jx^*)\sin z^* + \psi_{(m-j)2}(t^*)\sin[(m-j)x^*]\sin(2z^*) \quad , \tag{9.5}$$

$$T^*(x^*,z^*,t^*) = T_{m1}(t^*)\cos(mx^*)\sin z^* + T_{j1}(t^*)\cos(jx^*)\sin z^* + T_{(m-j)2}(t^*)\cos[(m-j)x^*]\sin(2z^*) + T_{02}(t^*)\sin(2z^*) \quad . \tag{9.6}$$

In these expressions, m and j are integral horizontal wavenumbers. As we see below, the six components, aside from the T_{02} term, represent the interacting triads that accomplish the exchange of stability from a solution having wavenumber m to one having wavenumber j via the catalytic (m-j,2) terms. The equations of the model are found by first substituting the expressions for ψ^* and T^* into the vorticity and thermodynamic equations (2.25)-(2.26) and then reducing the system to a set of seven ordinary differential equations using the Galerkin technique (see Chapter 3):

$$\dot{\psi}_{m1} = \zeta_{mj}\psi_{j1}\psi_{(m-j)2}/(4\sigma_{m1}) + PmT_{m1}/\sigma_{m1} - P\sigma_{m1}\psi_{m1}/a \quad , \tag{9.7}$$

$$\dot{\psi}_{j1} = -\zeta_{jm}\psi_{m1}\psi_{(m-j)2}/(4\sigma_{j1}) + PjT_{j1}/\sigma_{j1} - P\sigma_{j1}\psi_{j1}/a \quad , \tag{9.8}$$

$$\dot{\psi}_{(m-j)2} = -(m-j)\sigma_{m+j,0}\,\psi_{m1}\psi_{j1}/(4\sigma_{m-j,2}) + P(m-j)T_{(m-j)2}/\sigma_{m-j,2} - P\sigma_{m-j,2}\,\psi_{(m-j)2}/a \quad , \tag{9.9}$$

$$\dot{T}_{m1} = (m+j)[\psi_{j1}T_{(m-j)2} - \psi_{(m-j)2}T_{j1}]/4 + m\psi_{m1}T_{02} + m\,Ra\,\psi_{m1} - \sigma_{m1}T_{m1}/a \quad , \tag{9.10}$$

$$\dot{T}_{j1} = (m+j)[\psi_{m1}T_{(m-j)2} + \psi_{(m-j)2}T_{m1}]/4 + j\psi_{j1}T_{02} + j\,Ra\,\psi_{j1} - \sigma_{j1}T_{j1}/a \quad , \tag{9.11}$$

$$\dot{T}_{(m-j)2} = -(m+j)[\psi_{m1}T_{j1} + \psi_{j1}T_{m1}]/4 + (m-j)\,Ra\,\psi_{(m-j)2} - \sigma_{m-j,2}T_{(m-j)2}/a \quad , \tag{9.12}$$

$$\dot{T}_{02} = -(m\psi_{m1}T_{m1} + j\psi_{j1}T_{j1})/2 - 4\,T_{02}/a \quad , \tag{9.13}$$

in which

$$\sigma_{kn} = k^2a^2 + n^2 \quad , \tag{9.14}$$

and

$$\zeta_{kn} = (k+n)(\sigma_{k-n,2} - \sigma_{n1}) \quad . \tag{9.15}$$

The stationary solutions of this system include two primary branches P_m and P_j of the Lorenz type,

$$P_m = (\psi^s_{m1},0,0,T^s_{m1},0,0,T^s_{02}) \quad , \tag{9.16}$$

and

$$P_j = (0,\psi^s_{j1},0,0,T^s_{j1},0,T^s_{02}) \quad , \tag{9.17}$$

as well as secondary solutions S_{mj} involving the catalytic terms $\psi_{(m-j)2}$ and $T_{(m-j)2}$.

To see how stability is exchanged between the solutions, we must perform a linear analysis. We begin by considering the trivial solution for which all seven spectral components vanish. Following Chapter 4, we obtain a 7×7 determinant, the vanishing of which produces a seventh-degree polynomial equation in the characteristic exponent λ. This equation factors into

$$[\lambda^2\sigma_{m1} + \lambda(\frac{P+1}{a})\sigma^2_{m1} + m^2P(Ra_m-Ra)]\ [\lambda^2\sigma_{j1} + \lambda(\frac{P+1}{a})\sigma^2_{j1} + j^2P(Ra_j-Ra)]$$

$$\times\ [\lambda^2\sigma_{m-j,2} + \lambda(\frac{P+1}{a})\sigma^2_{m-j,2} + P\ \sigma^3_{m-j,2}/a^2 - (m-j)^2P\ Ra]\ [\lambda + 4/a] = 0 \quad , \tag{9.18}$$

in which Ra_m and Ra_j are given in (9.2) and (9.3). Each of the three quadratic factors has the form (2.62), and so all seven exponents are real. Now if the values of m and j are chosen so that $Ra_m < Ra_j < \sigma^3_{m-j,2}/[(m-j)^2a^2]$, then we have the following results: When $Ra < Ra_m$, there are seven negative exponents and the trivial solution is stable; when $Ra_m < Ra < Ra_j$, then there is one positive exponent λ_m and six negative ones, and the trivial solution is unstable; finally, when $Ra > Ra_j$ there are two positive exponents λ_m and λ_j. (The case $m = 3$ and $j = 2$ is illustrated in Fig. 9.5 below.) A third exponent may become positive when $Ra > \sigma^3_{m-j,2}/[(m-j)^2a^2]$, but this value of Ra is beyond the range of applicability of the model (cf. Fig. 7.1b). From these results, we conclude that the two bifurcation points Ra_m and Ra_j are represented, as required.

9.2.1 The goal form. We now develop a picture for the branching behavior of the convective solutions. Emanating from the bifurcation points Ra_m and Ra_j we find primary branches P_m and P_j (9.16) and (9.17). Each branch has the form (2.100)-(2.102); for example, the P_m branch obeys

$$\psi^s_{m1} = \pm \sqrt{8}\,(Ra-Ra_m)^{1/2}/\sigma_{m1} \quad , \tag{9.19}$$

$$T^s_{m1} = \pm \sqrt{8}\,\sigma_{m1}\,(Ra-Ra_m)^{1/2}/(ma) \quad , \tag{9.20}$$

$$T^s_{02} = -\,(Ra-Ra_m) \quad . \tag{9.21}$$

We may calculate the stability of this solution as we did in Section 4.2.2. Upon setting

$$\psi_{m1}(t^*) = \psi^s_{m1} + \psi'_{m1}(t^*) \quad , \tag{9.22}$$

$$\psi_{j1}(t^*) = \psi'_{j1}(t^*) \quad , \tag{9.23}$$

$$\psi_{(m-j)2}(t^*) = \psi'_{(m-j)2}(t^*) \quad , \tag{9.24}$$

$$T_{m1}(t^*) = T^s_{m1} + T'_{m1}(t^*) \quad , \tag{9.25}$$

$$T_{j1}(t^*) = T'_{j1}(t^*) \quad , \tag{9.26}$$

$$T_{(m-j)2}(t^*) = T'_{(m-j)2}(t^*) \quad , \tag{9.27}$$

$$T_{02}(t^*) = T^s_{02} + T'_{02}(t^*) \quad , \tag{9.28}$$

and substituting these forms into (9.7)-(9.13), we neglect all products of the perturbations. After assuming solutions of the form $\hat{B}\exp[\lambda t^*]$ for the primed variables in the resulting linear system, we arrive at the following determinant:

$$
\begin{array}{ccc:cccc}
\hat{\psi}_{m1} & \hat{T}_{m1} & \hat{T}_{02} & \hat{\psi}_{j1} & \hat{\psi}_{(m-j)2} & \hat{T}_{j1} & \hat{T}_{(m-j)2} \\
\end{array}
$$

$$
\left|\begin{array}{ccc:cccc}
\frac{-P\sigma_{m1}}{a}-\lambda & \frac{Pm}{\sigma_{m1}} & 0 & 0 & 0 & 0 & 0 \\
mRa_m & \frac{-\sigma_{m1}}{a}-\lambda & m\psi^s_{m1} & 0 & 0 & 0 & 0 \\
-mT^s_{m1} & -m\psi^s_{m1} & \frac{-4}{a}-\lambda & 0 & 0 & 0 & 0 \\
\hdashline
0 & 0 & 0 & \frac{-P\sigma_{j1}}{a}-\lambda & \frac{-\zeta_{jm}}{4\sigma_{j1}}\psi^s_{m1} & \frac{Pj}{\sigma_{j1}} & 0 \\
0 & 0 & 0 & \frac{-(m-j)\sigma_{m+j,0}\psi^s_{m1}}{4\sigma_{m-j,2}} & \frac{-P\sigma_{m-j,2}}{a}-\lambda & 0 & \frac{P(m-j)}{\sigma_{m-j,2}} \\
0 & 0 & 0 & j\ Ra_m & \frac{(m+j)T^s_{m1}}{4} & \frac{-\sigma_{j1}}{a}-\lambda & \frac{(m+j)\psi^s_{m1}}{4} \\
0 & 0 & 0 & \frac{-(m+j)T^s_{m1}}{4} & (m-j)Ra & \frac{-(m+j)\psi^s_{m1}}{4} & \frac{-\sigma_{m-j,2}}{a}-\lambda
\end{array}\right| = 0. \qquad (9.29)
$$

Although the above way of writing this 7 × 7 determinant may at first seem unnatural, we see now that it can be written as a product of 3 × 3 and 4 × 4 determinants. Moreover, the 3 × 3 determinant is the one we would obtain if we were analyzing the Lorenz model alone--only coefficients of the amplitudes of the primary branch P_m are involved. Thus, all the bifurcation points of the Lorenz model are represented in the Chang and Shirer model, and the properties of the smaller model carry over to the larger one. Consequently, the Chang and Shirer model satisfies the crucial requirement embodied in Modeling Principle Seven, leading us to conclude that it is a suitable extension of the Lorenz model.

New bifurcation points are introduced by the vanishing of the 4 × 4 determinant, which represents the effects of perturbations having the horizontal wavenumbers j and m-j. Some of the elements of the 4 × 4 determinant, specifically those depending on ψ^s_{m1} in the first two rows, originate from the $J(\psi^*,\tilde{\nabla}^2\psi^*)$ term in (2.25) and so might be expected to produce secondary branching that represents cell broadening. Indeed, the 4 × 4 determinant vanishes if the Rayleigh number satisfies a quadratic equation (given in Chang and Shirer, 1984), so that no more than two secondary bifurcation points on P_m are possible. Normally, only one bifurcation point, denoted by Ra_{mj}, exists on P_m, and so one secondary branch S_{mj} emanates from P_m at Ra_{mj}. Such secondary branches owe their existence to spectral components having wavenumbers other than m, and in general we must be careful to choose basis functions capable of capturing these important branches. Moreover, we noted in Section 9.1 that secondary bifurcation points often arise from double primary bifurcation points. It is easy to show that $Ra_{mj} \to Ra_m$ as $a \to a_{mj}$, and so we indeed find that the secondary points appear in the expected manner.

A similar calculation of the stability of the P_j branch yields no more than two secondary bifurcation points Ra_{jm} at which the secondary branch S_{mj} meets P_j. Again, the expected behavior $Ra_{jm} \to Ra_j$ as $a \to a_{mj}$ occurs. As shown in Chang and Shirer (1984), this secondary branch can be obtained analytically by setting the right sides of (9.7)-(9.13) to zero and then reducing the resulting seven nonlinear equations to a single one. The calculation is quite tedious and is not shown here; details of it can be found in Chang (1983).

An example for which m = 3 and j = 2 is shown schematically in Fig. 9.5, which shows that S_{32} connects P_3 and P_2 and hence effects a transfer of stability from P_3 to P_2. Because of the form of the solutions in the bifurcation diagram, we say that the branching behavior has a <u>goal form</u>. This name is suggested by the resemblance between the form of the primary branches and the goalposts of, and the form of the connecting branch and the crossbar of, the goal used in American football. In Fig. 9.5 we show the magnitude $|\psi|=[\psi_{m1}^2+\psi_{j1}^2+\psi_{(m-j)2}^2]^{1/2}$ and so the contributions of the individual components of ψ are not apparent. An inspection of Fig. 9.6 reveals that ψ_{m1} is the only active component when $Ra_3 < Ra < Ra_{32}$, all three are active when $Ra_{32} < Ra < Ra_{23}$, and finally only ψ_{j1} is nonzero when $Ra_{23} < Ra$. It is clear from Fig. 9.6c that the mechanism for stability transfer from P_3 to P_2 is provided by the catalytic term $\psi_{(m-j)2}$ whose role is to excite ψ_{j1} at the expense of ψ_{m1} (Figs. 9.6a,b). In Fig. 9.2a-c we show the stream function contours during the transitional process illustrated in Figs. 9.5 and 9.6--in Fig. 9.2a we show P_3, in Fig. 9.2b, S_{32}

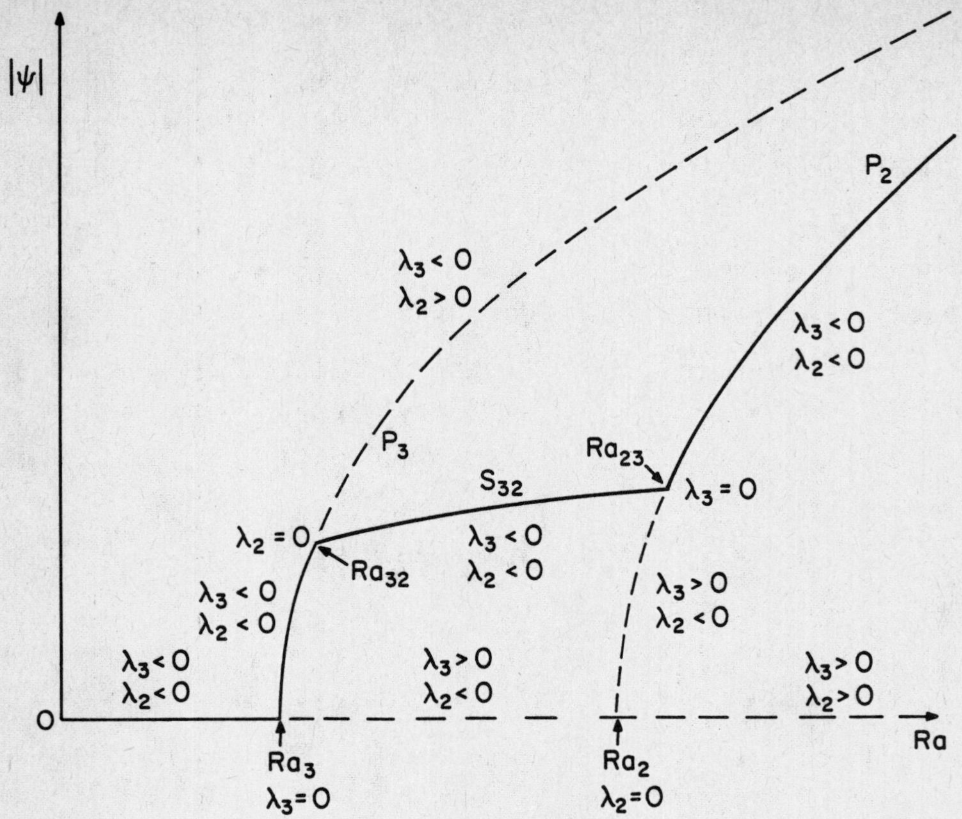

Fig. 9.5 Schematic bifurcation and stability diagram for the Chang and Shirer model with wavenumbers m=3 and j=2. The magnitudes of the stationary solutions are plotted as functions of Ra. Here Ra_{32} and Ra_{23} represent secondary bifurcation points, and Ra_3 and Ra_2 represent primary bifurcation points. Characteristic exponents associated with wavenumbers m and j on any solution branch P_m, P_j or S_{mj} are denoted by λ_m and λ_j, respectively. Stable and unstable solutions are labeled with solid and dashed lines, respectively. Here $P \sim 0.1$ and $a=0.2357 < a_{32} \cong 0.2874$ (cf. Fig. 9.4).

and in Fig. 9.2c, P_2. Thus, although we found in Section 7.1.3 that the most unstable wave is always m = 3 when Ra > Ra_{23} (cf. Fig. 7.5), we instead find that the wave j = 2 is the only one remaining in the nonlinear solution. This result agrees with those of Saltzman (1962) and van Delden (1984), who note that solutions dominated by a linearly unexpected wavenumber (which here is j = 2) appear in some nonlinear solutions to low-order models of Rayleigh-Bénard convection.

To see how the P_2 branch gains stability in the range Ra > Ra_{23}, we find it

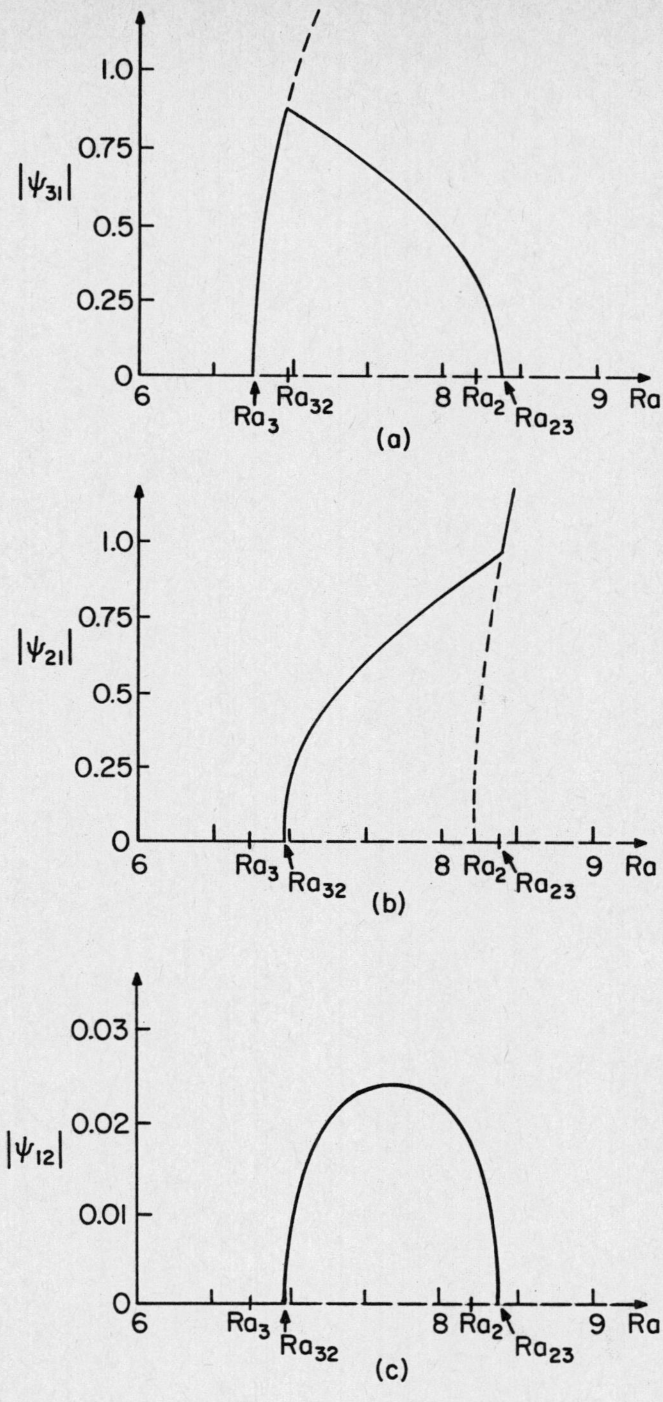

Fig. 9.6 Magnitudes of the individual stream function components as functions of Ra for the case given in Fig. 9.5. In (a) $|\Psi_{31}|$ is shown, in (b) $|\Psi_{21}|$ and in (c) $|\Psi_{12}|$. The components of the stable and unstable solutions are depicted by solid and dashed lines, respectively.

instructive to follow the exponents λ_3 and λ_2 of the conductive or convective solutions; these exponents must vanish at $Ra = Ra_3$ and $Ra = Ra_2$, respectively. We do not consider the other five exponents because they always have negative real parts and so do not affect the stability results. Whether we follow the upper path $0 \to P_3 \to S_{32} \to P_2$ or the lower path $0 \to P_2$, we must arrive at the conclusion that $\lambda_3 < 0$ and $\lambda_2 < 0$ on P_2 when $Ra > Ra_{23}$. This exercise of exponent tracing is a good way to check the consistency of the results, as we saw in Section 7.2.5 when we explored the applicability of minimizing the values of Ra at the regular turning points in the Veronis model of rotating Rayleigh-Bénard convection.

Not surprisingly, a consistent branching form is found in the Chang and Shirer model when $P \sim 0.1$. Such a small value of P is chosen because, as noted by Clever and Busse (1978), this is the value of P for which cell broadening is a predominantly two-dimensional process. From Fig. 9.5 we see that the conductive solution is stable in the range $0 < Ra < Ra_3$; that is, both exponents λ_3 and λ_2 are negative. At $Ra = Ra_3$, we find bifurcation to the primary branch P_3, and so λ_3 vanishes and λ_2 is negative. Beyond Ra_3, λ_3 is positive and the conductive solution is unstable, but at the point $Ra = Ra_2$, λ_2 is zero. If it were not for the positive λ_3 exponent, then the primary branch P_2 would be stable at supercritical values of Ra_2. Upon following P_2, we see that λ_3 vanishes at $Ra = Ra_{23}$. Beyond this point on P_2, both λ_3 and λ_2 are negative and the solution is stable.

This same result is obtained if we proceed along the conductive solution to P_3 and then to P_2 via the secondary solution, S_{32}. At Ra_{32}, λ_2 is zero, and for values of $Ra > Ra_{32}$, P_3 is unstable because $\lambda_2 > 0$. Both exponents are less than zero on the secondary solution, and thus it is stable. Once more, λ_3 vanishes at Ra_{23}. Relative to P_2, for $Ra < Ra_{23}$, λ_3 is positive and for $Ra > Ra_{23}$, λ_3 is negative. Hence, P_2 is found to be stable in the range $Ra > Ra_{23}$ <u>independent of the path taken to reach it</u>.

As we have seen, then, exponent tracing can be a powerful means for correct deduction of the typical branching picture. With this approach, we are able to verify the consistency of the branching diagram in Fig. 9.5, which is an example of the one in Fig. 9.4a.

<u>9.2.2 Further comments on secondary branching</u>. As noted at the end of Section

9.1, the above secondary branching results for $a < a_{32}$, together with the observation that connecting secondary branches cannot occur when $a > a_{32}$, depend on the plausible assumption that the branching diagram in Fig. 9.3 is correct: that is, that P_3 is unstable and P_2 is stable when $a = a_{32}$. Now we investigate whether there exists a different branching configuration in the case $a = a_{32}$ that is consistent with the appearance of goal forms in both the cases $a < a_{32}$ and $a > a_{32}$. Thus, we assume that goal forms occur when $a < a_{32}$ and $a > a_{32}$, leading to the situations depicted in Figs. 9.7a,b. Then we consider what must happen as $a \to a_{32}$ and the two secondary branches approach the Ra-axis and disappear at $a = a_{32}$. As we approach this limiting case, we find that λ_3 for the P_2 branch must be nonpositive when a approaches a_{32} from below (Fig. 9.7c), but must be nonnegative when a approaches a_{32} from above (Fig. 9.7d). When $a = a_{32}$ the only way both conditions can be satisfied is that $\lambda_3 = 0$ for P_2 (Fig. 9.7e). Similarly, we deduce that $\lambda_2 = 0$ for P_3 when $a = a_{32}$. Although these are conceivable conclusions, they lead to the requirement that two exponents must remain zero for all values of $Ra > Ra_c$, and this is an extremely atypical, or nongeneric, situation. Moreover, the system depicted in Fig. 9.7e does not have a form allowing verification that the index I(Ra) of the system is conserved, for the degrees of P_3 and P_2 are undefined. Hence, both forms in Figs. 9.7a and 9.7b cannot occur because they lead to an unlikely limiting case in Fig. 9.7e. Because Fig. 9.7a is correct, it follows that Fig. 9.7b is incorrect. Thus, as in Section 9.1, we conclude that the asymmetry of the secondary branching behavior for a near a_{mj} is the typical result; that is, we obtain a goal form only when $a < a_{mj}$.

However, when $a > a_{32}$, some unusual branching possibilities are found in the Chang and Shirer (1984) model for various values of the Prandtl number P; an example is shown in Fig. 9.8 for the case $a = 0.2924$. When $P = P_s \cong 0.3215$, a double secondary bifurcation point appears on the P_m branch at $Ra \cong 8.92$. For $P < P_s$, there is no secondary branching; but for $P > P_s$, the double point separates into two secondary bifurcation points, and an unstable secondary branch connects the two points (Fig. 9.8a). Via exponent tracing, we conclude that this secondary branch causes the portion of the primary branch P_3 between the two secondary bifurcation points to be stable. Moreover, as the value of P increases, the bifurcation

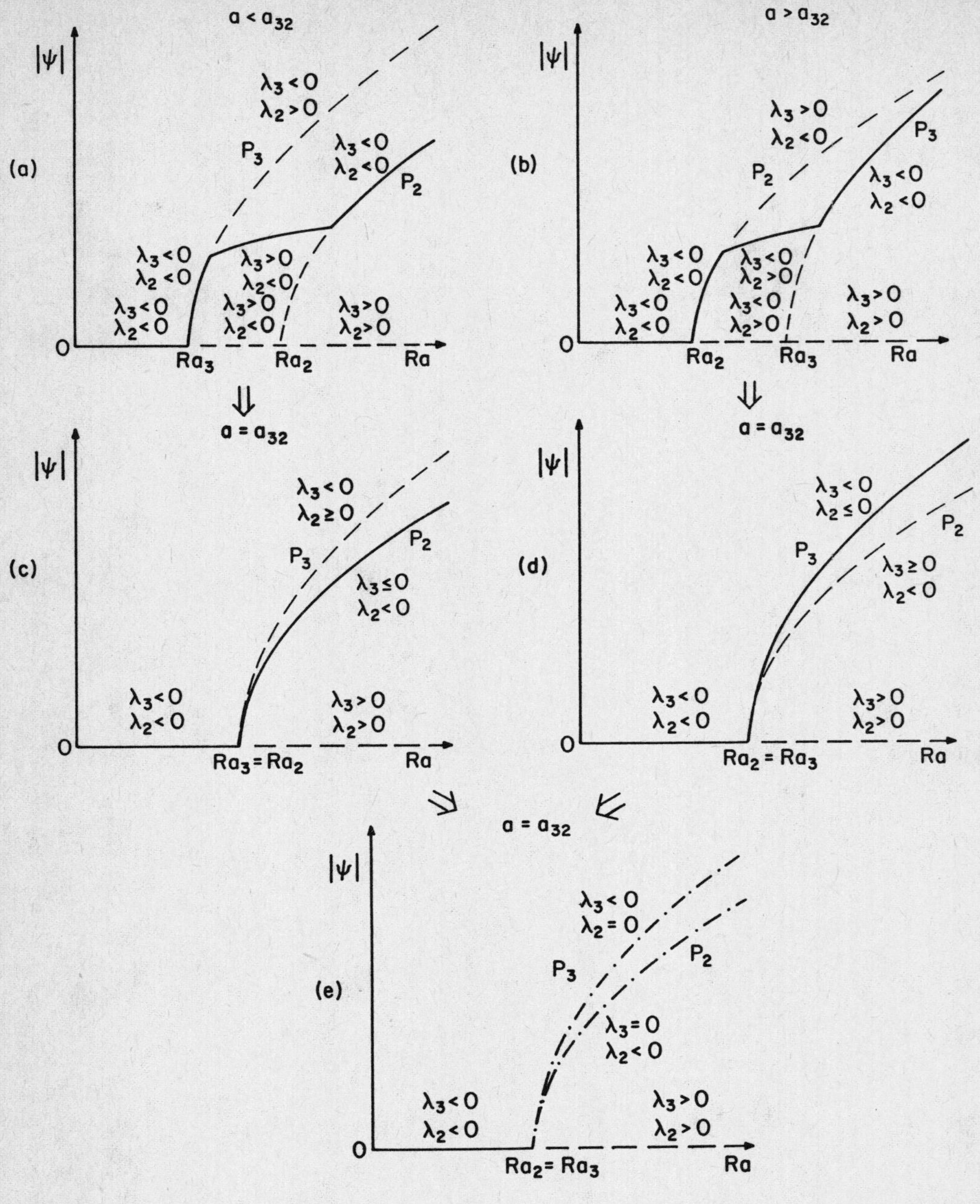

Fig. 9.7 Stability properties of primary branches P_2 and P_3 in the case that both goal forms in (a) and (b) are correct. As the value of a approaches that of a_{32}, the values of the characteristic exponents λ_2 and λ_3 are constrained as shown: the behavior in (c) follows from that in (a) and the behavior in (d) follows from that in (b). The only result consistent with both (c) and (d) is that given in (e). However, this last form is an unlikely one, thereby forcing the conclusion that only one of the diagrams in (a) and (b) is valid.

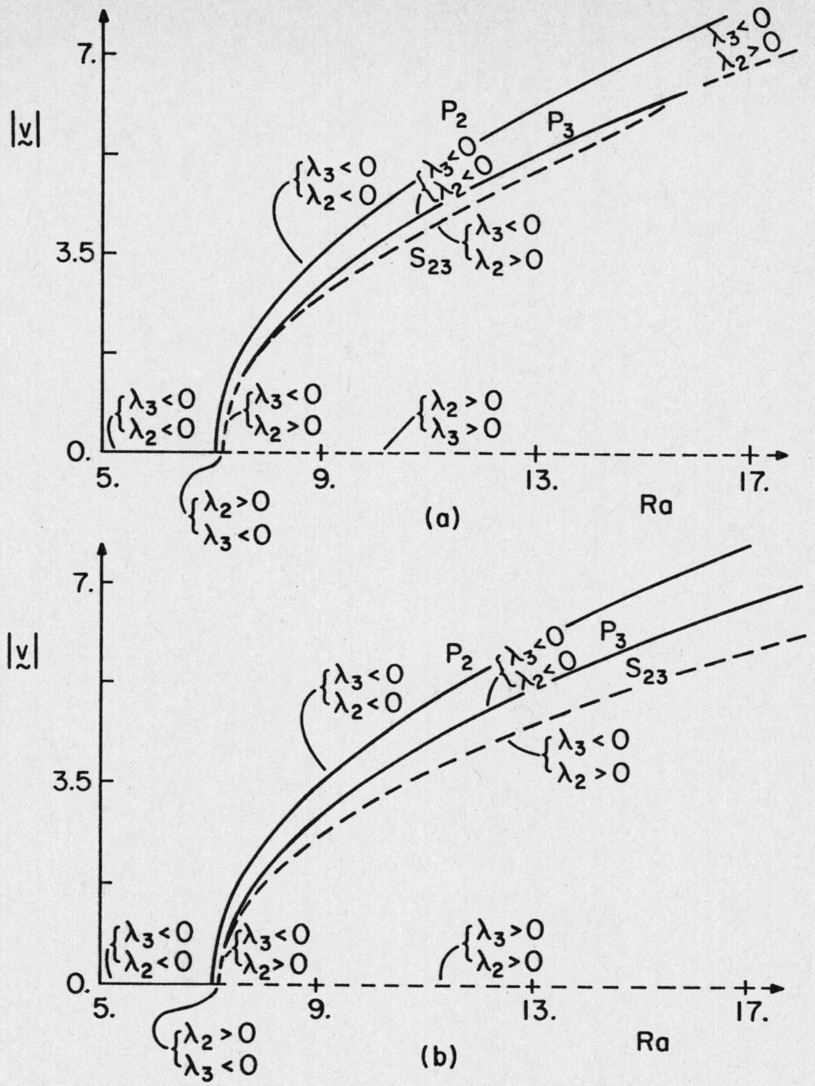

Fig. 9.8 Bifurcation and stability diagrams for the Chang and Shirer model when $a>a_{32}$; here $a=0.2924$ and $a_{32}\cong0.2874$. In (a) $P=0.36>P_s\cong0.3215$ and P_3 is stable for only a small portion; in (b) $P=5.0>P_\infty\cong4.7$ and P_3 is stable for most of its length. Here stable solutions are denoted by solid lines, unstable ones by dashed lines, and $|\underset{\sim}{v}|^2 = \sigma_{m1}^2\psi_{m1}^2 + \sigma_{j1}^2\psi_{j1}^2 + \sigma_{m-j,2}^2\psi_{(m-j)2}^2$.

point having the larger value moves along the P_3 branch until it becomes infinitely large at $P = P_\infty \cong 4.7$. When $P > P_\infty$, we have that the primary branch P_3 is stable for most of its length, because the first secondary point Ra_{23} approaches a value of approximately 7.33 that is very close to that of approximately 7.20 for Ra_3

(Fig. 9.8b). Thus, we find that both primary branches can be stable, even though stability is not exchanged from one to the other via a connecting secondary branch! A similar situation is found as well in the case $a < a_{32}$. For large values of P, the secondary branch disconnects from P_3, leading to two stable primary branches similar to those shown in Fig. 9.8b.

9.2.3 Ordering of bifurcation points and cell broadening. We saw in Section 9.1 that secondary branching is signaled by the existence of double primary bifurcation points. In addition, we discovered from Table 9.1 that there are many values a_{mj} of the aspect ratio for which double points may occur and that no triple points exist. When a and a_{mj} are related in the proper way, we found that secondary branches S_{mj} connecting primary branches P_m and P_j are possible and that stability can be exchanged from one primary branch to another. A significant observation is that this behavior is not restricted to a particular model having specific values for the wavenumbers m and j, but is appropriate to an entire family of models. Using this point of view, we can exploit the required relationship between a and a_{mj} and the resulting asymmetry in the secondary branching to deduce that cell broadening must occur in Rayleigh-Bénard convection when $P \sim 0.1$.

Suppose we choose a domain that has a certain aspect ratio a. We found in Section 7.1.2 that, as the value of Ra is increased, the expected number m of waves in the convective solution that first appears is given by $\alpha^2 = m^2a^2 = 1/2$ and $Ra_m = 27/4$ (see Fig. 9.2a for the case m = 3). The stability of the resulting primary branch P_m can be ascertained from the vanishing of the 4 × 4 determinant in (9.29). We may locate all possible secondary bifurcation points on P_m by varying the value of j over all the integers. In this way, we find that only the choices $j < m$ produce physically admissible bifurcation points $Ra_{mj} > Ra_m$ on P_m. The origin of this result can be traced to the requirement that $a < a_{mj}$ for there to be secondary branching. For example, when $a = \sqrt{2}/6 \cong 0.2357$, we find that m = 3 and P_3 is the first branching solution; in this case the only choices for j yielding $a_{3j} > a$ are j = 1 and j = 2 (see Table 9.1). Thus, only secondary branches involving smaller wavenumbers than that of P_m are possible, and so only stability exchanges from cells of one wavelength to ones of longer wavelengths are possible. In agreement with the modeling results of van Delden (1984), we conclude that cell broadening is the only possibility produced by smooth transitions between solutions. Significantly, cell broadening is observed in laboratory experiments (e.g. Krishnamurti, 1970a), although it is often linked to growth of perturbations in the (third) dimension perpendicular to the roll axis (e.g. Willis et al., 1972).

In order to discover how cell broadening occurs in a particular example, we onsider in Fig. 9.9 the case in which P_3 is the first branch. We find that $Ra_{32} < Ra_{31}$ so that a stability exchange to P_2 via S_{32} is expected. Because P_2 is stable to perturbations of wavenumber 3 for $Ra > Ra_{23}$, any further branching will be related to other wavenumbers. By recognizing that the Chang and Shirer (1984) model represents a family of models, we use it again with m = 2 to extend the branching results to larger values of Ra. To be plausible, this extension must produce consistent branching results, as we discuss below. Here we see from Table 9.1 that when m = 2, the only value of j for which $a < a_{mj}$ is j = 1, and so we expect to find only one other bifurcation point Ra_{21} on P_2. We discover that $Ra_{21} > Ra_{23}$, and so we suppose that a stability exchange from P_2 to P_1 would occur, as shown in Fig. 9.9. The expected cell broadening from wavenumber 3 to 1 as the value of Ra is increased is illustrated in Fig. 9.2.

We arrived at Fig. 9.9 by applying the Chang and Shirer model twice--once for the combination (m,j) = (3,2) and next for (m,j) = (2,1). We must ask whether it is reasonable to expect that we may extend the applicability of the model in this way. One test of the above reasoning is to see whether solutions of the type given in Fig. 9.2 are found in a model having more degrees of freedom. This test was performed by Chang and Shirer (1984), who integrated a grid-point model having 31 points in the vertical and 41 points in the horizontal. After finding the Fourier coefficients of the solutions to the grid-point model, Chang and Shirer used the amplitudes of the coefficients to identify the dominant harmonics. They found that, in the case of the primary branches, the solutions to the spectral model were in good agreement with the numerical solutions to the grid-point model. The secondary branches however, were found to be somewhat different in the two models.

A second test of the reasoning is to see whether consistent stability results are obtained independent of the path chosen through the branching diagram. As before in Section 9.2.1, we perform this test by determining the signs of the three

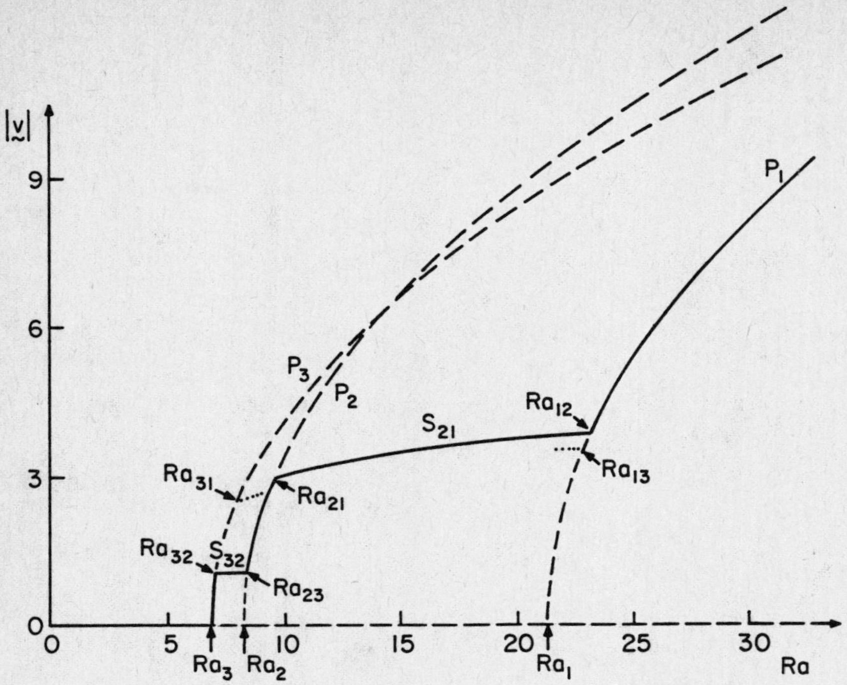

Fig. 9.9 Bifurcation and stability diagram obtained after two applications of the Chang and Shirer model. Three primary branches P_1, P_2, and P_3 and two secondary branches S_{32} and S_{21} are shown. Here, Ra_{mj} denotes a secondary bifurcation point and Ra_m denotes a primary bifurcation point. Stable solutions and ordinate are indicated as in Fig. 9.8a (after Chang and Shirer, 1984).

exponents λ_1, λ_2, and λ_3 that vanish at $Ra = Ra_1$, Ra_2, and Ra_3 on the conductive solution or that vanish at $Ra = Ra_{32}$, Ra_{31}, Ra_{23}, Ra_{21}, Ra_{13}, and Ra_{12} on the convective solution. The results are shown in Fig. 9.10. The arrows in this figure indicate the bifurcation points at which the exponents change sign (see Fig. 9.9). Between the bifurcation points, the signs of the exponents are given, and from this information, we are able to determine which exponent has changed sign at a particular bifurcation point. Finally, the solid lines represent the stable portions while the dashed lines represent the unstable portions of the branches.

If we proceed along the conductive solution, then we find three bifurcation points, each associated with a change in sign of λ_3, λ_2, and λ_1, respectively. The primary branch P_3 is the first one to bifurcate and this branch remains stable while the conductive state is no longer stable. Now P_3 is stable until the first critical

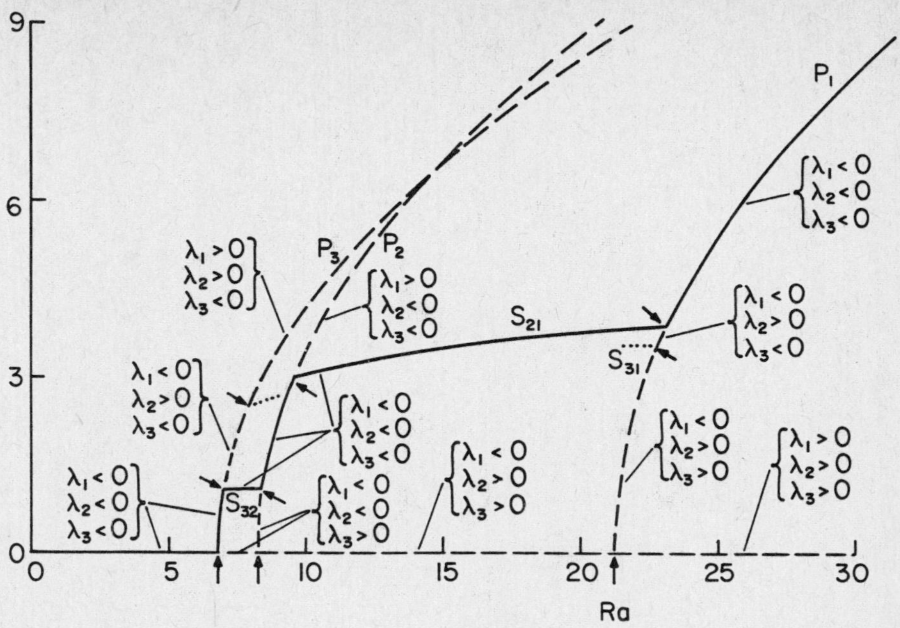

Fig. 9.10 Bifurcation and stability diagram showing the signs of the exponents near each bifurcation point for the case shown in Fig. 9.9. Here m denotes the wavenumber associated with the primary branch P_m, λ_m is the exponent associated with each wavenumber, and the arrows identify the bifurcation points. Stable solutions and ordinate indicated as in Fig. 9.8. The dots denote a portion of the (unstable) secondary branch S_{31} (after Chang and Shirer, 1984).

point on it is reached, at which λ_2 changes sign from negative to positive. Then stability is transferred to the second primary branch P_2 via a secondary branch. The primary branch P_2 becomes stable at the point where λ_3 becomes negative. We observe that if λ_1 had changed sign before λ_2, then there would have been a direct transfer from P_3 to P_1.

Repeating the above process, we see that P_2 is stable until we reach the next secondary bifurcation point along its path, where now λ_1 changes sign. Stability of P_2 is then lost and is exchanged with the third primary branch P_1 via a secondary branch. However, we note that P_1 is not stable at the first bifurcation point at which λ_3 changes sign but at the second at which λ_2 changes sign. This point is the one at which all the exponents become negative. This ordering, with λ_3 changing sign to negative followed by λ_2 changing sign, parallels in reverse order the sign changes of λ_3 and λ_2 along the trivial solution.

This ordering occurs generally for arbitrary choices of domain aspect ratio, as illustrated in Fig. 9.11. This figure is based on a domain aspect ratio $a = \sqrt{2}/18$ so that $m = 9$ is the first observed wavenumber and is the result of four applications $[(m,j) = (9,8); (8,7); (7,6); (6,4)]$ of the seven-component model. As in Fig. 9.10, the arrows mark the bifurcation points at which the appropriate exponents change sign.

To verify that the multiple branching picture in Fig. 9.11 is consistent, we investigate the last primary branch P_6. As we follow the conductive path, λ_9, λ_8, and λ_7 each become greater than zero before we finally reach the origin of P_6 at which $\lambda_6 = 0$. The primary branch P_6 is unstable there because $\lambda_7 > 0$, $\lambda_8 > 0$ and $\lambda_9 > 0$, and P_6 remains so until all the exponents become negative. This branch finally becomes stable when λ_7 changes sign because both λ_9 and λ_8 have previously changed sign at the two other bifurcation points on P_6. Oddly, λ_4 changes sign next, implying a transition from a solution having six waves to one having four waves. Thus we see that, although secondary branching always leads to a stable solution having a smaller wavenumber, some integers may be skipped in the process.

What is remarkable about the above behavior is that this consistent ordering of bifurcation points occurred on <u>all</u> primary branches in Fig. 9.11. Significantly, this ordering occurs in all other applications of the model as well, a result that indicates that the modeling approach is sound.

From the above discussion, we can speculate about the likely form of the branching behavior in the partial differential system. Because the value of domain aspect ratio a is not physically meaningful but the value of cell aspect ratio $\alpha = ma$ is, we should find that the solutions P_3 and P_2 in Fig. 9.9 correspond to P_9 and P_6 in Fig. 9.11. That is, we should discover that the wavelength ℓ of the cells corresponding to P_9 and P_3 are the same. Indeed, the wavelengths are $\ell = 2\sqrt{2}\, z_T$ in both cases. Similarly, $\ell = 3\sqrt{2}\, z_T$ for the cells associated with both P_6 and P_2. However, the number of secondary bifurcations involved in the cell broadening process increases as we decrease the domain aspect ratio a because more waves can fit into the domain. Three secondary branches occur between $Ra = 6.75$ and $Ra = 8.5$ in Fig.

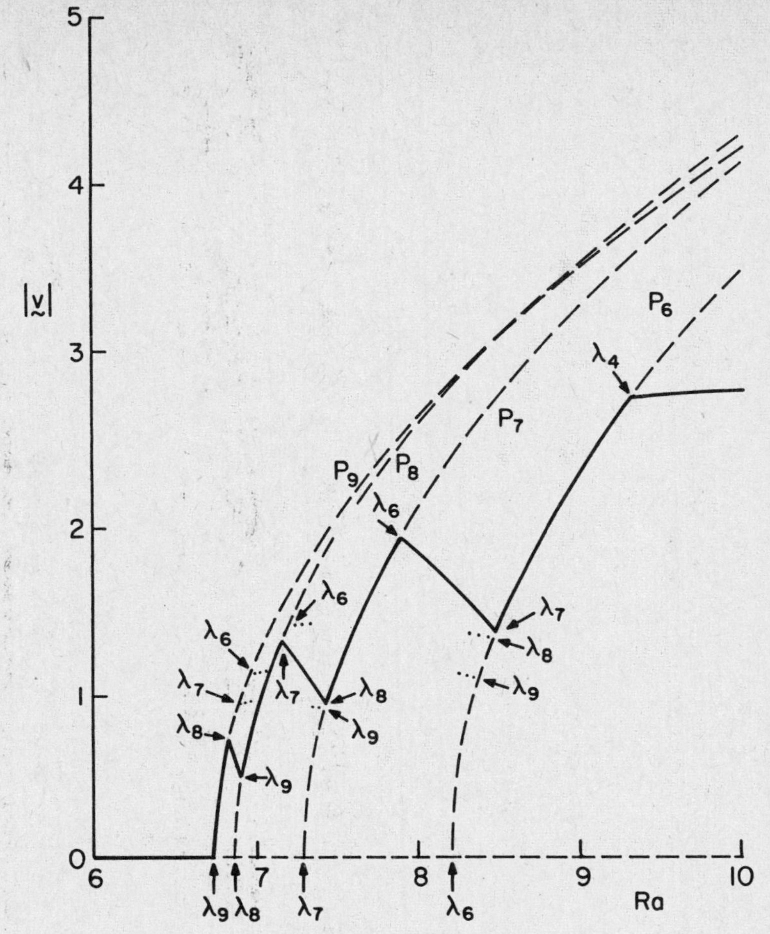

Fig. 9.11 Bifurcation and stability diagram showing which exponent λ_m changes sign at each bifurcation point, in the case for which the solution m=9 branches first. The labeling conventions follow those used in Figs. 9.8 and 9.10 (after Chang and Shirer, 1984).

9.11, but only one occurs in this range of Ra in Fig. 9.9. We may infer that as the first observed value of m increases, the number of secondary branches increases. Hence, the cell broadening process would approach a continuous one beginning at $\ell = 2\sqrt{2}\, z_T$ and would proceed until a transition to a three-dimensional solution would occur. Although use of a low-order system has discretized the representation of the process, we have nevertheless obtained an excellent model of it. A similar approach using variables for the wavenumbers presumably could be employed to model the transitions from two- to three-dimensional flows, and is a topic for future reseach.

At least for steady, two-dimensional Rayleigh-Bénard convection, the seven-component model of Saltzman (1962) or Chang and Shirer (1984) appears to provide the fundamental branching form upon which models of more complicated transitions can be built. As we have seen in this chapter, the origin of this form is traced to the fact that secondary branching is signaled by the occurrence of double primary bifurcation points on the conductive solution to the original partial differential equations.

By basing a general low-order model on a fundamental form, like the one discussed in this chapter, we in fact create a generic family of models. When studied as a whole, this family allows extension of the results into a much larger range of Rayleigh numbers than originally might have been expected. In this way, repeated study of a simple system of ordinary differential equations allows the development of a branching picture that otherwise could be obtained only from tedious investigation of a much larger model. Of course, the key to development of a suitable family of low-order models is to identify the basic branching form. Certainly the demonstration that a form is basic ultimately must be founded on an analysis of the properties of the original partial differential system. Unfortunately, this task is a very difficult one, but as noted in Section 4.3, some progress is being made through the comparison of attractors in both the partial differential equations and suitable Galerkin approximates of them (e.g., Temam, 1983; Constantin et al., 1985; Wells and Dutton, 1986).

CHAPTER 10

ALEXANDER-YORKE CONTINUATION: NUMERICALLY FINDING <u>ALL</u> THE STATIONARY SOLUTIONS IN A SPECTRAL MODEL

RONALD GELARO

Nonlinear truncated spectral models of the type we study usually exhibit multiple stationary solutions. As we have shown in previous chapters, much can be learned about the nonlinear properties of a model by studying these solutions. Moreover, it has been demonstrated elsewhere (e.g., Vickroy and Dutton, 1979) that understanding stationary behavior is useful in studying the asymptotic properties of the temporal solutions to a spectral model. Stationary solutions of spectral models are obtained by solving the limited set of quadratic equations obtained when the temporal derivatives are set to zero. In simple models such as those of Lorenz (1963) or Vickroy and Dutton (1979), the roots can be found algebraically. In higher order models, with ten or more degrees of freedom, recourse to numerical methods is usually required.

A standard procedure used to obtain the stationary solutions to a spectral model involves the Lyapunov-Schmidt Splitting Procedure with which we can express all the spectral components in terms of a single component and then use these expressions to form a polynomial equation in one variable (see Section 8.1); for example, the stationary solutions of the Lorenz model are governed by a cubic equation. The real roots of this polynomial equation are the stationary solutions to the system, and the values of the remaining spectral components are readily obtainable by substituting these roots back into the previous expressions. However, the success and practicality of this technique depend on many factors such as the number of components in the model, as well as the forms of the nonlinear terms. Consequently, in some cases, reducing the system to a single polynomial equation may be difficult, or even impossible, without altering the original truncation.

An alternative procedure is to compute the stationary solutions directly, that is, to obtain the solutions to the algebraic system, with little or no reduction in the original number of equations. These solutions can be found numerically via Alexander-Yorke Continuation (AYC) (Alexander and Yorke, 1978). AYC is an iterative method for finding the roots of an algebraic system by integrating a set of differential equations that we derive from the original algebraic set. As we demonstrate in this chapter, the use of AYC eventually may make it possible to compute all the stationary solutions in a spectral model, including those aphysical ones that may not be revealed in a single polynomial equation.

10.1 Theory and Development

AYC is a method for approximating all the complex solutions to an equation $F(x) = 0$, where the polynomial map $F(x)$ is defined by

$$F(x) = [F_1(x_1, \ldots, x_n), \ldots, F_n(x_1, \ldots, x_n)] \quad , \tag{10.1}$$

in which $F_1(x_1, \ldots, x_n), \ldots, F_n(x_1, \ldots, x_n)$ are independent polynomial functions. The basic idea of AYC is to obtain the solutions x of $F(x) = 0$ by integrating, until some time t, a system of differential equations derived from the original map (10.1). While AYC can be applied generally to systems of equations of any degree, we restrict the discussion here to cases in which (10.1) contains terms of no higher degree than quadratic. This, of course, is the case of interest from a hydrodynamic point of view, and derives from the fact that the nonlinear advective terms in the Navier-Stokes equations, and consequently in the spectral models we study, are second-degree. Thus, we consider the case in which the functions $F_n(x)$ in (10.1) have degree two or less.

10.1.1 Preliminary description. Before we develop the AYC method, we observe the following points concerning the development and presentation here:

1. To describe how AYC works, we need to define some additional polynomial maps that, in addition to the original map (10.1), are used to determine the correct set of differential equations.
2. The successful implementation of AYC requires the use of complex variables. The reasons for this are discussed later in the chapter.
3. Keeping the above in mind, we discuss most of the theory in real variables for conceptual and graphical convenience. We utilize complex variables when they become absolutely necessary.

The first step in describing the method is to introduce an auxiliary polynomial map $S_t(x;y,Z)$ parameterized by t, y and Z. This map is defined by setting

$$S_t(x;y,Z) = \begin{bmatrix} x_1^2 - y_1^2 \\ \cdot \\ \cdot \\ \cdot \\ x_n^2 - y_n^2 \end{bmatrix} + tx_1^2 Z_1 + \cdots + tx_n^2 Z_n \quad , \tag{10.2}$$

in which $y = (y_1, \ldots, y_n)^T$ is an n-vector and

$$Z = \begin{bmatrix} z_{11} & \cdots & z_{1n} \\ & \cdot & \\ & \cdot & \\ & \cdot & \\ z_{n1} & \cdots & z_{nn} \end{bmatrix} \quad , \tag{10.3}$$

is an $n \times n$ matrix with columns $Z_1, \ldots, Z_n$. For now, it suffices to say that the the matrix Z is included to ensure that the system remains general, or generic. For example, it ensures that trajectories in complex n-space do not intersect; such an event has probability zero in a general system. However, it is important to note in (10.2) that, at $t = 0$, the equation $S_0(x;y,Z) = 0$ becomes

$$S_0(x;y,Z) = \begin{bmatrix} x_1^2 - y_1^2 \\ \cdot \\ \cdot \\ \cdot \\ x_n^2 - y_n^2 \end{bmatrix} = 0 \quad , \tag{10.4}$$

which implies that the solutions x of (10.4) are the members of the set we call

$$\text{Zeros}(y) = \{x \mid x_i = \pm\, y_i,\ i = 1, \ldots, n\} \quad . \tag{10.5}$$

Thus, we expect there to be 2^n complex solutions x, and this is verified by Bezout's Theorem (Walker, 1950), which we discuss in the following subsection.

The next step in the development of AYC requires the use of the original polynomial map $F(x)$ and the auxiliary map $S_t(x;y,Z)$ to construct a new map $F_t(x)$, which we define as

$$F_t(x) = (1 - t)\, S_t(x;y,Z) + t\, F(x) \quad . \tag{10.6}$$

Note that at $t = 1$, we have $F_t(x) = F(x)$. Thus, the roots x of $F_t(x) = 0$ at $t = 1$ are the roots x of the original system $F(x) = 0$. From (10.6), we begin to see how the AYC method proceeds. If we know the roots of $F_t(x) = 0$ for various values of t, then we might be able to evolve, or integrate, (10.6) up to $t = 1$ to obtain the roots of the original equation $F(x) = 0$. Indeed, (10.6) is the foundation of the system of differential equations we need in order to carry out AYC.

10.1.2 Points at infinity and Bezout's Theorem. Having defined $S_t(x;y,Z)$ and $F_t(x)$, we are well along in the description of the AYC method. Next we must create a system of differential equations based on (10.6), then determine an appropriate set of initial conditions, and finally perform the integration. However, because we intend to use AYC to find all of the stationary solutions in a truncated spectral model, we must first introduce the process of homogenization of a polynomial map. Although this is not a part of the AYC method itself, we need to incorporate this feature into the method in order to represent certain roots, known as roots at infinity, that play a central role in any general algorithm for solving polynomial equations. Although the roots at infinity are not literally zeros of the system under consideration, they are closely related to finite zeros of a nearby system. We illustrate this relationship with the following example.

Consider the following pair of equations:

$$\varepsilon x_1^2 + x_1 - 3 = 0 \quad , \tag{10.7}$$

$$4x_2^2 - 4x_1^2 - 3 = 0 \quad . \tag{10.8}$$

Elementary algebra suggests that, for $\varepsilon > 0$, (10.7)-(10.8) has four solutions. For any solution point (x_1, x_2), the value of x_1 is given by solving (10.7) to obtain

$$x_1 = \left[-1 \pm \sqrt{1 + 12\varepsilon}\right]/(2\varepsilon) \quad , \tag{10.9}$$

and the value of x_2 is given by solving (10.8) to find

$$x_2 = \pm \left[4x_1^2 + 3\right]^{1/2}/2 \quad . \tag{10.10}$$

However, when $\varepsilon = 0$, the system (10.7)-(10.8) collapses to

$$x_1 - 3 = 0 \quad , \tag{10.11}$$

$$4x_2^2 - 4x_1^2 - 3 = 0 \quad , \tag{10.12}$$

which has exactly <u>two</u> solutions given by $(x_1,x_2) = (3, \pm\sqrt{39}/2)$. But what happened to the other two solutions? Their magnitudes became infinite, as we can see by examining the limit $\varepsilon \to 0$ in (10.9). In Fig. 10.1 we display this limiting behavior by setting $\varepsilon = 2$ in (10.9)-(10.10) and then letting $\varepsilon \to 0$. Apparently the two roots originally at $x_1 = -3/2$, $x_2 = \pm\sqrt{3}$ "go to infinity", while the other two remain

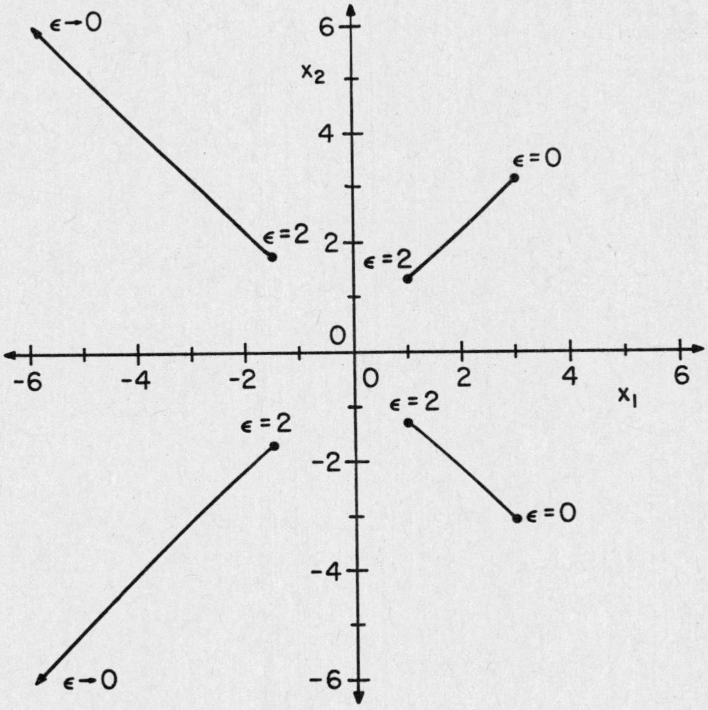

Fig. 10.1 Behavior of the four solutions to the pair of equations (10.7)-(10.8). When $\varepsilon=2$ there are four solutions $(x_1, x_2) = (-3/2, -\sqrt{3})$; $(-3/2, \sqrt{3})$; $(1, -\sqrt{7}/2)$; $(1, \sqrt{7}/2)$. But as $\varepsilon \to 0$, only <u>two</u> remain finite and approach the solutions $(x_1, x_2) = (3, -\sqrt{39}/2)$; $(3, \sqrt{39}/2)$ to (10.11)-(10.12).

finite. If we insist on regarding (10.11) as a degenerate case of the quadratic equation (10.7), then (10.11)-(10.12) has four solutions as in the nondegenerate case (10.7)-(10.8), in the sense that two of them are "at infinity".

The fact that we encountered two roots at infinity suggests that we need to define a set of points "at infinity" whose structure is sufficient to distinguish between these two roots. The mathematical formalism that leads to the definition of the set of points at infinity is the process of homogenization of a system of polynomial equations, or of a polynomial map. To describe this process in general, we examine an arbitrary n-component polynomial map G(x) of second degree:

$$G(x) = G(x_1, \ldots, x_n) \quad . \tag{10.13}$$

We then define a <u>homogeneous polynomial map</u> $\hat{G}(u) = \hat{G}(u_1, \ldots, u_{n+1})$ in $n + 1$ variables by setting

$$\hat{G}(u) = u_{n+1}^2 \, G(u_1/u_{n+1}, \ldots, u_n/u_{n+1}) \quad . \tag{10.14}$$

There is a very close correspondence between the roots of (10.13) and those of (10.14). The roots of (10.14) consist in a certain sense of those of (10.13) together with those we define below to be the roots at infinity.

We begin by setting up the correspondence between all the roots of (10.13) and some of the roots of (10.14). We note, by comparing the forms of (10.13) and (10.14), that the roots $x = (x_1,\ldots,x_n)$ of (10.13) can be identified with those $u = (u_1,\ldots,u_{n+1})$ of (10.14) by setting $u_{n+1} = 1$. This identification is given by

$$x \leftrightarrow u = (u_1, \ldots, u_n, u_{n+1}) = (x_1, \ldots, x_n, 1) = (x, 1) \quad . \tag{10.15}$$

As seen in Fig. 10.2, geometrically the set of roots of $G(x) = 0$ corresponds exactly to the set of roots of $\hat{G}(u) = 0$ on the hyperplane $u_{n+1} = 1$.

Unfortunately, an equally good identification is given by associating the root x of (10.13) with the root $u = (x/3, 1/3)$ of (10.14), as seen in Fig. 10.3. Under this identification, the set of roots of $G(x) = 0$ corresponds exactly to the set of roots of $\hat{G}(u) = 0$ on the hyperplane $u_{n+1} = 1/3$. In the same way, for any number $\xi_o \neq 0$,

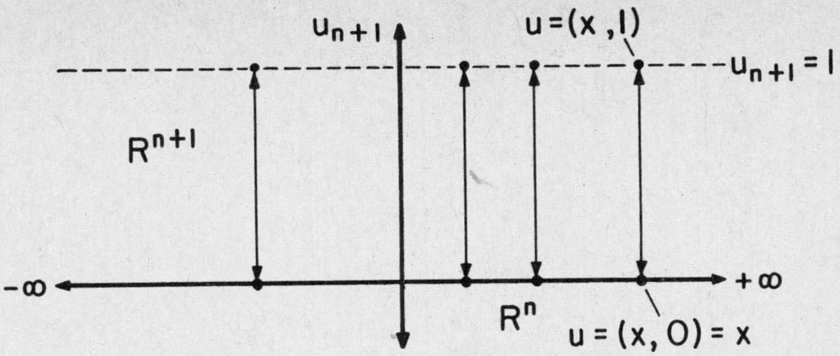

Fig. 10.2 Projections of the solutions x of $G(x) = 0$ in R^n as solutions $u = (x,1)$ of $\hat{G}(u) = 0$ in R^{n+1}.

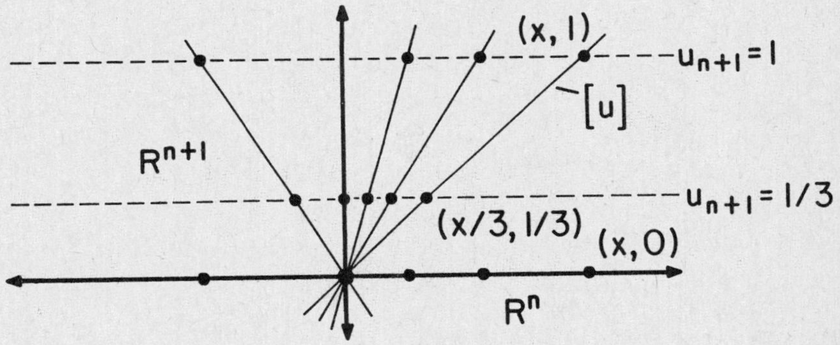

Fig. 10.3 Schematic representation of the root lines [u] as solutions to $\hat{G}(u) = 0$ in R^{n+1}. Each line corresponds to a particular solution x of $G(x) = 0$ in R^n.

the set of roots of $G(x) = 0$ corresponds exactly to the set of roots of $\hat{G}(u) = 0$ on the hyperplane $u_{n+1} = \xi_o$. The appropriate identification in this case is given by

$$x \leftrightarrow u = (\xi_o x, \xi_o) \quad . \tag{10.16}$$

We may carry out all these identifications <u>simultaneously</u> by matching the root x in R^n, not with any single point of R^{n+1}, but rather with the entire line, which we donote by $[(x,1)] = [u]$, determined by the origin and the point $(x,1)$ (Fig. 10.3).

The equation for this line is given using the parameter ξ by

$$u_i = \xi\, x_i \quad ; \quad i = 1, \ldots, n \quad , \tag{10.17}$$

$$u_{n+1} = \xi \quad . \tag{10.18}$$

Notice that the identification (10.16) is recovered from (10.17)-(10.18) by simply setting $\xi = \xi_o$. Furthermore we may recover x from u by calculating $x_i = u_i/u_{n+1}$, for $i = 1, \ldots, n$.

We have seen that each root x of $G(x) = 0$ corresponds to a line $[u] = [(x,1)]$. We may extend this correspondence to every point x of R^n, whether or not it is a root of $G(x) = 0$, by simply associating x with the line $[(x,1)]$ whose parametric equation is given by (10.17)-(10.18). Geometrically, these lines are depicted in Fig. 10.3. Under this association, <u>each point</u> of R^n corresponds to <u>one line</u> in R^{n+1}. Conversely, every line in R^{n+1} through the origin, except those also in R^n, corresponds exactly to one point x of R^n. That is, we have identified the set of points in R^n with the set of straight lines in the set difference $R^{n+1} - R^n$. We notice that any of the remaining lines--that is those in R^n--may be obtained as a limit of lines $[(x,1)]$ given as x approaches infinity in a suitable way. Now <u>every</u> line through the origin in R^{n+1} has an interpretation as a point of an extension of R^n. Such a line is identified either with a point of R^n or with a point at infinity.

The above discussion shows that we must associate points of R^n with entire lines of R^{n+1}. Thus, in order to associate roots x of $G(x) = 0$ with roots u of $\hat{G}(u) = 0$, we need to know that if $\hat{G}(u) = 0$ for a single point u on a line L, then $\hat{G}(v) = 0$ for any other point $v = \xi_o u$ on L. To see this fact, we use the important equality $[v] = [\xi_o u] = [u]$ that is valid for any scalar $\xi_o \neq 0$ and any point $u \neq 0$ in R^{n+1}. Thus we may speak of <u>root lines</u> of $\hat{G}(u) = 0$. The above formalism identifies the roots x of $G(x) = 0$ with those root lines [u] of $\hat{G}(u) = 0$ that do not lie in R^n. The remaining root lines we regard as the <u>roots</u> of $G(x) = 0$ <u>at infinity</u>.

To illustrate these ideas, we recall the example (10.7)-(10.8) given earlier in this section. To form the homogenized version of (10.7)-(10.8), we set $x_1 = u_1/u_3$ and $x_2 = u_2/u_3$, substitute them into (10.7)-(10.8), and multiply each equation by u_3^2 to obtain

$$\varepsilon u_1^2 + u_1 u_3 - 3u_3^2 = 0 \quad , \tag{10.19}$$

$$4u_2^2 - 4u_1^2 - 3u_3^2 = 0 \quad . \tag{10.20}$$

When $\varepsilon = 2$, the root lines of (10.19)-(10.20) are given by $[u_1,u_2,u_3] = [-3/2,-\sqrt{3},1]$; $[-3/2,\sqrt{3},1]$; $[1,-\sqrt{7}/2,1]$; $[1,\sqrt{7}/2,1]$. When $\varepsilon = 0$ the root lines are given by $[3,-\sqrt{39}/2,1]$; $[3,\sqrt{39}/2,1]$; $[1,-1,0]$; $[1,1,0]$, in which we have normalized the first two lines by requiring that $u_3 = 1$ when $u_3 \neq 0$. The last two lines are equally well represented as $[\xi_o,-\xi_o,0]$ and $[\xi_o,\xi_o,0]$ with $\xi_o \neq 0$; clearly $\xi_o = 1$ is a convenient choice. Now we see what has happened to the missing two roots of (10.7)-(10.8) when $\varepsilon = 0$: they have become the roots at infinity $[1,-1,0]$ and $[1,1,0]$.

Thus we find that we have four roots in the above example of a pair of quadratic equations, whether or not $\varepsilon = 0$. This observation is a special case of a general theorem, Bezout's Theorem, that relates the number N of roots of a system $G(x) = 0$ to the degrees of its components. To define these degrees, we begin by defining the degree of a monomial

$$\underset{\sim}{x}^{\underset{\sim}{a}} = x_1^{a_1} x_2^{a_2} \cdots x_n^{a_n} \quad , \tag{10.21}$$

to be

$$\deg(\underset{\sim}{x}^{\underset{\sim}{a}}) = a_1 + a_2 + \cdots + a_n \quad . \tag{10.22}$$

Here $\underset{\sim}{a}$ is a vector having the nonnegative integer components $(a_1, \ldots, a_n)^T$. Next we define the degree of a scalar polynomial function

$$f(x) = \sum_{\underset{\sim}{a}} c_{\underset{\sim}{a}} x^{\underset{\sim}{a}} \quad \text{, with the sum on } \underset{\sim}{a} \text{ finite} \quad , \tag{10.23}$$

to be

$$\deg[f(x)] = \max[\deg(\underset{\sim}{x}^{\underset{\sim}{a}})] \quad , \tag{10.24}$$

in which the maximum is taken over those monomials $\underset{\sim}{x}^{\underset{\sim}{a}}$ that appear in the sum (10.23), even if the corresponding coefficient $c_{\underset{\sim}{a}}$ is equal to zero. In this way, we may regard the linear polynomial function as a quadratic polynomial function, as we did in the above example when $\varepsilon = 0$.

Now Bezout's Theorem states that the number N of roots to the polynomial system $G(x) = 0$ is given by

$$N = \deg[G_1(x)]\ \deg[G_2(x)] \cdots \deg[G_n(x)] \quad . \tag{10.25}$$

The number N of roots must be suitably interpreted, however, because $G(x) = 0$ may be degenerate. A system $G(x) = 0$ is <u>degenerate</u> if it has infinitely many multiple roots. In an appropriate sense, fortunately, the probability of selecting a degenerate system is zero. For a nondegenerate system, the number N of roots refers to <u>all</u> the roots: finite or at infinity, complex or real, provided they are counted with the appropriate multiplicity.

From the above discussion, we see that in order to obtain a complete picture of the roots x of a system $G(x) = 0$, we must consider the set of root lines of the associated homogeneous system $\hat{G}(u) = 0$. These root lines are members of the sets of lines through the origin in R^{n+1}. This set of lines is called <u>projective space</u>. As we have seen, this set has the structure we need to distinguish roots at infinity, but in fact this structure is too subtle for us to specify explicitly here. Instead we obtain a convenient, though slightly ambiguous, representation of this space. To obtain this representation, we define the sphere S in R^{n+1} to comprise the set of points u for which

$$u_1^2 + u_2^2 + \cdots + u_{n+1}^2 = c^2 \quad , \tag{10.26}$$

in which c is a constant. Then we represent the line [u] as the intersection of [u] with S (Fig. 10.4). Any root in R^{n+1} is depicted by a point on the surface of S. Moreover, we now have a finite representation for the roots at infinity. These roots are simply the points that lie on the equator of S.

Although there is an apparent ambiguity because the line [u] intersects S at two <u>antipodal points</u> (Fig. 10.5), this ambiguity does not interfere with our analysis. If we consider any sphere S with antipodal points u and u' as shown in Fig. 10.5, then the fact that there is no interference can be illustrated as follows:

For two points u, u' ε S, the relationship [u] = [u'] implies that u and u' are either antipodal points or the same point. In order for [u] = [u'], we saw above that $u = \xi u'$; thus we have

$$|u| = |\xi||u'| \quad .$$

$$\text{But } |u| = |u'| = c, \text{ a constant} \quad ,$$

$$\text{so } |\xi| = 1, \text{ or } \xi = \pm 1 \quad .$$

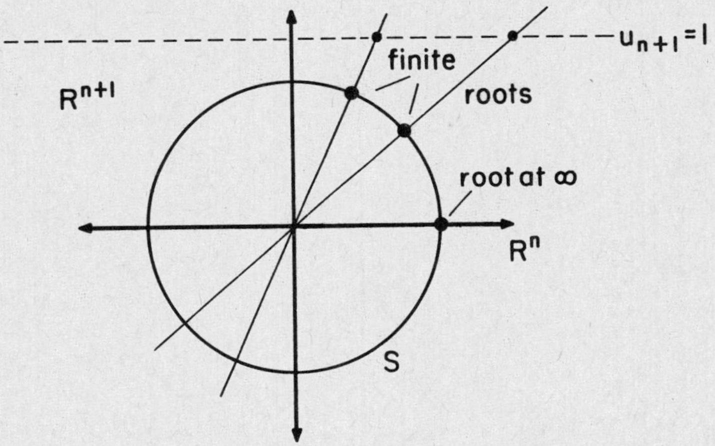

Fig. 10.4 Schematic depiction of roots in R^{n+1} represented by the points of intersection of the root lines [u] with the sphere S. Roots at infinity intersect S at its equator.

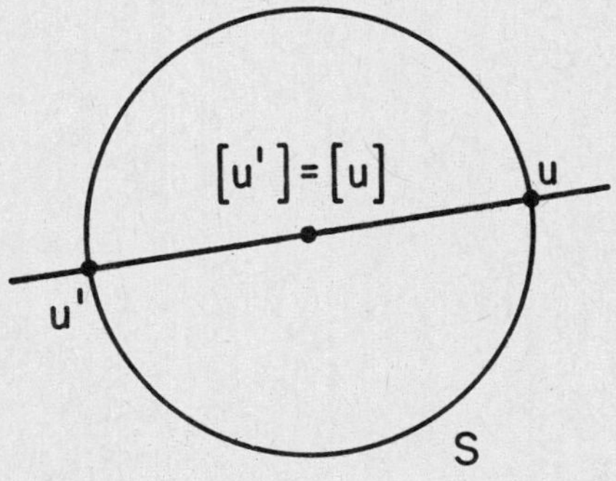

Fig. 10.5 Sphere S with antipodal points u, u' and corresponding line [u'] = [u].

The ambiguity is that $\xi = \pm 1$. However, if we recall the definition (10.17)-(10.18), which can be written as

$$x_i = \frac{u_i}{u_{n+1}} \quad , \qquad i = 1, \ldots, n \quad , \tag{10.27}$$

then we have also

$$x_i = \frac{u_i}{u_{n+1}} = \frac{\xi u_i'}{\xi u_{n+1}'} \quad , \qquad i = 1, \ldots, n \quad . \tag{10.28}$$

Thus, when $u_{n+1} \neq 0$, the variable ξ divides out, and <u>either</u> antipodal point corresponds to the <u>same</u> line--that is, to the same point of the projective space. In particular, the two points on the sphere correspond to a single finite root of the original system.

<u>10.1.3 The differential equations.</u> We return to the development of the AYC method that we began in Section 10.1.1 and now incorporate the homogenization process described above. The objective is to use (10.6) to compute the solutions to $\hat{F}(u) = 0$, which is the homogenized version of $F(x) = 0$. Using the substitution $x_i = u_i/u_{n+1}$, $i = 1, \ldots, n$, and recalling the general definition (10.14), we homogenize $F(x)$ and $S_t(x;y,Z)$ to obtain

$$\hat{F}_t(u) = (1 - t)\, \hat{S}_t(u;y,Z) + t\, \hat{F}(u) \quad , \tag{10.29}$$

which is the homogenized version of (10.6).

Using (10.26) and (10.29), we consider a smooth curve $u(t)$ that solves the system

$$\hat{F}_t(u(t)) = 0 \quad , \tag{10.30}$$

$$u^2(t) = c^2 \quad ; \tag{10.31}$$

for notational convenience, we regard u as an $(n+1) \times 1$ matrix. Differentiating (10.30) and (10.31) with respect to time t, we find that $u(t)$ satisfies the system of differential equations

$$D_u\hat{F}_t(u)\,\frac{du}{dt} + \frac{\partial}{\partial t}\,\hat{F}_t(u) = 0 \quad , \tag{10.32}$$

$$u^T\,\frac{du}{dt} = 0 \quad , \tag{10.33}$$

in which $D_u\hat{F}_t(u)$ denotes the $n \times (n + 1)$ matrix of partial derivatives of $\hat{F}_t(u)$ with respect to u. From the left sides of (10.32)-(10.33), we construct the $(n + 1) \times (n + 1)$ matrix $M_t(u)$, with upper $n \times (n + 1)$ part $D_u\hat{F}_t(u)$ and bottom row u^T, given by

$$M_t(u) = \begin{bmatrix} D_u\hat{F}_t(u) \\ u^T \end{bmatrix} \quad . \tag{10.34}$$

If we now multiply (10.32)-(10.33) by the matrix $M_t(u)^{-1}$, then we obtain the system of ordinary differential equations

$$\frac{du}{dt} = -\,M_t(u)^{-1} \begin{bmatrix} \partial\hat{F}_t(u)/\partial t \\ 0 \end{bmatrix} = -\begin{bmatrix} D_u\hat{F}_t(u) \\ u^T \end{bmatrix}^{-1} \begin{bmatrix} \partial\hat{F}_t(u)/\partial t \\ 0 \end{bmatrix} \quad . \tag{10.35}$$

It is this system that we wish to integrate numerically from $0 \leq t < 1$ in order to obtain solutions to the homogenized system $\hat{F}_t(u) = 0$ (10.29), and consequently the roots $x_i = u_i/u_{n+1}$, $i = 1, \ldots, n$. However, from (10.35) we see that the matrix $M_t(u)$ <u>must be invertible at all times</u> $0 \leq t < 1$ for the method to be successful. Unfortunately, this condition is often <u>not</u> satisfied for real variables, and it is now necessary to introduce complex variables. By applying Sard's Theorem (Milnor, 1965) to $\hat{F}_t(u)$, we find that in complex variables, $M_t(u)$ is invertible for almost all choices of initial conditions $\pm\, y_i$ and Z, whenever $t \neq 1$ and $\hat{F}_t(u) = 0$.

There are several reasons for this result, but the most basic and conceptual reason arises from the codimension of the system. The <u>codimension</u> of a subset of a space is the difference between the dimension of the subset and the dimension of the ambient space. According to intuition, the appropriate depiction of these dimensions in real variables is as shown in Fig. 10.6a. Here, we represent the space of real variables as a dashed line, and the singular set of points for which $M_t(u)$ is noninvertible is then represented as points x on the line. Because the line has dimension one, and the singular points have dimension zero, the codimension is one. However, intuition requires that there be codimension greater than one to ensure that $M_t(u)$ is invertible. From Fig. 10.6a, we see that, if at least one singular point x lies between the initial conditions at $t = 0$ and the root at $t = 1$, then the trajectory cannot avoid this point, and $M_t(u)$ is not invertible at some time t for which $0 \leq t < 1$. In complex variables, the dimension of the space increases, but the dimension of the singular set remains the same. According to Sard's Theorem, the appropriate representation is as shown schematically in Fig. 10.6b. In this figure, the space has dimension two, while the singular set has dimension zero. Thus, the codimension is two and Sard's Theorem is satisfied. In this case, the extra dimension of the space allows almost all trajectories to avoid singular points in their paths to that $M_t(u)$ is almost always invertible.

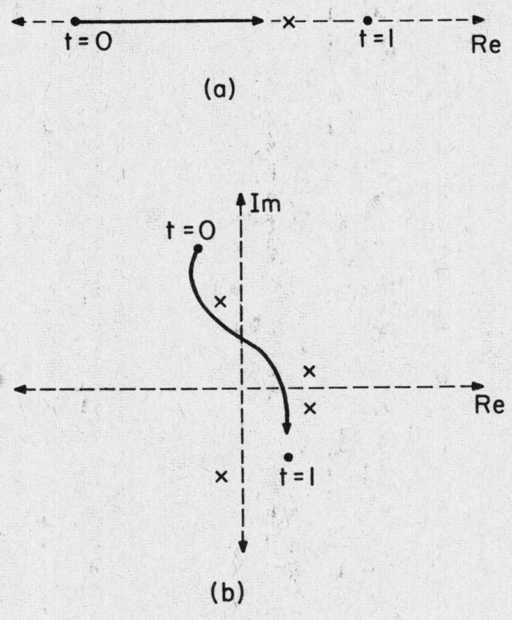

Fig. 10.6 Schematic representation of real (a) and complex (b) spaces according to Sard's Theorem. Trajectories may encounter singular points x at which the matrix $M_t(u)$ is noninvertible. In (a) the codimension of the subset is one, while in (b) the codimension of the subset is two.

If we rework the AYC method in complex variables, then the only obvious change in the equations occurs in (10.33). Because each equation in the system must have a real and an imaginary part, the new form of (10.33) becomes

$$u^* \frac{du}{dt} = 0 \quad , \tag{10.36}$$

in which $u^* = \bar{u}^T$ is the <u>transpose</u> <u>conjugate</u> of u. The variables u are now of the form $u = \mathrm{Re}(u) + i\,\mathrm{Im}(u)$ so that the real part of (10.36) is

$$\frac{d}{dt}\{[\mathrm{Re}(u)]^2 + [\mathrm{Im}(u)]^2\} = 0 \quad , \tag{10.37}$$

which, as before, maintains the trajectories on the surface of the sphere S. The imaginary part of (10.36) is of no significance and affects only the rates of motion along the trajectories.

From (10.32) and (10.36) we construct the new continuation equations in complex variables

$$\frac{du}{dt} = -\begin{bmatrix} D_u\hat{F}_t(u) \\ u^* \end{bmatrix}^{-1} \begin{bmatrix} \partial\hat{F}_t(u)/\partial t \\ 0 \end{bmatrix} \quad . \tag{10.38}$$

The solutions u(t) of the initial value problem given by (10.38) and $u(0) = (x,1)$, where x is chosen as any member of Zeros(y) (10.5), are well-defined for $0 \le t < 1$. It follows that for almost any choices of y and Z, the roots of $\hat{F}_t(u) = 0$ are all distinct and simple, as long as $0 \le t < 1$. By integrating all possible such initial value problems to some time $t < 1$, we obtain all 2^n solutions to $\hat{F}_t(u) = 0$; then we obtain all the solutions to $\hat{F}(u) = 0$ as the limit

$$u(1) = \lim_{t \to 1} [u(t)] \quad . \tag{10.39}$$

Finally, from these roots we obtain all the solutions to the original equation $F(x) = 0$ by selecting those for which $u_{n+1} \neq 0$ and setting

$$x_i = u_i/u_{n+1} \quad , \qquad i = 1, \ldots n \quad . \tag{10.40}$$

This is the fundamental strategy of the AYC method.

10.2 Numerical Integration and Newton's Method

Having derived the continuation equation (10.38), we now integrate it numerically. Although several sophisticated integration routines exist, we can integrate (10.38) to a reasonable degree of accuracy by using a simple Euler method. In this case, we write (10.38) in the form

$$u_{t+\Delta t} = u_t - \Delta t \left\{ \begin{bmatrix} D_u\hat{F}_t(u) \\ \\ u^* \end{bmatrix}_t^{-1} \begin{bmatrix} \partial\hat{F}_t(u)/\partial t \\ \\ 0 \end{bmatrix}_t \right\} . \qquad (10.41)$$

Thus, we obtain the trajectories u(t) on the surface of S as the sum of small straight line segments. For a particular iteration of (10.41), the result of the integration is depicted in Fig. 10.7. Because of the step-like progression of this linear approximation, the point $u_{t+\Delta t}$ obtained from (10.41) actually misses the trajectory $\hat{F}_t(u) = 0$, especially when this trajectory is strongly nonlinear. However, it was shown in Section 10.1.3 that, in order to obtain the correct roots, the solutions u(t) must satisfy $\hat{F}_t(u) = 0$ at all times. As a result, we must correct the solutions $u_{t+\Delta t}$ given by (10.41) before the next integration, or continuation, step is performed. To perform the correction and obtain a better approximation of the roots u(t), we use the Newton-Raphson scheme, which is commonly referred to as simply Newton's method. This is an iterative method that we apply at a fixed time t.

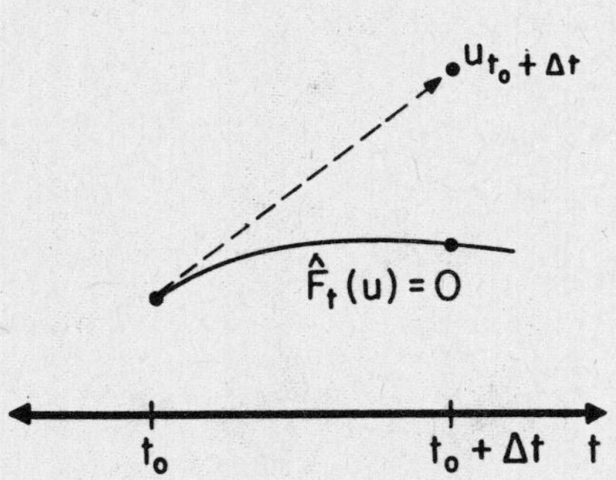

Fig. 10.7 Schematic representation of the result of a single iteration (dashed line) of (10.41). Because (10.41) represents a linear approximation, the numerical solution $u_{t+\Delta t}$ may "miss" the trajectory $\hat{F}_t(u)=0$.

The method is obtained by truncating a Taylor series after the first two terms leaving

$$f(x_{n+1}) = f(x_n) + (x_{n+1} - x_n)\, f'(x_n) \quad . \tag{10.42}$$

If we set $f(x_{n+1}) = 0$ in (10.42), then the result is the general form of the Newton correction given by

$$x_{n+1} = x_n - \frac{f(x_n)}{f'(x_n)} \quad . \tag{10.43}$$

Geometrically, Newton's method involves a succession of tangent lines that, in most cases, converges to the correct root. The method is shown in Fig. 10.8a. The correct root x_∞ occurs where f(x) meets the abscissa. The point x_o depicts the initial guess from which the first of a succession of tangent lines is drawn until there is convergence. The success of the method depends on the character of the curve f(x), and even more importantly, on the initial guess x_o. But the method can fail, as shown in Fig. 10.8b; in this case x_o is near a relative minimum so that convergence never occurs. We discuss such problems shortly.

In the present application, the proper form of (10.43) is only a slight variation of the continuation step given in (10.41). Here, it is useful to think of the ordinate y in Fig. 10.8 as the residual of $\hat{F}_t(u) = 0$. The actual derivation of the equation is unimportant, but it can be shown that, in this case, the proper form is that of the differential equation

$$\frac{du}{dn} = - \begin{bmatrix} D_u\hat{F}_t(u) \\ u^* \end{bmatrix}^{-1} \begin{bmatrix} \hat{F}_t(u) \\ 0 \end{bmatrix} \quad . \tag{10.44}$$

It may be noted that (10.44) differs from the continuation equation (10.38) <u>only</u> in the upper $n \times (n + 1)$ part of the far right matrix in each equation. We integrate (10.44) numerically at a fixed time t as

$$u_{n+1} = u_n - \Delta n \left\{ \begin{bmatrix} D_u\hat{F}_t(u) \\ u^* \end{bmatrix}_n^{-1} \begin{bmatrix} \hat{F}_t(u) \\ 0 \end{bmatrix}_n \right\} \quad . \tag{10.45}$$

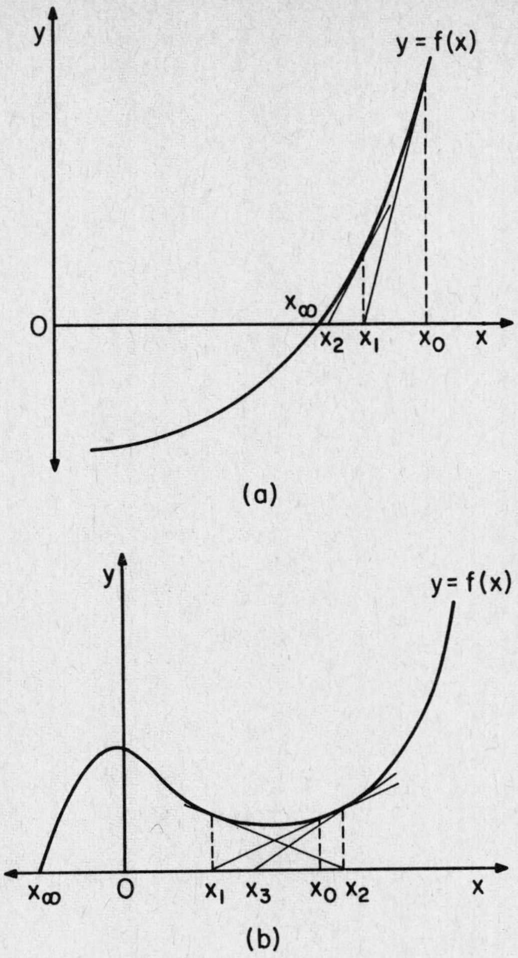

Fig. 10.8 Geometric representation of Newton's method. In (a), the initial guess x_o is improved using a succession of tangent lines that converge on the root x_∞. An example in which the method fails is given in (b). In this case, the initial guess x_o falls near a relative minimum of f(x) and the method does not converge (after Kellison, 1975).

Here Δn is a "false" time-step, which is actually more like a space-step, and we set $\Delta n = 1$. Although the derivations of (10.44) and (10.45) are not shown here, both are clearly compatible with the general form (10.43).

Thus, the AYC method can be viewed as a succession of integration steps and corrections as shown in Fig. 10.9. Here the points $n_o, \ldots, n_2$ correspond to the points x_n in Fig. 10.8 where the tangent lines intersect the abscissa. In Fig. 10.9, the next continuation step (10.41) would be performed with the point $u(n_2)$ as the initial condition.

10.3 Bisection/Doubling of the Time-Step Δt

At this level of development, the AYC method performs well in most cases. The use of complex variables ensures that $M_t(u)$ is almost always invertible, and the Newton correction step ensures that the solutions $u(t)$ satisfy $\hat{F}_t(u) = 0$ to some prescribed degree of accuracy. These two conditions are the vital ones from a theoretical point of view.

Significantly, in applications of the AYC method, we can detect multiple roots of $\hat{F}(u) = \hat{F}_1(u) = 0$, in spite of the fact that the roots of $\hat{F}_t(u) = 0$ are distinct for $t < 1$. Consequently, any multiple roots must appear at $t = 1$, as illustrated by the two trajectories given in Fig. 10.10a. Because these two trajectories converge to the same root at $t = 1$, the root has multiplicity two. However, if we obtain trajectories that coincide at some time $t < 1$ (Fig. 10.10b), then we must conclude that numerical error has caused AYC to fail.

Fortunately, experience with the AYC method has led us to a technique for circumventing the problem of erroneous convergence. This technique derives from the manner by which the Newton method generally fails. That is, the method may produce iterates that converge to the wrong root (Fig. 10.11). This difficulty occurs when the trajectory lies near the boundary of the basin of attraction of a point on another trajectory; here this basin is that determined by solutions to the differential equation (10.44) for Newton's method.

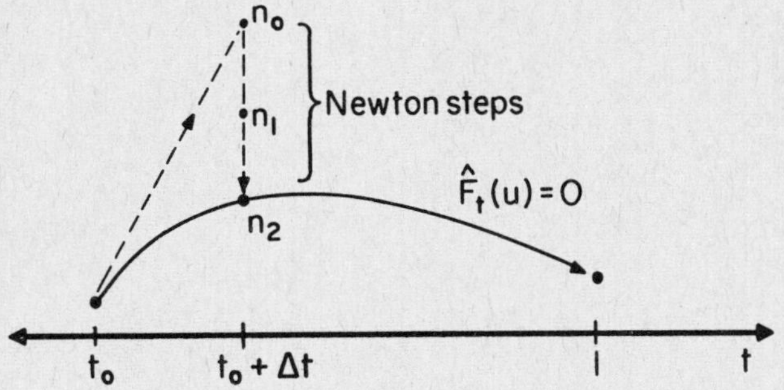

Fig. 10.9 As in Fig. 10.7, except a Newton correction is performed at fixed time $t_o+\Delta t$ so that the numerical solution again satisfies $\hat{F}_t(u)=0$.

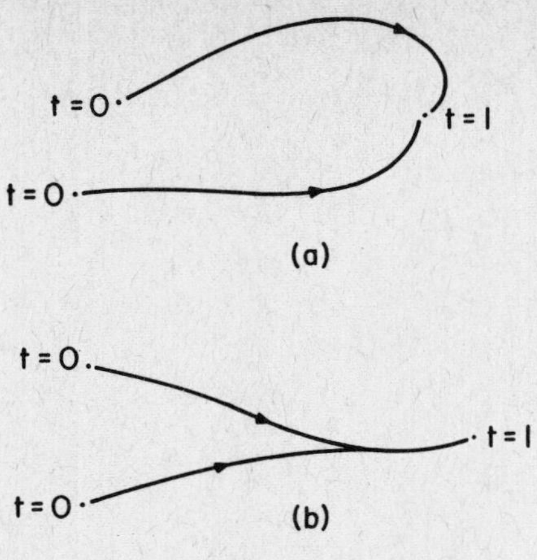

Fig. 10.10 Schematic representation of ways AYC might produce multiple roots. In (a), AYC correctly finds a root of multiplicity two because the trajectories meet only at t=1. In (b) the root has spuriously high multiplicity because the trajectories converge at t<1.

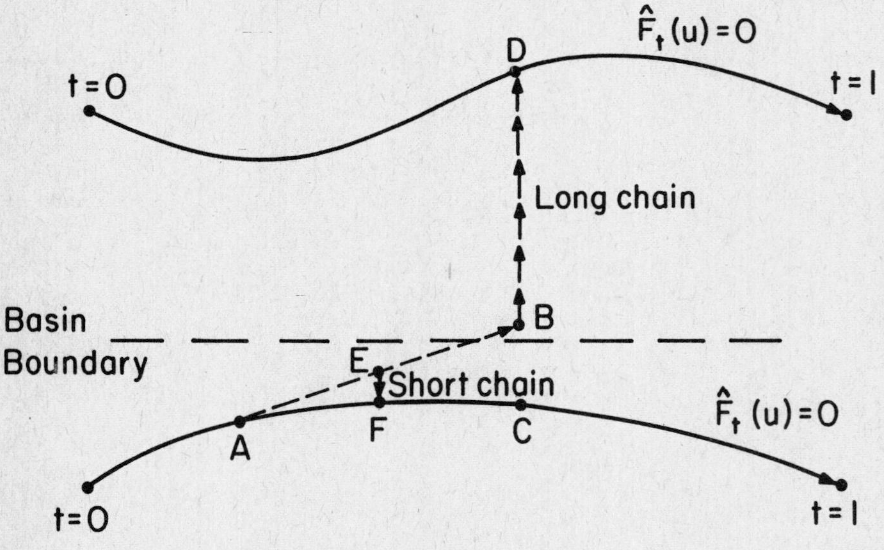

Fig. 10.11 The apparent cause of track-jumping is illustrated by the continuation step originating at A producing a point B that is in the Newton basin of attraction of the point D, rather than in the basin of the desired point C. Because the time step Δt is relatively small, it follows that both B and C are near A and consequently that B is near C. Thus B must lie near the boundary of the wrong basin, and so a large number of Newton iterates are necessary to carry B to the wrong point D. The incorrect iteration can be circumvented by choosing a smaller time step $\Delta t/2$ to produce point E. Then Newton's method converges quickly to the correct point F.

In this case, for a given value of Δt, the continuation step may produce an initial guess that converges to another root, as shown in Fig. 10.11, and this behavior we call track-jumping. Consequently, certain roots appear with erroneously high multiplicities, while others do not appear at all. Although, as noted above, AYC can find roots having high multiplicities, it is built into the method that these roots have unique trajectories up to t = 1. Therefore, the behavior of track-jumping should be detected; of course it must be eliminated.

A fairly reliable indication that track-jumping is occurring is reflected by the number of Newton corrections required to obtain an acceptable residual of $\hat{F}_t(u) = 0$ (Fig. 10.11). In systems having as many as five components, we have found that a time-step of $\Delta t = 0.05$ requires approximately three to five Newton corrections to obtain an acceptably small residual ($\sim 10^{-13}$). When the number of corrections is significantly larger than this, then the scheme may be converging to the wrong root. In most cases, the closeness and curvature of the trajectories appear to be the underlying problems. An effective way to handle the track-jumping problem is to regulate the size of the continuation time-step Δt throughout the entire integration. When the number of corrections is large, indicating that the scheme may be converging to the wrong root, then we simply repeat the preceding continuation step with a smaller value of Δt. This process can be repeated several times for a given continuation step until the number of Newton corrections falls within an acceptable range. In cases where few or no corrections are needed, the value of Δt may be increased to make the scheme more efficient. We can think of decreasing Δt as "slowing down" the integration near difficult regions on the trajectory, and increasing Δt as "speeding up" the integration in regions where the trajectory is relatively smooth or isolated. This procedure is demonstrated schematically in Fig. 10.12. Here, we see that the value of Δt is decreased where the trajectories are close together in order to prevent the continuation step from producing an initial guess in the (Newton) basin of attraction of another trajectory (see Fig. 10.11).

The point here is that sometimes no single time-step Δt is applicable over the entire path of the trajectory. Although a very small value of Δt may be chosen initially to avoid this problem, such a small value of Δt usually would lead to very inefficient integrations.

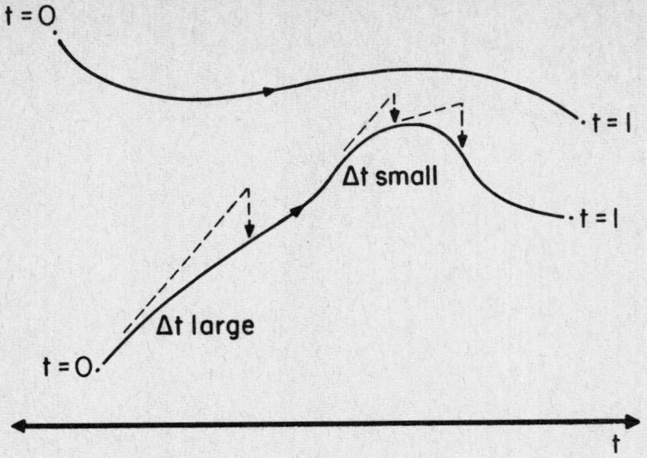

Fig. 10.12 Schematic representation of the AYC method modified so that the value of Δt can be increased or decreased to accomodate the character and proximity of the trajectories and their Newton basins of attraction.

A good general procedure is to choose a number C of corrections as the critical value (so far three to five seems reasonable). When the number of corrections is greater than C, then the value of Δt should be cut in half or <u>bisected</u>. When the number of corrections is smaller than C, then the value of Δt can be <u>doubled</u>. Obviously, the scheme should not be allowed to bisect the value of Δt indefinitely during any given iteration. Thus, a critical value M of bisections should be permitted before the routine is interrupted and the initial value of Δt is re-evaluated. It should be noted that the values of C and M are obtained empirically, and should be chosen according to the behavior of the particular system of equations.

Assuming the necessary differential equations have been derived as discussed in the previous sections, we can use the flow-chart in Fig. 10.13 to illustrate a typical computer algorithm based on the AYC method.

10.4 Examples: The General Two-Equation Quadratic System

In this section, we illustrate the elements of the AYC method necessary for solving a two-component quadratic system. Here, the algebra is not very lengthy and the necessary expressions can be computed easily. It should be noted that, for

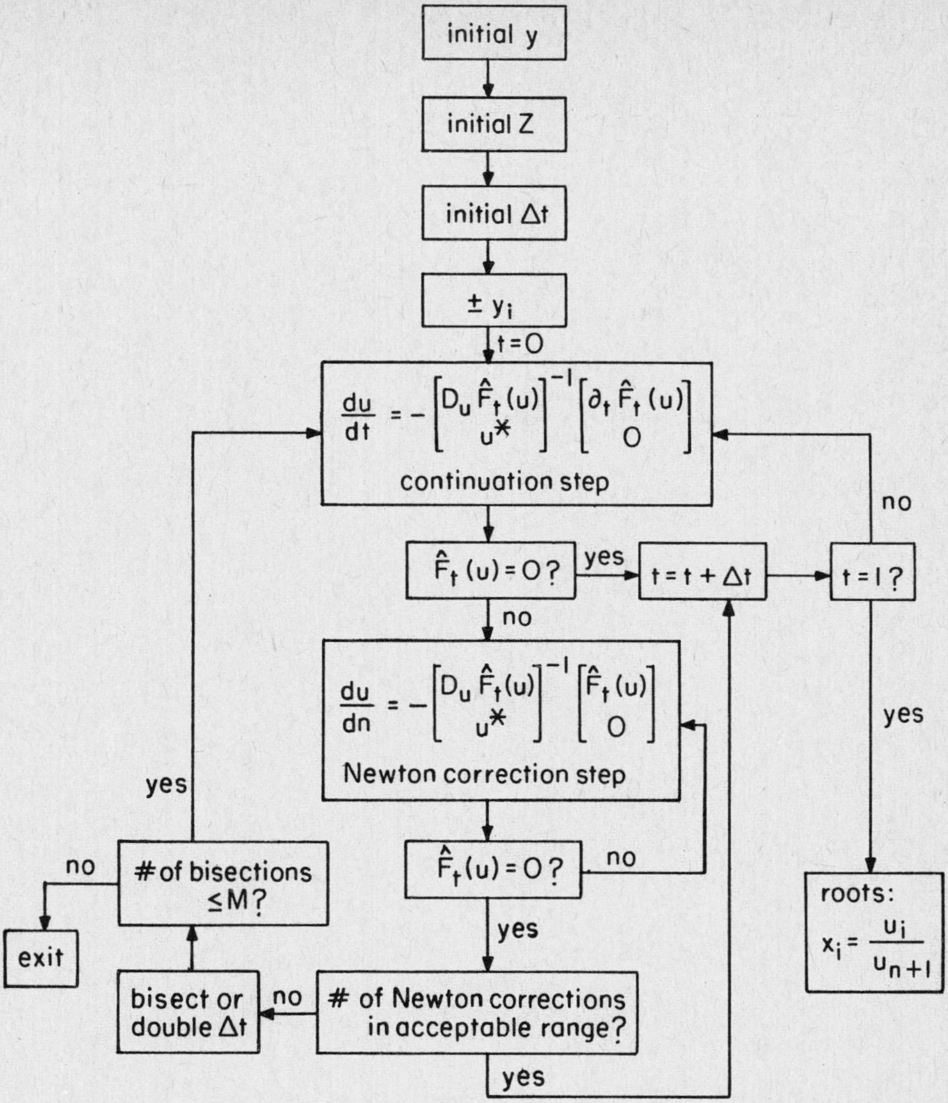

Fig. 10.13 Flow chart illustrating a typical algorithm based on the AYC method for obtaining one of the 2^n roots to an n-equation quadratic system.

larger spectral systems, the use of a symbolic manipulator (e.g. Section 3.3) is required to perform these calculations within a reasonable amount of time.

In this example, we apply the AYC method to a two-component quadratic system, in which the general form of the polynomial map F(x) is given by

$$F_1(x) = a_1x_1 + b_1x_2 + c_1x_1^2 + d_1x_1x_2 + e_1x_2^2 + f_1 \quad , \tag{10.46}$$

$$F_2(x) = a_2x_1 + b_2x_2 + c_2x_1^2 + d_2x_1x_2 + e_2x_2^2 + f_2 \quad . \tag{10.47}$$

Any two-component quadratic equation F(x) = 0 can be generated from (10.46)-(10.47) by choosing the appropriate values for the coefficients a_i, ..., f_i, i = 1,2. We use AYC to obtain the solutions to two specific examples in the following subsections.

Following the procedure in Section 10.1.1, we define the auxiliary polynomial map $S_t(x;y,Z)$ in (10.2) to be

$$S_t(x;y,Z) = \begin{bmatrix} x_1^2 - y_1^2 \\ x_2^2 - y_2^2 \end{bmatrix} + tx_1^2 \begin{bmatrix} z_{11} \\ z_{21} \end{bmatrix} + tx_2^2 \begin{bmatrix} z_{12} \\ z_{22} \end{bmatrix} \quad , \tag{10.48}$$

in which the matrix Z is

$$Z = \begin{bmatrix} z_{11} & z_{12} \\ z_{21} & z_{22} \end{bmatrix} \quad . \tag{10.49}$$

Expanding (10.48), we obtain

$$S_t(x;y,Z) = \begin{cases} x_1^2 - y_1^2 + tx_1^2 z_{11} + tx_2^2 z_{12} \quad , & (10.50) \\ x_2^2 - y_2^2 + tx_1^2 z_{21} + tx_2^2 z_{22} \quad . & (10.51) \end{cases}$$

Now, according to (10.6), we construct $F_t(x) = (1 - t)S_t(x;y,Z) + tF(x)$ giving

$$F_t(x) = \begin{cases} (1 - t)[x_1^2 - y_1^2 + tx_1^2 z_{11} + tx_2^2 z_{12}] \\ \qquad + t[a_1x_1 + b_1x_2 + c_1x_1^2 + d_1x_1x_2 + e_1x_2^2 + f_1] \quad , & (10.52) \\ (1 - t)[x_2^2 - y_2^2 + tx_1^2 z_{21} + tx_2^2 z_{22}] \\ \qquad + t[a_2x_1 + b_2x_2 + c_2x_1^2 + d_2x_1x_2 + e_2x_2^2 + f_2] \quad . & (10.53) \end{cases}$$

Using the substitution $x_i = u_i/u_3$, $i = 1,2$, and, recalling the definition (10.14), we homogenize (10.52)-(10.53) to obtain

$$\hat{F}_t(u) = \begin{cases} u_3^2\{(1-t)[\frac{u_1^2}{u_3^2} - y_1^2 + t\frac{u_1^2}{u_3^2} z_{11} + t\frac{u_2^2}{u_3^2} z_{12}] + \\ \quad t[a_1 \frac{u_1}{u_3} + b_1 \frac{u_2}{u_3} + c_1 \frac{u_1^2}{u_3^2} + d_1 \frac{u_1 u_2}{u_3^2} + e_1 \frac{u_2^2}{u_3^2} + f_1]\} , & (10.54) \\ \\ u_3^2\{(1-t)[\frac{u_2^2}{u_3^2} - y_2^2 + t\frac{u_1^2}{u_3^2} z_{21} + t\frac{u_2^2}{u_3^2} z_{22}] + \\ \quad t[a_2 \frac{u_1}{u_3} + b_2 \frac{u_2}{u_3} + c_2 \frac{u_1^2}{u_3^2} + d_2 \frac{u_1 u_2}{u_3^2} + e_2 \frac{u_2^2}{u_3^2} + f_2]\} . & (10.55) \end{cases}$$

Because we seek the curve $u(t)$ that satisfies the implicit differential equation (10.32), we must compute the $n \times (n+1) = 2 \times 3$ matrix

$$D_u\hat{F}_t(u) = \begin{bmatrix} \frac{\partial}{\partial u_1}(\hat{F}_t(u))_1 & \frac{\partial}{\partial u_2}(\hat{F}_t(u))_1 & \frac{\partial}{\partial u_3}(\hat{F}_t(u))_1 \\ \\ \frac{\partial}{\partial u_1}(\hat{F}_t(u))_2 & \frac{\partial}{\partial u_2}(\hat{F}_t(u))_2 & \frac{\partial}{\partial u_3}(\hat{F}_t(u))_2 \end{bmatrix} , \qquad (10.56)$$

and the vector

$$\frac{\partial}{\partial t}\hat{F}_t(u) = \begin{bmatrix} \frac{\partial}{\partial t}(\hat{F}_t(u))_1 \\ \\ \frac{\partial}{\partial t}(\hat{F}_t(u))_2 \end{bmatrix} , \qquad (10.57)$$

in which the subscripts 1 and 2 on $\hat{F}_t(u)$ in (10.56)-(10.57) correspond to (10.54) and (10.55), respectively. Differentiating (10.54)-(10.55), we find

$$\frac{\partial}{\partial u_1}\left(\hat{F}_t(u)\right)_1 = 2u_1(1-t) + 2u_1t(z_{11} - z_{11}t + c_1) + t(a_1u_3 + d_1u_2) = \eta_{11} \quad , \tag{10.58}$$

$$\frac{\partial}{\partial u_2}\left(\hat{F}_t(u)\right)_1 = 2u_2z_{12}t(1-t) + t(b_1u_3 + d_1u_1 + 2e_1u_2) = \eta_{12} \quad , \tag{10.59}$$

$$\frac{\partial}{\partial u_3}\left(\hat{F}_t(u)\right)_1 = 2u_3y_1^2(t-1) + t(a_1u_1 + b_1u_2 + 2f_1u_3) = \eta_{13} \quad , \tag{10.60}$$

$$\frac{\partial}{\partial u_1}\left(\hat{F}_t(u)\right)_2 = 2u_1z_{21}t(1-t) + t(a_2u_3 + 2c_2u_1 + d_2u_2) = \eta_{21} \quad , \tag{10.61}$$

$$\frac{\partial}{\partial u_2}\left(\hat{F}_t(u)\right)_2 = 2u_2(1-t) + 2u_2t(z_{22} - z_{22}t + e_2) + t(b_2u_3 + d_2u_1) = \eta_{22} \quad , \tag{10.62}$$

$$\frac{\partial}{\partial u_3}\left(\hat{F}_t(u)\right)_2 = 2u_3y_2^2(t-1) + t(a_2u_1 + b_2u_2 + 2f_2u_3) = \eta_{23} \quad , \tag{10.63}$$

and

$$\frac{\partial}{\partial t}\left(\hat{F}_t(u)\right)_1 = u_1^2(z_{11} - 1 - 2z_{11}t + c_1) + u_2^2z_{12}(1-2t) + u_3^2(y_1^2 + f_1) + a_1u_1u_3 + b_1u_2u_3 + d_1u_1u_2 + e_1u_2^2 = \gamma_{11} \quad , \tag{10.64}$$

$$\frac{\partial}{\partial t}\left(\hat{F}_t(u)\right)_2 = u_2^2(z_{22} - 1 - 2z_{22}t + e_2) + u_1^2z_{21}(1-2t) + u_3^2(y_2^2 + f_2) + a_2u_1u_3 + b_2u_2u_3 + c_2u_1^2 + d_2u_1u_2 = \gamma_{21} \quad . \tag{10.65}$$

From (10.36) we obtain the lower row of $M_t(u)$, given by the elements

$$\bar{u}_1 = \eta_{31} \quad , \tag{10.66}$$

$$\bar{u}_2 = \eta_{32} \quad , \tag{10.67}$$

$$\bar{u}_3 = \eta_{33} \quad , \tag{10.68}$$

which together with (10.58)-(10.63) give

$$M_t(u) = \begin{bmatrix} D_u\hat{F}_t(u) \\ \\ u^* \end{bmatrix} = \begin{bmatrix} \eta_{11} & \eta_{12} & \eta_{13} \\ \eta_{21} & \eta_{22} & \eta_{23} \\ \eta_{31} & \eta_{32} & \eta_{33} \end{bmatrix} \quad . \tag{10.69}$$

Thus, the differential system (10.38) has the form

$$\frac{du}{dt} = - \begin{bmatrix} \eta_{11} & \eta_{12} & \eta_{13} \\ \eta_{21} & \eta_{22} & \eta_{23} \\ \eta_{31} & \eta_{32} & \eta_{33} \end{bmatrix}^{-1} \begin{bmatrix} \gamma_{11} \\ \gamma_{21} \\ 0 \end{bmatrix} \quad . \tag{10.70}$$

If we denote the elements of $M_t(u)^{-1}$ by ζ_{ij} and expand (10.70), then we obtain the differential equations for the continuation step, given by

$$\frac{du_1}{dt} = - \zeta_{11}\gamma_{11} - \zeta_{12}\gamma_{21} \quad , \tag{10.71}$$

$$\frac{du_2}{dt} = - \zeta_{21}\gamma_{11} - \zeta_{22}\gamma_{21} \quad , \tag{10.72}$$

$$\frac{du_3}{dt} = - \zeta_{31}\gamma_{11} - \zeta_{32}\gamma_{21} \quad . \tag{10.73}$$

The Newton correction step (10.44) follows directly, except that the elements γ_{11}, γ_{21} in (10.70) are replaced by (10.54) and (10.55), respectively.

In the following two subsections, we examine specific examples in which we use AYC to obtain the roots of systems of equations based on (10.46)-(10.47). Some numerical results are shown as a reference.

10.4.1 Example 1: Four finite roots. As a first example, we choose the values of the coefficients a_i, ..., f_i in (10.46)-(10.47) that yield the system

$$F_1(x) = x_1^2 + 1 = 0 \quad , \tag{10.74}$$

$$F_2(x) = (x_2 - 3)(x_2 - 1/2) = 0 \quad , \tag{10.75}$$

whose roots are $x_1 = \pm\, i$, $x_2 = 1/2, 3$. One of the $2^2 = 4$ pairs of solutions is given by $x_1 = i$, $x_2 = 3$, which we obtain numerically from the initial conditions whose signs are $u_1 = + y_1$, $u_2 = + y_2$, $u_3 = 1$. All initial values are given in Table 10.1. Trajectory values for u_1 and u_3 from $t = 0$ to $t = 1$ are given in Table 10.2. The columns in Table 10.2 are defined as follows:

t_i: initial time at which each prediction is made.

$t_i + \Delta t$: new time obtained by adding previous value of Δt to t_i. The first continuation prediction is performed at $t_i + \Delta t$ in each step.

B/D: denotes whether the previous value of Δt must be bisected (B) or doubled (D) depending on the number of corrections required for the continuation prediction at $t = t_i + \Delta t$.

t_f: time for which the subsequent column values are obtained. If there is no bisection or doubling of Δt, then $t_f = t_i + \Delta t$.

Continuation values

u_{1R}: real part of u_1 produced at t_f by continuation step.

u_{1I}: imaginary part of u_1 produced at t_f by continuation step.

$||\hat{F}_t(u)_1||$: norm of the residual of $\hat{F}_t(u)_1$ at t_f obtained using u_{1R} and u_{1I} from continuation step.

#cor.: the number of Newton corrections at t_f required to obtain an acceptable residual for $||\hat{F}_t(u)_1||$ (i.e., $||\hat{F}_t(u)_1|| \sim \leq 10^{-13}$).

Corrected values

u_{1R}: corrected value of real part of u_1 at t_f.

u_{1I}: corrected value of imaginary part of u_1 at t_f.

u_{3R}: corrected value of real part of u_3 at t_f.

u_{3I}: corrected value of imaginary part of u_3 at t_f.

Table 10.1 Initial values for examples (10.74)-(10.75) and (10.76)-(10.77).

	Real	Imaginary
$\pm u_1 = y_1$	4.0769995310	1.1127470975
$\pm u_2 = y_2$	0.3374556690	1.6625309799
u_3	1.0000000000	0.0000000000
z_{11}	0.9873260090	2.0095222609
z_{12}	− 1.3477123965	0.9345622100
z_{21}	− 4.9336488793	− 0.1330221763
z_{22}	0.3344729080	1.7362096738

$\Delta t = 0.05$

Table 10.2 Trajectory values for (10.74)-(10.75) using initial conditions $u_1 = +y_1$, $u_2 = +y_2$ given in Table 10.1.

				Continuation Forecast (at t_f)				Corrected Forecast (at t_f)			
t_i	$t_i + \Delta t$	B/D	t_f	u_{1R}	u_{1I}	$\|\|\hat{F}_t(u)_1\|\|$	# cor.	u_{1R}	u_{1I}	u_{3R}	u_{3I}
			0					4.077	1.113	1.000	0.000
0	.05	B	.025	4.131	1.318	0.114	4	4.058	1.311	1.031	0.070
.025	.05	-	.05	3.957	1.497	0.128	4	3.912	1.438	1.022	0.134
.05	.075	-	.075	3.739	1.525	0.109	4	3.741	1.492	0.999	0.184
.075	.10	-	.10	3.575	1.525	0.081	4	3.585	1.512	0.975	0.225
.10	.125	-	.125	3.440	1.522	0.059	3	3.450	1.517	0.953	0.263
.125	.15	-	.15	3.324	1.517	0.042	3	3.332	1.515	0.934	0.298
.15	.175	-	.175	3.223	1.511	0.030	3	3.230	1.509	0.919	0.332
.175	.20	-	.20	3.133	1.503	0.021	3	3.139	1.502	0.906	0.365
.20	.225	-	.225	3.054	1.495	0.014	3	3.059	1.494	0.897	0.398
.225	.25	-	.25	2.983	1.486	0.009	3	2.987	1.485	0.890	0.429
.25	.275	-	.275	2.918	1.476	0.006	3	2.921	1.476	0.885	0.459
.275	.30	-	.30	2.859	1.466	0.005	3	2.862	1.466	0.883	0.488
.30	.325	-	.325	2.805	1.455	0.005	3	2.808	1.455	0.882	0.516
.325	.35	D	.375	2.704	1.433	0.023	4	2.714	1.434	0.888	0.569
.375	.425	B	.40	2.666	1.420	0.007	3	2.667	1.420	0.891	0.593
.40	.425	D	.45	2.583	1.395	0.033	4	2.589	1.394	0.906	0.640
.45	.50	-	.50	2.509	1.364	0.040	4	2.512	1.362	0.923	0.680
.50	.55	B	.525	2.480	1.348	0.013	3	2.480	1.347	0.935	0.699
.525	.55	D	.575	2.412	1.313	0.058	4	2.414	1.311	0.963	0.733
.575	.625	-	.625	2.345	1.271	0.073	4	2.345	1.267	0.995	0.759
.625	.675	B	.65	2.312	1.245	0.024	3	2.312	1.244	1.016	0.771
.65	.675	D	.70	2.241	1.194	0.112	4	2.238	1.190	1.062	0.789
.70	.75	-	.75	2.155	1.129	0.151	4	2.146	1.122	1.118	0.797
.75	.80	B	.775	2.096	1.086	0.052	3	2.091	1.083	1.152	0.798
.775	.80	-	.80	2.030	1.041	0.062	3	2.024	1.038	1.189	0.796
.80	.825	-	.825	1.949	0.989	0.075	3	1.940	0.984	1.230	0.791
.825	.85	-	.85	1.844	0.925	0.091	3	1.830	0.919	1.275	0.782
.85	.875	-	.875	1.705	0.846	0.113	3	1.684	0.836	1.321	0.768
.875	.90	-	.90	1.514	0.742	0.143	3	1.482	0.727	1.367	0.746
.90	.925	-	.925	1.241	0.600	0.193	4	1.184	0.576	1.408	0.715
.925	.95	-	.95	0.812	0.397	0.300	4	0.656	0.348	1.441	0.668
.95	.975	2B	.95625	0.453	0.273	0.056	4	0.401	0.268	1.448	0.653
.95625	.9625	B	.959375	0.233	0.228	0.033	4	0.188	0.248	1.451	0.642
.959375	.9625	B	.960938	0.053	0.263	0.019	4	0.054	0.296	1.451	0.635
.960938	.9625	-	.9625	-0.062	0.374	0.021	4	-0.036	0.381	1.449	0.627
.9625	.964063	-	.964063	-0.107	0.465	0.013	4	-0.095	0.460	1.445	0.620
.964063	.965625	D	.967188	-0.193	0.609	0.034	4	-0.172	0.592	1.436	0.606
.967188	.970313	-	.970313	-0.236	0.711	0.019	4	-0.227	0.701	1.426	0.593
.970313	.973438	D	.976563	-0.323	0.900	0.055	4	-0.307	0.876	1.407	0.567
.976563	.982813	-	.982813	-0.373	1.033	0.034	4	-0.365	1.019	1.386	0.542
.982813	.989063	-	.989063	-0.416	1.151	0.024	4	-0.411	1.142	1.364	0.516
.989063	.995313	D*	1.00	-0.484	1.342	0.059	4	-0.473	1.323	1.323	0.473

$t_i = 1.0$: $x_1 = u_1/u_3$ $x_{1R} = 8.6E-17$ $x_{1I} = 1.0$ $x_{2R} = 3.0$ $x_{2I} = 1.E-17$

D* - time step Δt multiplied by 1.75 rather than 2.0 so that final time is 1.00.

The value of x_1 anywhere on the trajectory is given by $x_1 = u_1/u_3$ using the corrected values of u_1 and u_3.

In Table 10.2, we begin with an initial time-step of $\Delta t = 0.05$. This is immediately bisected during the first iteration. We see that the value $\Delta t = 0.025$ is satisfactory until $t_i = 0.325$, at which time a series of bisections and doublings occurs until we again obtain $\Delta t = 0.025$ at $t_i = 0.775$. Another difficult region on the trajectory appears at $t_i = 0.95$. The value of Δt is subsequently bisected four times, and then gradually increased again to a value of $\Delta t = 6.25 \times 10^{-3}$. These difficult regions are also reflected by growing values of $||\hat{F}_t(u)_1||$ up to the points where Δt is finally bisected (e.g., $t_i = 0.75$ to $t_i = 0.925$), as well as by relatively sharp changes in the values of u_1. It may be noted that the changes in the values of u_{3R} and u_{3I} do not increase or decrease drastically at any time during the integration, nor does u_3 approach zero. The values of x_{1R} and x_{1I} at the bottom of the table are obtained from the values in the last row and produced the root $x_1 = i$. The component u_2 of the trajectory proceeds in a similar manner. For the initial conditions given in Table 10.1, we obtain at $t = 1$ the values $u_{2R} = 3.971$ and $u_{2I} = 1.420$. By dividing these values by the final values for u_{3R} and u_{3I} in Table 10.2, we obtain the numerical solution corresponding to the root $x_2 = 3$.

10.4.2 Example 2: One finite root. An example in which roots at infinity occur is given by choosing the coefficients in (10.46)-(10.47) so that the resulting system is

$$F_1(x) = x_1 - 4 = 0 \quad , \tag{10.76}$$

$$F_2(x) = x_2 - 3 = 0 \quad . \tag{10.77}$$

Of course, this system is linear; however, if we regard it as a degenerate quadratic system, then it acquires infinitely many roots at infinity. In this case, the AYC method generates the finite root $x_1 = 3$, $x_2 = 4$ and three of the infinite roots. Using the same initial conditions as in the preceding example (Table 10.1), we obtain the finite root using the initial conditions $u_1 = + y_1$, $u_2 = + y_2$, $u_3 = 1$. However, for any of the three remaining pairs of initial conditions, we obtain roots x_1 and x_2 at infinity. Two of the components of the trajectory for initial conditions $u_1 = - y_1$, $u_2 = + y_2$, $u_3 = 1$ are given in Table 10.3.

In Table 10.3, we again begin with an initial value of $\Delta t = 0.05$, which is bisected during the first iteration. Relatively fewer bisections (and consequently fewer iterations) are required here than in Table 10.2. Because we expect a solution at infinity, the value of u_3 must approach zero. This is indeed the case as the predicted values at $t_f = 1.0$ are $u_{3R} = -5.6 \times 10^{-15}$ and $u_{3I} = 5.8 \times 10^{-15}$. However, it is interesting to note that the magnitude of u_3 decreases very slowly up to $t_i = 0.975$, and then drops off very drastically during the Newton correction step at $t = 1.0$. This behavior is common in other cases as well. Similarly, it should be noted that real roots, such as $x_1 = 4$, $x_2 = 3$ in this case, often remain complex until the last correction step at $t = 1.0$. Thus, it is difficult to determine where a trajectory may be headed during the integration, and it often undergoes drastic changes near $t = 1.0$.

10.5 Larger Spectral Models

As mentioned in the introduction to this chapter, a great advantage of AYC is that it can be used to obtain directly the stationary solutions in a spectral model, with little or no reduction of the original system. Thus, the use of AYC makes it possible to find the stationary solutions in large spectral models, which is ordinarily difficult because the reduction of these models to single stationary polynomial equations may be arduous or impossible.

However, as we increase the number of equations in the spectral system, then obviously we increase the number of differential equations we must integrate to perform AYC. The consequence is that computing the polynomial maps $\hat{S}_t(u;y,Z)$ and $\hat{F}_t(u)$ becomes a lengthy algebraic problem that requires the use of a symbolic manipulator. Moreover, the dimension of the matrix $M_t(u)$ in (10.38) increases, and it may become time consuming and costly to compute its inverse.

As a general rule, in spectral models consisting of five or more equations, it is more efficient to solve (10.38) as a system of linear inhomogeneous algebraic equations in du/dt, and then to perform an Euler step. Thus, we rewrite (10.38) as

$$\begin{bmatrix} D_u\hat{F}_t(u) \\ u^* \end{bmatrix} \begin{bmatrix} \frac{du}{dt} \end{bmatrix} = - \begin{bmatrix} \partial\hat{F}_t(u)/\partial t \\ 0 \end{bmatrix} \quad , \tag{10.78}$$

Table 10.3 Trajectory values for (10.76)-(10.77) using initial conditions $u_1 = -y_1$, $u_2 = +y_2$ given in Table 10.1.

				Continuation Forecast (at t_f)				Corrected Forecast (at t_f)			
t_i	$t_i + \Delta t$	B/D	t_f	u_{1R}	u_{1I}	$\|\|\hat{F}_t(u)_1\|\|$	# cor.	u_{1R}	u_{1I}	u_{3R}	u_{3I}
			0					-4.077	-1.113	1.000	0.000
0	.05	B	.025	-4.155	-1.308	0.119	4	-4.079	-1.312	1.017	0.071
.025	.05	-	.05	-3.987	-1.505	0.118	4	-3.934	-1.438	0.990	0.136
.05	.075	-	.075	-3.758	-1.522	0.096	4	-3.760	-1.488	0.948	0.186
.075	.10	-	.10	-3.592	-1.516	0.070	4	-3.602	-1.504	0.905	0.228
.10	.125	-	.125	-3.454	-1.512	0.051	3	-3.464	-1.507	0.865	0.267
.125	.15	-	.15	-3.334	-1.507	0.038	3	-3.342	-1.505	0.828	0.305
.15	.175	-	.175	-3.229	-1.502	0.027	3	-3.236	-1.501	0.795	0.342
.175	.20	-	.20	-3.136	-1.497	0.019	3	-3.141	-1.497	0.765	0.378
.20	.225	-	.225	-3.053	-1.493	0.013	3	-3.058	-1.493	0.738	0.414
.225	.25	-	.25	-2.978	-1.490	0.009	3	-2.983	-1.490	0.714	0.450
.25	.275	-	.275	-2.912	-1.487	0.006	3	-2.916	-1.487	0.693	0.484
.275	.30	-	.30	-2.852	-1.484	0.005	3	-2.855	-1.485	0.674	0.517
.30	.325	-	.325	-2.798	-1.482	0.006	3	-2.801	-1.483	0.657	0.549
.325	.35	-	.35	-2.750	-1.481	0.008	3	-2.752	-1.481	0.642	0.579
.35	.375	D	.40	-2.660	-1.478	0.038	4	-2.671	-1.480	0.617	0.635
.40	.45	B	.425	-2.631	-1.477	0.012	3	-2.634	-1.477	0.604	0.660
.425	.45	D	.475	-2.566	-1.475	0.053	4	-2.575	-1.475	0.581	0.705
.475	.525	-	.525	-2.519	-1.471	0.063	4	-2.525	-1.471	0.557	0.742
.525	.575	B	.55	-2.506	-1.471	0.018	3	-2.508	-1.471	0.545	0.759
.55	.575	D	.60	-2.473	-1.468	0.079	4	-2.479	-1.469	0.519	0.785
.60	.65	-	.65	-2.455	-1.466	0.092	4	-2.460	-1.467	0.488	0.802
.65	.70	-	.70	-2.451	-1.467	0.109	4	-2.458	-1.468	0.452	0.809
.70	.75	B	.725	-2.457	-1.469	0.032	3	-2.459	-1.469	0.430	0.807
.725	.75	D	.775	-2.469	-1.474	0.146	4	-2.477	-1.479	0.381	0.791
.775	.825	-	.825	-2.503	-1.493	0.183	3	-2.514	-1.501	0.321	0.752
.825	.875	-	.875	-2.562	-1.534	0.238	4	-2.576	-1.552	0.245	0.678
.875	.925	-	.925	-2.648	-1.624	0.325	4	-2.665	-1.665	0.152	0.542
.925	.975	B	.95	-2.715	-1.749	0.126	3	-2.716	-1.772	0.093	0.432
.95	.975	-	.975	-2.766	-1.906	0.169	4	-2.754	-1.948	0.034	0.268
.975	1.00	-	1.00	-2.770	-2.179	0.250	4	-2.641	-2.339	-5.6E-15	5.8E-15

$t_i = 1.0$: $x_1 = u_1/u_3$ $x_{1R} = 1.5E+13$ $x_{1I} = 4.3E+14$

and calculate du/dt at each time t using a Gaussian elimination routine. Once the solutions du/dt are found, we may obtain the predicted values $u_{t+\Delta t}$ by solving

$$u_{t+\Delta t} = u_t + \Delta t \left.\frac{du}{dt}\right|_t \quad . \tag{10.79}$$

The Newton correction step is performed in an analogous manner.

Applying Bezout's Theorem to an n-component quadratic system G(x) = 0, we expect that there would be 2^n roots in the case that they are simple. Thus, if we find 2^n simple roots, then we are certain that we have found all the solutions. However, if the system is degenerate, then typically we would find that some of the complex roots at infinity would not appear in conjugate pairs. In this situation, it is necessary to perturb at random the original system G(x) = 0; with probability one, the resulting system would have simple roots. Then the isolated roots of the original system are approximated by appropriate ones to the perturbed system. In the example presented below, we did not implement this last step.

We are able to demonstrate the success of applying AYC to a larger spectral model by using the technique to obtain the stationary solutions to the five-component spectral model of quasi-geostrophic flow examined by Gelaro (1983) and Gelaro and Shirer (1986). In this case, we seek the solutions of

$$F(x) = \begin{cases} - D_1x_3x_4 + D_1x_2x_5 - V_1x_1 - h_1 = 0 , & (10.80) \\ - D_2x_1x_3 - D_3x_1x_5 + B_2x_3 - V_2x_2 - h_2 = 0 , & (10.81) \\ D_2x_1x_2 + D_3x_1x_4 - B_3x_2 - V_3x_3 - h_3 = 0 , & (10.82) \\ - D_4x_1x_3 - D_5x_1x_5 + B_4x_5 - V_4x_4 - h_4 = 0 , & (10.83) \\ D_4x_1x_2 + D_5x_1x_4 - B_5x_4 - V_5x_5 - h_5 = 0 , & (10.84) \end{cases}$$

in which the coefficients D_i, B_i, V_i and h_i represent the effects of physical processes such as heating, rotation and viscosity. These coefficients are analogues of a_i, ..., f_i in (10.46)-(10.47). Here the auxiliary polynomial map $S_t(x;y,Z)$ takes the form

$$S_t(x;y,Z) = \begin{bmatrix} x_1^2 - y_1^2 \\ x_2^2 - y_2^2 \\ x_3^2 - y_3^2 \\ x_4^2 - y_4^2 \\ x_5^2 - y_5^2 \end{bmatrix} + tx_1^2 \begin{bmatrix} z_{11} \\ z_{21} \\ z_{31} \\ z_{41} \\ z_{51} \end{bmatrix} + tx_2^2 \begin{bmatrix} z_{12} \\ z_{22} \\ z_{32} \\ z_{42} \\ z_{52} \end{bmatrix} + tx_3^2 \begin{bmatrix} z_{13} \\ z_{23} \\ z_{33} \\ z_{43} \\ z_{53} \end{bmatrix} + tx_4^2 \begin{bmatrix} z_{14} \\ z_{24} \\ z_{34} \\ z_{44} \\ z_{54} \end{bmatrix} + tx_5^2 \begin{bmatrix} z_{15} \\ z_{25} \\ z_{35} \\ z_{45} \\ z_{55} \end{bmatrix} , \qquad (10.85)$$

and the resulting increase in algebraic manipulations needed to obtain the AYC equations is obvious. Gelaro and Shirer (1986) note that (10.80)-(10.84) can be reduced to a ninth-degree polynomial equation in x_1, and so there are at most nine finite roots. Because we expect $2^5 = 32$ roots from the application of AYC to (10.80)-(10.84), we conclude that at least 23 are roots at infinity.

Here we discuss one example in which we have used AYC to compute the roots of (10.80)-(10.84). The values of the dimensionless parameters D_i, B_i, V_i, and h_i for this case are given in Table 10.4; this example is irrotational because $B_i = 0$ (Gelaro and Shirer, 1986). A cross section of the real stationary solutions to the ninth-degree polynomial equation for this example is shown in Fig. 10.14. For the range of values of h_1 shown, the real roots of the stationary polynomial equation yield a cross section of a typical folded solution surface known as a cusp surface (see Sections 6.3.2 and 8.3). We use AYC to compute the roots of (10.80)-(10.84) when $h_1 = 0$. Thus, from Fig. 10.14 we expect to obtain, among the $2^5 = 32$ solutions, the three real roots $x_1 = 0$, $x_1 = \pm 0.462$, as well as 29 complex roots or roots at infinity.

Table 10.4 Values of the dimensionless parameters in (10.80)-(10.84) used to obtain solutions in Table 10.6.

D_i	B_i	V_i	h_i
$D_1 = -0.67906109$	---	$V_1 = 0.04$	$h_1 = 0$
$D_2 = -0.42441318$	$B_2 = 0$	$V_2 = 0.08$	$h_2 = 0.3$
$D_3 = -0.76394372$	$B_3 = 0$	$V_3 = 0.08$	$h_3 = 0$
$D_4 = -0.01697652$	$B_4 = 0$	$V_4 = 0.40$	$h_4 = 0$
$D_5 = -0.58932801$	$B_5 = 0$	$V_5 = 0.40$	$h_5 = 0$

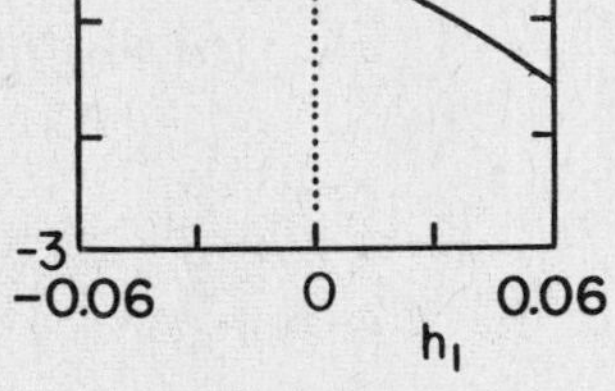

Fig. 10.14 Cross section of the real stationary solutions to the ninth-degree polynomial equation for (10.80)-(10.84). The dotted line indicates the value of h_1 at which the solutions to (10.80)-(10.84) are computed using AYC (after Gelaro and Shirer, 1986).

The initial conditions y and Z for this example are given in Table 10.5. The approximate values of u_1, u_6, x_1 and x_2 at t = 1 for all 32 permutations of the initial conditions $\pm y_i$ are given in Table 10.6. The various combinations of the signs of the initial conditions are given on the left of the table. Values of x_1 that correspond to roots of the original stationary polynomial equation are marked by an R or a C at the far right of Table 10.6; these symbols are also defined at the bottom of the table.

We note that the values of x_1 corresponding to the three real roots in Fig. 10.14 are obtained from initial conditions number 1, 2 and 6 (generally, values less than $\sim 10^{-10}$ may be considered as zeros). Complex conjugate roots (marked C) of the stationary polynomial equation are obtained from initial conditions number 8 and 17. Note that the x_1-components of these roots are purely imaginary. Those roots with no symbols in the far right column of Table 10.6 are roots at infinity. These roots are recognized easily by examining the values of u_6, which we may recall would approach zero in the definition $x_i = u_i/u_6$, i = 1, ..., 5. However, because $u_1, \ldots, u_5$ may also approach zero, some of the components x_i of these roots might be finite. For example, for initial condition number 3, the values of <u>both</u> u_1 and u_6 nearly vanish at t = 1. Thus, upon dividing to obtain x_i, we find that the component x_1 is finite, while the component x_2 is obviously approaching infinity; in this case we have a root at infinity. Therefore, we must consider the value of u_6 to determine whether or not a root is finite.

Those roots marked C* in Table 10.6 are complex roots that appear in the stationary polynomial equation, but appear to be roots at infinity. However, the values of these roots are difficult to determine accurately even after several bisections of Δt during the final approach to t = 1. As a result, they occur with erroneously high multiplicity. We see this by noting that there are eight roots (two conjugate pairs of multiplicity two) marked C*. Thus, the number of symbols in the far right column of the table totals 13 rather than nine (corresponding to each root of the stationary polynomial equation) owing to the two extra pairs of roots. We may recall from the two-equation example in the previous section that many roots undergo drastic changes in magnitude at t = 1. Because we have interrupted the calculations of the roots marked C*, we note that they appear to be headed toward infinity, but this is not as evident as in the remaining cases.

Table 10.5 Initial conditions y and Z used to obtain solutions in Table 10.6.

	Real	Imaginary
$\pm u_1 = y_1$ =	0.7230921784995831	0.7369950023192549
$\pm u_2 = y_2$ =	0.9141404891885487	0.8518879687708429
$\pm u_3 = y_3$ =	0.8840635189538087	0.6373894765545333
$\pm u_4 = y_4$ =	0.8677653250250335	0.4700866884158237
$\pm u_5 = y_5$ =	0.0106323415517527	0.8330139898502149
u_6 =	1.0000000000000000	0.0000000000000000
z_{11} =	0.9023927561098255	0.9172307097762861
z_{12} =	0.3818495354385543	0.0360209881832853
z_{13} =	0.7794802191784127	0.3526923123952189
z_{14} =	0.1008320380477111	0.4307614984985637
z_{15} =	0.6770806213055599	0.1856302413462861
z_{21} =	0.0200559926097895	0.4496638380550069
z_{22} =	0.5174790403290911	0.0578997267359069
z_{23} =	0.6900871337357335	0.6194251800219717
z_{24} =	0.5057669582794959	0.4597752112484973
z_{25} =	0.2067486974883655	0.1025153654629845
z_{31} =	0.7543539698954623	0.6034854484366461
z_{32} =	0.8317270705864055	0.5589934148450405
z_{33} =	0.8684169900747055	0.1795612068428685
z_{34} =	0.2616145211798183	0.9536362927495157
z_{35} =	0.3672869841094623	0.6209954607060893
z_{41} =	0.4203899072513751	0.9333804061791365
z_{42} =	0.8167732445560207	0.5002159207495853
z_{43} =	0.6503364597754375	0.4000754991627797
z_{44} =	0.5474249660234303	0.6838703309319869
z_{45} =	0.1763973186374711	0.9035510969754789
z_{51} =	0.8337306323463663	0.8704240303245773
z_{52} =	0.7189685725994343	0.4799952717010997
z_{53} =	0.4092545858373791	0.1355701242272221
z_{54} =	0.1301295545961879	0.5606462367885509
z_{55} =	0.1927113748527695	0.1104522270453485

Table 10.6 Roots of (10.80)-(10.84) obtained via AYC using parameter values in Tables 10.4 and 10.5.

	$y_1, \ldots, y_5$	u_{1R}	u_{1I}	u_{6R}	u_{6I}	x_{1R}	x_{1I}	x_{2R}	x_{2I}	
1.	- - - - -	0.410E-19	-0.863E-18	0.716	0.076	-0.690E-19	-0.120E-17	-3.750	-0.824E-16	R
2.	- - - - +	-0.806	-0.248	1.745	0.538	-0.462	0.127E-16	-0.573	0.000	R
3.	- - - + -	-0.995E-24	0.153E-23	0.335E-23	0.307E-23	0.066	0.397	-0.101E+24	-0.140E+24	
4.	- - - + +	-0.644E-14	-0.574E-13	-0.109E-12	0.159E-12	-0.227	0.195	-0.789E+13	-0.407E+13	
5.	- - + - -	0.127E-20	-0.459E-21	0.211E-20	0.704E-20	-0.010	-0.183	-0.170E+21	-0.160E+21	
6.	- - + - +	0.886	0.433	1.920	0.937	0.462	0.482E-15	-0.573	0.462E-14	R
7.	- - + + -	-0.457E-7	0.353E-6	0.191E-5	0.247E-6	0.256E-17	0.185	-0.560E+6	0.227E+7	C*
8.	- - + + +	-2.157	0.525	-0.595	-2.442	0.485E-13	-0.883	0.373	-0.308E-12	C
9.	- + - - -	-0.332E-7	0.101E-5	0.139E-5	0.455E-7	-0.147E-16	0.730	0.120E+7	-0.179E+6	C*
10.	- + - - +	0.941E-7	-0.128E-5	0.175E-5	0.129E-6	-0.238E-15	-0.730	0.105E+7	0.788E+6	C*
11.	- + - + -	0.836E-24	0.129E-23	0.442E-23	-0.217E-23	0.037	0.309	0.283E+24	0.123E+24	
12.	- + - + +	-0.943E-15	-0.694E-15	0.178E-14	-0.529E-15	-0.380	-0.503	-0.430E+15	0.788E+15	
13.	- + + - -	-0.108E-13	-0.192E-14	0.314E-14	-0.136E-13	-0.040	-0.786	0.443E+14	0.618E+14	
14.	- + + - +	-0.723E-13	-0.330E-13	-0.200E-12	0.383E-12	0.969E-2	0.184	0.349E+13	-0.117E+13	
15.	- + + + -	-0.144E-18	0.400E-19	-0.633E-20	-0.260E-18	-0.141	-0.557	-0.394E+19	0.251E+19	
16.	- + + + +	-0.172E-6	-0.265E-6	-0.143E-5	0.928E-6	-0.294E-16	0.185	0.413E+6	-0.160E+7	C*
17.	+ - - - -	0.928	1.371	1.552	-1.051	0.381E-16	0.883	0.373	-0.571E-16	C
18.	+ - - - +	-0.134E-15	0.802E-16	-0.111E-15	-0.181E-15	0.873E-2	-0.734	0.737E+16	-0.549E+16	
19.	+ - - + -	0.869E-18	0.115E-17	0.113E-17	-0.225E-17	-0.252	0.512	0.343E+18	-0.222E+18	
20.	+ - - + +	0.219E-6	-0.355E-6	0.192E-5	0.119E-5	0.301E-16	-0.185	0.780E+6	0.513E+6	C*
21.	+ - + - -	-0.143E-6	0.963E-6	0.132E-5	0.196E-6	-0.244E-15	0.730	-0.134E+7	0.200E+6	C*
22.	+ - + - +	-0.419E-18	0.315E-17	0.108E-16	-0.748E-17	-0.162	0.179	0.784E+17	0.121E+18	
23.	+ - + + -	-0.325E-13	0.160E-13	-0.174E-13	0.232E-13	1.113	0.566	0.552E+14	0.252E+14	
24.	+ - + + +	0.134E-6	-0.996E-6	0.136E-5	0.184E-6	-0.273E-16	-0.730	-0.118E+7	-0.881E+6	C*
25.	+ + - - -	-0.444E-14	-0.505E-14	0.717E-14	-0.594E-14	-0.021	-0.723	-0.546E+14	0.106E+15	
26.	+ + - - +	0.151E-22	0.154E-23	0.213E-23	-0.207E-22	0.765E-3	0.729	-0.138E+23	0.651E+23	
27.	+ + - + -	0.845E-13	0.101E-12	0.419E-12	0.793E-12	0.143	-0.031	0.147E+13	-0.720E+12	
28.	+ + - + +	-0.780E-14	-0.898E-14	-0.108E-12	-0.114E-13	0.080	0.075	-0.129E+14	-0.477E+13	
29.	+ + + - -	0.354E-6	0.132E-6	-0.716E-6	0.191E-5	0.609E-16	-0.185	-0.133E+7	-0.861E+6	C*
30.	+ + + - +	2.869	-1.084	0.296E-24	-0.265E-24	0.720E+25	0.279E+25	-5.729	-1.076	
31.	+ + + + -	-0.164E-17	-0.193E-17	-0.218E-17	0.307E-17	-0.168	0.652	0.262E+17	0.138E+18	
32.	+ + + + +	-0.300E-14	-0.155E-14	0.960E-14	-0.197E-13	0.329E-2	-0.154	0.282E+14	0.555E+14	
										13

R - Real root of ninth-degree stationary polynomial equation.
C - Complex root of ninth-degree stationary polynomial equation.
* - Number of Newton corrections exceeds acceptable range after ten bisections at t = 1.

Ideally, in addition to the five finite solutions in this example, there should be 27 roots at infinity consisting of 13 complex conjugate pairs and one real one. From Table 10.6, we see that this behavior does not occur. This result is tied to the ambiguity problem discussed in Section 10.1.2, and we suggest a possible solution to this problem below. In summary, we make the following observations from examination of several cases such as the one in Table 10.6:

- Among the $2^5 = 32$ trajectories, we obtain the nine roots yielded by the stationary polynomial equation in the original work, in addition to those at infinity. Unfortunately some of these roots at infinity occur with erroneously high multiplicities.
- Some complex conjugate pairs of roots of the ninth-degree stationary polynomial equation were revealed by AYC to be roots at infinity. This implies that the stationary behavior of a model may be governed by a polynomial equation of lower order than that obtained by reducing the system to a single polynomial equation (see Vickroy and Dutton, 1979 or Gelaro and Shirer, 1986). In the above example the suggested order is five.
- It is of interest to know the multiplicities of the roots at infinity. Those roots of multiplicity one would remain infinite, while those with greater multiplicities might become finite, for different values of hidden parameters -- those that are not included in the model but that are part of a physical problem (see Chapter 8).
- By identifying those roots at infinity having multiplicity one, we can greatly reduce the number of trajectories that we must follow after some initial run, because these roots would <u>never</u> be solutions to the model and so are irrelevant. Thus, AYC can become very efficient in succeeding runs at different parameter values, making the production of a bifurcation diagram an efficient procedure. For example, we might expect to follow those solutions associated with initial conditions number 1, 2, 6, 8, and 17 in Table 10.6.

- Unfortunately, the nonlinear parts of spectral models such as (10.80)-(10.84) are highly degenerate, and this implies that there are an infinite number of roots at infinity. This is related to the ambiguity problem discussed at the end of Section 10.1.2.
- A solution to the above ambiguity problem might be to somehow perturb the spectral equations by adding to the system very small quadratic terms. These terms may alter the finite solutions very slightly, but should also separate roots at infinity into finitely many identifiable conjugate pairs. Initial tests with this procedure indicated that it showed some merit and may be a step in resolving this problem.

CHAPTER 11

TYPICAL BRANCHING FORMS: PERIODIC SOLUTIONS

ROBERT J. PYLE

Throughout the previous discussion of the solutions to spectral systems, we noted that there were two fundamentally different ways by which stationary solutions could lose stability to other solutions. The first is signaled by the vanishing of a single characteristic exponent and the second by the vanishing of the real parts of a conjugate pair of exponents. So far, we have concentrated on the first case, in which a new stationary solution branches from the old one. In this chapter we begin to discuss in more detail the second case, in which a temporally periodic solution emanates from the stationary one. This process is known as Hopf bifurcation, and in the first section below we explain why Hopf bifurcation is expected to produce a temporally periodic solution. Later in the chapter, we consider some of the constraints on the branching behavior that are imposed on the periodic solutions. Finally we introduce a spectral model of a physical system possessing branching periodic solutions that can be obtained analytically.

11.1 Hopf Bifurcation

Whether we consider systems of partial differential equations or systems of ordinary differential equations, we have seen in Chapters 2 and 4 that we may examine the stability of a stationary solution x^s by determining the temporal solutions to the problem linearized about x^s. In both cases, the pure solutions to the linear equations have the form

$$A(t) = \hat{A} \exp[(\lambda_r + i\lambda_i)t] \quad , \tag{11.1}$$

in which λ_r represents the rate of growth or decay of the solution away from or toward x^s. We may use a trigonometric identity to rewrite (11.1) as

$$A(t) = \hat{A} \exp(\lambda_r t)[\cos(\lambda_i t) + i \sin(\lambda_i t)] \quad . \tag{11.2}$$

In general, the amplitude $\hat{A} = \hat{A}_r + i\hat{A}_i$ is complex, and so we may express (11.2) as

$$A(t) = \{[\hat{A}_r \cos(\lambda_i t) - \hat{A}_i \sin(\lambda_i t)] + i[\hat{A}_r \sin(\lambda_i t) + \hat{A}_i \cos(\lambda_i t)]\} \exp(\lambda_r t)$$

$$= [\hat{B}_r(t) + i\,\hat{B}_i(t)] \exp(\lambda_r t) = \hat{B}(t) \exp(\lambda_r t) \quad . \tag{11.3}$$

Now we see that $A(t)$ is composed of a complex periodic component $\hat{B}(t)$ having a period $T = 2\pi/\lambda_i$ and an amplifying or decaying component $\exp(\lambda_r t)$ having a rate λ_r (Fig. 11.1a,c); in the case $\lambda_r = 0$ of neutral stability, the variation in $A(t)$ is given entirely by the periodic component $\hat{B}(t)$ (Fig. 11.1b). In the nonlinear problem, we expect that an exchange of stability to a new solution would occur at a

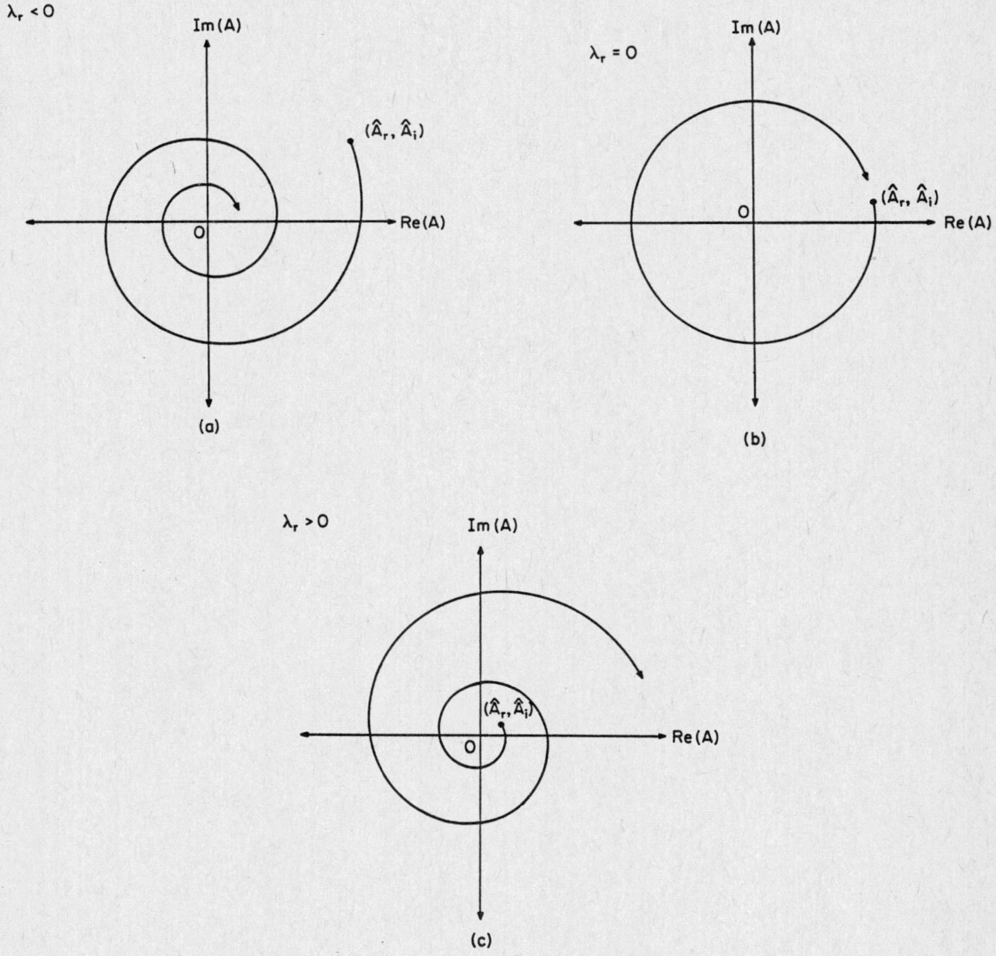

Fig. 11.1 Examples of linear solutions when $\lambda_i \neq 0$ in the cases of decay ($\lambda_r < 0$), (a); neutrality ($\lambda_r = 0$), (b); and amplification ($\lambda_r > 0$), (c). The initial conditions in each case are $\hat{A} = (\hat{A}_r, \hat{A}_i)$.

critical value R_H of the control parameter R given by setting $\lambda_r = 0$. It is easy to see from Fig. 11.1b that a plausible candidate for the new solution is a periodic one having period $T = 2\pi/\lambda_i$; significantly, the above two-dimensional case provides the correct picture for the n-dimensional one.

But how can a temporally periodic solution, along which there is motion in phase space, be created from a stationary point? A reasonable way is for the amplitude of the periodic solution to approach zero as $R \to R_H$, as shown in Fig. 11.2. Periodic solutions created in this way we call closed orbits, or simply orbits, because the motion in phase space involves revolutions around a stationary point much as a planet revolves about a star (Fig. 11.3).

Thus we can imagine that a periodic solution could emanate from a stationary one, but for this event to occur in the nonlinear problem, we must suppose that the outwardly spiraling solution shown in Fig. 11.1c actually approaches an orbit. This behavior occurs if sufficiently large perturbations spiral in toward the origin, while small perturbations spiral out, thereby creating a closed curve P(t) toward

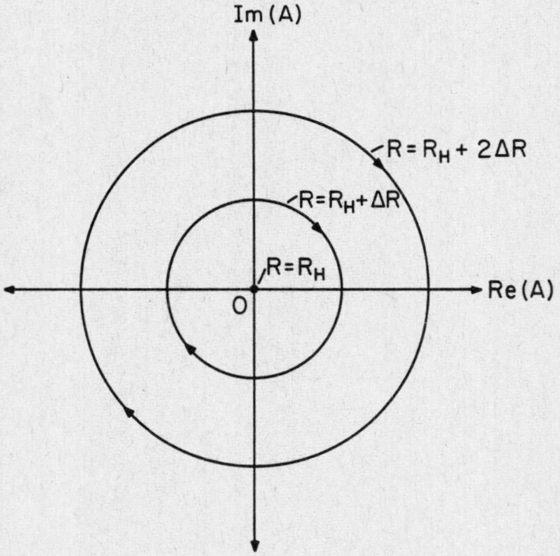

Fig. 11.2 Examples of a temporally periodic solution branching from a stationary solution A=0 at $R=R_H$; note that the amplitude of the solution, or the radius of the circle, increases from 0 as $|R-R_H|$ increases.

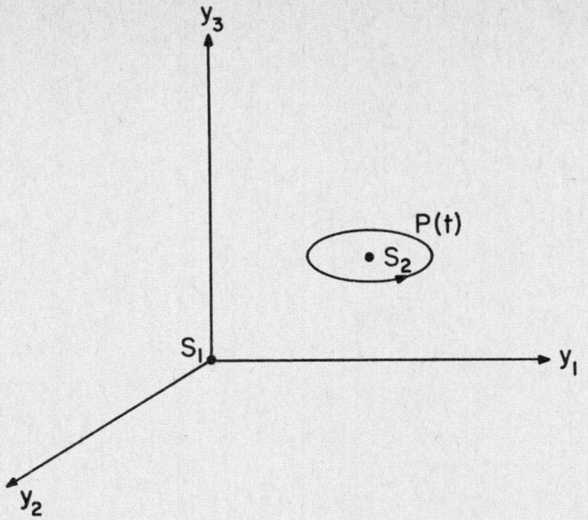

Fig. 11.3 Examples of solutions to a typical low-order model. Stationary solutions are represented by points S_1 and S_2 and a branching periodic one is represented by an orbit P(t) about S_2.

which all perturbations tend (Fig. 11.4). It is easy to see that in two dimensions, this mechanism produces a stable periodic solution that grows from the trivial one, but as we discover below, this mechanism applies to n-dimensional systems as well.

In Section 6.1 we noted that hydrodynamic problems are examples of forced dissipative systems in which nontrivial solutions are possible when forcing and dissipation balance. In that section we argued that dissipation can in many situations overwhelm the forcing, leading to the decay of arbitrarily large perturbations and the existence of a globally unique trivial solution. Once the magnitude of the forcing is increased sufficiently, small perturbations of the trivial solution would amplify, but large perturbations would decay. As we show in Section 17.3.3 this phenomenon leads to the eventual confinement of the solutions to a bounded region of phase space. In the present context, this observation means that the spiraling solutions cannot grow without bound and must converge toward some limiting path. Fortunately, this expanding solution becomes confined in the n-dimensional problem to a two-dimensional surface known as the <u>center manifold</u>, and this surface can be adequately pictured as the two-dimensional plane of Fig. 11.4 (see Section 2 of

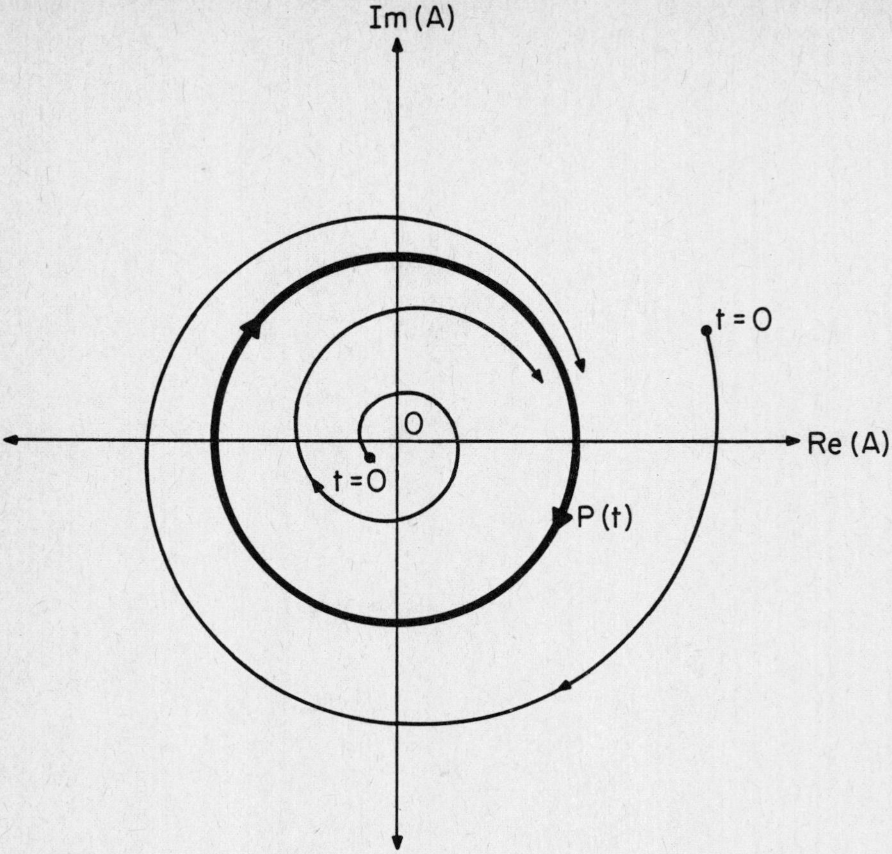

Fig. 11.4 A two-dimensional example of a small perturbation spiraling out from the origin 0 and a large perturbation spiraling in toward 0. The limiting boundary is a periodic solution P(t).

Marsden and McCracken, 1976). Thus even in the nonlinear problem we expect that outwardly spiraling trajectories may approach a temporally periodic solution, as shown in Fig. 11.4. It is easy to create simple examples whose solutions match those in Fig. 11.4, and we present one of them in Chapter 14.

The above results were formalized and proved by Hopf (1942) and have been summarized in the Hopf Bifurcation Theorem (see Section 3 in Marsden and McCracken, 1976 or Section 3.4 in Guckenheimer and Holmes, 1983). There are versions of this theorem for partial differential equations, but here we only present one for ordinary differential equations.

Hopf Bifurcation Theorem. For an n-dimensional ordinary differential system $\dot{y} = f(y,R)$, suppose that $f(0,R) = 0$ for all values of the control parameter R and that the differential matrix $Df(0,R)$ has a pair of complex conjugate eigenvalues, or characteristic exponents, $\lambda(R) = \lambda_r(R) + i\lambda_i(R)$ and $\lambda(R) = \lambda_r(R) - i\lambda_i(R)$. Furthermore, suppose that there is a value R_H of R such that $\lambda_r(R_H) = 0$, $\lambda_r(R) > 0$ for $R > R_H$, and $\partial\lambda_r/\partial R > 0$ when $R = R_H$. Then bifurcating from $y = 0$ at $R = R_H$ there exists a unique periodic solution whose squared amplitude grows approximately as $|R - R_H|$ and whose period T obeys

$$\lim_{R \to R_H} [T(R)] = \lim_{R \to R_H} [2\pi/\lambda_i(R)] = 2\pi/\omega_o \quad . \tag{11.4}$$

Here R_H is the *Hopf bifurcation point* and ω_o is the *limiting frequency* of the periodic solution. Moreover, at $R = R_H$, the stability of the stationary solution is exchanged with that of the periodic solution when the branching is supercritical. When the branching is subcritical, locally stability is lost. Finally, transcritically branching solutions are impossible, at least in the classical case discussed here (see Section 11.2). In Section 14.1 we give a simple example illustrating supercritically branching behavior as a prelude to showing how to calculate the stability of a periodic solution.

The requirement that a complex conjugate pair of characteristic exponents crosses the imaginary axis with nonzero speed (Fig. 11.5) is a crucial hypothesis, for it leads to the conclusion that only one periodic solution emanates from the trivial solution. For example, if this hypothesis is removed, then according to Chafee (1968) a pair of supercritically bifurcating solutions may be expected to appear. This result is not structurally stable, however; that is, it is easy to perturb the system of equations, causing the exponents to cross with nonzero speed and causing one periodic solution to disappear. Significantly, the single periodic solution expected from the Hopf Bifurcation Theorem is structurally stable: The solution does not disappear when the equations are altered slightly, although the value of R_H and the dependence of the amplitude on $|R - R_H|$ might vary slightly.

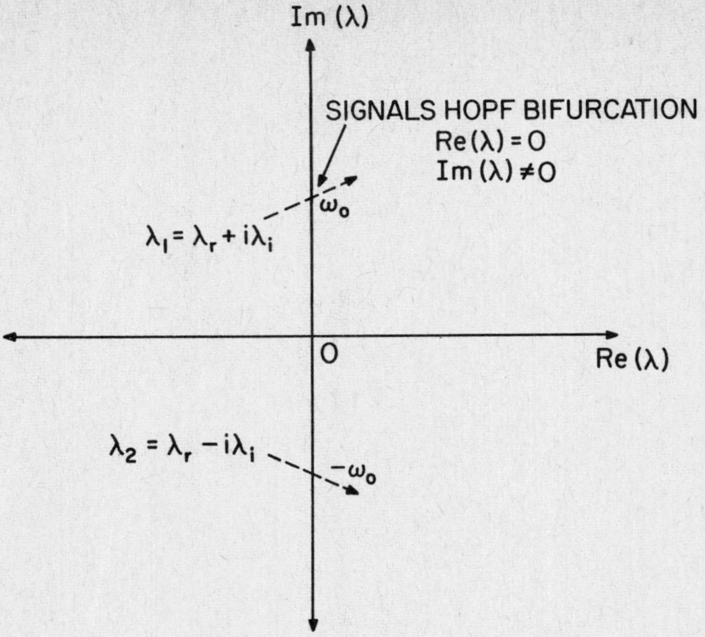

Fig. 11.5 A Hopf bifurcation occurs when the conjugate pair λ_1 and λ_2 of characteristic exponents crosses the Im(λ) axis with nonzero speed. The limiting frequency ω_o of the branching periodic solution is the value of λ_i at $R=R_H$.

11.2 Symmetry Requirements

We saw in Section 6.2 that in typical hydrodynamic problems, the presence of a parameter range in which a unique solution exists places restrictions on the admissible forms for the polynomial equations governing the magnitudes of the branching stationary solutions. Similar restrictions apply to the branching periodic solutions whose existence is implied by the Hopf Bifurcation Theorem. That is, we assume that the hypotheses of the theorem are satisfied, implying that a branching solution having amplitude $\hat{A} \propto |R - R_H|^{1/2}$ is temporally periodic. In this section, we use these restrictions to illustrate that only supercritical and subcritical branching solutions are possible.

As we saw in Section 3.1.2, a propagating wave of a single horizontal wavenumber m may be represented as

$$f(x,t) = A_m(t)\,\sin(\frac{2m\pi x}{L}) + B_m(t)\,\cos(\frac{2m\pi x}{L}) \quad . \tag{11.5}$$

If we set

$$A_m(t) = \hat{A}\cos(\omega t) \quad , \tag{11.6}$$

$$B_m(t) = -\hat{A}\sin(\omega t) \quad , \tag{11.7}$$

then we may rewrite (11.5) as

$$f(x,t) = \hat{A}\sin(-\omega t + \frac{2m\pi x}{L}) \quad . \tag{11.8}$$

We found that in phase space a linearly translating wave of fixed amplitude $\hat{A}$ was represented by a circular trajectory having radius $\hat{A}$ (see Fig. 3.2) and so we might expect that a branching periodic solution in a spectral model would take the form (11.6)-(11.7) in certain special circumstances. We illustrate such circumstances in Section 11.3 where we discuss a nonlinear model whose periodic solutions we can obtain analytically.

Because the periodic solution of amplitude $\hat{A}$ originates from a stationary solution that is at the center of the orbit, we conclude that $\hat{A} \to 0$ as $R \to R_H$ (see Fig. 11.2). In most applications, it is convenient to shift the origin of the phase space to the location of the stationary solution so that it is given by $\hat{A} = 0$. In general we must obtain $\hat{A}$ via a power series expansion in $|R - R_H|^{1/2}$ (see Chapter 13), but in some cases $\hat{A}$ can be shown to satisfy a polynomial equation (see Section 11.3.4). Any such equation governing $\hat{A}$ must not have a constant term; moreover the polynomial function must be of odd degree so that there may exist a range $-\infty < R < R_u$ for which the trivial solution is unique (see Section 6.2). Consequently, the simplest form governing $\hat{A}$ would be a cubic polynomial equation

$$C_3\hat{A}^3 + C_1\hat{A} = 0 \quad , \tag{11.9}$$

in which the amplitude $|\hat{A}|$ of the periodic solution is given by

$$|\hat{A}|^2 = -C_1/C_3 \quad . \tag{11.10}$$

Clearly, $C_1 \propto |R - R_H|$ in order that a conclusion of the Hopf Bifurcation Theorem is satisfied: the squared amplitude of the periodic solution must decay linearly to zero as R approaches the bifurcation point R_H. Solutions to (11.9) are seen to produce the usual trident branching form that we obtained for stationary solutions (Fig. 11.6; compare with Fig. 6.2); as in the case of stationary solutions, the branching direction depends on the sign of the function $C_1(R - R_H)$.

To obtain a complete picture of the branching behavior in the phase space given by A_m, B_m, and R, we note that the positive solution (11.10) to (11.9) can be combined with the expressions in (11.6)-(11.7) to give the temporal behavior of A_m B_m:

$$A_m(t) = (-C_1/C_3)^{1/2} \cos(\omega t) \quad , \tag{11.11}$$

$$B_m(t) = -(-C_1/C_3)^{1/2} \sin(\omega t) \quad . \tag{11.12}$$

At t = 0 and t = T/2 = π/ω, we have $B_m = 0$, and so A_m takes on the trident form (Fig. 11.7a). Similarly, at t = T/4 and t = 3T/4, we have $A_m = 0$ and B_m takes on the

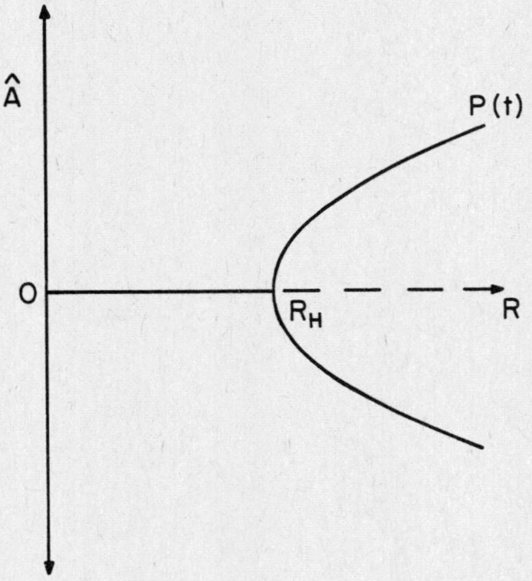

Fig. 11.6 Representation of a periodic solution P(t) branching supercritically from a trivial one. Here the amplitude of the solution is $|\hat{A}|$ and the Hopf bifurcation point is R_H. Stable solutions are denoted by solid lines, unstable ones by dashed lines.

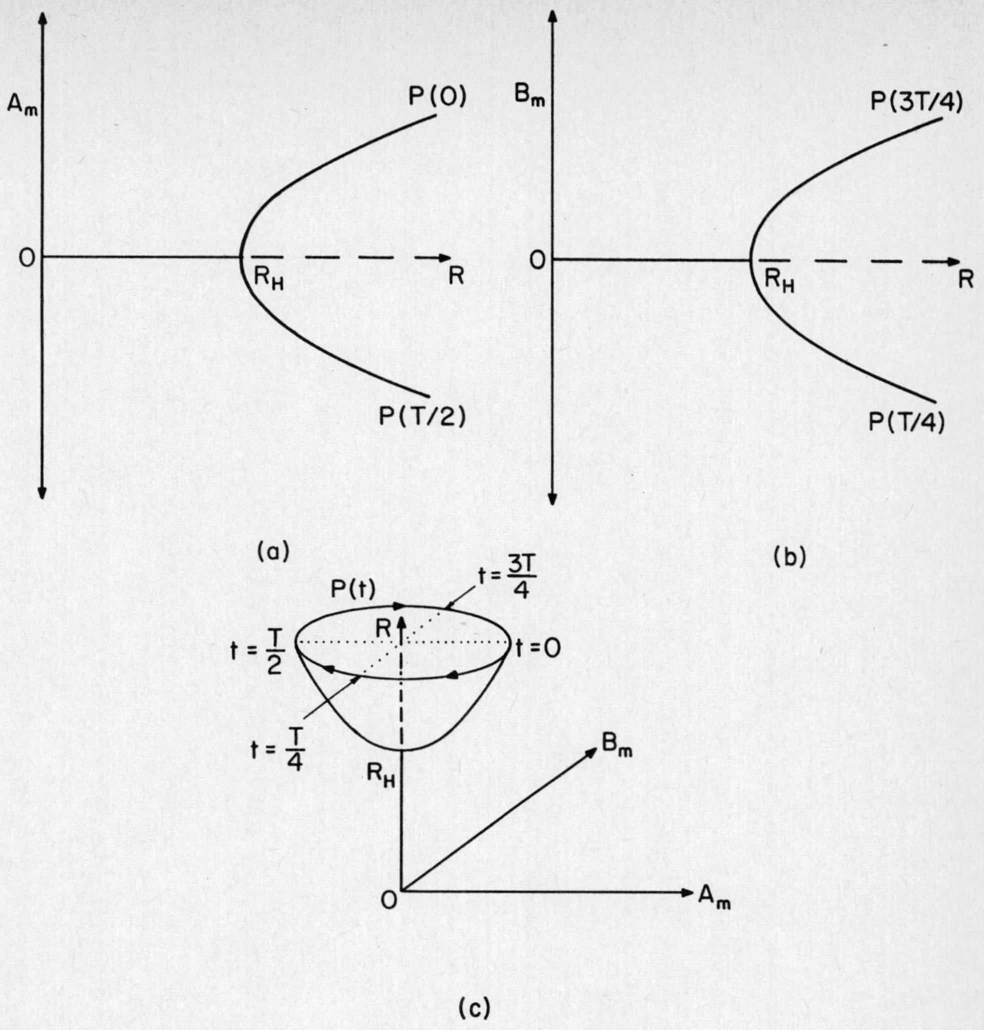

Fig. 11.7 Bifurcation diagram for the supercritically branching periodic solution P(t) also shown in Fig. 11.6. In (a) the solution at t=0 (upper curve) and t=T/2 (lower curve) is given, in (b) at t=T/4 (lower curve) and t=3T/4 (upper curve), and in (c) at all times t. The sense of the temporal variation is given in (c) by the arrows. Stable and unstable solutions are denoted by solid and dashed lines, respectively.

trident form (Fig. 11.7b). Next we observe that the forms in Fig. 11.7a,b are cross sections through a three-dimensional figure that resembles a bowl, as illustrated in Fig. 11.7c. The resulting figure can be imagined as a trident spinning about the R-axis at the frequency ω, and either subcritical or supercritical branching is produced in this manner. In general ω may be a function of R (see Chapter 13), and ω gives the rate of travel around the orbit, as shown by the arrows in Fig. 11.7c.

Another conceivable form for the amplitude polynomial equation is the one for the shifted trident:

$$C_3\hat{A}^3 + C_2\hat{A}^2 + C_1\hat{A} = 0 \quad ; \tag{11.13}$$

we found in Section 6.3.1 that this produces transcritical branching. This form is illustrated in Figs. 11.8 and 11.9 in the case $C_1 \propto R - R_H$, with the amplitude $\hat{A}$ as ordinate in Fig. 11.8 and the magnitude $|\hat{A}|$ used in Fig. 11.9. This form is unacceptable for the following fundamental reasons: First, because $C_1 \propto R - R_H$, we

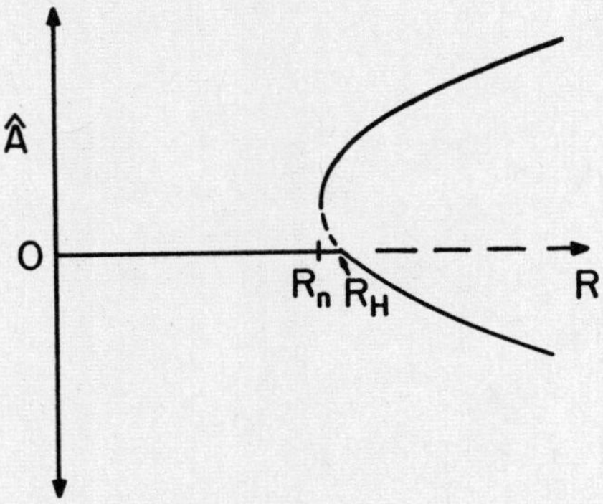

Fig. 11.8 Hypothesized shifted trident showing the amplitude coefficient $\hat{A}$ of a periodic solution as a function of R. The hypothetical solution meets the trivial solution at $R = R_H$. Clearly the slope of the branching solution is finite at $R=R_H$, in contradiction to the form required by the Hopf Bifurcation Theorem (compare with Fig. 11.9).

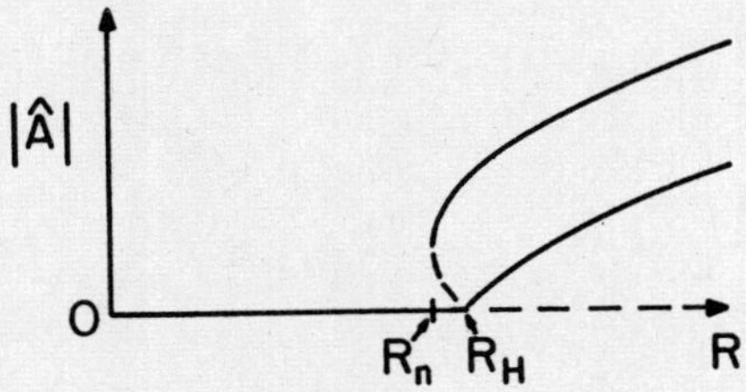

Fig. 11.9 Hypothesized shifted trident showing the magnitude $|\hat{A}|$ of the amplitude $\hat{A}$ of transcritically branching periodic solutions. Apparently two solutions meet the trivial one at $R=R_H$, in contradiction to the uniqueness requirement of the Hopf Bifurcation Theorem (compare with Fig. 11.8).

conclude that $\hat{A} \propto |R - R_H|$ for small $\hat{A}$; but from the Hopf Bifurcation Theorem, we know that the form should be $\hat{A} \propto |R - R_H|^{1/2}$. Second, the conclusion that $\hat{A} \propto |R - R_H|^{1/2}$ implies in turn that $\partial\hat{A}/\partial R \to \infty$ as $R \to R_H$; however, from Fig. 11.8, we clearly see that the slope of the transcritical curve is finite. Alternatively we might imagine that the bifurcating solution could be obtained by spinning the form in Fig. 11.8 about the R-axis. In this case, the slope argument above shows that this form must violate the hypotheses of the Hopf Bifurcation Theorem. To see this contradiction, we show in Fig. 11.9 the absolute value $|\hat{A}|$ of $\hat{A}$, in which it is obvious that the slope of the branching solution is finite. Moreover, apparently two bifurcating solutions appear at $R = R_H$, but the Hopf Bifurcation Theorem ensures that only one can appear. As the above transcritical behavior originates from the even-degree term in the amplitude polynomial equation (11.13), we conclude generally that only odd-degree terms can be accepted.

The next possible case to consider is a quintic polynomial equation for $\hat{A}$ given by

$$C_5\hat{A}^5 + C_3\hat{A}^3 + C_1\hat{A} = 0 \quad . \tag{11.14}$$

In this case we can represent $|\hat{A}|$ by the form in Fig. 11.10a; as before, upon representing $\hat{A}$ as a function of A_m and B_m, we obtain the form in Fig. 11.10b. If we take cross sections parallel to the $A_m - B_m$ plane, then we find the orbits illustrated in Fig. 11.11. In contrast to the difficulties encountered in the shifted trident case above, there are no problems finding the orbits here. The circles are concentric with common centers at zero, and we find that this characteristic is the crucial one.

As we begin moving up the R-axis in Fig. 11.10b, we observe that for $R < R_1$ there is no orbit, but that at $R = R_1 = R_n$, suddenly an orbit appears. As R increases in value, two orbits split off the first one, an inner one having radius A_{in}, and an outer one having radius A_{out}. As we move up the R-axis toward R_2, the magnitude of A_{in} decreases and the magnitude of A_{out} increases. Furthermore, as we continue toward R_3, A_{in} decreases to a very small value and A_{out} increases in magnitude. At the bifurcation point R_H, the inner orbit shrinks to a point and

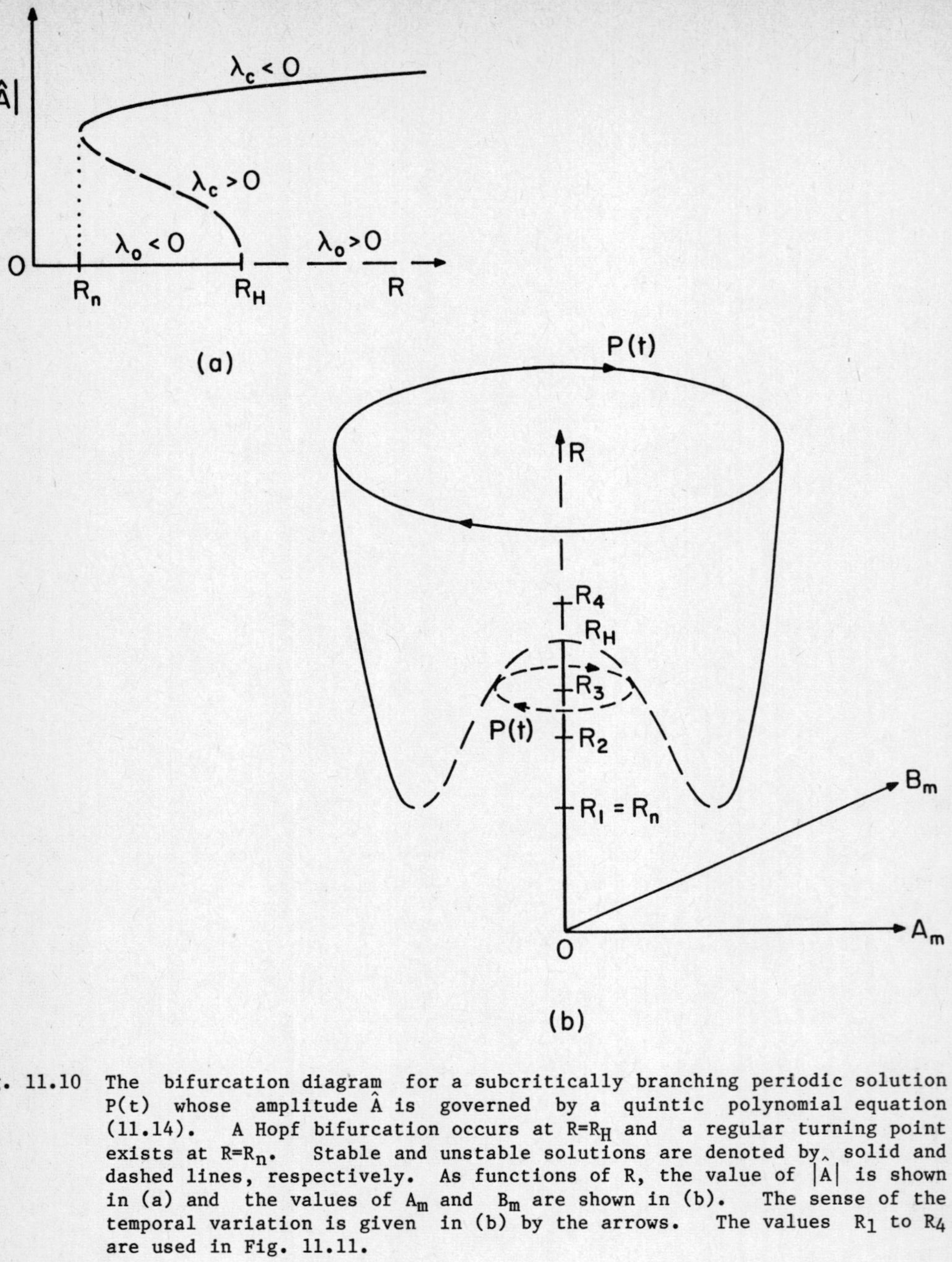

Fig. 11.10 The bifurcation diagram for a subcritically branching periodic solution P(t) whose amplitude $\hat{A}$ is governed by a quintic polynomial equation (11.14). A Hopf bifurcation occurs at $R=R_H$ and a regular turning point exists at $R=R_n$. Stable and unstable solutions are denoted by solid and dashed lines, respectively. As functions of R, the value of $|\hat{A}|$ is shown in (a) and the values of A_m and B_m are shown in (b). The sense of the temporal variation is given in (b) by the arrows. The values R_1 to R_4 are used in Fig. 11.11.

disappears. Finally when we reach R_4, the outer orbit is the only one remaining. Following an analysis paralleling that for the cubic case, we do not allow the quintic $\hat{A}$ polynomial equation to contain even powers of $\hat{A}$. Such an inclusion would cause the same type of problem we saw above with the shifted trident.

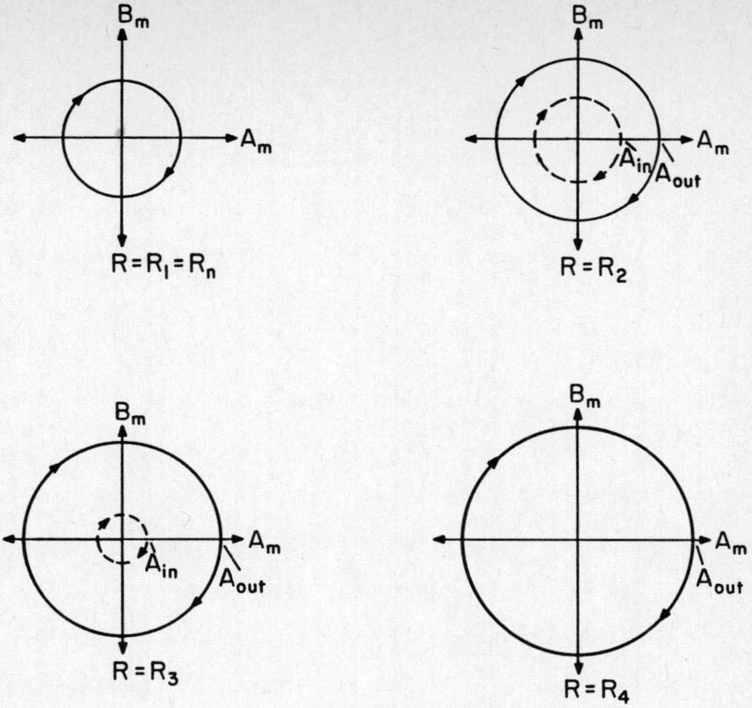

Fig. 11.11 Cross sections perpendicular to the R-axis at the four values R_1 to R_4 of R given in Fig. 11.10. Here A_{in} and A_{out} are the radii of the dashed and solid orbits, respectively. The arrows give the sense of the temporal variation.

Thus to summarize, we find that the symmetry requirements are reflected in the form of the $\hat{A}$ polynomial equation: as with stationary solutions, only odd-degree polynomials are possible, but in the periodic solution case, only odd powers of $\hat{A}$ are admissible. As a consequence, the possible terms are severely limited in the $\hat{A}$ polynomial equations governing the amplitudes of branching periodic solutions. The above discussion is motivated in part by the supposition that sinusoidal forms can be found for periodic solutions to nonlinear spectral modes. These do exist (e.g. Shirer, 1980; Mitchell and Dutton, 1981), as we show in the next section.

11.3 Sinusoidal Forms That Solve the Nonlinear Equations

We noted in Section 11.1 that a traveling wave A(t) of amplitude $\hat{A}$ often corresponds to a periodic solution in phase space. In particular, this periodic solution appears as a closed orbit when it is displayed in terms of the real and imaginary parts of A (see Fig. 11.2). To represent such a periodic solution in a spectral model, we must therefore have at least two spectral components for each horizontal and vertical wavenumber pair (m,n), one for the real part and the other for the imaginary part of the amplitude. This situation occurs, for example, if we include both sin(mx) sin(nz) and cos(mx) sin(nz) as basis functions when we form the spectral equations.

A physical system in which propagating waves might be expected is shallow convection occurring within an environment having a height-dependent basic wind $\underset{\sim}{V}(z)$. Examples of such systems include cloud streets, which are bands of clouds that commonly develop behind cold fronts as cold air masses pour over warmer water (see Chapter 12). These rolls provide the most likely atmospheric examples of Rayleigh-Bénard convection, and so study of Rayleigh-Bénard convection in the presence of a height-dependent background wind is a natural extension of the problem. We find in this section that inclusion of a basic wind causes the time-independent solutions obtained earlier in the monograph to become temporally periodic, with their periods given by functions of certain Fourier coefficients of $\underset{\sim}{V}$ and $\partial^2 \underset{\sim}{V}/\partial z^2$.

11.3.1 Incorporation of the basic wind. Here we use the Boussinesq system to model two-dimensional shallow convection (see Section 2.1 for further details). Typically in the Boussinesq system, convection is regarded as a perturbation on a motionless hydrostatic basic state in which the basic temperature field varies linearly with height. When the equations are written in this form, the trivial solution corresponds to the conductive state and a nontrivial solution corresponds to a convective state.

Here we modify the system to include an arbitrary background flow $\underset{\sim}{V}(z)$ in the basic state, but convection still is represented by a superimposed perturbation. This basic current is of much larger temporal and spatial scales than the perturbations so that $\underset{\sim}{V}$ can be taken to be independent of both time and the eddy effects incorporated in the eddy viscosity ν and the eddy thermometric conductivity κ. In this model, which is based on one discussed by Shirer (1980), the presence of a basic current adds important terms to the equations and the trivial solution is still available to the system.

To incorporate the basic wind, we first take the x-axis and the unit vector $\underset{\sim}{i}$ to be perpendicular to the roll axis and then take the y-axis and the unit vector $\underset{\sim}{j}$ to be parallel to the roll axis as shown in Fig. 11.12. Since the model is two-dimensional, all variations in the y-direction or along the cloud band axis, are neglected. The basic wind vector $\underset{\sim}{V}$ may be directed at any angle to the roll, but for the present purposes we need only consider the component U of $\underset{\sim}{V}$ that is perpendicular to the roll. If we denote the eastward coordinate by x_c and the unit vector $\underset{\sim}{i}_c$ and the northward coordinate by y_c and the unit vector $\underset{\sim}{j}_c$, then the reference wind velocity can be written as

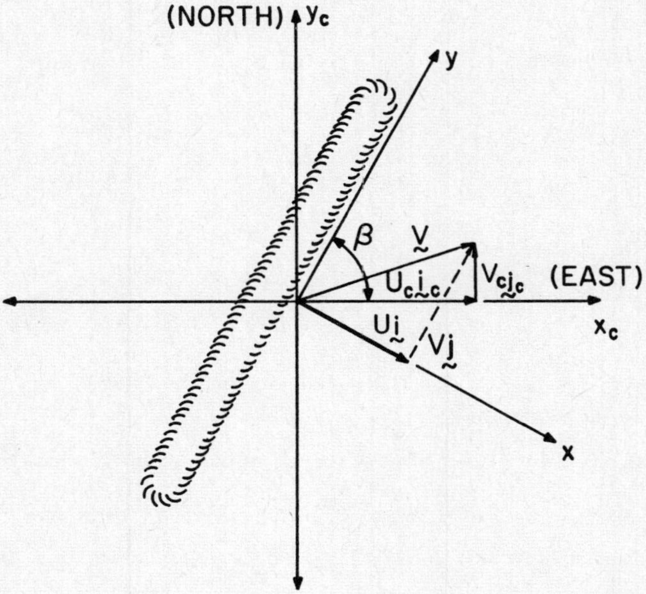

Fig. 11.12 The cloud street coordinate system used in the Shirer (1980) model. The wavy line denotes a cloud band oriented along the y-axis. Eastward and northward directions are denoted by x_c and y_c, respectively. The orientation angle β is the angle between the roll axis and east. Only the perpendicular wind component U enters the system here; the parallel wind component V is denoted by the dashed arrow (after Shirer, 1980).

$$\underset{\sim}{V}(z) = U_c(z)\underset{\sim}{i}_c + V_c(z)\underset{\sim}{j}_c = U(z)\underset{\sim}{i} + V(z)\underset{\sim}{j} \quad . \tag{11.15}$$

Because we neglect components along the roll, we neglect $V(z)$ here; however, if we retain the Coriolis force, then we cannot neglect $V(z)$, as we discover in Chapter 12. With $\underset{\sim}{V}(z)$ denoting the basic wind profile, then together with the perturbation $\underset{\sim}{v}'$, we write the total wind in the cloud street coordinate system as

$$\underset{\sim}{V}(z) + \underset{\sim}{v}'(x,z,t) = [U(z) + u'(x,z,t)]\underset{\sim}{i} + w'(x,z,t)\underset{\sim}{k} \quad . \tag{11.16}$$

Using the expansions (2.2)-(2.4) and (2.6)-(2.8) for the state variables $p(x,z,t)$, $\rho(x,z,t)$ and $T(x,z,t)$ and using the stream function definition (2.13)-(2.14), we write the dimensional equations as (cf. (2.17)-(2.18))

$$\frac{\partial}{\partial t}(\nabla^2\psi) + J(\psi,\nabla^2\psi) - \frac{g}{T_{oo}}\frac{\partial T'}{\partial x} + U\frac{\partial}{\partial x}(\nabla^2\psi) - \frac{\partial^2 U}{\partial z^2}\frac{\partial\psi}{\partial x} - \nu\nabla^4\psi = 0 \quad , \tag{11.17}$$

$$\frac{\partial T'}{\partial t} + J(\psi,T') + U\frac{\partial T'}{\partial x} - \frac{\Delta_z T}{z_T}\frac{\partial\psi}{\partial x} - \kappa\nabla^2 T' = 0 \quad . \tag{11.18}$$

To create a dimensionless system, we add to the definitions (2.20)-(2.24) and (2.27)-(2.30) the expressions

$$U(z) = |\underset{\sim}{V}(z_T)|U^*(z^*)\pi \quad , \tag{11.19}$$

$$Re = |\underset{\sim}{V}(z_T)|z_T/\nu \quad , \tag{11.20}$$

in which $|\underset{\sim}{V}(z_T)|$ is the wind speed at the top z_T of the domain and Re is a Reynolds number that provides a measure of the wind stress at the top of the domain. Now we may write the Boussinesq system (11.17)-(11.18) in the dimensionless form

$$\frac{\partial}{\partial t^*}(\tilde{\nabla}^2\psi^*) + J(\psi^*,\tilde{\nabla}^2\psi^*) - P\frac{\partial T^*}{\partial x^*} + \underline{Re\, P\, U^*\frac{\partial}{\partial x^*}(\tilde{\nabla}^2\psi^*)} - \underline{Re\, P\frac{\partial^2 U^*}{\partial z^{*2}}\frac{\partial\psi^*}{\partial x^*}} - \frac{P}{a}\tilde{\nabla}^4\psi^* = 0 \quad , \tag{11.21}$$

$$\frac{\partial T^*}{\partial t^*} + J(\psi^*,T^*) + \underline{Re\, P\, U^*\frac{\partial T^*}{\partial x^*}} - Ra\frac{\partial\psi^*}{\partial x^*} - \frac{1}{a}\tilde{\nabla}^2 T^* = 0 \quad . \tag{11.22}$$

This is the system considered by Shirer (1980), except that he uses a different dimensionless form for the background wind U(z) and he uses a different domain in the vertical. If we assume that the inversion height z_T provides a cap on the vertical extent of the convective circulation, then we may use the domain $0 \leq x^* \leq 2\pi$, $0 \leq z^* \leq \pi$, as we have done throughout the monograph. Use of this domain does not alter significantly any of the results reported by Shirer (1980) but provides a more realistic setting for the model. For boundary conditions, we assume that the flow is cyclically continuous in the horizontal so that the background wind can advect the rolls across the domain, and we assume that the upper and lower boundaries are rigid, stress-free, and conducting. Thus we require that (cf. (2.42)-(2.44))

$$\chi^*(0,z^*) = \chi^*(2\pi,z^*), \text{ for all variables } \chi^*(x^*,z^*) \quad , \tag{11.23}$$

$$\psi^*(x^*,0) = \psi^*(x^*,\pi) = \tilde{\nabla}^2\psi^*(x^*,0) = \tilde{\nabla}^2\psi^*(x^*,\pi) = T^*(x^*,0) = T^*(x^*,\pi) = 0 \quad . \tag{11.24}$$

Upon comparison of (2.25)-(2.26) with (11.21)-(11.22), we see that the three underlined terms have been added to the Boussinesq equations. These terms are the ones that allow the temporal solutions to develop. As we discuss in more detail in Chapter 12, the wind component U perpendicular to the roll can act in some cases as a source of energy for the circulation, but in other cases as a sink. Here we note that, when we use the definitions (2.46)-(2.47) for roll kinetic energy KE and available potential energy AE, we obtain

$$\frac{\partial}{\partial t^*}(KE + AE) = GA + RS - DI \quad , \tag{11.25}$$

in which the energy generation GA and dissipation rate DI are given in (2.51)-(2.52). The new term RS is given by

$$RS = Re\ P\int_0^{2\pi}\int_0^{\pi} U^*\psi^* \frac{\partial}{\partial x^*}(\tilde{\nabla}^2\psi^*)\, dz^*dx^* - Re\ P\int_0^{2\pi}\int_0^{\pi} \frac{\partial^2 U^*}{\partial z^{*2}}\psi^* \frac{\partial\psi^*}{\partial x^*}\, dz^*dx^*$$

$$- Re\ P\int_0^{2\pi}\int_0^{\pi} U^*T^* \frac{\partial T^*}{\partial x^*}\, dz^*dx^* \quad . \tag{11.26}$$

The last two integrals vanish owing to cyclic continuity in the horizontal. The first integral can be manipulated as

$$RS = Re\ P\int_0^{2\pi}\int_0^{\pi} [\frac{\partial}{\partial x^*}(U^*\psi^* \frac{\partial^2\psi^*}{\partial x^{*2}}) - U^* \frac{\partial\psi^*}{\partial x^*}\frac{\partial^2\psi^*}{\partial x^{*2}} + \frac{\partial}{\partial z^*}(U^*\psi^* \frac{\partial^2\psi^*}{\partial x^*\partial z^*}) - \frac{\partial U^*}{\partial z^*}\psi^* \frac{\partial^2\psi^*}{\partial x^*\partial z^*}$$

$$- U^* \frac{\partial\psi^*}{\partial z^*}\frac{\partial^2\psi^*}{\partial x^*\partial z^*}]\ dz^*dx^*$$

$$= -\ Re\ P\int_0^{2\pi}\int_0^{\pi} [\frac{\partial}{\partial x^*}(\frac{\partial U^*}{\partial z^*}\psi^* \frac{\partial\psi^*}{\partial z^*}) - \frac{\partial\psi^*}{\partial x^*}\frac{\partial\psi^*}{\partial z^*}\frac{\partial U^*}{\partial z^*}]\ dz^*dx^*$$

$$= Re\ P\int_0^{2\pi}\int_0^{\pi} \frac{\partial\psi^*}{\partial x^*}\frac{\partial\psi^*}{\partial z^*}\frac{\partial U^*}{\partial z^*}\ dz^*dx^*$$

$$= -\ Re\ P\int_0^{2\pi}\int_0^{\pi} u^*w^* \frac{\partial U^*}{\partial z^*}\ dz^*dx^* \quad . \tag{11.27}$$

Upon application of the boundary conditions (11.23)-(11.24), we find that only the fourth term in the first line of (11.27) survives; this term can be rewritten in the more convenient forms given in the third and fourth lines. Now we see that the magnitude of RS measures the vertical momentum flux owing to the background flow, and RS is sometimes called a shear production term. We refer to the term as the Reynolds stress because a similar term appears in turbulence theory and serves as a measure of how severely the shearing basic wind field stresses the fluid. In Chapter 12 we discuss the effects of this term on cloud street development.

11.3.2 The spectral equations. The domain we consider is the usual rectangular one in which the variables satisfy the boundary conditions (11.23)-(11.24). Thus, we may use sinusoidal functions to represent ψ^* and T^*. A truncation based on the one (2.73)-(2.74) for the Lorenz model is

$$\psi^*(x^*,z^*,t^*) = \psi_{m1}(t^*)\sin(mx^*)\sin z^* + \phi_{m1}(t^*)\cos(mx^*)\sin z^* \quad , \tag{11.28}$$

$$T^*(x^*,z^*,t^*) = T_{m1}(t^*)\cos(mx^*)\sin z^* +$$

$$\theta_{m1}(t^*)\sin(mx^*)\sin z^* + T_{02}(t^*)\sin(2z^*) \quad , \tag{11.29}$$

in which m is an integer representing the number of cells in the domain.

We have included the two new coefficients ϕ_{m1} and θ_{m1} in the spectral expansion in order to incorporate the new linear terms of the Boussinesq system (11.21)-(11.22) into the spectral system of equations. To see why we choose these particular coefficients, we insert (11.28)-(11.29) into (11.21)-(11.22), multiply the result by the appropriate basis functions, integrate in the x^*-direction only, use the orthogonality properties (3.56)-(3.58) of the eigenfunctions, and keep in the spectral model only those terms whose integrands have the form $\sin^2(mx^*)$ or $\cos^2(mx^*)$. As an example, we consider the two underlined terms $\mathrm{Re}\, P\, U^* \partial(\tilde{\nabla}^2\psi^*)/\partial x^*$ and $\mathrm{Re}\, P\, (\partial^2 U^*/\partial z^{*2})(\partial\psi^*/\partial x^*)$ in (11.21). First, we note that

$$\tilde{\nabla}^2\psi^* = -(m^2a^2 + 1)[\psi_{ml} \sin(mx^*) + \phi_{ml} \cos(mx^*)] \sin z^* \quad . \qquad (11.30)$$

If we multiply (11.21) by $\sin(mx^*) \sin z^*$ and write only the temporal derivative and the underlined terms, then we have

$$- (m^2a^2 + 1)[\underbrace{\dot{\psi}_{ml} \sin^2(mx^*)}_{\boxed{1}} + \underbrace{\dot{\phi}_{ml} \cos(mx^*) \sin(mx^*)}_{\boxed{2}}] \sin^2 z^*$$

$$\sim \mathrm{Re}\, P\, U^* m(m^2a^2 + 1)[\underbrace{\psi_{ml} \cos(mx^*) \sin(mx^*)}_{\boxed{3}} - \underbrace{\phi_{ml} \sin^2(mx^*)}_{\boxed{4}}] \sin^2 z^*$$

$$+ \mathrm{Re}\, P \frac{\partial^2 U^*}{\partial z^{*2}} m[\underbrace{\psi_{ml} \cos(mx^*) \sin(mx^*)}_{\boxed{5}} - \underbrace{\phi_{ml} \sin^2(mx^*)}_{\boxed{6}}] \sin^2 z^* \quad . \qquad (11.31)$$

Upon integrating in the x^*-direction and using the above orthogonality properties, we note that only the first, fourth and sixth terms survive, leaving

$$- (m^2a^2 + 1)\, \dot{\psi}_{ml} \sin^2 z^* \sim - \mathrm{Re}\, P\, U^* m(m^2a^2 + 1)\phi_{ml} \sin^2 z^*$$

$$- \mathrm{Re}\, P \frac{\partial^2 U^*}{\partial z^{*2}}\, m\, \phi_{ml} \sin^2 z^* \quad . \qquad (11.32)$$

Finally, we integrate (11.32) in the z^*-direction, and note that we must introduce two functions of the Fourier coefficients of the perpendicular wind field U^*:

$$\Sigma_1 = \frac{2}{\pi} \int_0^\pi U^* \sin^2 z^* \, dz^* \quad , \tag{11.33}$$

$$\Sigma_3 = - \frac{1}{\pi} \int_0^\pi \frac{\partial^2 U^*}{\partial z^{*2}} \sin^2 z^* \, dz^* \quad . \tag{11.34}$$

The form of the definition (11.34) for Σ_3 conforms to the definitions used in Section 12.3. Thus, we discover that the wind field can alter the magnitude of the Fourier coefficient ψ_{m1} only via interaction with ϕ_{m1}, whose attendant basis function is 90° out of phase with the one associated with ψ_{m1}. But as we noted in Section 11.2, inclusion of both $\sin(mx^*)$ and $\cos(mx^*)$ in a spectral expansion (e.g. (11.5)) often leads to orbits in phase space (see Fig. 11.7). Thus we conclude that the wind field might induce temporally periodic solutions. We demonstrate below that it actually does so when we show that Hopf bifurcation occurs in the system.

When we use procedures similar to those outlined above, we obtain the five-component model of Shirer (1980):

$$\dot{\psi}_{m1} = m \, Re \, P(\Sigma_1 - 2\Sigma_3/\sigma_{m1}) \, \phi_{m1} + mP \, T_{m1}/\sigma_{m1} - \sigma_{m1} \, P\psi_{m1}/a \quad , \tag{11.35}$$

$$\dot{\phi}_{m1} = - m \, Re \, P(\Sigma_1 - 2\Sigma_3/\sigma_{m1}) \, \psi_{m1} - mP \, \theta_{m1}/\sigma_{m1} - \sigma_{m1} \, P\phi_{m1}/a \quad , \tag{11.36}$$

$$\dot{T}_{m1} = m \, \psi_{m1} \, T_{02} - m \, Re \, P \, \Sigma_1 \theta_{m1} + m \, Ra \, \psi_{m1} - \sigma_{m1} \, T_{m1}/a \quad , \tag{11.37}$$

$$\dot{\theta}_{m1} = - m \, \phi_{m1} \, T_{02} + m \, Re \, P \, \Sigma_1 T_{m1} - m \, Ra \, \phi_{m1} - \sigma_{m1} \, \theta_{m1}/a \quad , \tag{11.38}$$

$$\dot{T}_{02} = m(\phi_{m1} \, \theta_{m1} - \psi_{m1} \, T_{m1})/2 - 4 \, T_{02}/a \quad , \tag{11.39}$$

in which

$$\sigma_{m1} = m^2 a^2 + 1 \quad . \tag{11.40}$$

The appropriate definitions for the energy quantities are (cf. (2.84)-(2.86))

$$KE = \sigma_{m1}(\psi_{m1}^2 + \phi_{m1}^2)/2 \quad , \tag{11.41}$$

$$AE = P(T_{m1}^2 + \theta_{m1}^2 + 2T_{02}^2)/2 \quad , \tag{11.42}$$

$$GA = mP(Ra + 1)(\psi_{ml}\, T_{ml} - \phi_{ml}\, \theta_{ml}) \quad , \tag{11.43}$$

$$DI = P[\sigma_{ml}^2(\psi_{ml}^2 + \phi_{ml}^2) + \sigma_{ml}(T_{ml}^2 + \theta_{ml}^2) + 8\, T_{02}^2]/a \quad , \tag{11.44}$$

so that the energetics is controlled by a form similar to (2.86) for the Lorenz model. Conspicuously absent here is any representation of the Reynolds stress (11.27); as we find in Section 12.4.1, because we have included only one vertical wavenumber in the expansion (11.28) for the stream function, all energy contributions from the perpendicular wind component vanish. As we see below, however, the fact that Σ_3 is in only the first two equations of (11.35)-(11.39) allows the wind field to be able to alter the critical value of the Rayleigh number.

11.3.3 Stability properties. We note that (11.35)-(11.39) admits the trivial solution $\psi_{ml} = \phi_{ml} = T_{ml} = \theta_{ml} = T_{02} = 0$. Thus, the first step in the analysis of the solutions to (11.35)-(11.39) is to consider the stability of the trivial solution. The determinant that produces the characteristic equation is

$$\begin{matrix} \psi_{ml} & \phi_{ml} & T_{ml} & \theta_{ml} & T_{02} \end{matrix}$$

$$\begin{vmatrix} -\sigma_{ml}P/a-\lambda & m\,Re\,P(\Sigma_1-2\Sigma_3/\sigma_{ml}) & mP/\sigma_{ml} & 0 & 0 \\ -m\,Re\,P(\Sigma_1-2\Sigma_3/\sigma_{ml}) & -\sigma_{ml}\,P/a-\lambda & 0 & -m\,P/\sigma_{ml} & 0 \\ m\,Ra & 0 & -\sigma_{ml}/a-\lambda & -m\,Re\,P\,\Sigma_1 & 0 \\ 0 & -m\,Ra & m\,Re\,P\,\Sigma_1 & -\sigma_{ml}/a-\lambda & 0 \\ 0 & 0 & 0 & 0 & -4/a-\lambda \end{vmatrix} = 0 \quad . \tag{11.45}$$

Obtaining the characteristic exponents λ is not an easy task when the determinant is written in this form. One exponent is clearly seen to be $\lambda = -4/a$ because it is the only factor in the last row and last column. The remaining 4×4 determinant can be rewritten in a more convenient form if we introduce complex variables in the original linearized equations and then re-order the columns and rows to rewrite (11.45) as

$$\begin{array}{cc|cc} \psi_{ml} + i\,\phi_{ml} & T_{ml} - i\,\theta_{ml} & \psi_{ml} - i\,\phi_{ml} & T_{ml} + i\,\theta_{ml} \end{array}$$

$$\left|\begin{array}{cc|cc} A & B & 0 & 0 \\ C & D & 0 & 0 \\ \hline 0 & 0 & \bar{A} & \bar{B} \\ 0 & 0 & \bar{C} & \bar{D} \end{array}\right| = 0 \quad , \qquad (11.46)$$

in which

$$A = -\,(\sigma_{ml}P/a + \lambda) - im\ Re\ P(\Sigma_1 - 2\Sigma_3/\sigma_{ml}) \quad , \qquad (11.47)$$

$$B = mP/\sigma_{ml} \quad , \qquad (11.48)$$

$$C = m\ Ra \quad , \qquad (11.49)$$

$$D = -\,(\sigma_{ml}/a + \lambda) - im\ Re\ P\ \Sigma_1 \quad , \qquad (11.50)$$

and the overbar denotes a complex conjugate. Clearly this form factors into a product of two quadratic polynomial functions, and so the characteristic equation (11.46) can be written as

$$(\lambda + 4/a)(\lambda^2 + E\lambda + F)(\lambda^2 + \bar{E}\lambda + \bar{F}) = 0 \quad , \qquad (11.51)$$

in which E and F are given by

$$E = \sigma_{ml}(P + 1)/a + im\ Re\ P(2\Sigma_1 - 2\Sigma_3/\sigma_{ml}) \quad , \qquad (11.52)$$

$$F = -\,m^2\ Re^2\ P^2\ \Sigma_1(\Sigma_1 - 2\Sigma_3/\sigma_{ml}) - m^2P(Ra - \sigma_{ml}^3/m^2a^2)/\sigma_{ml}$$

$$+ im\ Re\ P[\sigma_{ml}(P + 1)\Sigma_1 - 2\Sigma_3]/a \quad . \qquad (11.53)$$

The characteristic equation (11.51) has the roots

$$\lambda = \begin{cases} -\,4/a \\ \dfrac{-\,E \pm G^{1/2}}{2} \\ \dfrac{-\,\bar{E} \pm \bar{G}^{1/2}}{2} \end{cases} \quad , \qquad (11.54)$$

in which

$$G = \{\sigma_{ml}(P + 1)/a - im\ 2Re\ P\ \Sigma_3(P - 1)/[\sigma_{ml}(P + 1)]\}^2$$

$$+ 4m^2P\{Ra - \sigma_{ml}^3/(m^2a^2) - 4Re^2P^2\Sigma_3^2/[\sigma_{ml}(P + 1)^2]\}/\sigma_{ml} \quad . \tag{11.55}$$

Thus when

$$Ra = Ra_H = \frac{\sigma_{ml}^3}{m^2a^2} + \frac{4Re^2P^2\Sigma_3^2}{\sigma_{ml}(P + 1)^2} \quad , \tag{11.56}$$

we see that the plus roots in (11.54) give

$$\lambda = \pm\ i\omega_o = \pm\ im\ Re\ P\{\Sigma_1 - 2\Sigma_3/[\sigma_{ml}(P + 1)]\} \quad ; \tag{11.57}$$

that is, a Hopf bifurcation is signaled because at $Ra = Ra_H$ there is a purely imaginary conjugate pair of characteristic exponents. Before we can be sure that a unique bifurcating periodic solution exists, however, we must check that $\partial\lambda_r/\partial Ra \neq 0$ at $Ra = Ra_H$. This tedious calculation is made much simpler if we first note that $\partial\lambda_r/\partial Ra = \mathrm{Real}(\partial\lambda/\partial Ra)$; therefore, we have

$$\left.\frac{\partial\lambda_r}{\partial Ra}\right|_{Ra = Ra_H} = \mathrm{Real}\left\{\pm \frac{G^{-1/2}}{4} \left.\frac{\partial G}{\partial Ra}\right|_{Ra = Ra_H}\right\} = \frac{m^2a\sigma_{ml}^2P(P + 1)^3}{\sigma_{ml}^4(P + 1)^4 + 4m^2a^2Re^2P^2\Sigma_3^2(P - 1)^2} \quad , \tag{11.58}$$

and so the exponents indeed cross the imaginary axis with nonzero speed (Fig. 11.5). We conclude that a unique temporal solution having a squared amplitude proportional to $|Ra - Ra_H|$ exists, but we do not know whether it branches subcritically or supercritically. In Chapter 13 we discuss a general method for determining the branching direction, but as we see in the next subsection, in this particular model we can obtain this solution analytically.

We see from (11.57) that the limiting frequency ω_o of the periodic solution is a function of the Fourier coefficients Σ_1 and Σ_3 of the roll-perpendicular wind component $\underset{\sim}{i}U^*(z^*)$. If we set $U^* = 0$, then Σ_1 and Σ_3 vanish and the frequency of the periodic solution is zero. Although we are not interested in the case $U^* = 0$ from a physical standpoint, we note that this leads to two zero characteristic exponents as a degenerate case of Hopf bifurcation. We have encountered double zero-valued exponents in Section 9.1 in a different context when we discussed secondary branching of stationary solutions. There, the aspect ratio a was the dimensionless parameter whose value was varied in order to produce a pair of zero exponents. Near the critical value a_{mj} of a (see (9.4)), we found that the exponents became $\lambda_m \sim +\varepsilon$ and and $\lambda_j \sim -\varepsilon$, and this signaled secondary branching (Bauer et al., 1975). But here we find that introducing a different parameter, a Fourier coefficient of the background wind, changes the two exponents into conjugate pairs $\lambda \sim \pm i\varepsilon$, and we obtain branching periodic solutions rather than a stationary secondary branch connecting two stationary solutions. Thus, we see that having a pair of vanishing exponents marks a system as being highly singular; variation or introduction of one set of parameters leads to a richer branching tree of stationary solutions, while variation of a different set leads to temporally periodic solutions. Identification of these two sets, in the sense discussed in Chapter 8, is not yet fully resolved.

11.3.4 Primary periodic solutions. Given that a branching periodic solution is expected, we next find a solution to the nonlinear set (11.35)-(11.39). As we note in Chapter 13, in most cases we obtain the solution approximately using a power series method, but sometimes we can obtain the solution analytically. If we assume that the component T_{02} is time-independent, then the system (11.35)-(11.38) is linear in time and so admits trigonometric solutions. But this approach is feasible only if we can solve (11.39) in a manner that ensures that T_{02} remains time-independent. For example, if we choose ψ_{m1}, ϕ_{m1}, T_{m1}, θ_{m1} to be

$$\psi_{m1}(t^*) = \hat{\psi}\cos(\omega t^*) \quad , \tag{11.59}$$

$$\phi_{m1}(t^*) = \hat{\psi}\sin(\omega t^*) \quad , \tag{11.60}$$

$$T_{m1}(t^*) = -\hat{T}\cos(\omega t^*) \quad , \tag{11.61}$$

$$\theta_{m1}(t^*) = \hat{T}\sin(\omega t^*) \quad , \tag{11.62}$$

then (11.39) gives

$$\dot{T}_{02} = \frac{m}{2}\,\hat{\psi}\hat{T}[\sin^2(\omega t^*) + \cos^2(\omega t^*)] - 4\,T_{02}/a$$

$$= \frac{m}{2}\,\hat{\psi}\hat{T} - 4\,T_{02}/a \quad . \tag{11.63}$$

Because of a fortuitous nonlinear form in (11.39), we see that T_{02} may be time-independent while the other coefficients may vary with time.

A more general form for (11.59)-(11.62) containing phase angles η and ε is

$$\psi_{m1}(t^*) = \hat{\psi}\cos(-\omega t^* + \eta) \quad , \tag{11.64}$$

$$\phi_{m1}(t^*) = \hat{\psi}\sin(-\omega t^* + \eta) \quad , \tag{11.65}$$

$$T_{m1}(t^*) = \hat{T}\sin(-\omega t^* + \varepsilon) \quad , \tag{11.66}$$

$$\theta_{m1}(t^*) = \hat{T}\cos(-\omega t^* + \varepsilon) \quad . \tag{11.67}$$

These forms also allow the T_{02}-coefficient to be time-independent, although now the T_{02}-equation depends on $\sin(\varepsilon - \eta)$. Thus we complete our specification of the form of the branching periodic solution by setting

$$T_{02} = \hat{T}_{02} \quad . \tag{11.68}$$

Substitution of (11.64)-(11.68) into (11.35)-(11.39) leads after lengthy calculation to the following results:

$$\hat{\psi} = [8(Ra - Ra_H)]^{1/2}/\sigma_{m1} \quad , \tag{11.69}$$

$$\hat{T} = \sigma_{m1}[8(Ra - Ra_H)]^{1/2}/[ma\sin(\varepsilon - \eta)] \quad , \tag{11.70}$$

$$\hat{T}_{02} = -(Ra - Ra_H) \quad , \tag{11.71}$$

$$\cot(\varepsilon - \eta) = 2ma\,Re\,P\,\Sigma_3/[\sigma^2_{m1}(P + 1)] \quad , \tag{11.72}$$

$$\omega = m\,Re\,P\{\Sigma_1 - 2\Sigma_3/[\sigma_{m1}(P + 1)]\} \quad , \tag{11.73}$$

in which Ra_H is defined in (11.56) and we have corrected an error in the specification of $\hat{T}$ given in Shirer (1980). Significantly, the amplitudes (11.69)-(11.71) of the periodic solution have the anticipated functional dependence on $Ra - Ra_H$, and only odd-degree terms appear in the governing cubic polynomial equation in $\hat{T}$. Moreover, the solution has nearly the same form as that in (2.100)-(2.102) for the Lorenz model, although both the phasing of the thermal and momentum fields and the amplitude of the thermal perturbation $\hat{T}$ are altered by Σ_3. As we have seen in previous models, when we recognize that ω/m is the cell frequency (see Section 7.2.3), we see that the solutions depend only on the cell aspect ratio $\alpha = ma$. Moreover, when we insert (11.64)-(11.68) into the energy definitions (11.41)-(11.44), we see that

$$KE = \sigma_{m1} \hat{\psi}^2/2 \quad , \tag{11.74}$$

$$AE = P(\hat{T}^2 + 2\hat{T}_{02}^2)/2 \quad , \tag{11.75}$$

$$GA = mP(Ra + 1)\hat{\psi}\hat{T} \sin(\varepsilon - \eta) \quad , \tag{11.76}$$

$$DI = P[\sigma_{m1}^2 \hat{\psi}^2 + \sigma_{m1} \hat{T}^2 + 8 \hat{T}_{02}^2]/a \quad , \tag{11.77}$$

so that the temporally periodic solution is energetically steady. In addition, this solution exists only when $Ra > Ra_H$, and so we expect it to be stable. To see what this solution corresponds to physically, we combine (11.28)-(11.29) and (11.64)-(11.67) to find that

$$\psi^*(x^*,z^*,t^*) = \hat{\psi} \sin(mx^* - \omega t^* + \eta) \sin z^* \quad , \tag{11.78}$$

$$T^*(x^*,z^*,t^*) = \hat{T} \sin(mx^* - \omega t^* + \varepsilon) \sin z^* + \hat{T}_{02} \sin(2z^*) \quad . \tag{11.79}$$

Now (11.78)-(11.79) have the form (11.8) for a linearly translating wave: As time increases, the crest of the waveform in (11.78)-(11.79) moves horizontally toward positive values of x^* at a speed ω/m. Thus we conclude that the periodic solution corresponds to a stable convective roll or cloud street of aspect ratio α propagating with a constant amplitude downstream at a rate ω/m that depends on the Fourier coefficients Σ_1 and Σ_3 of the roll-perpendicular wind field.

We discover by combining (11.69)-(11.72) and (11.74)-(11.77) that the available energy and dissipation rate depend DI on the difference $\varepsilon - \eta$ in phase angles, and that the magnitude of DI is minimized if $|\varepsilon - \eta| = 90°$. From (11.72) we observe that $|\varepsilon - \eta|$ depends on the curvature coefficient Σ_3 that depends on $\partial^2 U^*/\partial z^{*2}$, and that $|\varepsilon - \eta| = 90°$ when $\Sigma_3 = 0$. Consequently the vanishing of this Fourier coefficient leads to the minimum rate of energy dissipation for a given energy generation (see Section 6.1). If we assume that the system adopts its most efficient solution, then we conclude that the branching roll would develop in a way that minimizes the effects of Σ_3. We find in the next chapter that with application of an equivalent principle, the minimization of the value of Ra_H with respect to both Σ_3 and α, we may obtain both the expected orientation of the rolls with respect to the background wind field and the preferred aspect ratio of the cell.

CHAPTER 12

THE EXPECTED BRANCHING SOLUTION: PREFERRED WAVELENGTHS AND ORIENTATIONS

DAVID J. STENSRUD

We have seen that a number of mechanisms affect the exchange of stability between solutions in hydrodynamic problems. In general, the forcing effects are represented by control parameters such as the Rayleigh number Ra, and these parameters are in turn functions of other parameters such as the cell aspect ratio α or the dimensionless Coriolis parameter f^*. Parameters such as α represent possible responses of the fluid, and typically the expected response is the one that is associated with the minimum value of the control parameter. For classical Rayleigh-Bénard convection, we found in Section 7.1.2 that the smallest value of the critical Rayleigh number Ra_c occurs when $\alpha^2 = 1/2$. Additional parameters such as f^* serve to alter the values of response parameters such as α^2 and the corresponding minima of control parameters such as Ra (see Section 7.2.2). However, these additional parameters cannot be regarded as response parameters; that is, minimizing with respect to them makes no physical sense, since they are not free to seek optimizing values.

Both Rayleigh-Bénard and rotating Rayleigh-Bénard convection are normally treated as two-dimensional problems; indeed, the first flows observed when motion appears are two-dimensional (see, for example, Krishnamurti, 1970a). But these experiments necessarily occur in three-dimensional vessels, and coherent rolls occur only if there is a preferred orientation for them in the horizontal plane. In a laboratory vessel, the rolls tend to be aligned parallel to the shorter wall (Stork and Müller, 1972). To model this phenomenon, appropriate boundary effects must be represented in the problem if the complete character of the initial branching solution is to be captured. That is, additional parameters must be introduced into the model in order to ensure that the model represents situations having finite probability, in accordance with Modeling Principle Five (see Section 1.3 and the introduction to Chapter 8).

Two-dimensional rolls are also seen in the three-dimensional atmosphere, manifested in many cases as cloud streets or stratocumulus decks with varying cloud

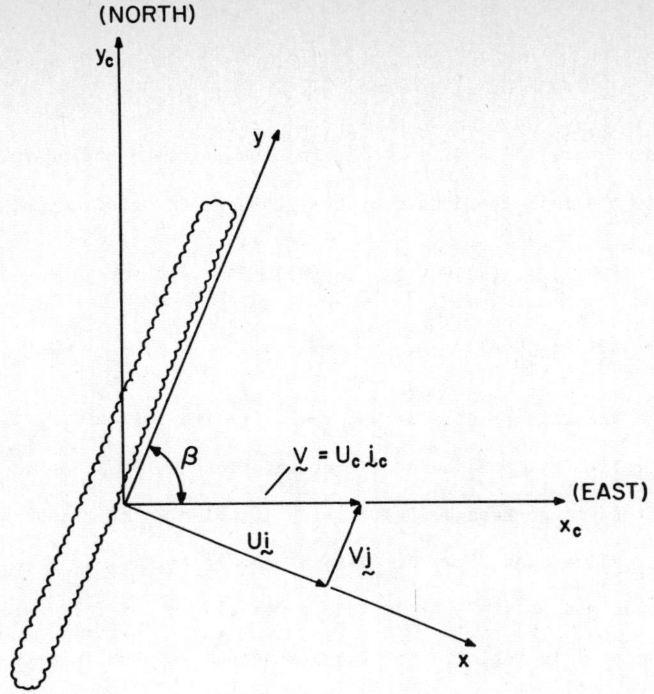

Fig. 12.1 Coordinate system showing the standard eastward and northward axes x_c and y_c and the roll coordinates x and y. The orientation angle β is defined as the angle between east and the cloud axis y. For clarity, we have chosen a wind velocity for which V_c=0 (cf. Fig. 11.12).

bases. These rolls have well-defined horizontal wavelengths and orientations, and so again there are two response parameters to determine. As in Rayleigh-Bénard convection, one of these is the cell aspect ratio $\alpha = 2z_T/\ell$, where ℓ is the horizontal wavelength of the cell and z_T is the depth of the circulation, which is usually given by the altitude of the inversion capping the boundary layer. However, since there are no side walls in the atmosphere, the horizontal orientation of the rolls is determined by the vertically varying horizontal wind profile.

In the atmosphere, we find that the horizontal wind profile influences the convective processes and, for wind speeds greater than a few meters per second, produces a preferred alignment of the circulations (Brown, 1980). The preferred alignment can be expressed in terms of an orientation angle β, where β is defined as the angle between the cloud axis and some direction, say east (Fig. 12.1). Thus, the reference wind velocity can be written as

$$\underset{\sim}{V}(z) = \underset{\sim}{i}_c U_c(z) + \underset{\sim}{j}_c V_c(z) \quad , \tag{12.1}$$

in which $\underset{\sim}{i}_c$ and $\underset{\sim}{j}_c$ are the unit vectors in the eastward and northward directions, respectively. In the roll coordinate system, this wind vector can be represented as

$$\underset{\sim}{V}(z) = \underset{\sim}{i}[U_c(z)\sin(\beta) - V_c(z)\cos(\beta)] + \underset{\sim}{j}[U_c(z)\cos(\beta) + V_c(z)\sin(\beta)]$$

$$= \underset{\sim}{i}U(z) + \underset{\sim}{j}V(z) \quad , \tag{12.2}$$

where U(z) is the velocity profile perpendicular to the roll and V(z) is the profile parallel to the roll. By introducing the orientation angle β, we reduce the degrees of freedom in the Rayleigh-Bénard instability problem so that the three-dimensional problem in $(\underset{\sim}{i}_c,\underset{\sim}{j}_c,\underset{\sim}{k})$ becomes a two-dimensional one in $(\underset{\sim}{i},\underset{\sim}{k})$. To see this reduction, we note that variations in the $\underset{\sim}{j}$ direction parallel to the roll are neglected and that as the value of β is varied, the two-dimensional system in $(\underset{\sim}{i},\underset{\sim}{k})$ is turned, or rotated, about the vertical axis in the three-dimensional system in $(\underset{\sim}{i}_c,\underset{\sim}{j}_c,\underset{\sim}{k})$. As this rotation occurs, the wind field U(z) represented in the two-dimensional system is altered and so may be regarded as a function of β. This dependence on β can be easily seen in Fig. 12.1 by assuming a unidirectional wind $\underset{\sim}{V} = \underset{\sim}{i}_c U_c$. If the horizontal axis of the two-dimensional system is aligned perpendicular to the wind direction (β = 90°), then the entire wind field is represented, because $U = U_c$ and V = 0. If the axis of the system is aligned parallel to the wind direction (β = 0°), then none of the wind field is represented because U = 0 and $V = U_c$. As we note below, the intensity of the wind field is represented by a second control parameter, the Reynolds number Re.

The Shirer (1980) model that was introduced in Section 11.3 is appropriate for the study of cloud streets in a non-neutral, irrotational atmosphere. We recall that the critical value Ra_H of the Rayleigh number in this model is (11.56) or

$$Ra_H = (\alpha^2 + 1)^3/\alpha^2 + 4Re^2P^2\Sigma_3^2/[(\alpha^2 + 1)(P + 1)^2] \quad , \tag{12.3}$$

in which α is the cell aspect ratio and Σ_3 is a Fourier coefficient (11.34) of the background wind in the cross-roll direction (see also (12.35) below). We note that the first term depends only on the value of the cell aspect ratio α, and is associated with Rayleigh-Bénard convection in an environment at rest. However, the second depends upon both α and the Fourier coefficient Σ_3 of the background wind. As the alignment, or the value of β, varies, the value of Σ_3^2 also varies and for some value of β, reaches the minimum value given by $\Sigma_3 = 0$. Thus for this situation, the atmosphere can respond not only by choosing a value of α, but also by choosing a value of β, which together minimize the value of the critical Rayleigh number Ra_H.

In this chapter, we continue to examine methods for finding the expected critical values of the parameters controlling bifurcations between solutions. Previously, in Chapter 7, we studied the time-independent solutions of the convective equations in an environment at rest. We now investigate several models that incorporate a basic shearing wind in the environment (Stensrud, 1985; Shirer, 1986; Stensrud and Shirer, 1987). These models of cloud street behavior require a second controlling parameter, the Reynolds number Re, that is a measure of the wind stress upon the fluid. As in Chapter 11, we find that this extra degree of freedom converts the stationary solutions of the Boussinesq system into temporally periodic ones, and then the analysis proceeds analogously to the one described in Chapter 7.

We begin by reviewing the three instability mechanisms associated with the development of boundary layer rolls: the Rayleigh-Bénard instability, the parallel instability and the inflection point instability. We then discuss the Shirer (1980, 1986) models for the pure Rayleigh-Bénard instability and the pure parallel instability cases. For these cases, there is only one controlling parameter, either the Rayleigh number Ra or the Reynolds number Re. Next, we introduce the Stensrud and Shirer (1987) model of the pure inflection point instability mechanism, for which there is only one controlling parameter, the Reynolds number. Lastly, we examine the Shirer (1986) model for the mixed thermal and parallel instability modes, for which there are two controlling parameters: Ra and Re. We discover that for this last case, we must be careful to minimize the values of both Ra and Re in order for the results to be applicable to the atmosphere.

12.1 The Three Mechanisms of Cloud Street Formation

The Rayleigh-Bénard instability occurs when a fluid is heated uniformly from below and cooled uniformly from above. We find that when the temperature gradient, represented by the Rayleigh number Ra, exceeds a critical value, roll circulations are produced to replace the motionless, conductive state. This instability is manifested by convective perturbations extracting energy from the basic thermal state (Shirer, 1986). The background mean wind causes a transition from free convective cellular patterns to linear patterns as the wind speed exceeds a critical value of only a few meters per second (Brown, 1980). Indeed, the mean wind shear produces a stabilizing effect (Kuettner, 1971), and consequently, the convective rolls have alignments that minimize the magnitude of the perpendicular component of the wind shear in the roll coordinate system (Shirer, 1980).

The parallel instability was first studied by Lilly (1966). A roll is able to extract energy from the large-scale wind shear parallel to the roll axis through the Coriolis terms. Lilly's initial analysis suggests that the parallel instability has an effect only when the values of the Reynolds number are small, leading most investigators to believe that the mechanism is of secondary importance (Brown, 1980). However, from interpretation of the bifurcation and stability theorems, we recognize that the manifestation of the parallel instability at small Reynolds numbers makes it an important instability mechanism to examine, since we generally seek the smallest value of the control parameter at which the first, or preferred, bifurcation occurs. Indeed, some investigators believe that the parallel instability has a significant effect on the development of cloud streets (Etling, 1971; Gammelsrød, 1975).

The inflection point instability can be viewed as a generalized Kelvin-Helmholtz type instability (Brown, 1980). When an inflection point exists in the large-scale wind profile perpendicular to the roll axis, a roll may extract energy from this component of the wind shear. An inflection point in the velocity profile is a necessary, but not a sufficient condition for the existence of this instability mechanism (Rayleigh, 1880; Drazin and Howard, 1966; see Fig. 12.2). However, using a nonlinear low-order model to study the modes arising from the inflection point instability yields a fortuitous bonus: the bifurcation and stability theorems used to analyze its solutions give both necessary and sufficient conditions for an

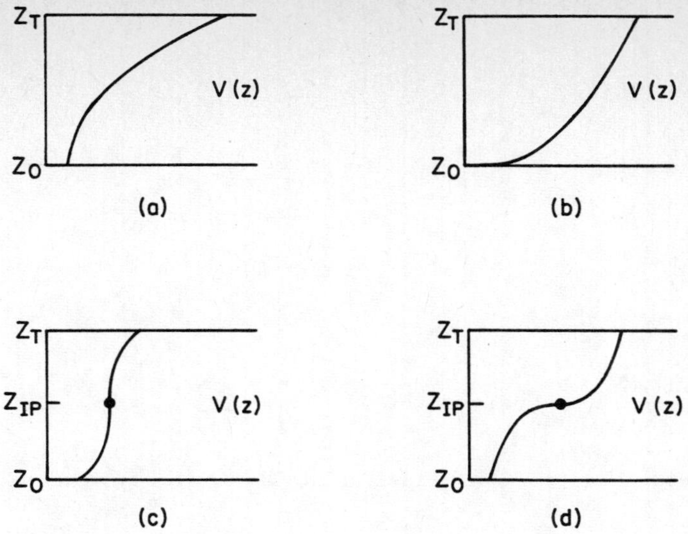

Fig. 12.2 Vertical wind profiles between heights z_O and z_T in the domain; the inflection point heights are labeled z_{IP}. These profiles are stable (a), stable (b), stable even though an inflection point exists in the profile (c), and possibly unstable (d) (after Drazin and Howard, 1966).

instability and a branching nonlinear solution to occur. Thus, low-order models are ideally suited for the study of the inflection point instability mechanism, as well as the other two instability mechanisms.

The three instability mechanisms can be divided into two distinct groups. The Rayleigh-Bénard and the parallel instabilities affect the cloud street orientations in basically the same way, with the preferred orientations being the ones that minimize the vertical wind shear in the component perpendicular to the roll. In contrast, the preferred orientations for the inflection point instability are those that maximize the vertical wind shear in the component perpendicular to the roll. In general, the preferred wavelengths for all three mechanisms are in the range of one to eight times the depth z_T of the boundary layer (Kelly, 1984).

12.2 Energetics

The appropriate system of equations for studying development of boundary layer rolls is the two-dimensional shallow Boussinesq system for a rotating fluid that is forced both thermally and dynamically. As in Section 11.3, we consider the circulations to be perturbations imposed upon a hydrostatic, stratified, horizontally moving flow, but here we add the Coriolis force. This system is written in the roll coordinate system as (cf. (11.17)-(11.18))

$$\frac{\partial\nabla^2\psi}{\partial t} + J(\psi,\nabla^2\psi) + U\frac{\partial\nabla^2\psi}{\partial x} - \frac{\partial\psi}{\partial x}\frac{\partial^2 U}{\partial z^2} + f\frac{\partial v'}{\partial z} - \frac{g}{T_{oo}}\frac{\partial T'}{\partial x} - \nu\nabla^4\psi = 0 \quad , \tag{12.4}$$

$$\frac{\partial v'}{\partial t} + J(\psi,v') + U\frac{\partial v'}{\partial x} + \frac{\partial\psi}{\partial x}\frac{\partial V}{\partial z} - f\frac{\partial\psi}{\partial z} - \nu\nabla^2 v' = 0 \quad , \tag{12.5}$$

$$\frac{\partial T'}{\partial t} + J(\psi,T') + U\frac{\partial T'}{\partial x} - \frac{\Delta_z T}{z_T}\frac{\partial\psi}{\partial x} - \kappa\nabla^2 T' = 0 \quad , \tag{12.6}$$

in which ψ, v', and T' are the stream function, roll-parallel velocity component, and temperature of the convective perturbation, and in which $U(z)$ and $V(z)$ are the height-dependent roll-perpendicular and roll-parallel components of the background wind. For a dry atmosphere, $\Delta_z T/z_T \sim (\gamma_e - \gamma_d)$, where γ_e and γ_d are the environmental and dry adiabatic lapse rates, respectively.

The two-dimensional shallow Boussinesq system can be expressed in a dimensionless form (cf. (11.21)-(11.22) and (7.23)-(7.25)) as

$$\frac{\partial\tilde\nabla^2\psi^*}{\partial t^*} + J(\psi^*,\tilde\nabla^2\psi^*) + \text{Re}\,P\,U^*\frac{\partial\tilde\nabla^2\psi^*}{\partial x^*} - \text{Re}\,P\frac{\partial\psi^*}{\partial x^*}\frac{\partial^2 U^*}{\partial z^{*2}}$$

$$+ \frac{f^*P}{a}\frac{\partial v^*}{\partial z^*} - P\frac{\partial T^*}{\partial x^*} - \frac{P}{a}\tilde\nabla^4\psi^* = 0 \quad , \tag{12.7}$$

$$\frac{\partial v^*}{\partial t^*} + J(\psi^*,v^*) + \text{Re}\,P\,U^*\frac{\partial v^*}{\partial x^*} + \text{Re}\,P\frac{\partial\psi^*}{\partial x^*}\frac{\partial V^*}{\partial z^*} - \frac{f^*P}{a}\frac{\partial\psi^*}{\partial z^*}$$

$$- \frac{P}{a}\tilde\nabla^2 v^* = 0 \quad , \tag{12.8}$$

$$\frac{\partial T^*}{\partial t^*} + J(\psi^*,T^*) + \text{Re}\,P\,U^*\frac{\partial T^*}{\partial x^*} - \text{Ra}\frac{\partial\psi^*}{\partial x^*} - \frac{1}{a}\tilde\nabla^2 T^* = 0 \quad . \tag{12.9}$$

Here we used the dimensionless forms (2.20)-(2.24), (2.27), and (11.19) for x,z,t,ψ, T,∇^2, and U and the additional forms

$$v' = v^*\,\kappa\pi/z_T \quad , \tag{12.10}$$

$$V = V^*|\underset{\sim}{V}(z_T)|\pi \quad , \tag{12.11}$$

$$f = f^*\nu\pi^2/z_T^2 \quad , \tag{12.12}$$

in which $|\underset{\sim}{V}(z_T)|$ is the wind speed at the domain height z_T. As before, we define the Prandtl number $P = \nu/\kappa$ (2.29) and the domain aspect ratio $a = 2z_T/L$ (2.30), and we recall that the Reynolds number Re (11.20) is

$$Re = |\underset{\sim}{V}(z_T)|z_T/\nu \quad , \tag{12.13}$$

and the Rayleigh number (2.28) is

$$Ra = gz_T^3\Delta_z T/(\nu\kappa T_{oo}\pi^4) \quad . \tag{12.14}$$

In order to clarify the available energy sources and instability mechanisms for the roll circulations, we review the energetics analysis of Kaylor and Faller (1972). For two-dimensional flow, it is appropriate to divide the total kinetic energy into two parts: one part is the kinetic energy of the motion parallel to the roll, or the longitudinal kinetic energy, and the other part is the kinetic energy of the motion within the roll, or the roll kinetic energy. We define KE to be the roll kinetic energy

$$KE = \frac{1}{2}\int_0^\pi\int_0^{2\pi} |\tilde{\nabla}\psi^*|^2\, dx^*dz^* \quad , \tag{12.15}$$

LKE to be the longitudinal kinetic energy,

$$LKE = \frac{1}{2}\int_0^\pi\int_0^{2\pi} v^{*2}\, dx^*dz^* \quad , \tag{12.16}$$

and AE to be the available potential energy

$$AE = \frac{1}{2}\int_0^\pi\int_0^{2\pi} PT^{*2}\, dx^*dz^* \quad . \tag{12.17}$$

We can transform the equations (12.7)-(12.9) into energy equations by multiplying (12.7)-(12.9) by ψ^*, v^* and T^*, respectively, and then integrating the results over the horizontally cyclic domain. Thus, we obtain

$$\frac{\partial}{\partial t^*}(KE) = \int_0^{\pi}\int_0^{2\pi} Re\, P\left[\frac{\partial \psi^*}{\partial x^*}\frac{\partial \psi^*}{\partial z^*}\frac{\partial U^*}{\partial z^*}\right] dx^*dz^* + \int_0^{\pi}\int_0^{2\pi} Pa^{-1}\left[-f^*v^*\frac{\partial \psi^*}{\partial z^*}\right] dx^*dz^*$$

I III

$$+ \int_0^{\pi}\int_0^{2\pi}\left[PT^*\frac{\partial \psi^*}{\partial x^*}\right] dx^*dz^* + \int_0^{\pi}\int_0^{2\pi} Pa^{-1}\left[-|\tilde{\nabla}^2\psi^*|^2\right] dx^*dz^* \quad , \quad (12.18)$$

IV V

$$\frac{\partial}{\partial t^*}(LKE) = \int_0^{\pi}\int_0^{2\pi} Re\, P\left[-v^*\frac{\partial \psi^*}{\partial x^*}\frac{\partial V^*}{\partial z^*}\right] dx^*dz^* + \int_0^{\pi}\int_0^{2\pi} Pa^{-1}\left[f^*v^*\frac{\partial \psi^*}{\partial z^*}\right] dx^*dz^*$$

II III

$$+ \int_0^{\pi}\int_0^{2\pi} Pa^{-1}\left[-|\tilde{\nabla}v^*|^2\right] dx^*dz^* \quad , \quad (12.19)$$

VI

$$\frac{\partial}{\partial t^*}(AE) = \int_0^{\pi}\int_0^{2\pi} Ra\left[PT^*\frac{\partial \psi^*}{\partial x^*}\right] dx^*dz^* + \int_0^{\pi}\int_0^{2\pi} Pa^{-1}\left[-|\tilde{\nabla}T^*|^2\right] dx^*dz^* \quad .$$

IV VII (12.20)

Terms (I) and (II) in equations (12.18)-(12.20) are Reynolds stresses (cf. (11.27)) (Dutton, 1976). Term (I) depends on the wind shear component U^* perpendicular to the roll axis, directly contributes to the roll kinetic energy, and represents the energy source for the inflection point instability. Term (II) depends on the wind shear component V^* parallel to the roll axis and represents the energy source for the parallel instability. Energy introduced into LKE by (II) can be transferred from the longitudinal kinetic energy to the roll kinetic energy by (III), and so amplify the overturning circulations. It is apparent that for these transfer terms to be nonzero, the Coriolis parameter must be included. Terms (IV) in (12.18) and (12.20) measure the magnitude of the energy generation and so represent the sources for the Rayleigh-Bénard instability. Terms (V), (VI) and (VII) represent the energy losses owing to dissipation. As we discussed in Section 6.1, instability and roll amplification occur when the energy sources are larger in magnitude than the energy sinks.

12.3 The Rayleigh-Bénard and Parallel Instabilities

We begin with the dimensionless two-dimensional shallow Boussinesq system (12.7)-(12.9) for a rotating fluid in a shearing environment. Since the smallest spectral model of rotating convection was studied by Veronis (1966) (see Section 7.2), the present Shirer (1986) model is based on the Veronis system. Thus, one wavenumber is used to represent the vertical velocity field, two are used to represent the horizontal velocity field, and two are used for the thermal perturbation. We extend the Veronis model here as we did the Lorenz model in Section 11.3.2, and so the appropriate forms for the expansions are (cf. (7.28) and (11.28)-(11.29))

$$\psi^*(x^*,z^*,t^*) = \psi_{11}(t^*)\sin(x^*)\sin(z^*) + \phi_{11}(t^*)\cos(x^*)\sin(z^*) \quad , \qquad (12.21)$$

$$\begin{aligned} v^*(x^*,z^*,t^*) = {} & v_{11}(t^*)\sin(x^*)\cos(z^*) + \chi_{11}(t^*)\cos(x^*)\cos(z^*) \\ & + v_{20}(t^*)\sin(2x^*) + \chi_{20}(t^*)\cos(2x^*) \quad , \end{aligned} \qquad (12.22)$$

$$\begin{aligned} T^*(x^*,z^*,t^*) = {} & T_{11}(t^*)\cos(x^*)\sin(z^*) + \theta_{11}(t^*)\sin(x^*)\sin(z^*) \\ & + T_{02}(t^*)\sin(2z^*) \quad . \end{aligned} \qquad (12.23)$$

For simplicity we have set $m = 1$ in (12.21)-(12.23) so that $a = \alpha$. We now substitute these expansions into (12.7)-(12.9) and use the Galerkin technique discussed in Chapter 3 to form the spectral system in roll coordinates. If we denote temporal derivatives by an overdot, then the resulting spectral system is written as

$$\begin{aligned} \dot{\psi}_{11} = {} & -\{f^*P/[\alpha(\alpha^2+1)]\}v_{11} - [P(\alpha^2+1)/\alpha]\psi_{11} \\ & + \text{Re}\, P[[2\Sigma_2 + (\alpha^2-1)\Sigma_1]/(\alpha^2+1)]\phi_{11} + [P/(\alpha^2+1)]T_{11} \quad , \end{aligned} \qquad (12.24)$$

$$\begin{aligned} \dot{\phi}_{11} = {} & -\{f^*P/[\alpha(\alpha^2+1)]\}\chi_{11} - [P(\alpha^2+1)/\alpha]\phi_{11} \\ & - \text{Re}\, P[[2\Sigma_2 + (\alpha^2-1)\Sigma_1]/(\alpha^2+1)]\psi_{11} - [P/(\alpha^2+1)]\theta_{11} \quad , \end{aligned} \qquad (12.25)$$

$$\begin{aligned} \dot{v}_{11} = {} & \text{Re}\, P\Sigma_2\chi_{11} + \text{Re}\, P\Sigma_4\phi_{11} + (f^*P/\alpha)\psi_{11} - [P(\alpha^2+1)/\alpha]v_{11} \\ & - \psi_{11}v_{20} - \phi_{11}\chi_{20} \quad , \end{aligned} \qquad (12.26)$$

$$\begin{aligned} \dot{\chi}_{11} = {} & -\text{Re}\, P\Sigma_2 v_{11} - \text{Re}\, P\Sigma_4\psi_{11} + (f^*P/\alpha)\phi_{11} - [P(\alpha^2+1)/\alpha]\chi_{11} \\ & - \psi_{11}\chi_{20} + \phi_{11}v_{20} \quad , \end{aligned} \qquad (12.27)$$

$$\dot{v}_{20} = (1/2)v_{11}\psi_{11} - (1/2)\chi_{11}\phi_{11} - 4P\alpha v_{20} + \text{Re}\ P(\Sigma_1 + \Sigma_2)\chi_{20} \quad , \qquad (12.28)$$

$$\dot{\chi}_{20} = (1/2)v_{11}\phi_{11} + (1/2)\chi_{11}\psi_{11} - 4P\alpha\chi_{20} - \text{Re}\ P(\Sigma_1 + \Sigma_2)v_{20} \quad , \qquad (12.29)$$

$$\dot{T}_{11} = \text{Ra}\ \psi_{11} - [(\alpha^2 + 1)/\alpha]T_{11} - \text{Re}\ P\Sigma_1\theta_{11} + \psi_{11}T_{02} \quad , \qquad (12.30)$$

$$\dot{\theta}_{11} = -\ \text{Ra}\ \phi_{11} - [(\alpha^2 + 1)/\alpha]\theta_{11} + \text{Re}\ P\Sigma_1 T_{11} - \phi_{11}T_{02} \quad , \qquad (12.31)$$

$$\dot{T}_{02} = (1/2)[-\psi_{11}T_{11} + \phi_{11}\theta_{11}] - (4/\alpha)T_{02} \quad . \qquad (12.32)$$

Here the Fourier coefficients are defined as (cf. (11.33)-(11.34))

$$\Sigma_1 = 2\pi^{-1} \int_0^\pi U^* \sin^2(z^*)\ dz^* \quad , \qquad (12.33)$$

$$\Sigma_2 = 2\pi^{-1} \int_0^\pi U^* \cos^2(z^*)\ dz^* \quad , \qquad (12.34)$$

$$\Sigma_3 = \pi^{-1} \int_0^\pi \frac{\partial U^*}{\partial z^*} \sin(2z^*)\ dz^* \quad , \qquad (12.35)$$

$$\Sigma_4 = \pi^{-1} \int_0^\pi \frac{\partial V^*}{\partial z^*} \sin(2z^*)\ dz^* \quad , \qquad (12.36)$$

in which V^* and U^* denote components of the mean wind that are parallel to and perpendicular to the roll axis, respectively. In creating the above model, we used integration by parts to show that $\Sigma_1=\Sigma_2-\Sigma_3$ so that $(\alpha^2+1)\Sigma_1-2\Sigma_3=(\alpha^2-1)\Sigma_1+2\Sigma_2$.

<u>12.3.1 Spectral model energetics</u>. To elucidate the available energy sources for the roll, we form energy equations from (12.24)-(12.32). The perturbation roll kinetic energy is equivalent in the spectral system to

$$2KE = (\alpha^2 + 1)[\psi_{11}^2 + \phi_{11}^2] \quad , \qquad (12.37)$$

the perturbation longitudinal kinetic energy is equivalent to

$$2LKE = v_{11}^2 + \chi_{11}^2 + 2(v_{20}^2 + \chi_{20}^2) \quad , \qquad (12.38)$$

and the perturbation available potential energy is equivalent to

$$2AE = P[T_{11}^2 + \theta_{11}^2 + 2T_{02}^2] \quad . \tag{12.39}$$

From these equations, we find in the dimensionless spectral system that

$$\dot{KE} = -\underbrace{[f^*P/\alpha][\psi_{11}v_{11} + \phi_{11}\chi_{11}]}_{\text{III}} + \underbrace{P[\psi_{11}T_{11} - \phi_{11}\theta_{11}]}_{\text{IV}}$$

$$\underbrace{- [P(\alpha^2 + 1)^2/\alpha][\psi_{11}^2 + \phi_{11}^2]}_{\text{V}} \quad , \tag{12.40}$$

$$\dot{LKE} = \underbrace{\mathrm{Re}\ P\ \Sigma_4[v_{11}\phi_{11} - \chi_{11}\psi_{11}]}_{\text{II}} + \underbrace{(f^*P/\alpha)[v_{11}\psi_{11} + \chi_{11}\phi_{11}]}_{\text{III}}$$

$$\underbrace{-\{[P(\alpha^2 + 1)/\alpha][v_{11}^2 + \chi_{11}^2] + 8P\alpha[v_{20}^2 + \chi_{20}^2]\}}_{\text{VI}} \quad , \tag{12.41}$$

$$\dot{AE} = \underbrace{\mathrm{Ra}\ P[T_{11}\psi_{11} - \theta_{11}\phi_{11}]}_{\text{IV}}$$

$$\underbrace{- \{P[(\alpha^2 + 1)/\alpha][T_{11}^2 + \theta_{11}^2] + [8P/\alpha]T_{02}^2\}}_{\text{VII}} \quad . \tag{12.42}$$

Many of the forms contributing to energy changes in (12.40)-(12.42) are analogs of those in (12.18)-(12.20) for the original equations. The first term on the right side of the roll kinetic energy equation (12.40) represents the mechanism by which energy of the form LKE can be transferred to the form KE. For (III) to be nonzero, the Coriolis terms must be included in the model. We note that there is no Reynolds stress (I) that would represent the energy source for the inflection point instability. When a model has only one vertical wavenumber, (I) integrates to zero and so the inflection point instability mechanism is effectively filtered (see Section 12.4). The second term in (12.40) represents energy generation (IV), provided that $\mathrm{Ra} > 0$ in (12.42), and allows energy to be extracted from the basic thermal state represented by Ra. The last term (V) measures the dissipation rate.

The first term in the longitudinal kinetic energy equation (12.41) is a Reynolds stress (II). Since (II) includes Σ_4 (12.36), it depends on the wind shear parallel to the roll axis and provides the energy source for the parallel instability. This energy source becomes activated by transfers owing to (III). The last term (VI) gives the dissipation rate.

In the equation (12.42) for the available potential energy, (IV) represents energy generation when Ra > 0. As noted above, this term is involved in the transfer of energy from AE to KE, and represents the energy source for the Rayleigh-Bénard instability. Finally, (VII) measures the dissipation rate. Thus, the energy source terms in the spectral system are of the same type as the energy source terms in the original partial differential equations, except that the Reynolds stress (I) representing the energy source for the inflection point instability is absent from the spectral model. This observation suggests that the spectral model (12.24)-(12.32) should be able to capture both the Rayleigh-Bénard and parallel instability mechanisms.

12.3.2 Orientation angles. We now introduce the definition of the orientation angle (12.2) into the Fourier coefficients of the wind to identify another degree of freedom in the problem. Thus, we may express the wind shear coefficients Σ_3 and Σ_4 as

$$\Sigma_3 = s_3 \sin(\beta) - s_4 \cos(\beta) \quad , \tag{12.43}$$

$$\Sigma_4 = s_3 \cos(\beta) + s_4 \sin(\beta) \quad , \tag{12.44}$$

in which

$$s_3 = \pi^{-1} \int_0^\pi \frac{\partial U_c^*}{\partial z^*} \sin(2z^*)\, dz^* \quad , \tag{12.45}$$

$$s_4 = \pi^{-1} \int_0^\pi \frac{\partial V_c^*}{\partial z^*} \sin(2z^*)\, dz^* \quad , \tag{12.46}$$

and U_c^* and V_c^* are the dimensionless background wind components in the standard eastward/northward coordinate system (Fig. 12.1).

We assume that the preferred values of the orientation angle β and cell aspect ratio α are those that produce the lowest acceptable critical values of the control parameters, which here are either Ra_H or Re_H. Because the values of either Ra_H or Re_H are usually given by solutions to a low-degree polynomial equation, these preferred values can be determined easily for a given wind profile with its Fourier coefficeints as data (Shirer and Brümmer, 1986; Stensrud and Shirer, 1987). In the rest of this section, we summarize the expressions for the preferred values of β and then in Section 12.5 we present some results using simple wind profiles.

12.3.3 Special cases: $f^* = 0$. The irrotational case will be examined again to discover whether the results agree with those obtained by Shirer (1980) and discussed in Section 11.3. As before, stability is lost via a Hopf bifurcation and we find that the Hopf bifurcation point Ra_H is given by

$$Ra_H = (\alpha^2 + 1)^3/\alpha^2 + 4Re^2P^2\Sigma_3^2/[(\alpha^2 + 1)(P + 1)^2] \quad , \tag{12.47}$$

in agreement with (11.56). We do not express this bifurcation point as a critical value of Re because the energetics analysis revealed that Σ_3 does not provide energy to the roll. The minimum value of Ra_H occurs when $\Sigma_3 = 0$ and $\alpha^2 = 1/2$; this result eliminates Re from the problem and produces the same value for Ra_H as that encountered in classical Rayleigh-Bénard convection. In this case, we see from (11.57) that the limiting frequency of the periodic solution is given by $|\omega_o| = Re\ P|\Sigma_1|$, so that the roll is simply moving downwind at a rate depending on the roll-perpendicular component U. Here we refer to this special case as model MT, where the T refers to the inclusion of thermal effects. From the expression (12.43) for Σ_3, we have that the minimum value of Ra_H occurs when

$$\Sigma_3 = s_3\sin(\beta) - s_4\cos(\beta) = 0 \quad , \tag{12.48}$$

which yields

$$\tan(\beta) = s_4/s_3 \quad . \tag{12.49}$$

This form produces the same orientation angles as those found by Shirer (1980). When the roll adopts this angle, it feels no effects from the cross-roll component of the wind shear.

We find that if we integrate Σ_3 by parts to obtain an expression dependent upon the second derivative of the wind $\partial^2 U^*/\partial z^{*2}$, then we again obtain (11.34), which is

$$\Sigma_3 = -\pi^{-1} \int_0^\pi \frac{\partial^2 U^*}{\partial z^{*2}} \sin^2(z^*)\, dz^* \quad . \tag{12.50}$$

Since $\sin^2(z^*) > 0$ for $0 < z^* < \pi$, we can see that in order for Σ_3 to be zero, either the second derivative of the cross-roll wind profile must be identically zero throughout the domain, or there must be an inflection point $(\partial^2 U^*/\partial z^{*2} = 0)$ in the roll-perpendicular wind profile at some level within the domain. For example, if $U_c^*(z^*) = z^{*2}/\pi^3$ and $V_c^*(z^*) = 0$, then the orientation angle produced by (12.49) is $\beta = 0°$. For this orientation angle $U(z^*) = V_c^*(z^*) = 0$, so that $\partial^2 U^*/\partial z^{*2} = 0$ throughout the domain. A more complicated profile would require that the second derivative of the cross-roll wind component be zero somewhere in the domain, so that the integral can equal zero.

In Section 12.4 we discover that for the pure inflection point instability case, an inflection point is a necessary, but not a sufficient condition for this third instability mechanism to exist. But, we have seen here that for ordinary Rayleigh-Bénard convection, the existence of an inflection point in the component of the wind perpendicular to the roll axis is necessary in order to determine a preferred value of the orientation angle. Thus, finding an inflection point in the roll-perpendicular wind profile does not necessarily indicate that the inflection point instability mechanism is dominating the characteristics of the flow.

12.3.4 Special cases: $Ra_H = 0$. This case allows an examination of the parallel instability modes that occur in the absence of thermal effects. Following Stensrud and Shirer (1987), we refer to this special case as model Mf, where the f refers to the inclusion of the Coriolis terms in the model. As in the Rayleigh-Bénard case, the conductive solution loses stability via a Hopf bifurcation. We find that only one root exists for which the value of the critical Reynolds number, denoted here by Re_p, is both real and positive. This root is given by

$$Re_p^2 = G_1/G_2 \quad , \tag{12.51}$$

where

$$G_1 = 4[(\alpha^2 + 1)^3 + f^{*2}]\,(\alpha^2 + 1)^3 \quad , \tag{12.52}$$

$$G_2 = \alpha^2[s_3 \cos(\beta) + s_4 \sin(\beta)]^2 f^{*2}$$

$$- \alpha^2\,[s_3\sin(\beta) - s_4\cos(\beta)]^2\,(\alpha^2 - 1)^2(\alpha^2 + 1)^2 \quad . \tag{12.53}$$

It is apparent that the minimum value of Re_p occurs when G_2 is a maximum. From (12.53) we see that this maximum value occurs when $\tan(\beta) = s_4/s_3$, and from (12.44) we see that this orientation maximizes Σ_4, the energy source for the parallel instability. This value of β is the same as that found previously in (12.49) for the irrotational case, and again the roll-perpendicular component vanishes. Thus, the parallel and thermal instabilities, when examined in the absence of other effects, yield the same orientation angles. For this orientation angle, the critical value of Re_p is given by

$$Re_p^2 = 4(\alpha^2 + 1)^3[(\alpha^2 + 1)^3 + f^{*2}]/[\alpha^2 f^{*2}(s_3^2 + s_4^2)] \quad . \tag{12.54}$$

The limiting frequency ω_o of the branching solution is given by $Re = Re_p$ in

$$|\omega_o| = Re|\Sigma_1 - f^*\Sigma_4/[2(\alpha^2 + 1)^2]| \quad , \tag{12.55}$$

so that now the parallel wind shear contributes to the roll propagation rate. However, the minimum value of Re_p^2 with respect to α^2 depends upon f^{*2}; differentiating Re_p^2 with respect to α^2 and setting the result to zero leads to the requirement that

$$(\alpha^2 + 1)^3(5\alpha^2 - 1) + f^{*2}(2\alpha^2 - 1) = 0 \quad , \tag{12.56}$$

so that $1/5 < \alpha^2 < 1/2$. A similar dependence was first discussed for the Veronis (1966) model in Section 7.2.2, where a different restriction on α^2 was found.

12.3.5 Special cases: $\Sigma_3 = 0$ and $P = 1$. We have seen that the preferred orientation angle is given by $\Sigma_3 = 0$ for both the irrotational case when $f^* = 0$, and the neutrally stratified case when $Ra_H = 0$. Thus, it is natural to investigate the non-neutral, rotational case when $\Sigma_3 = 0$; however, because Ra_H is governed by a cubic polynomial equation, simple analytical solutions have been found only when $P = 1$. As before, the conductive solution loses stability via a Hopf bifurcation and we find that the critical value of the Rayleigh number is

$$Ra_H = [(\alpha^2 + 1)^3 + f^{*2}]/\alpha^2 - f^{*2}Re^2\Sigma_4^2/[4(\alpha^2 + 1)^3] \quad , \tag{12.57}$$

and that the limiting frequency ω_o obeys (12.55). The first bracketed term in the equation is the usual critical Rayleigh number (7.37) for convection in a rotating fluid (Veronis, 1966). However, the second term is a destabilizing effect owing to the presence of rotation and roll-parallel wind shear; we found previously that it contributed to creation of roll kinetic energy. We know that Σ_4 is a Fourier coefficient of the wind parallel to the roll axis, so that a maximum value for Σ_4 would yield a minimum value for Ra_H. As we saw in the case $Ra_H = 0$ above, maximizing Σ_4 is a manifestation of the parallel instability mechanism (Lilly, (1966), by which the roll can extract energy from the mean wind shear parallel to the roll axis. The fact that inclusion of rotation in the model is essential for the existence of this instability mechanism can be seen directly from (12.57).

The form of (12.57) indicates that there is only one instability mechanism, and that it has as special cases the two mechanisms of Rayleigh-Bénard and parallel instabilities (Shirer, 1986). This result suggests that it may not be correct to view the Rayleigh-Bénard and parallel instability mechanisms as being separate ones leading to solutions having different roll geometries (Etling, 1971; Asai and Nakasuji, 1973). Thus, the Shirer (1986) model effectively links the two mechanisms. Before discussing the expected orientations associated with various wind profiles, we first discuss a model for the third instability mechanism in the following section.

12.4 The Inflection Point Instability

A model appropriate for study of the inflection point instability modes is that of Stensrud and Shirer (1987), who extended the analysis of Shirer (1986) by including two vertical wavenumbers. We again begin with the two-dimensional shallow Boussinesq system, but for a neutral, irrotational atmosphere. The Rayleigh number is now zero by definition, thereby eliminating the modes originating from the Rayleigh-Bénard instability, and because we have no thermal dissipation we set P = 1. Also, the Coriolis terms are set to zero, and this effectively filters the parallel instability. Because we are interested only in the stability properties of the conductive solution $\psi^* = 0$, we begin with the two-dimensional, linear version of the Boussinesq equation (12.7) in roll coordinates,

$$\frac{\partial \tilde{\nabla}^2 \psi^*}{\partial t^*} + \mathrm{Re}\, U^* \frac{\partial \tilde{\nabla}^2 \psi^*}{\partial x^*} - \mathrm{Re}\, \frac{\partial \psi^*}{\partial x^*} \frac{\partial^2 U^*}{\partial z^{*2}} - a^{-1} \tilde{\nabla}^4 \psi^* = 0 \quad . \tag{12.58}$$

An appropriate form for the spectral expansion of ψ^* is

$$\psi^*(x^*,z^*,t^*) = \psi_{1q}(t^*)\sin(x^*)\sin(qz^*) + \phi_{1q}(t^*)\cos(x^*)\sin(qz^*)$$

$$+ \psi_{1n}(t^*)\sin(x^*)\sin(nz^*) + \phi_{1n}(t^*)\cos(x^*)\sin(nz^*) \quad , \tag{12.59}$$

where q and n are integral vertical wavenumbers. Since this model has two vertical wavenumbers q and n, we refer to it as model M2(q,n). For most applications, we choose q = 1 and n = 2. We now substitute (12.59) into (12.58) and use the Galerkin technique discussed in Chapter 3 to form the spectral system. For $a = \alpha$ as before, the resulting linear spectral system is

$$\dot{\psi}_{1q} = \mathrm{Re}\{H_2(q)\phi_{1q} + H_3(n,q)\phi_{1n}\} - D(q)\psi_{1q} \quad , \tag{12.60}$$

$$\dot{\phi}_{1q} = -\,\mathrm{Re}\{H_2(q)\psi_{1q} + H_3(n,q)\psi_{1n}\} - D(q)\phi_{1q} \quad , \tag{12.61}$$

$$\dot{\psi}_{1n} = \mathrm{Re}\{H_2(n)\phi_{1n} + H_3(q,n)\phi_{1q}\} - D(n)\psi_{1n} \quad , \tag{12.62}$$

$$\dot{\phi}_{1n} = -\,\mathrm{Re}\{H_2(n)\psi_{1n} + H_3(q,n)\psi_{1q}\} - D(n)\phi_{1n} \quad . \tag{12.63}$$

For the integers m and r, we have introduced the functions

$$H_2(r) = \Sigma_5 - [(\alpha^2 - 3r^2)/(\alpha^2 + r^2)]\Sigma_7(r) \quad , \tag{12.64}$$

$$H_3(m,r) = [(-\alpha^2 + 2mr + r^2)/(\alpha^2 + r^2)]\Sigma_9(m,r)$$

$$+ [(\alpha^2 + 2mr - r^2)/(\alpha^2 + r^2)]\Sigma_{11}(m,r) \quad , \tag{12.65}$$

$$D(r) = (\alpha^2 + r^2)/\alpha \quad , \tag{12.66}$$

and we have defined the Fourier coefficients

$$\Sigma_5 = \pi^{-1} \int_0^\pi U^*(z^*)\, dz^* = [\Sigma_1 + \Sigma_2]/2 \quad , \tag{12.67}$$

$$\Sigma_7(r) = \pi^{-1} \int_0^\pi U^*(z^*)\cos(2rz^*)\, dz^* \quad , \tag{12.68}$$

$$\Sigma_9(m,r) = \pi^{-1} \int_0^\pi U^*(z^*)\cos[(m + r)z^*]\, dz^* \quad , \tag{12.69}$$

$$\Sigma_{11}(m,r) = \pi^{-1} \int_0^\pi U^*(z^*)\cos[(m - r)z^*]\, dz^* \quad . \tag{12.70}$$

As before U^* denotes the component of the mean wind that is perpendicular to the roll axis.

12.4.1 Spectral model energetics. In order to elucidate the available energy sources for model M2, we form a perturbation roll kinetic energy equation from (12.60)-(12.63). The perturbation roll kinetic energy is equivalent to

$$2KE = (\alpha^2 + q^2)(\psi_{1q}^2 + \phi_{1q}^2) + (\alpha^2 + n^2)(\psi_{1n}^2 + \phi_{1n}^2) \quad , \tag{12.71}$$

and this leads to

$$\begin{aligned} 2\dot{KE} = {} & \underbrace{Re(q^2 - n^2)[\Sigma_{11}(n,q) - \Sigma_9(n,q)](\psi_{1n}\phi_{1q} - \phi_{1n}\psi_{1q})}_{\mathrm{I}} \\ & \underbrace{- \alpha^{-1}(\alpha^2 + q^2)^2[\psi_{1q}^2 + \phi_{1q}^2]}_{\mathrm{V}} \underbrace{- \alpha^{-1}(\alpha^2 + n^2)^2[\psi_{1n}^2 + \phi_{1n}^2]}_{\mathrm{V}} \quad . \end{aligned} \tag{12.72}$$

The first term on the right side of (12.72), which includes the Fourier coefficients $\Sigma_9(n,q)$ and $\Sigma_{11}(n,q)$, is a Reynolds stress. This term (I) represents the energy source for the inflection point instability, since it depends on the mean wind shear perpendicular to the roll. It is apparent from (12.72) that at least two vertical harmonics, or wavenumbers, are needed for this mechanism to exist. This fact is easily demonstrated by setting either $m = 0$ or $r = 0$ in (12.69) and (12.70) to conclude that $\Sigma_9 = \Sigma_{11}$. In this case, term (I) is zero and does not contribute to the roll kinetic energy KE. The last two terms (V) represent dissipation rates. Since the spectral model energetics only includes an energy source for the inflection point instability, we expect that this model should be able to reproduce the modes arising from this instability mechanism.

12.4.2 Orientation angles. As in Section 12.3.2, we can introduce the definition of the orientation angle (12.2) into the Fourier coefficients of the wind to identify another degree of freedom in the problem. Thus, we may express the wind shear coefficients as

$$\Sigma_5 = s_5 \sin(\beta) - s_6 \cos(\beta) \quad , \tag{12.73}$$

$$\Sigma_7(r) = s_7(r)\sin(\beta) - s_8(r)\cos(\beta) \quad , \tag{12.74}$$

$$\Sigma_9(m,r) = s_9(m,r)\sin(\beta) - s_{10}(m,r)\cos(\beta) \quad , \tag{12.75}$$

$$\Sigma_{11}(m,r) = s_{11}(m,r)\sin(\beta) - s_{12}(m,r)\cos(\beta) \quad , \tag{12.76}$$

in which we have defined

$$s_5 = \pi^{-1} \int_0^\pi U_c^*(z^*)\, dz^* \quad , \tag{12.77}$$

$$s_6 = \pi^{-1} \int_0^\pi V_c^*(z^*)\, dz^* \quad , \tag{12.78}$$

$$s_7(r) = \pi^{-1} \int_0^\pi U_c^*(z^*)\cos(2rz^*)\, dz^* \quad , \tag{12.79}$$

$$s_8(r) = \pi^{-1} \int_0^\pi V_c^*(z^*)\cos(2rz^*)\, dz^* \quad , \tag{12.80}$$

$$s_9(m,r) = \pi^{-1} \int_0^\pi U_c^*(z^*)\cos[(m+r)z^*]\, dz^* \quad , \tag{12.81}$$

$$s_{10}(m,r) = \pi^{-1} \int_0^\pi V_c^*(z^*)\cos[(m+r)z^*]\, dz^* \quad , \tag{12.82}$$

$$s_{11}(m,r) = \pi^{-1} \int_0^\pi U_c^*(z^*)\cos[(m-r)z^*]\, dz^* \quad , \tag{12.83}$$

$$s_{12}(m,r) = \pi^{-1} \int_0^\pi V_c^*(z^*)\cos[(m-r)z^*]\, dz^* \quad . \tag{12.84}$$

As before, U^*_c and V^*_c are the dimensionless background wind components in the standard coordinate system (Fig. 12.1). As in Section 12.3, we assume that the preferred values of orientation angle β and cell aspect ratio α are those that produce the lowest acceptable value of the critical Reynolds number Re_H.

12.4.3 Preferred roll geometry. The stability of the basic solution to a model is determined by performing a linear analysis of the equations. The linearization of M2(q,n) about the conductive solution is given by (12.60)-(12.63). We find that the characteristic exponents λ of (12.60)-(12.63) are governed by a quartic polynomial equation. This polynomial equation can itself be factored into two quadratic equations. Neutral stability and bifurcation are given by the vanishing of the real part of one of the roots to the quadratic equation. A Hopf bifurcation to a temporally periodic solution is given by $\lambda = \pm i\omega_o$, where ω_o is the limiting frequency. As in Stensrud and Shirer (1987), we find that when this form is substituted into either quadratic equation, we obtain complex terms. Since only real values of the frequency ω_o are acceptable as solutions, we set the imaginary terms to zero and solve for ω_o. Thus, using (12.64) and (12.66) we have that

$$|\omega_o| = Re_i|[H_2(n)D(q) + H_2(q)D(n)]/[D(n) + D(q)]| \quad . \tag{12.85}$$

We then substitute this expression for ω_o back into the real part of either quadratic equation to obtain

$$Re_i^2[H_2(n) - H_2(q)]^2D(n)D(q) + Re_i^2[H_3(n,q)H_3(q,n)][D(n) + D(q)]^2$$
$$+ [D(n) + D(q)]^2D(n)D(q) = 0 \quad , \tag{12.86}$$

where $H_2(r)$ and $H_3(m,r)$ are defined in (12.64)-(12.65) and Re_i is the critical Reynolds number for the inflection point instability. It is apparent that real roots to (12.86) can exist only if $H_3(n,q)H_3(q,n) < 0$, so that $Re_i^2 > 0$. In this case, a Hopf bifurcation, or instability, might occur since all the other terms are positive.

We find that it is possible to obtain a simple expression for the preferred orientation angle β for the inflection point modes. We substitute the expressions (12.74)-(12.76) for the Fourier coefficients into the equation (12.86) governing the value of the critical Reynolds number Re_i and then take the derivative of this equation with respect to β. Finally we use the simple fact that the minimum value of Re_i occurs when $\partial Re_i/\partial\beta = 0$ to obtain

$$\tan(2\beta) = B_1/B_2 \quad , \tag{12.87}$$

in which

$$\begin{aligned} B_1 = &- \left[2a_6^2 s_7(n)s_8(n) + 2a_5^2 s_7(q)s_8(q)\right. \\ &\left. - 2a_5a_6\left(s_7(n)s_8(q) + s_7(q)s_8(n)\right)\right] (\alpha^2 + n^2)(\alpha^2 + q^2) \\ &- \left[2a_1a_3 s_{10}(n,q)s_9(n,q) + 2a_2a_4 s_{12}(n,q)s_{11}(n,q)\right. \\ &\left. + (a_1a_4 + a_2a_3)\left(s_{10}(n,q)s_{11}(n,q) + s_9(n,q)s_{12}(n,q)\right)\right] (2\alpha^2 + n^2 + q^2)^2 \quad , \end{aligned} \tag{12.88}$$

$$\begin{aligned} B_2 = &\left[a_6^2\left(s_8^2(n) - s_7^2(n)\right) + a_5^2\left(s_8^2(q) - s_7^2(q)\right)\right. \\ &\left. + 2a_5a_6\left(s_7(n)s_7(q) - s_8(n)s_8(q)\right)\right] (\alpha^2 + n^2)(\alpha^2 + q^2) \\ &+ \left[a_1a_3\left(s_{10}^2(n,q) - s_9^2(n,q)\right) + a_2a_4\left(s_{12}^2(n,q) - s_{11}^2(n,q)\right)\right. \\ &\left. + (a_1a_4 + a_2a_3)\left(s_{10}(n,q)s_{12}(n,q) - s_9(n,q)s_{11}(n,q)\right)\right] (2\alpha^2 + n^2 + q^2)^2 \quad , \end{aligned} \tag{12.89}$$

and where

$$a_1 = (-\alpha^2 + 2nq + q^2)/(\alpha^2 + q^2) \quad , \tag{12.90}$$

$$a_2 = (\alpha^2 + 2nq - q^2)/(\alpha^2 + q^2) \quad , \tag{12.91}$$

$$a_3 = (-\alpha^2 + 2qn + n^2)/(\alpha^2 + n^2) \quad , \tag{12.92}$$

$$a_4 = (\alpha^2 + 2qn - n^2)/(\alpha^2 + n^2) \quad , \tag{12.93}$$

$$a_5 = (\alpha^2 - 3q^2)/(\alpha^2 + q^2) \quad , \tag{12.94}$$

$$a_6 = (\alpha^2 - 3n^2)/(\alpha^2 + n^2) \quad . \tag{12.95}$$

For any given wind profile, we can easily calculate the appropriate Fourier coefficients and substitute them into the right side of (12.87) to obtain a value for β. Once we have the preferred value for β, we can substitute its value into the expression (12.86) governing Re_i. We perform these calculations for a range of values of α until we find the one associated with the minimum value of Re_i. The resulting values of α, β, and Re_i are the preferred values at which a bifurcation to a temporally periodic solution occurs first.

12.5 A Comparison of the Pure Instability Modes

Idealized wind profiles are often used to represent the mean wind in the boundary layer. In this section, we use very simple wind profiles to compare the model results for the cases of pure Rayleigh-Bénard instability, pure parallel instability, and pure inflection point instability. These comparisons provide an understanding of the differences between modes excited by the three instability mechanisms. We note that the dimensionless forms (11.19) and (12.11) for U^* and V^* imply that $U_c^{*2}(\pi) + V_c^{*2}(\pi) = 1/\pi^2$.

We discovered in Section 12.3 that the Rayleigh-Bénard and parallel instability mechanisms produce the same preferred orientation angle given by $\Sigma_3 = 0$. The Rayleigh-Bénard instability also yields expected values of $\alpha^2 = 1/2$ and $Ra_H = 6.75$ for any given wind profile. The parallel instability produces a value of Re_p that depends on both the given wind profile (see (12.54)) and the value of f^*, the latter determining a preferred value of the cell aspect ratio α that obeys $1/5 < \alpha^2 < 1/2$. Here, we choose $f^* = 0.5$ so that $\alpha^2 \approx 0.216$ is the expected value obtained from (12.56). Thus, although the value of the preferred orientation angle is the same, the preferred value of the cell wavelength ℓ is 1.52 times larger for the parallel mode than for the thermal one. For the inflection point instability mechanism, the expected values of both the orientation angle β and the cell aspect ratio α depend on the given wind profile.

12.5.1 Linear and quadratic wind profiles. We begin by examining the roll geometries given by the pure instability cases when the wind profile is a simple linear one

$$U_c^*(z^*) = z^*/\pi^2 \quad , \tag{12.96}$$

$$V_c^*(z^*) = 0 \quad . \tag{12.97}$$

The values of the relevant Fourier coefficients are given in Table 12.1. We know that for the inflection point modes, an inflection point in the wind profile is a necessary condition for instability, and so no inflection point modes should exist for this profile. Indeed, we find that for M2(1,2) the values of Re_i^2 obtained from (12.86) are negative, so that no instability occurs in this case (Table 12.2). For both the Rayleigh-Bénard and parallel modes, we find from (12.49) that β is indeterminate because both s_3 and s_4 vanish. Thus we see, in agreement with some observations of Kuettner (1959), that curvature must be present in the wind profile for there to be clearly defined rolls.

One of the simplest idealized wind profiles that has a nonconstant shear is a quadratic profile. We choose

$$U_c^*(z^*) = z^{*2}/\pi^3 \quad , \tag{12.98}$$

$$V_c^*(z^*) = 0 \quad , \tag{12.99}$$

and note that this wind profile also has no inflection point. As expected, the inflection point model M2(1,2) gives no instability. However, we find that Rayleigh-Bénard and parallel modes are possible with $\beta = 0°$ for both; for this profile we have $\alpha^2 \simeq 0.216$ and $Re_p \simeq 512$ from Mf (Table 12.2) and $\alpha^2 = 1/2$ and $Ra_H = 6.75$ from MT.

12.5.2 A sinusoidal profile. A more interesting wind profile is one that contains an inflection point at a height z_{IP} in the domain. We choose

$$U_c^*(z^*) = \left(\sin(z^*) + \varepsilon \sin(2z^*) + 1\right)/\pi \quad , \tag{12.100}$$

$$V_c^*(z^*) = 0 \quad , \tag{12.101}$$

where we vary the value of ε between 0.0 and 1.0, and so vary the value of z_{IP}. In Table 12.1 we give the important Fourier coefficients of the wind profile and in Table 12.2 we show the critical Reynolds numbers for the two dynamic modes. For $\varepsilon = 0.0$, we expect that the Rayleigh-Bénard and parallel instabilities dominate,

Table 12.1 Fourier Coefficients for Simple Wind Profiles

Profile	s_3	$s_7(1)$	$s_7(2)$	$s_9(1,2)$	$s_{11}(1,2)$
Linear	0.	0.	0.	$-2/9\pi^2$	$-2/\pi^2$
Quadratic	$-1/\pi^3$	$1/2\pi^3$	$1/8\pi^3$	$-2/9\pi^3$	$-2/\pi^3$
Sinusoidal	$4/3\pi^2$	$-2/3\pi^2$	$-2/15\pi^2$	$-4\varepsilon/5\pi^2$	$4\varepsilon/3\pi^2$

Table 12.2 Preferred Critical Reynolds Numbers for Simple Wind Profiles

	Parallel Mode [Mf] ($f^*=0.5$)			Inflection Point Mode [M2(1,2)]		
Profile	β	α^2	Re_p	β	α^2	Re_i
Linear	–	–	∞	–	–	Imag.
Quadratic	0°	0.216	512.	–	–	Imag.
Sinusoidal						
ε = 0.0	0°	0.216	122.	–	–	Imag.
0.1	0°	0.216	122.	90°	1.84	400.
0.2	0°	0.216	122.	90°	1.59	187.
0.3	0°	0.216	122.	90°	1.40	119.
0.4	0°	0.216	122.	90°	1.29	86.7
0.5	0°	0.216	122.	90°	1.23	68.2
0.6	0°	0.216	122.	90°	1.18	56.2
0.7	0°	0.216	122.	90°	1.15	47.8
0.8	0°	0.216	122.	90°	1.14	41.6
0.9	0°	0.216	122.	90°	1.12	36.8
1.0	0°	0.216	122.	90°	1.11	33.1

since the wind profile does not contain an inflection point. However, as the value of ε is increased, we expect that the inflection point instability would begin to have an effect on the roll development. For all of these profiles, the values of Ra_H and Re_p are the same, since $Ra_H = 6.75$ for any given wind profile, and since the analysis of Shirer (1986) for Mf includes only one vertical wavenumber, which here is represented in (12.100)-(12.101) by $\sin(z^*)$. Thus, from Mf, we have $Re_p \simeq 122$, $\alpha^2 \simeq 0.216$ and $\beta = 0°$ for any value of ε (Table 12.2). For $\varepsilon = 0.0$ (Fig. 12.3a), M2(1,2) yields only negative values of Re_i^2, so that no instability occurs yielding inflection point modes. However, when $\varepsilon = 0.3$ (Fig. 12.3b), $Re_i \simeq 119$, $\beta = 90°$ and $\alpha^2 \simeq 1.40$, so that instability occurs for the inflection point mode at a lower value of Re_c than for the parallel mode; of the two dynamic modes, then, the inflection point mode dominates. From this type of comparison, it is impossible to determine whether the Rayleigh-Bénard mode (Ra > 0) or the pure inflection point mode (Ra = 0) actually approximates the characteristics of the flow. We can only conclude which of the two dynamic instability mechanisms more greatly influences the response. As

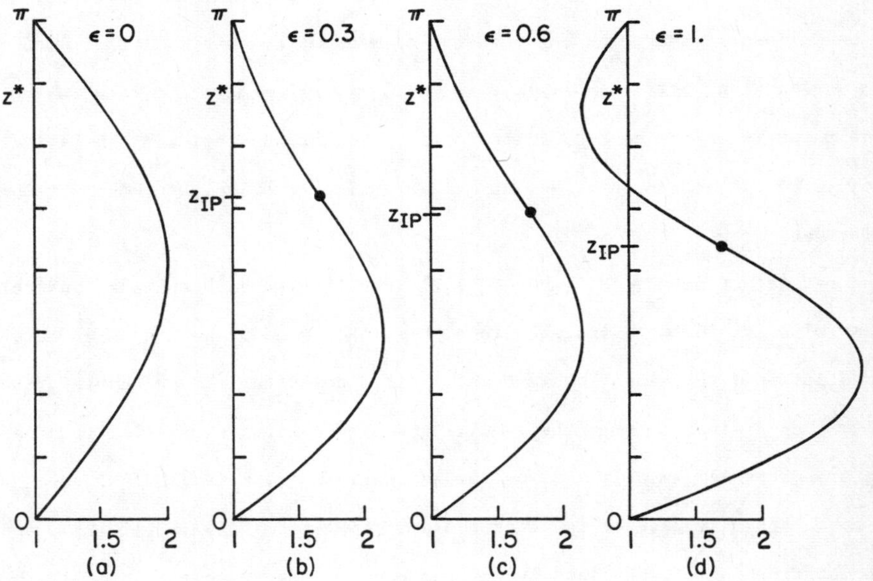

Fig. 12.3 Vertical wind profiles given by $\pi U_c^*(z^*)=\sin(z^*)+\varepsilon\sin(2z^*)+1$ and $V_c^*(z^*)=0$ for the cases $\varepsilon=0.0$ (a), $\varepsilon=0.3$ (b), $\varepsilon=0.6$ (c), and $\varepsilon=1.0$ (d). Here the inflection point height is labeled z_{IP} (from Stensrud and Shirer, 1987).

discovered by Stensrud and Shirer (1987), a comparison between the results of Mf for the parallel modes and M2 for the inflection point modes is an accurate way to determine for the general case which of these two dynamic instability mechanisms are dominant. As we further increase the value of ε, we find that the value of Re_i continues to decrease. At $\varepsilon = 0.6$ (Fig. 12.3c), $Re_i \approx 56.2$ and $\alpha^2 \approx 1.18$ and at $\varepsilon = 1.0$ (Fig. 12.3d), $Re_i \approx 33.1$ and $\alpha^2 \approx 1.11$. Thus, once the value of ε is greater than approximately 0.3, the inflection point instability is dominant.

If we examine Fig. 12.3, then we can see that for $\varepsilon = 0.0$ (Fig. 12.3a) the wind profile has no inflection point, so the parallel instability mode is the only one possible. Once $\varepsilon = 0.3$ (Fig. 12.3b), we find that the wind profile now contains an inflection point that is slightly above the center of the domain. In this case, the inflection point instability mode occurs before the parallel instability one, although the values of Re_i and Re_p are nearly equal. When $\varepsilon = 0.6$ (Fig. 12.3c) and $\varepsilon = 1.0$ (Fig. 12.3d), the values of Re_i remain less than that of Re_p, and so the inflection point mode still occurs before the parallel one. We can see from Fig. 12.3 that as the value of ε increases, the inflection point moves closer to the domain center and the wind shear at the inflection point is stronger. This observation is in agreement with the results of Brümmer and Latif (1985), who found from a more general stability analysis that for a neutral atmosphere, the nearer the inflection point is to the center of the domain, the more unstable is the basic flow. In this way, the inflection point height plays an important role in the development of cloud streets.

The results from MT, Mf and M2(1,2) for the three separate instability mechanisms also yield some insight into how the wind shear form affects the characteristics of the individual modes. If the parallel or Rayleigh-Bénard instabiilty mode dominates, then the resulting roll is aligned parallel to the wind shear vector. This alignment maximizes the generation of longitudinal kinetic energy from the mean shear $\partial V^*/\partial z^*$ of the longitudinal flow (term (II) in (12.19)), and can affect the overturning circulations by the exchange of energy from LKE to KE through the action of the Coriolis force (terms (III) in (12.18)-(12.19)). This alignment also produces a lower value for Ra_H (12.47), which suggests that the wind shear can affect the vertical heat flux. However, if the inflection point instability dominates, then the roll is aligned perpendicular to the wind shear vector. This alignment maximizes the generation of roll kinetic energy from the mean shear $\partial U^*/\partial z^*$ of the cross flow, which directly contributes to the generation of roll kinetic energy (term (I) in (12.18)). Thus, in these very simple cases, we see that the preferred orientation angles yield alignments that maximize the particular energy source terms for the various instability mechanisms.

12.5.3 The Ekman profile. One commonly used wind profile for approximating the mean wind in the boundary layer is the Ekman profile, and it has been used extensively for study of the formation of cloud streets (Lilly, 1966; Asai and Nakasuji, 1973). We define a 0° orientation to denote rolls that are aligned parallel to the westerly geostrophic wind vector $\underset{\sim}{V}_g^*$, with positive orientations being to the left of this wind vector (Fig. 12.1). For an Ekman profile, the inflection point instability is characteristically associated with orientation angles of 10° to 20° and the Rayleigh-Bénard and parallel instabilities are associated with orientation angles of -10° to -20°.

The Ekman profile can be written as

$$U_c^*(z^*) = |\underset{\sim}{V}_g^*|[1 - \exp(-z^*/D^*) \cos(z^*/D^*)] \quad , \qquad (12.102)$$

$$V_c^*(z^*) = |\underset{\sim}{V}_g^*|\exp(-z^*/D^*) \sin(z^*/D^*) \quad , \qquad (12.103)$$

in which $|\underset{\sim}{V}_g^*|$ is chosen so that $U_c^{*2}(\pi) + V_c^{*2}(\pi) = 1/\pi^2$:

$$|\underset{\sim}{V}_g^*|^2 = 1/\{\pi^2[1-2\exp(-\pi/D^*)\cos(\pi/D^*) + \exp(-2\pi/D^*)]\} \quad . \qquad (12.104)$$

Here D is the Ekman depth and $D^* = D\pi/z_T$ is the dimensionless Ekman depth; πD^* is the lowest altitude at which $V_c^* = 0$, implying that the Ekman profile is parallel to the geostrophic wind vector $\underset{\sim}{V}_g^*$ (Fig. 12.4). For heights $z^* < \pi D^*$, we have $V_c^* > 0$ so that the wind vector $\underset{\sim}{V}_c^*$ is oriented to the left of $\underset{\sim}{V}_g^*$, with this angle approaching 45° as $z^* \to 0$. For $\pi D^* < z^* < 2\pi D^*$, we have $V_c^* < 0$ so that $\underset{\sim}{V}_c^*$ is to the right of $\underset{\sim}{V}_g^*$, and as $z^* \to \infty$, the wind vector $\underset{\sim}{V}_c^*$ becomes coincident with the geostrophic one $\underset{\sim}{V}_g^*$. Here we vary the value of D^* from $D^* = 0.5$ to $D^* = 3.0$, which is equivalent to varying the domain height z_T from approximately 6D to D. Faller and Kaylor (1966) indicate that

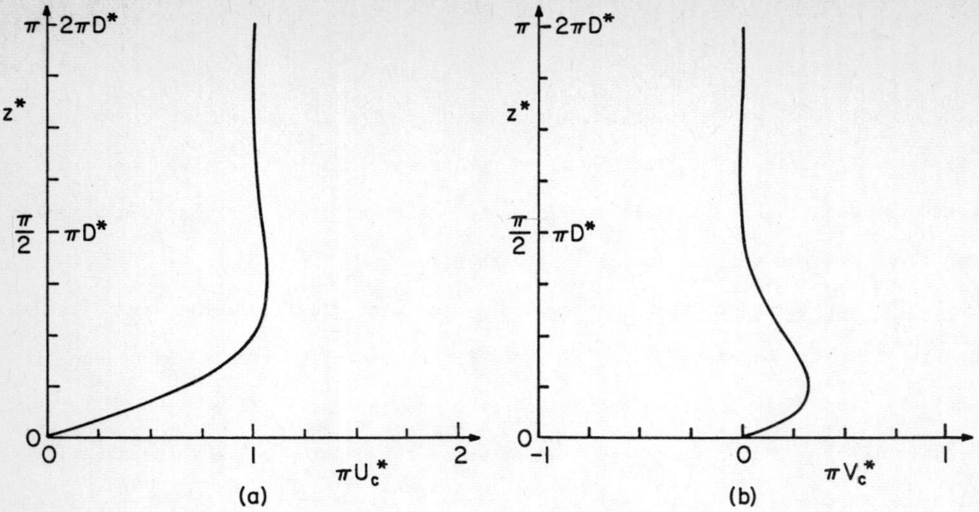

Fig. 12.4 The U_c^*-component (a) and the V_c^*-component (b) of the Ekman profile when the dimensionless Ekman depth $D^*=1/2$. Note that $\pi D^*=\pi/2$ is the lowest height at which $V_c^*=0$ implying that $\underset{\sim}{V}_c^*$ is parallel to $\underset{\sim}{V}_g^*$.

when D is used as a vertical scaling parameter, the average circulation depth z_T is 4D to 6D for most studies using an Ekman profile. This corresponds approximately to a value of D^* between 0.5 and 0.8. However, observations of boundary layer rolls over the North Sea suggest that values of D^* between 2.0 and 3.0 are more reasonable (Brümmer, 1985).

In Fig. 12.5, we summarize the results from MT, Mf and M2(1,2) for D^* = 0.5, 1.0, 2.0 and 3.0. We use vertical wavenumbers one and two because this wavenumber choice usually produces the lowest value of Re_i; however, when a different wavenumber choice produces the best results, the preferred values of the orientation angle β are still within the indicated range of -20° to 20°. For D^* = 0.5 (indicated by triangles), we find that all three models have negative orientation angles with β = -18° (open triangles) from MT and Mf and β = -10° (darkened triangles) from M2(1,2). However, as we increase the value of D^* to 1.0 (circles), we find that the orientation angles have shifted toward positive values, with β = 18° from MT and Mf and β = 8° from M2(1,2). As we increase the value of D^* still further, the

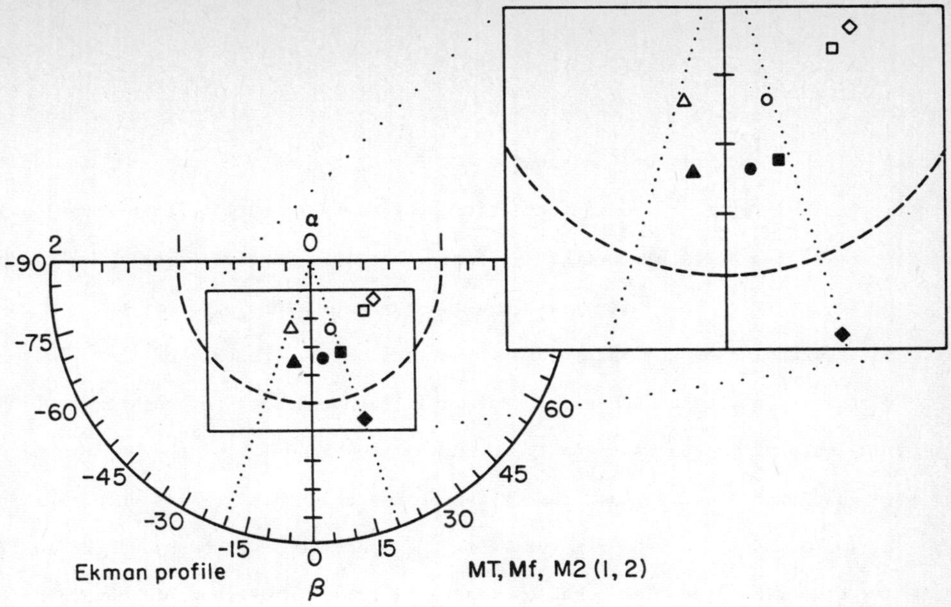

Fig. 12.5 A summary of the results from MT and Mf (open symbols) and M2(1,2) (darkened symbols) for the Ekman profile with $D^*=0.5$ (triangles), 1.0 (circles), 2.0 (squares) and 3.0 (diamonds).

orientation angles shift to even larger positive values of β. For example, from M2(1,2) with $D^* = 2.0$ (squares) we find that $\beta = 16°$, and with $D^* = 3.0$ (diamonds) we find that $\beta = 20°$. This dependence of β on D^* was first described by Shirer (1986) for the pure parallel modes of Mf. However, both the pure inflection point modes of M2(1,2) and the Rayleigh-Bénard modes exhibit the same behavior. Thus, we discover a shift in orientation angles as the value of D^*, or the domain height, is varied.

The wide range of preferred values of β produced by the various models using the Ekman profile indicate that associating negative orientations with the pure parallel instability mode and positive orientations with the pure inflection point instability mode is incorrect. The preferred orientation angles are strongly dependent on the value of the Ekman depth D. Unfortunately, most of the studies using the Ekman profile to examine the formation of cloud streets use D as a vertical scaling parameter. However, the sensitivity of the model results to the value of D indicates that it may be unwise to use D in this way.

12.6 The General Case of Mixed Instability Mechanisms

The stability of the conductive solution to the Shirer (1986) model for the general case of mixed Rayleigh-Bénard and parallel instability modes is determined by performing a linear analysis of the equations. Therefore, we seek the characteristic exponents that are roots of the characteristic polynomial equation; this equation is the determinant of a certain matrix. We find that this matrix can be partitioned into three submatrices: a six-by-six, a two-by-two, and a one-by-one. A Hopf bifurcation is signaled by the vanishing of the real part of a pair of the roots of the characteristic polynomial equation. Here this cannot happen for the roots of the linear or the quadratic equations that result from the expansion of the one-by-one or the two-by-two submatrices. Thus, the sixth-degree polynomial equation, resulting from the expansion of the six-by-six submatrix, governs the development of the rolls.

The sixth-degree polynomial equation can be factored into two cubic equations by changing the variables into complex form as described in Section 11.3.3. A Hopf bifurcation is given by assuming that $\lambda = \pm i\omega$. When this form is substituted into the cubic equation, a coupled system in Ra and ω is obtained:

$$b_1\omega^3 + b_2\omega^2 + b_3\omega + b_4 = 0 \quad , \tag{12.105}$$

$$c_1\omega^2 + c_2\omega + c_3 = 0 \quad , \tag{12.106}$$

in which the definitions of b_1 to b_4 and c_1 to c_3, some of which are functions of Ra, are given in Shirer (1986). Only the real roots ω of (12.105)-(12.106) yield Hopf bifurcation points. The common roots of these two equations can be found either by using the Euclidean Algorithm (Richards, 1959; see Appendix B) or the method of eliminants (Richards, 1959; see Appendix C). The equation that results can be viewed as either a cubic equation in Ra_H or a cubic equation in Re_H^2.

This situation is considerably more complicated than the ones encountered previously when the values of a control parameter were governed by linear equations such as (12.3), (12.54), or (12.57). Now, one or three branching periodic solutions are possible, and when there are three, they compete with one another for attainment of the globally smallest values. We find that we must be careful to seek

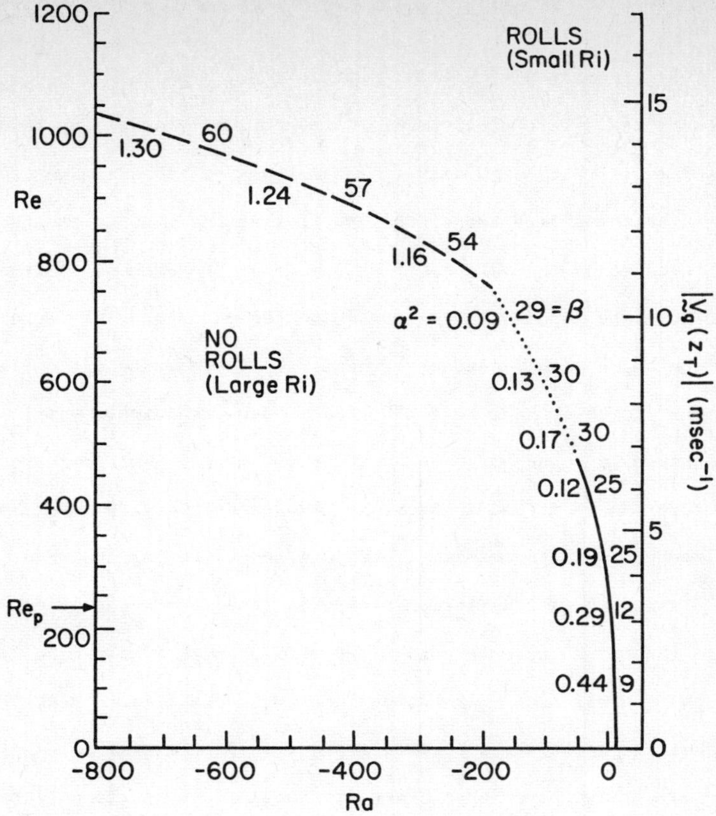

Fig. 12.6 The critical values of Re and Ra for the three roll modes obtained from the Shirer (1986) model for the Ekman profile. Here $D^*=1.0$, $\nu=14\ m^2sec^{-1}$, $f^*=0.5$, P=1; a few preferred values of α^2 are shown to the left of the lines and a few preferred values of β (in degrees) are shown to the right. Three different modes may produce global minima as denoted by the three line types (after Shirer, 1986).

simultaneous minima in both Ra_H and Re_H in order for the results to be independent of whether we view the problem in terms of Ra or Re.

For the Ekman profile with P = 1, z_T = 1 km and f^* = 0.5, the results are summarized in Fig. 12.6. We see that for a given value of Ra_H, or for a given stratification, rolls develop if the value of the wind speed exceeds a certain value given by the critical Reynolds number Re_H, or when Ra and Re have values that are above and to the right of the curves. This result amounts to requiring that the value of a Richardson number Ri, where

$$Ri = -Ra(Re^2P)^{-1} \quad , \tag{12.107}$$

be either sufficiently small and positive, or negative. This observation is in agreement with the results of other investigators (Brown, 1972; Wippermann et al., 1978) who showed that rolls can exist only in a statically stable atmosphere having a small value for the Richardson number. Three types of modes are evident and these are denoted by the three line types; the particular one that is excited depends on which line is crossed as the values of Ra and Re vary. The solid line denotes the mode linked to both the pure Rayleigh-Bénard and the pure parallel instabilities. As Re increases, the value of α^2 decreases from 1/2 and the orientation angle slowly increases from 9° to 25°. Near Re = 450, there are relatively small jumps in the preferred values of α^2 and β. Both increase as a new minimum overtakes the original one, much as we found in Section 7.2.4 and Fig. 7.9 when we considered rotating Rayleigh-Bénard convection. There are smooth variations in α^2 and β again until Re ≃ 750 when a third minimum overtakes the second one and a much shorter wavelength cell (having a much larger value of α^2) appears at a much larger value of β. Thus, the general problem contains much more complicated behavior, including discontinuous variations in the preferred geometries of the rolls.

In this chapter, we have considered several models of cloud street behavior. The technique for finding the critical values of the controlling parameters was extended to temporally periodic solutions and the analysis yielded preferred orientations in agreement with those obtained from larger models of cloud street formation. We also discovered that the addition of a second controlling parameter complicated the analysis and required simultaneous minimum values of both the controlling parameters.

Of course, associating the minimum values of Ra and Re with the expected characteristics of the roll carries with it the implied assumption that the nonlinear solution branches supercritically so that it may acquire the stability lost by the conductive, or basic, solution. We realize, however, that this may not be the case, and we must determine whether the branching solution is stable or not. This determination usually is linked to the branching direction of the periodic solution (Section 11.1). A method for computing the branching direction that does not require knowledge of the periodic solution is the topic of the next chapter.

CHAPTER 13

ON COMPUTING THE BRANCHING DIRECTION OF BIFURCATING PERIODIC SOLUTIONS

HAMPTON N. SHIRER

When studying the stability of stationary solutions, we have noted that a temporally periodic solution emanates from the stationary one at a Hopf bifurcation point, which occurs when the roots, or characteristic exponents, of the characteristic equation are purely imaginary and when the exponents cross the imaginary axis with nonzero speed (see Section 11.1). The Hopf bifurcation point of primary interest is the one R_H at which the stationary solution loses stability as the value of R increases. However, once R_H has been located, we do not know whether the branching periodic solution is stable, or observable, unless we know the direction in which it branches. If the solution exists for $R > R_H$, then it branches supercritically, and we expect it to be stable; if it exists for $R < R_H$, then it branches subcritically, and we expect it to be unstable. Determination of the branching direction depends on consideration of the nonlinear governing system. In some cases, such as the ones presented in Sections 11.3 and 14.1, we can calculate the solution explicitly and determine the branching direction easily. But in most cases, as with the Lorenz model in Section 4.2.2, we cannot find the solution analytically, and so we must use a suitable approximation.

A procedure developed for complex variables by Joseph and Sattinger (1972) and Iooss and Joseph (1980) was cast in real variables by Kloeden and Wells (1983) and is an alternative method to the one given in Marsden and McCracken (1976). The procedure, which can be applied to either partial differential or ordinary differential systems, begins with the realization that a bifurcating periodic solution approaches the stationary solution from which it emanates as the value of R approaches that of R_H (see Section 11.1). Because the amplitude of the periodic solution approaches zero as R approaches R_H, it is natural to attempt to expand the periodic solution as a power series in $(R-R_H)$ having temporally periodic coefficients. This attempt must fail, however, because the power series would make sense for <u>both</u> positive and negative values of $(R-R_H)$, implying falsely that periodic solutions branch both supercritically and subcritically in any given bifurcation.

Instead, the procedure rests on the idea of expanding both the solution and $(R-R_H)$ in terms of a new arbitrary parameter ε. Although the new parameter appears to be an artificial one introduced to facilitate the calculations, it turns out to be closely related to the amplitude of the periodic solution. Thus, we expand $(R-R_H)$ in terms of the amplitude rather than the reverse. Similar power series expansions apply to branching stationary solutions, but we do not review them here.

When the partial differential system is considered, the functions in the expansion can suggest the eigenfunctions necessary for representing the dominant character of the solution; indeed, Kloeden (1986a) proposed that these functions provide the appropriate truncation for representing branching periodic solutions in a low-order spectral model. For example, the power series solution, when determined to high enough order for the branching direction to be found, gives the basis functions used to create the five-component Veronis model of rotating Rayleigh-Bénard convection. This procedure then, might provide an analytical, objective approach for developing qualitatively faithful low-order models of many hydrodynamic flows.

In this chapter, we outline the power series method of Kloeden and Wells (1983), and then we apply it to a system of ordinary differential equations, the Lorenz model. Use of the method necessitates that a lot of algebra be performed, but this algebra can often be done symbolically with a computer. We wish to thank Prof. Kloeden for providing a detailed set of notes, upon which much of Section 13.2 is based.

13.1 Outline of the Method

As we describe the power series approach, we illustrate the computations by applying them to a set of ordinary differential equations whose branching periodic solution we know explicitly. By carrying out this calculation, we demonstrate that we get consistent results; application to a typical hydrodynamic system is given in Section 13.2. When appropriate, we comment on how the calculations could be extended to the case of partial differential equations. Additional detail is given in Kloeden and Wells (1983).

The system we consider first is (see Chapter 14)

$$\frac{dy_1}{dt} = y_2 + y_1[\delta-\eta(y_1^2 + y_2^2)] \quad , \qquad (13.1)$$

$$\frac{dy_2}{dt} = - y_1 + y_2[\delta-\eta(y_1^2 + y_2^2)] \quad , \tag{13.2}$$

in which $\eta = \pm 1$. At $\delta = \delta_o = 0$, the trivial solution $y_1 = 0$ and $y_2 = 0$ bifurcates to the solution

$$y_1 = \sqrt{\delta/\eta}\,\sin(t) \quad , \tag{13.3}$$

$$y_2 = \sqrt{\delta/\eta}\,\cos(t) \quad . \tag{13.4}$$

When $\eta = 1$ we obtain a supercritical branch because the solution exists only when $\delta > 0$; when $\eta = -1$ we obtain a subcritical solution because it exists only when $\delta < 0$. We show in Chapter 14 that this periodic solution is asymptotically orbitally stable when $\eta = 1$. In contrast, when $\eta = -1$ we expect to find an unstable branch. Of course, we may find an infinite number of essentially the same periodic solutions by introducing a phase angle ϕ into the arguments of the trigonometric functions; this introduction has the only effect of altering the initial conditions at $t = 0$.

13.1.1 The power series expansions. We note from (13.3)-(13.4) that the amplitude of the periodic solution depends on the distance $|\delta-\delta_o|$ between the parameter value δ and its bifurcation value $\delta_o = 0$. In general the frequency ω depends on $|\delta-\delta_o|$ as well; as $R \to R_H$ and $\delta \to \delta_o$, we have $\omega \to \omega_o$, in which ω_o is the imaginary part of the characteristic exponent $\lambda(R_H)$ of the system linearized about the stationary solution. The fact that $\omega = 1$ is independent of δ here is a special case. For the general case, it is convenient to formulate the problem in terms of a parameter ε that in some sense relates the amplitude and the frequency of the periodic solution to this distance $|\delta-\delta_o|$.

To see how we might define ε appropriately, we recall from Section 11.2 that, in some low-order models, the amplitude $\hat{A}$ of a periodic solution

$$\underset{\sim}{p}(t) = \hat{A}\begin{bmatrix} \sin(\omega_o t) \\ \cos(\omega_o t) \end{bmatrix} \quad , \tag{13.5}$$

is controlled by a polynomial equation of the form

$$\hat{A}\,[C_1 + C_3\,\hat{A}^2 + C_5\,\hat{A}^4 + \cdots + C_{2\ell+1}\hat{A}^{2\ell}] = 0 \quad , \tag{13.6}$$

in which ℓ is a positive integer and the frequency ω_o is independent of δ. The symmetry requirements on the branching solution, which follow from a conclusion of the Hopf Bifurcation Theorem, are reflected in there being only even powers in the bracketed portion of the polynomial function. Moreover, we have $C_1 \sim (\delta-\delta_o)$ so that $\hat{A} \to 0$ as $\delta \to \delta_o$. Thus, for the very small values of $\hat{A}$ for which a power series expansion would be valid, we have either that $\hat{A} \sim \sqrt{\delta_o-\delta}$ or that $\hat{A} \sim \sqrt{\delta-\delta_o}$, depending on the sign of C_3, and so the bifurcation is either subcritical or supercritical (Fig. 13.1). If we assume that the simplest relation between $\hat{A}$ and ε holds, which is

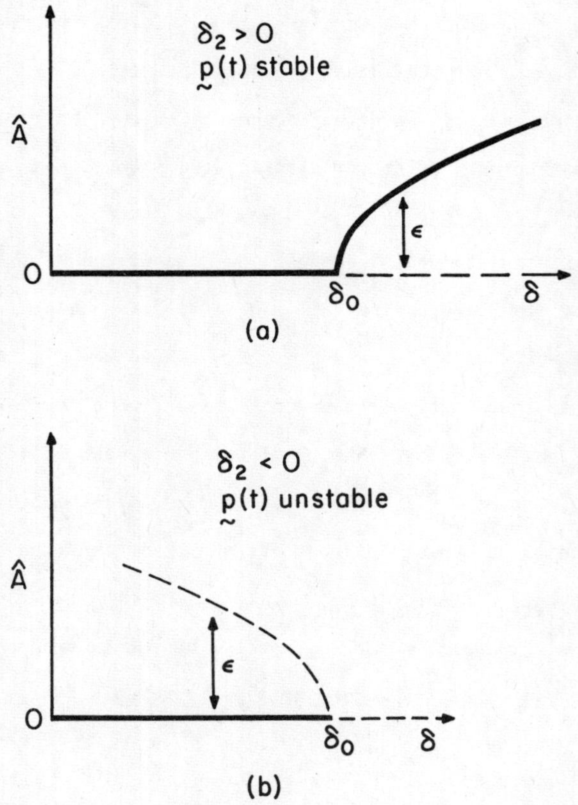

Fig. 13.1 The relationship between the amplitude $\hat{A}$ of a branching periodic solution $\underset{\sim}{p}(t)$ and the parameter ε. With $\hat{A} \sim \varepsilon$, $\delta \sim \delta_o+\delta_2\varepsilon^2$, and δ_o the Hopf bifurcation point, we find that $\delta_2>0$ corresponds to supercritical branching (a) and $\delta_2<0$ to subcritical branching (b). Here stable solutions are denoted by solid lines, unstable ones by dashed lines.

$\hat{A} \sim \varepsilon$, then we conclude that $\varepsilon \sim \sqrt{|\delta-\delta_o|}$ is the appropriate relation between ε and $\delta-\delta_o$. In this case, then, the periodic solution (13.5) may be regarded as

$$\underset{\sim}{p}(t) = \varepsilon\, \underset{\sim}{p}_o(t) \quad , \tag{13.7}$$

$$\underset{\sim}{p}_o(t) = \begin{bmatrix} \sin(\omega_o t) \\ \cos(\omega_o t) \end{bmatrix} \quad , \tag{13.8}$$

$$\delta = \delta_o + \delta_2\, \varepsilon^2 \quad , \tag{13.9}$$

$$\omega = \omega_o \quad , \tag{13.10}$$

where now $\varepsilon \geq 0$ can be interpreted as the amplitude of the periodic solution whose temporal variation is controlled by $\underset{\sim}{p}_o(t)$. Here the sign of δ_2 provides the direction of the branching solution. When $\delta_2 > 0$, we have a supercritical branch because the value of δ increases as the value of ε increases, and the periodic solution exists only for $\delta > \delta_o$ (Fig. 13.1a). When $\delta_2 < 0$, we have a subcritical branch and the solution exists only for $\delta < \delta_o$ (Fig. 13.1b).

Only in special cases does the periodic solution have the simple form given in (13.7)-(13.10). Usually more terms involving higher powers of ε are needed in the expression (13.7) for $\underset{\sim}{p}(t)$, as can be seen, for example, if a subcritical branch contains a regular turning point and becomes stable (Fig. 13.2a). Such an occurrence means that higher order terms are needed in the expressions for δ and ω as well. The most general way of writing the branching periodic solution is therefore

$$\underset{\sim}{p}(\tau,\varepsilon) = \varepsilon \underset{\sim}{p}_o(\tau) + \varepsilon^2 \underset{\sim}{p}_1(\tau) + \varepsilon^3 \underset{\sim}{p}_2(\tau) + \cdots \quad , \tag{13.11}$$

$$\delta(\varepsilon) = \delta_o + \delta_1\varepsilon + \delta_2\varepsilon^2 + \cdots \quad , \tag{13.12}$$

$$\omega(\varepsilon) = \omega_o + \omega_1\varepsilon + \omega_2\varepsilon^2 + \cdots \quad , \tag{13.13}$$

in which we have rescaled time via $t = \tau/\omega(\varepsilon)$ so that the periodic solution has period 2π for all values of ε, and in which $\underset{\sim}{p}$ is a vector having n components for

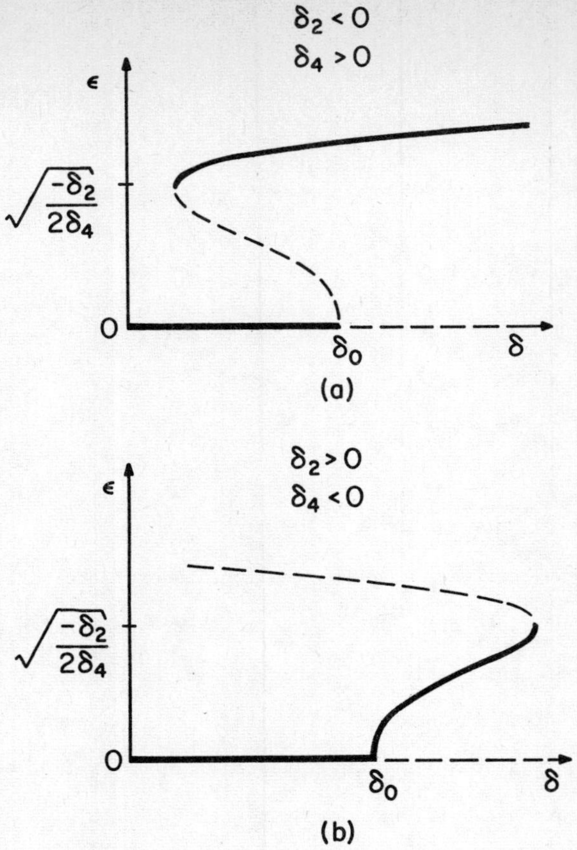

Fig. 13.2 Approximate branching forms and stabilities of the periodic solution (13.16) when the signs of δ_2 and δ_4 are opposite. A regular turning point occurs when $\varepsilon^2 \cong -\delta_2/(2\delta_4)$. In (a) an initially subcritical solution becomes stable at the turning point and is an example of a snap-through bifurcation owing to a finite-amplitude instability. In (b) an initially stable supercritical solution becomes unstable at the turning point. Here stable solutions are denoted by solid lines, unstable ones by dashed lines.

specifying a periodic solution to an n-coefficient system. We observe that $|\underset{\sim}{p}(\tau,\varepsilon)| \sim \varepsilon$ as $\varepsilon \to 0$, and so ε may be interpreted loosely as a measure of the amplitude of the bifurcating periodic solution. We note that the symmetry requirements for bifurcating periodic solutions are satisfied only if $\delta_{2k-1} = \omega_{2k-1} = 0$ for all positive integers k in (13.12)-(13.13). That is, (13.12)-(13.13) should be of the form

$$\delta(\varepsilon) = \delta_o + \delta_2\varepsilon^2 + \delta_4\varepsilon^4 + \cdots \quad , \qquad (13.14)$$

$$\omega(\varepsilon) = \omega_o + \omega_2\varepsilon^2 + \omega_4\varepsilon^4 + \cdots \quad . \tag{13.15}$$

We include the odd terms in (13.12)-(13.13), because demonstrating that these terms actually vanish is a useful check on the calculations. The goal of the present calculation is to determine the sign of δ_2; but, along the way, we find at least the expressions for $\underset{\sim}{p}_o$, $\underset{\sim}{p}_1$, and ω_2, and thereby find some of the characteristics of the periodic solution itself. We note that in the case of partial differential equations, $\underset{\sim}{p}_k$ depends on the spatial variables as well; normally the solution is separable so that spatially periodic solutions are sought.

Before outlining the method for calculating δ_2, we observe that in some cases more terms in the power series (13.11), (13.14)-(13.15) must be retained. For example, in order to determine whether a branching solution changes direction at a regular turning point, and thus changes stability, we must find the sign of δ_4 as well as that of δ_2. If $\delta_2 < 0$ but $\delta_4 > 0$, then there is a turning point at approximately $\varepsilon^2 = -\delta_2/(2\delta_4)$ when $|\delta_2|$ is small enough (Fig. 13.2a). If, in addition this value of ε^2 is sufficiently small so that the power series

$$\underset{\sim}{p}(\tau,\varepsilon) = \varepsilon\underset{\sim}{p}_o(\tau) + \varepsilon^2\underset{\sim}{p}_1(\tau) + \varepsilon^3\underset{\sim}{p}_2(\tau) + \varepsilon^4\underset{\sim}{p}_3(\tau) + \varepsilon^5\underset{\sim}{p}_4(\tau) \quad , \tag{13.16}$$

is able to represent the periodic solution $\underset{\sim}{p}(\tau)$ well enough, then $\underset{\sim}{p}(\tau)$ becomes stable at a finite amplitude for which $\varepsilon^2 > -\delta_2/(2\delta_4)$ (Fig. 13.2a). This situation is known as a snap-through bifurcation that is caused by a finite-amplitude instability, and the occurrence of this bifurcation is controlled by δ_4. The reverse situation of an initially stable, supercritical solution changing direction at a turning point is also described by δ_4, as illustrated in Fig. 13.2b. The procedure we outline below can be extended easily to the calculation of the necessary higher-order terms in the power series if the above types of information are sought.

<u>13.1.2 The linear differential equations</u>. We begin with an n-equation ordinary differential system

$$\frac{d\underset{\sim}{x}}{dt} = \underset{\sim}{f}(\underset{\sim}{x},\delta) \quad , \tag{13.17}$$

in which the vectors $\underset{\sim}{x}$ and $\underset{\sim}{f}$ are

$$\underset{\sim}{x} = \begin{bmatrix} x_1 \\ x_2 \\ \vdots \\ x_n \end{bmatrix} , \tag{13.18}$$

$$\underset{\sim}{f} = \begin{bmatrix} f_1 \\ f_2 \\ \vdots \\ f_n \end{bmatrix} , \tag{13.19}$$

and δ is the bifurcation parameter. In the sample system (13.1)-(13.2), we have $x_1 = y_1$, $x_2 = y_2$ and

$$f_1 = y_2 + y_1[\delta - \eta(y_1^2 + y_2^2)] , \tag{13.20}$$

$$f_2 = - y_1 + y_2[\delta - \eta(y_1^2 + y_2^2)] . \tag{13.21}$$

We next find a stationary solution $\underset{\sim}{x} = \underset{\sim}{x}^s(\delta)$ and then homogenize $f(\underset{\sim}{x},\delta)$ about $\underset{\sim}{x}^s$ by writing

$$\underset{\sim}{x} = \underset{\sim}{x}^s + \underset{\sim}{x}' , \tag{13.22}$$

$$\frac{d\underset{\sim}{x}'}{dt} = A(\delta)\underset{\sim}{x}' + \underset{\sim}{N}(\underset{\sim}{x}') , \tag{13.23}$$

in which $A(\delta)$ is an $n \times n$ matrix whose characteristic exponents govern the stability of $\underset{\sim}{x}^s$, and in which $\underset{\sim}{N}(\underset{\sim}{x}')$ represents the nonlinear terms. For partial differential systems, A and $\underset{\sim}{N}$ become operators, and they can be written in similar matrix forms. In the example (13.1)-(13.2), we have

$$A(\delta) = \begin{bmatrix} \delta & 1 \\ -1 & \delta \end{bmatrix} , \tag{13.24}$$

$$\underset{\sim}{N}(\underset{\sim}{y}) = \begin{bmatrix} -\eta y_1(y_1^2 + y_2^2) \\ -\eta y_2(y_1^2 + y_2^2) \end{bmatrix} \quad . \tag{13.25}$$

We examine the characteristic equation given by $\det(A - I_n\lambda) = 0$ to determine the Hopf bifurcation point given by

$$\lambda = \pm\, i\, \omega_o \quad , \tag{13.26}$$

$$\delta = \delta_o \quad . \tag{13.27}$$

In the example, $\delta_o = 0$ and $\omega_o = 1$ because $\lambda = \pm\, i$ when $\delta = 0$.

In order to insert the power series (13.11)-(13.13) into (13.23), we must first rescale time via

$$\tau = t\, \omega(\varepsilon) \quad , \tag{13.28}$$

and we rewrite (13.23) as

$$\omega \frac{d\underset{\sim}{x}'}{d\tau} = A(\delta)\underset{\sim}{x}' + \underset{\sim}{N}(\underset{\sim}{x}') \quad . \tag{13.29}$$

A rescaling is necessary in order to account for the fact that the frequency ω itself varies with δ and so with ε; the proposed scaling has the advantage of ensuring that the resulting temporal solutions are 2π-periodic in τ.

Substitution of (13.11)-(13.13) into (13.29) yields the set of systems

Order ε

$$\omega_o \frac{d\underset{\sim}{p}_o}{d\tau} = A(\delta_o)\, \underset{\sim}{p}_o \quad , \tag{13.30}$$

Order ε^{k+1}

$$\omega_o \frac{d\underset{\sim}{p}_k}{d\tau} = A(\delta_o)\underset{\sim}{p}_k + \underset{\sim}{g}_k(\underset{\sim}{p}_o,\ldots,\underset{\sim}{p}_{k-1};\ \omega_o,\ldots,\omega_k;\ \delta_o,\ldots,\delta_k) \quad ,$$

$$k = 1,2,\ldots \quad . \tag{13.31}$$

The inhomogeneous terms $\underset{\sim}{g}_k$ originate from the products in the nonlinear terms $\underset{\sim}{N}(\underset{\sim}{x}')$ as well as from products involving the solutions to the systems of lower order. To calculate δ_2 and ω_2, it suffices to consider only the systems of order ε, ε^2, and ε^3; but if $\delta_2 = 0$, then δ_4 is needed and so the systems of order ε^4 and ε^5 must be considered as well. When seeking stationary solutions to (13.29) by the power series method, we obtain equations similar to (13.30) and (13.31), with the left sides set to zero and the frequency coefficients ω_k omitted.

For the system (13.23)-(13.25), we retain the first three terms in the power series expressions to write

$$y_1(\tau,\varepsilon) = \varepsilon y_{11}(\tau) + \varepsilon^2 y_{12}(\tau) + \varepsilon^3 y_{13}(\tau) \quad , \tag{13.32}$$

$$y_2(\tau,\varepsilon) = \varepsilon y_{21}(\tau) + \varepsilon^2 y_{22}(\tau) + \varepsilon^3 y_{23}(\tau) \quad , \tag{13.33}$$

$$\omega(\varepsilon) = 1 + \varepsilon\omega_1 + \varepsilon^2\omega_2 \quad , \tag{13.34}$$

$$\delta(\varepsilon) = 0 + \varepsilon\delta_1 + \varepsilon^2\delta_2 \quad , \tag{13.35}$$

in which we have already used $\omega_o = 1$ in (13.34) and $\delta_o = 0$ in (13.35). Upon substituting (13.28) and (13.32)-(13.35) into (13.1), we obtain

$$\begin{aligned}(\varepsilon \frac{dy_{11}}{d\tau} + \varepsilon^2 \frac{dy_{12}}{d\tau} + \varepsilon^3 \frac{dy_{13}}{d\tau})(1 + \varepsilon\omega_1 + \varepsilon^2\omega_2) &= (\varepsilon y_{21} + \varepsilon^2 y_{22} + \varepsilon^3 y_{23}) \\ &+ (0 + \varepsilon\delta_1 + \varepsilon^2\delta_2)(\varepsilon y_{11} + \varepsilon^2 y_{12} + \varepsilon^3 y_{13}) \\ &- \eta(\varepsilon y_{11} + \varepsilon^2 y_{12} + \varepsilon^3 y_{13})\big((\varepsilon y_{11} + \varepsilon^2 y_{12} + \varepsilon^3 y_{13})^2 \\ &+ (\varepsilon y_{21} + \varepsilon^2 y_{22} + \varepsilon^3 y_{23})^2\big) \quad ,\end{aligned} \tag{13.36}$$

which can be rewritten as

$$\varepsilon\left(\frac{dy_{11}}{d\tau} - y_{21}\right) + \varepsilon^2\left(\frac{dy_{12}}{d\tau} - y_{22} - \delta_1 y_{11} + \omega_1\frac{dy_{11}}{d\tau}\right)$$

$$+ \varepsilon^3\left(\frac{dy_{13}}{d\tau} - y_{23} - \delta_1 y_{12} + \omega_1\frac{dy_{12}}{d\tau} - \delta_2 y_{11} + \omega_2\frac{dy_{11}}{d\tau}\right.$$

$$\left. + \eta y_{11}^3 + \eta y_{11} y_{21}^2\right)$$

$$+ \varepsilon^4 (\quad) + \cdots = 0 \quad . \tag{13.37}$$

A similar form can be obtained from (13.2). When the coefficients of the ε, ε^2, and ε^3 terms are required to each vanish separately, then we obtain the systems of order ε, ε^2, and ε^3:

Order ε

$$\frac{dy_{11}}{d\tau} = y_{21} \quad , \tag{13.38}$$

$$\frac{dy_{21}}{d\tau} = - y_{11} \quad , \tag{13.39}$$

Order ε^2

$$\frac{dy_{12}}{d\tau} = y_{22} + \delta_1 y_{11} - \omega_1 \frac{dy_{11}}{d\tau} = y_{22} + g_{11} \quad , \tag{13.40}$$

$$\frac{dy_{22}}{d\tau} = - y_{12} + \delta_1 y_{21} - \omega_1 \frac{dy_{21}}{d\tau} = - y_{12} + g_{12} \quad , \tag{13.41}$$

Order ε^3

$$\frac{dy_{13}}{d\tau} = y_{23} + \delta_1 y_{12} - \omega_1 \frac{dy_{12}}{d\tau} + \delta_2 y_{11} - \omega_2 \frac{dy_{11}}{d\tau}$$

$$- \eta y_{11}^3 - \eta y_{11} y_{21}^2 = y_{23} + g_{21} \quad , \tag{13.42}$$

$$\frac{dy_{23}}{d\tau} = - y_{13} + \delta_1 y_{22} - \omega_1 \frac{dy_{22}}{d\tau} + \delta_2 y_{21} - \omega_2 \frac{dy_{21}}{d\tau}$$

$$- \eta y_{21} y_{11}^2 - \eta y_{21}^3 = - y_{13} + g_{22} \quad . \tag{13.43}$$

We note that the nonlinear terms of the original equation do not enter here until the system of order ε^3 is considered. This behavior is not always the case, however.

13.1.3 The Fredholm Alternative. We seek periodic solutions to (13.38)-(13.43) having period 2π. These always exist in the system of order ε, but, owing to the inhomogeneous terms, they only exist in special cases for the systems of higher order. We must determine ω_k and δ_k in such a way that resonating terms are eliminated from the right sides of (13.31), thereby allowing 2π-periodic solutions to exist. As we see below, the compatibility conditions are necessary and sufficient to determine ω_k and δ_k. When k is odd, we simply obtain $\omega_k = \delta_k = 0$. In application of the power series method to finding branching stationary solutions, we note that only one compatibility condition is required, and this condition determines δ_k.

The appropriate way to find ω_k and δ_k is to use the Fredholm Alternative, a theorem that gives necessary and sufficient conditions for a linear inhomogeneous 2π-periodic system to have particular solutions of period 2π (Iooss and Joseph, 1980). In the two-dimensional case, such a system is given by

$$\frac{d}{d\tau}\begin{bmatrix} z_1(\tau) \\ z_2(\tau) \end{bmatrix} = A(\tau)\begin{bmatrix} z_1(\tau) \\ z_2(\tau) \end{bmatrix} + \begin{bmatrix} h_1(\tau) \\ h_2(\tau) \end{bmatrix} , \qquad (13.44)$$

in which the 2×2 matrix $A(\tau)$ and the inhomogeneous terms $h_1(\tau)$ and $h_2(\tau)$ are 2π-periodic in τ. Associated with this system are the corresponding homogeneous system

$$\frac{d}{d\tau}\begin{bmatrix} x_1(\tau) \\ x_2(\tau) \end{bmatrix} = A(\tau)\begin{bmatrix} x_1(\tau) \\ x_2(\tau) \end{bmatrix} , \qquad (13.45)$$

and its adjoint system

$$\frac{d}{d\tau}\begin{bmatrix} y_1(\tau) \\ y_2(\tau) \end{bmatrix} = -\,A(\tau)^T\begin{bmatrix} y_1(\tau) \\ y_2(\tau) \end{bmatrix} , \qquad (13.46)$$

in which the superscript T denotes a transpose. We notice that if $\underset{\sim}{x}(\tau)$ is a solution of the homogeneous system and if $\underset{\sim}{y}(\tau)$ is a solution of its adjoint, then the dot product $\underset{\sim}{y}(\tau)\cdot\underset{\sim}{x}(\tau) = \underset{\sim}{y}(\tau)^T\underset{\sim}{x}(\tau)$ is constant. We show this fact by calculating

$$\frac{d}{d\tau}(\underset{\sim}{y}^T\underset{\sim}{x}) = \underset{\sim}{y}^T \frac{d\underset{\sim}{x}}{d\tau} + \underset{\sim}{x}^T \frac{d\underset{\sim}{y}}{d\tau}$$

$$= \underset{\sim}{y}^T A\underset{\sim}{x} + \underset{\sim}{x}^T(-A^T\underset{\sim}{y}) = \underset{\sim}{y}^T A\underset{\sim}{x} - \underset{\sim}{y}^T A\underset{\sim}{x} = 0 \quad , \tag{13.47}$$

in which we have used some standard relationships involving matrix products (e.g. Kolman, 1970)

Next we suppose that $\underset{\sim}{\alpha}_1(\tau)$ and $\underset{\sim}{\alpha}_2(\tau)$ are two independent solutions of the homogeneous system (13.45). We may define uniquely two vectors $\underset{\sim}{\beta}_1(0)$ and $\underset{\sim}{\beta}_2(0)$ by requiring that

$$\underset{\sim}{\beta}_1(0)\cdot\underset{\sim}{\alpha}_1(0) = 1 \quad , \tag{13.48}$$

$$\underset{\sim}{\beta}_2(0)\cdot\underset{\sim}{\alpha}_2(0) = 1 \quad , \tag{13.49}$$

$$\underset{\sim}{\beta}_1(0)\cdot\underset{\sim}{\alpha}_2(0) = 0 \quad , \tag{13.50}$$

$$\underset{\sim}{\beta}_2(0)\cdot\underset{\sim}{\alpha}_1(0) = 0 \quad . \tag{13.51}$$

Then we let $\underset{\sim}{\beta}_1(\tau)$ and $\underset{\sim}{\beta}_2(\tau)$ be the solutions of the adjoint system (13.46) with initial conditions $\underset{\sim}{\beta}_1(0)$ and $\underset{\sim}{\beta}_2(0)$, respectively. It follows from (13.47) that

$$\underset{\sim}{\beta}_1(\tau)\cdot\underset{\sim}{\alpha}_1(\tau) = 1 \quad , \tag{13.52}$$

$$\underset{\sim}{\beta}_2(\tau)\cdot\underset{\sim}{\alpha}_2(\tau) = 1 \quad , \tag{13.53}$$

$$\underset{\sim}{\beta}_1(\tau)\cdot\underset{\sim}{\alpha}_2(\tau) = 0 \quad , \tag{13.54}$$

$$\underset{\sim}{\beta}_2(\tau)\cdot\underset{\sim}{\alpha}_1(\tau) = 0 \quad , \tag{13.55}$$

for all τ.

To arrive at the Fredholm Alternative, we assume that the solutions of the homogeneous system (13.45) are 2π-periodic. It follows that any solution of (13.44) is 2π-periodic if and only if any one particular solution is 2π-periodic. We note that the vector function defined by setting

$$\underset{\sim}{z}(\tau) = \{[\int_0^\tau \underset{\sim}{\beta}_1(s)^T \underset{\sim}{h}(s)\, ds]\, \underset{\sim}{\alpha}_1(\tau) + [\int_0^\tau \underset{\sim}{\beta}_2(s)^T \underset{\sim}{h}(s)\, ds]\, \underset{\sim}{\alpha}_2(\tau)\}/2 \quad , \tag{13.56}$$

is a particular solution of (13.44). Therefore, because $\underset{\sim}{z}(0) = 0$, the vector function $\underset{\sim}{z}(\tau)$ is 2π-periodic if and only if $\underset{\sim}{z}(2\pi) = 0$. However, $\underset{\sim}{\alpha}_1(2\pi)$ and $\underset{\sim}{\alpha}_2(2\pi)$ are independent vectors, and so $\underset{\sim}{z}(2\pi) = 0$ if and only if the coefficients of both vectors in (13.56) vanish separately; that is if the inner products obey

$$(\underset{\sim}{\beta}_1,\underset{\sim}{h}) = \frac{1}{2\pi}\int_0^{2\pi} \underset{\sim}{\beta}_1(\tau)^T \underset{\sim}{h}(\tau)\, d\tau = 0 \quad , \tag{13.57}$$

and

$$(\underset{\sim}{\beta}_2,\underset{\sim}{h}) = \frac{1}{2\pi}\int_0^{2\pi} \underset{\sim}{\beta}_2(\tau)^T \underset{\sim}{h}(\tau)\, d\tau = 0 \quad . \tag{13.58}$$

Thus, we have arrived at the theorem we seek:

> Fredholm Alternative. Provided that the homogeneous system (13.45) has 2π-periodic solutions, then the 2π-periodic system (13.44) has 2π-periodic solutions if and only if both (13.57) and (13.58) hold.

The generalization to an n-dimensional system

$$\frac{d\underset{\sim}{u}}{d\tau} = A(\tau)\underset{\sim}{u} + \underset{\sim}{h}(\tau) \quad , \tag{13.59}$$

where $\underset{\sim}{u} = (u_1,\ldots,u_n)^T$ is straightforward (Iooss and Joseph, 1980). For partial differential systems, $A(\tau)$ becomes an operator with $A(\tau)^T$ equal to the ordinary adjoint of $A(\tau)$; also the inner products corresponding to (13.57) and (13.58) also involve integration over the spatial coordinates (Kloeden and Wells, 1983).

13.1.4 Determination of the branching direction. As noted above, we use the Fredholm Alternative to show that $\omega_1 = \delta_1 = 0$ in the ordinary differential system (13.40)-(13.41) and to find the values of ω_2 and δ_2 in (13.42)-(13.43); the sign of δ_2 gives the branching direction. We begin by finding a solution to (13.38)-(13.39) as well as two solutions to the adjoint system

$$\frac{dw_1}{d\tau} = w_2 \quad , \tag{13.60}$$

$$\frac{dw_2}{d\tau} = - w_1 \quad . \tag{13.61}$$

In this example, but not in general, the adjoint and original systems are the same so that the system is self-adjoint. General solutions to (13.38)-(13.39) and (13.60)-(13.61) are

$$v_1(\tau) = c_1 \cos(\tau) + s_1 \sin(\tau) \quad , \tag{13.62}$$

$$v_2(\tau) = s_1 \cos(\tau) - c_1 \sin(\tau) \quad . \tag{13.63}$$

For convenience we normalize (13.62)-(13.63) with respect to the inner product by defining the norm $||\underset{\sim}{v}||$ via

$$||\underset{\sim}{v}||^2 = \frac{1}{2\pi} \int_0^{2\pi} \{ [v_1, v_2] \begin{bmatrix} v_1 \\ v_2 \end{bmatrix} \} \, d\tau = c_1^2 + s_1^2 \quad . \tag{13.64}$$

The simplest choices for solutions to (13.38)-(13.39) have a norm of one and are specified by $c_1 = 1$ and $s_1 = 0$ or $c_1 = 0$ and $s_1 = 1$ in (13.62)-(13.63); here we arbitrarily choose the latter so that

$$y_{11}(\tau) = \sin(\tau) \quad , \tag{13.65}$$

$$y_{21}(\tau) = \cos(\tau) \quad , \tag{13.66}$$

and for the solutions to (13.60)-(13.61) we use both simple possibilities so that

$$w_{11}(\tau) = \cos(\tau) \quad , \tag{13.67}$$

$$w_{21}(\tau) = - \sin(\tau) \quad , \tag{13.68}$$

$$w_{12}(\tau) = \sin(\tau) \quad , \tag{13.69}$$

$$w_{22}(\tau) = \cos(\tau) \quad . \tag{13.70}$$

For there to be a 2π-periodic solution to (13.40)-(13.41), we require that $(\underset{\sim}{w}_1, \underset{\sim}{g}_1) = 0$ or that

$$\frac{1}{2\pi}\int_0^{2\pi}\left\{[\cos(\tau), -\sin(\tau)]\begin{bmatrix}\delta_1\sin(\tau)-\omega_1\cos(\tau)\\ \delta_1\cos(\tau)+\omega_1\sin(\tau)\end{bmatrix}\right\}d\tau = 0 \quad . \tag{13.71}$$

This yields $\omega_1 = 0$. Similarly, $(\underset{\sim}{w}_2,\underset{\sim}{g}_1) = 0$ gives $\delta_1 = 0$, and we have the expected results. In this case, (13.40)-(13.41) becomes a homogeneous system because $g_{11} = 0$ and $g_{12} = 0$, and so it has the simple solution $y_{12} = y_{22} = 0$. Of course there are other solutions, but we may choose any one we wish; here the trivial solution is the most convenient one.

For the existence of a 2π-periodic solution to the equations of order ε^3, we apply the Fredholm Alternative to g_{21} and g_{22}, which with the aid of (13.65)-(13.66) simplify to

$$g_{21} = (\delta_2 - \eta)\sin(\tau) - \omega_2\cos(\tau) \quad , \tag{13.72}$$

$$g_{22} = (\delta_2 - \eta)\cos(\tau) + \omega_2\sin(\tau) \quad . \tag{13.73}$$

From applying the Fredholm Alternative to (13.72)-(13.73), we obtain $\omega_2 = 0$ and $\delta_2 = \eta$. Because we find that $\delta_2 > 0$ when $\eta = 1$, we expect that a supercritical, stable branching periodic solution emanates from the trivial one at $\delta = \delta_o$, and this behavior is indeed what we have in (13.3)-(13.4). Moreover, when $\eta = -1$, we have $\delta_2 < 0$, and we obtain a subcritical, unstable branching periodic solution; again, this result is what we expect from (13.3)-(13.4).

Incidentally, with the above choices for ω_2 and δ_2, we find that the system of order ε^3 becomes homogeneous and so $y_{13} = y_{23} = 0$ is the most convenient choice. Thus, the periodic solution to the third order is

$$y_1(\tau,\varepsilon) = \varepsilon\sin(\tau) \quad , \tag{13.74}$$

$$y_2(\tau,\varepsilon) = \varepsilon\cos(\tau) \quad , \tag{13.75}$$

$$\delta(\varepsilon) = \eta\varepsilon^2 \quad , \tag{13.76}$$

$$\omega(\varepsilon) = \omega_o = 1 \quad . \tag{13.77}$$

But this is equivalent to (13.3)-(13.4)! Thus, we see that the power series approach gives the correct answer in this case. We note that the above arbitrary choices in the solutions could be made in many different ways. The only effect of changing the choices is that the phasing of the periodic solution changes and so the specific role of ε in the functions $\delta(\varepsilon)$, $\omega(\varepsilon)$, etc. changes. These changes do not alter the fact that to each value of δ, there corresponds at most essentially one periodic solution.

13.2 The Lorenz System

From the calculations presented in Section 4.2.2, we know that a Hopf bifurcation occurs on the convective solution to the Lorenz model at a value (4.44) of the normalized Rayleigh number $r = r_H$ given by (Fig. 13.3)

$$r_H = \frac{P(P + b + 3)}{P - b - 1} , \tag{13.78}$$

for which $b = 4/(1+a^2)$ and a is the aspect ratio, and for which we require the Prandtl number $P > b + 1$. Because numerical integrations of the Lorenz system at $b = 8/3$, $r = 28$, and $P = 10$ give aperiodic trajectories (see Fig. 15.9), we conclude that the branching periodic solution is subcritical and unstable in this case. We summarize here the calculations necessary for demonstrating that indeed $\delta_2 < 0$ as expected.

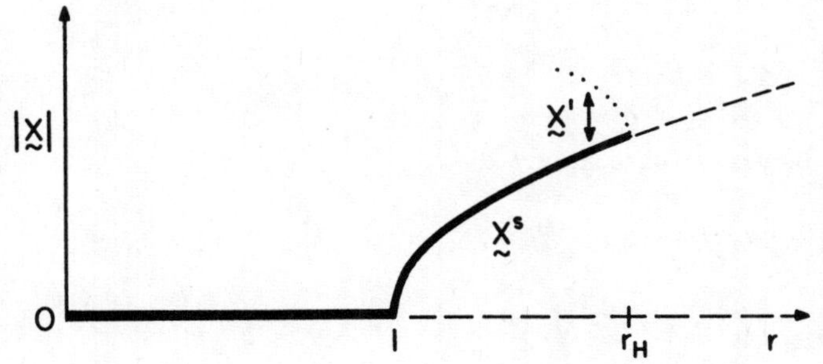

Fig. 13.3 Bifurcation diagram for the Lorenz model (13.79)-(13.81). A transition from the conductive to the convective solution $\underset{\sim}{X}^s$ occurs at $r=r_c=1$, and a loss of stability occurs at $r=r_H$. The branching periodic solution is subcritical, as denoted by the dotted lines, and the difference between the periodic solution and $\underset{\sim}{X}^s$ is denoted by $\underset{\sim}{X}'$. Stable solutions are denoted by solid lines, unstable ones by the dashed lines.

The Lorenz (1963) model (2.80)-(2.82) is

$$\frac{dX}{dt^*} = - PX + PY \quad , \tag{13.79}$$

$$\frac{dY}{dt^*} = rX - Y - XZ \quad , \tag{13.80}$$

$$\frac{dZ}{dt^*} = -bZ + XY \quad . \tag{13.81}$$

We transform the model to apply to a deviation about one of the stationary convective solutions (X^s,Y^s,Z^s); the branching results are identical for both convective solutions. Here we choose $(X^s,Y^s,Z^s) = \left(\sqrt{b(r-1)}, \sqrt{b(r-1)}, (r-1)\right)$ (Fig. 13.3). Thus, we write

$$X' = X - \sqrt{b(r-1)} \quad , \tag{13.82}$$

$$Y' = Y - \sqrt{b(r-1)} \quad , \tag{13.83}$$

$$Z' = Z - (r-1) \quad , \tag{13.84}$$

in which the primes denote deviations from the stationary solution (X^s,Y^s,Z^s). The differential system governing the deviations is then

$$\omega \frac{dX'}{d\tau} = - PX' + PY' \quad , \tag{13.85}$$

$$\omega \frac{dY'}{d\tau} = X' - Y' - \delta Z' - X'Z' \quad , \tag{13.86}$$

$$\omega \frac{dZ'}{d\tau} = \delta X' + \delta Y' - bZ' + X'Y' \quad , \tag{13.87}$$

in which the bifurcation parameter δ is

$$\delta = [b(r-1)]^{1/2} \quad , \tag{13.88}$$

the bifurcation point is

$$\delta_o = [b(P + b + 1)(P + 1)/(P - b - 1)]^{1/2} \quad , \tag{13.89}$$

the frequency ω_o at $r = r_H$ is

$$\omega_o = [2Pb(P + 1)/(P - b - 1)]^{1/2} \quad , \tag{13.90}$$

and we have rescaled time t^* via (13.28).

The next step is to write X', Y', Z', δ, and ω in power series of the forms (13.11), (13.14)-(13.15); in these forms, the parameters δ_1 and ω_1 are both assumed to vanish. Accordingly, we have

$$X'(\tau,\varepsilon) = \varepsilon\, X_o(\tau) + \varepsilon^2\, X_1(\tau) + \varepsilon^3\, X_2(\tau) + \cdots \quad , \tag{13.91}$$

$$Y'(\tau,\varepsilon) = \varepsilon\, Y_o(\tau) + \varepsilon^2\, Y_1(\tau) + \varepsilon^3\, Y_2(\tau) + \cdots \quad , \tag{13.92}$$

$$Z'(\tau,\varepsilon) = \varepsilon\, Z_o(\tau) + \varepsilon^2\, Z_1(\tau) + \varepsilon^3\, Z_2(\tau) + \cdots \quad , \tag{13.93}$$

$$\delta(\varepsilon) = \delta_o + \varepsilon^2 \delta_2 + \cdots \quad , \tag{13.94}$$

$$\omega(\varepsilon) = \omega_o + \varepsilon^2 \omega_2 + \cdots \quad , \tag{13.95}$$

and these represent properly the actual branching periodic solution provided that ε is small in magnitude. Substituting the power series (13.91)-(13.95) into (13.85)-(13.87) and requiring the coefficients of the ε, ε^2, and ε^3 terms to vanish separately, we obtain the systems

Order ε

$$\omega_o \frac{d}{d\tau} \begin{bmatrix} X_o \\ Y_o \\ Z_o \end{bmatrix} = A(\delta_o) \begin{bmatrix} X_o \\ Y_o \\ Z_o \end{bmatrix} \quad , \tag{13.96}$$

Order ε^2

$$\omega_o \frac{d}{d\tau} \begin{bmatrix} X_1 \\ Y_1 \\ Z_1 \end{bmatrix} = A(\delta_o) \begin{bmatrix} X_1 \\ Y_1 \\ Z_1 \end{bmatrix} + \begin{bmatrix} 0 \\ -X_o Z_o \\ X_o Y_o \end{bmatrix} \quad , \tag{13.97}$$

Order ε^3

$$\omega_o \frac{d}{d\tau}\begin{bmatrix} X_2 \\ Y_2 \\ Z_2 \end{bmatrix} = A(\delta_o)\begin{bmatrix} X_2 \\ Y_2 \\ Z_2 \end{bmatrix} + \begin{bmatrix} -\omega_2 \dfrac{dX_o}{d\tau} \\ -\omega_2 \dfrac{dY_o}{d\tau} - \delta_2 Z_o - X_o Z_1 - X_1 Z_o \\ -\omega_2 \dfrac{dZ_o}{d\tau} + \delta_2 X_o + \delta_2 Y_o + X_o Y_1 + X_1 Y_o \end{bmatrix} , \tag{13.98}$$

in which we have used

$$A(\delta_o) = \begin{bmatrix} -P & P & 0 \\ 1 & -1 & -\delta_o \\ \delta_o & \delta_o & -b \end{bmatrix} . \tag{13.99}$$

The solutions to the system of order ε (13.96) are most easily found by substituting exponential forms for X_o, Y_o, and Z_o into (13.96). That is, we assume

$$X_o(\tau) = C_1 \exp(i\tau) , \tag{13.100}$$

$$Y_o(\tau) = C_2 \exp(i\tau) , \tag{13.101}$$

$$Z_o(\tau) = C_3 \exp(i\tau) , \tag{13.102}$$

and substitute (13.100)-(13.102) into (13.96) to obtain the linear homogeneous system

$$-(P + i\,\omega_o)\,C_1 + PC_2 = 0 , \tag{13.103}$$

$$C_1 - (1 + i\omega_o)\,C_2 - \delta_o C_3 = 0 , \tag{13.104}$$

$$\delta_o C_1 + \delta_o C_2 - (b + i\,\omega_o)\,C_3 = 0 . \tag{13.105}$$

If (13.103)-(13.105) is written in matrix form, then we find that the determinant of the coefficients of the C_i vanishes, and so the homogeneous system has a nontrivial solution. The linear dependence in the system, which derives from the fact that δ_o is a bifurcation point, allows us to make a convenient choice for the undetermined constant, and the choice we make eliminates the need for a denominator in expressing C_1, C_2, and C_3. Thus, with the aid of (13.89) and (13.90), we find

$$X_o(\tau) = (P\delta_o)\cos(\tau) + (iP\delta_o)\sin(\tau) \quad , \tag{13.106}$$

$$Y_o(\tau) = (P\delta_o)\cos(\tau) - (\omega_o\delta_o)\sin(\tau) + i[(\delta_o\omega_o)\cos(\tau) + (P\delta_o)\sin(\tau)] \quad , \tag{13.107}$$

$$Z_o(\tau) = (\omega_o^2)\cos(\tau) + [(P+1)\omega_o]\sin(\tau) + i\{[-(P+1)\omega_o]\cos(\tau) + (\omega_o^2)\sin(\tau)\} \quad . \tag{13.108}$$

The real and imaginary parts of (13.106)-(13.108) give two linearly independent solutions, but we need only one. We obtain an arbitrary solution to (13.96) by choosing the real part of (13.106)-(13.108), and normalizing it with respect to the inner product given in (13.57) via

$$N_o^2 = \frac{1}{2\pi}\int_0^{2\pi} \underset{\sim}{X}_o(\tau)^T \underset{\sim}{X}_o(\tau)\, d\tau \quad , \tag{13.109}$$

in which $\underset{\sim}{X}_o(\tau) = (X_o(\tau), Y_o(\tau), Z_o(\tau))^T$. Thus we find that

$$X_o(\tau) = \left(\frac{P\delta_o}{N_o}\right)\cos(\tau) \quad , \tag{13.110}$$

$$Y_o(\tau) = \left(\frac{P\delta_o}{N_o}\right)\cos(\tau) - \left(\frac{\omega_o\delta_o}{N_o}\right)\sin(\tau) \quad , \tag{13.111}$$

$$Z_o(\tau) = \left(\frac{\omega_o^2}{N_o}\right)\cos(\tau) + \left(\frac{(P+1)\omega_o}{N_o}\right)\sin(\tau) \quad , \tag{13.112}$$

in which

$$2N_o^2 = 2P^2\delta_o^2 + [\delta_o^2 + (P+1)^2 + \omega_o^2]\omega_o^2 \quad . \tag{13.113}$$

With these solutions, the inhomogeneous term $\underset{\sim}{g}_1$ in the system of order ε^2 (13.97) becomes

$$g_{11} = 0 \quad , \tag{13.114}$$

$$g_{12} = \{-P\delta_o\omega_o^2[1 + \cos(2\tau)] - P\delta_o\omega_o(P+1)\sin(2\tau)\}/(2N_o^2) \quad , \tag{13.115}$$

$$g_{13} = \{P^2\delta_o^2\,[1 + \cos(2\tau)] - (P\omega_o\delta_o^2)\sin(2\tau)\}/(2N_o^2) \quad . \tag{13.116}$$

Because $\omega_1 = \delta_1 = 0$ is the condition given by the Fredholm Alternative for there to be a particular 2π-periodic solution to (13.97), we see from (13.114)-(13.116) that a reasonable arbitrary choice for the form of this particular solution is

$$X_1(\tau) = X_{10} + X_{11}\cos(2\tau) + X_{12}\sin(2\tau) \quad , \tag{13.117}$$

$$Y_1(\tau) = Y_{10} + Y_{11}\cos(2\tau) + Y_{12}\sin(2\tau) \quad , \tag{13.118}$$

$$Z_1(\tau) = Z_{10} + Z_{11}\cos(2\tau) + Z_{12}\sin(2\tau) \quad . \tag{13.119}$$

Although we could have added any multiple of (13.106)-(13.108) to (13.117)-(13.119) to obtain another solution, this addition unnecessarily complicates the calculations. Substitution of (13.117)-(13.119) into (13.97) and (13.114)-(13.116) and equating the coefficients of the constant, $\sin(2\tau)$ and $\cos(2\tau)$ terms produces a system of nine linear equations in nine unknowns. That is, we obtain the nine-equation system

$\underline{\omega_o \dfrac{dX_1}{d\tau}}$

$$\text{const:} \quad P X_{10} - P Y_{10} = 0 \quad , \tag{13.120}$$

$$\cos(2\tau): \quad P X_{11} + 2\,\omega_o X_{12} - P Y_{11} = 0 \quad , \tag{13.121}$$

$$\sin(2\tau): \quad -2\,\omega_o X_{11} + P X_{12} - P Y_{12} = 0 \quad , \tag{13.122}$$

$\underline{\omega_o \dfrac{dY_1}{d\tau}}$

$$\text{const:} \quad X_{10} - Y_{10} - \delta_o Z_{10} = P\delta_o\,\omega_o^2/[2N_o^2] \quad , \tag{13.123}$$

$$\cos(2\tau): \quad X_{11} - Y_{11} - 2\,\omega_o Y_{12} - \delta_o Z_{11} = P\,\delta_o\,\omega_o^2\,/[2N_o^2] \quad , \tag{13.124}$$

$$\sin(2\tau): \quad X_{12} + 2\,\omega_o Y_{11} - Y_{12} - \delta_o Z_{12} = P\,\delta_o\omega_o(P+1)/[2N_o^2] \quad , \tag{13.125}$$

$\underline{\omega_o \frac{dZ_1}{d\tau}}$

$$\text{const:} \quad \delta_o X_{10} + \delta_o Y_{10} - b Z_{10} = - P^2\delta_o^2/[2N_o^2] \quad , \tag{13.126}$$

$$\cos(2\tau): \quad \delta_o X_{11} + \delta_o Y_{11} - b Z_{11} - 2 \omega_o Z_{12} = - P^2\delta_o^2/[2N_o^2] \quad , \tag{13.127}$$

$$\sin(2\tau): \quad \delta_o X_{12} + \delta_o Y_{12} + 2 \omega_o Z_{11} - b Z_{12} = P \omega_o\delta_o^2/[2N_o^2] \quad . \tag{13.128}$$

With the aid of a symbolic manipulator, we were able to obtain the following expressions for the coefficients in (13.117)-(13.119)

$$X_{10} = Y_{10} = - \frac{P\left(P\delta_o^2 + b\omega_o^2\right)}{4\delta_o N_o^2} \quad , \tag{13.129}$$

$$Z_{10} = - P \frac{\omega_o^2}{2N_o^2} \quad , \tag{13.130}$$

$$X_{11} = \{P^2\delta_o\omega_o^2[8\omega_o^4 + 2\omega_o^2(b^2 + \delta_o^2 + 2(1+P)^2) + b^2(1+P)^2 + \delta_o^2(Pb-\delta_o^2)] - P^4\delta_o^5\}/D \quad , \tag{13.131}$$

$$X_{12} = \{P^2\delta_o\omega_o[4\omega_o^4(1+P) + \omega_o^2(b^2(1+P) + \delta_o^2(2P-4-3b)) - 2\delta_o^2 bP(1+P)]\}/D \quad , \tag{13.132}$$

$$Y_{11} = \{P\delta_o\omega_o^2[8\omega_o^4(1+2P) + 2\omega_o^2(b^2(1+2P) + 2P(1+P)^2 + \delta_o^2(3P-3b-4)) + P(b^2(1+P)^2 - \delta_o^2(3Pb+4b+\delta_o^2))] - P^4\delta_o^5\}/D \quad , \tag{13.133}$$

$$Y_{12} = \{P\delta_o\omega_o[-16\omega_o^6 - 4\omega_o^4(b^2+ \delta_o^2 + (P+1)(P+2)) + \omega_o^2(\delta_o^2(2P^2 + 2\delta_o^2 - 4P - 5Pb) - b^2(P+1)(P+2)) + 2P^2\delta_o^2(\delta_o^2 - b - Pb)]\}/D \quad , \tag{13.134}$$

$$Z_{11} = \{P\delta_o^2\omega_o^2[24\omega_o^4 + 2\omega_o^2(2(P+1)(P+2) + b + 7Pb - 3\delta_o^2)$$

$$+ 2P(2b(1+P)^2 - 3P\delta_o^2)]\}/D \quad , \tag{13.135}$$

$$Z_{12} = \{P\delta_o^2\omega_o[4\omega_o^4(1+7P-3b) + 2\omega_o^2(P+1)(4P(1+P) - b(P+2) - 2\delta_o^2)$$

$$- 4P^2\delta_o^2(1+P)]\}/D \quad , \tag{13.136}$$

in which

$$D = N_o^2\{64\omega_o^6 + 16\omega_o^4[(P+1)^2 + b^2 - 2\delta_o^2]$$

$$+ 4\omega_o^2[b^2(1+P)^2 + \delta_o^2(2b-2Pb-4P-4P^2+\delta_o^2)] + 4\delta_o^4P^2\} \quad . \tag{13.137}$$

Since (13.131)-(13.136) were found by using Cramer's Rule on a six-equation subset of (13.120)-(13.128), the expression for D is obtained from the determinant of the matrix of the homogeneous part of the system.

Now we consider the system of order ε^3 and note that we do not need to find the periodic solutions $X_2(\tau)$, $Y_2(\tau)$, and $Z_2(\tau)$ in order to obtain the branching direction; we need only apply the Fredholm Alternative to the inhomogeneous term $\tilde{g}_2(\tau)$ to obtain ω_2 and δ_2. First, however, we must solve the adjoint system

$$\omega_o \frac{d}{d\tau}\begin{bmatrix} W_1 \\ W_2 \\ W_3 \end{bmatrix} = - A(\delta_o)^T \begin{bmatrix} W_1 \\ W_2 \\ W_3 \end{bmatrix} \quad , \tag{13.138}$$

to obtain the pair of solutions

$$W_{11}(\tau) = (Pb)\cos(\tau) - [(1+b)\omega_o]\sin(\tau) \quad , \tag{13.139}$$

$$W_{21}(\tau) = -(Pb)\cos(\tau) - (P\omega_o)\sin(\tau) \quad , \tag{13.140}$$

$$W_{31}(\tau) = (P\delta_o)\cos(\tau) \quad , \tag{13.141}$$

and

$$W_{12}(\tau) = \left[(1+b)\omega_o\right]\cos(\tau) + (Pb)\sin(\tau) \quad , \qquad (13.142)$$

$$W_{22}(\tau) = (P\omega_o)\cos(\tau) - (Pb)\sin(\tau) \quad , \qquad (13.143)$$

$$W_{32}(\tau) = (P\delta_o)\sin(\tau) \quad . \qquad (13.144)$$

These are the real and imaginary parts of an exponential solution of the form (13.100)-(13.102).

Upon substituting (13.110)-(13.113) and (13.117)-(13.119) into the inhomogeneous term $\underset{\sim}{g}_2$ of (13.98), we obtain the forms

$$g_{21} = \frac{P\omega_2\delta_o}{N_o}\sin(\tau) \quad , \qquad (13.145)$$

$$g_{22} = (c_1\omega_2 + c_2\delta_2 + c_3)\sin(\tau) + (c_4\omega_2 + c_5\delta_2 + c_6)\cos(\tau)$$
$$+ c_7\cos(\tau)\cos(2\tau) + c_8\cos(\tau)\sin(2\tau)$$
$$+ c_9\sin(\tau)\cos(2\tau) + c_{10}\sin(\tau)\sin(2\tau) \quad , \qquad (13.146)$$

$$g_{23} = (d_1\omega_2 + d_2\delta_2 + d_3)\sin(\tau) + (d_4\omega_2 + d_5\delta_2 + d_6)\cos(\tau)$$
$$+ d_7\cos(\tau)\cos(2\tau) + d_8\cos(\tau)\sin(2\tau)$$
$$+ d_9\sin(\tau)\cos(2\tau) + d_{10}\sin(\tau)\sin(2\tau) \quad , \qquad (13.147)$$

in which

$$c_1 = P\delta_o/N_o \quad , \qquad (13.148)$$

$$c_2 = -(P+1)\omega_o/N_o \quad , \qquad (13.149)$$

$$c_3 = -(P+1)\omega_o X_{10}/N_o \quad , \qquad (13.150)$$

$$c_4 = \omega_o\delta_o/N_o \quad , \qquad (13.151)$$

$$c_5 = -\omega_o^2/N_o \quad , \qquad (13.152)$$

$$c_6 = -(\omega_o^2 X_{10} + P\delta_o Z_{10})/N_o \quad , \tag{13.153}$$

$$c_7 = -(P\delta_o Z_{11} + \omega_o^2 X_{11})/N_o \quad , \tag{13.154}$$

$$c_8 = -(P\delta_o Z_{12} + \omega_o^2 X_{12})/N_o \quad , \tag{13.155}$$

$$c_9 = -(P+1)\omega_o X_{11}/N_o \quad , \tag{13.156}$$

$$c_{10} = -(P+1)\omega_o X_{12}/N_o \quad , \tag{13.157}$$

$$d_1 = \omega_o^2/N_o \quad , \tag{13.158}$$

$$d_2 = -\omega_o\delta_o/N_o \quad , \tag{13.159}$$

$$d_3 = -\omega_o\delta_o X_{10}/N_o \quad , \tag{13.160}$$

$$d_4 = -(P+1)\omega_o/N_o \quad , \tag{13.161}$$

$$d_5 = 2P\delta_o/N_o \quad , \tag{13.162}$$

$$d_6 = (P\delta_o Y_{10} + P\delta_o X_{10})/N_o \quad , \tag{13.163}$$

$$d_7 = (P\delta_o Y_{11} + P\delta_o X_{11})/N_o \quad , \tag{13.164}$$

$$d_8 = (P\delta_o Y_{12} + P\delta_o X_{12})/N_o \quad , \tag{13.165}$$

$$d_9 = -\omega_o\delta_o X_{11}/N_o \quad , \tag{13.166}$$

$$d_{10} = -\omega_o\delta_o X_{12}/N_o \quad . \tag{13.167}$$

Finally, application of the Fredholm Alternative via $(\underset{\sim}{W}_1, \underset{\sim}{g}_2) = 0$ and $(\underset{\sim}{W}_2, \underset{\sim}{g}_2) = 0$ yields the pair of equations

$$e_1\omega_2 + e_2\delta_2 = e_3 \quad , \tag{13.168}$$

$$e_4\omega_2 + e_5\delta_2 = e_6 \quad , \tag{13.169}$$

in which

$$e_1 = 2\delta_o\omega_o(P+b+1) \quad , \tag{13.170}$$

$$e_2 = -\ 4P\delta_o^2 \quad , \tag{13.171}$$

$$\begin{aligned} e_3 = {} & 3P\delta_o^2\, X_{10} + \left[\omega_o^2(b-P-1) + P\delta_o^2\right] X_{11}/2 \\ & + \omega_o b(P+1)\, X_{12} + P\delta_o^2\, (Y_{10} + Y_{11}/2) \\ & + P\delta_o b\, (Z_{10} + Z_{11}/2) + P\omega_o\delta_o Z_{12}/2 \quad , \end{aligned} \tag{13.172}$$

$$e_4 = -\ 2\omega_o^2\delta_o \quad , \tag{13.173}$$

$$e_5 = 2\delta_o^2\omega_o \quad , \tag{13.174}$$

$$\begin{aligned} e_6 = {} & -\ 2\omega_o\delta_o^2\, X_{10} - \omega_o b(P+1)\, X_{11} \\ & + \left[(b-P-1)\omega_o^2 + P\delta_o^2\right] X_{12}/2 + P\delta_o^2\, Y_{12}/2 \\ & - P\delta_o\omega_o \left(Z_{10} + Z_{11}/2\right) + Pb\delta_o\, Z_{12}/2 \quad . \end{aligned} \tag{13.175}$$

Because the coefficient matrix in (13.168)-(13.169) has a determinant $8P\delta_o^3(\omega_o^2-\delta_o^2)$ that is nonzero when $P > b + 1$, we know that there is a unique solution for ω_2 and δ_2 for each value of P and b.

For the case $P = 10$ and $b = 8/3$ studied by Lorenz (1963), we find that $\delta_2 = -\ 7.085\times10^{-3}$ and $\omega_2 = -\ 2.150\times10^{-2}$; thus, an unstable subcritically branching solution occurs. This solution does not gain stability at a regular turning point, however, as might be expected. Instead, an aperiodic solution is seen whose behavior resembles that observed in turbulent flows (see Section 15.3.2). Here we note that numerical evaluation of (13.168)-(13.169) for a wide range of values of P and b reveals that $\delta_2 < 0$ for all values for which the Hopf bifurcation point exists, that is for $0 < b < P - 1$ (Fig. 13.4a). Moreover, as $b \to 0$ we have that $\delta_2 \to \infty$ and as $b \to P - 1$, we have that $\delta_2 \to 0$. Thus, Fig. 4B.1 produced in Marsden and

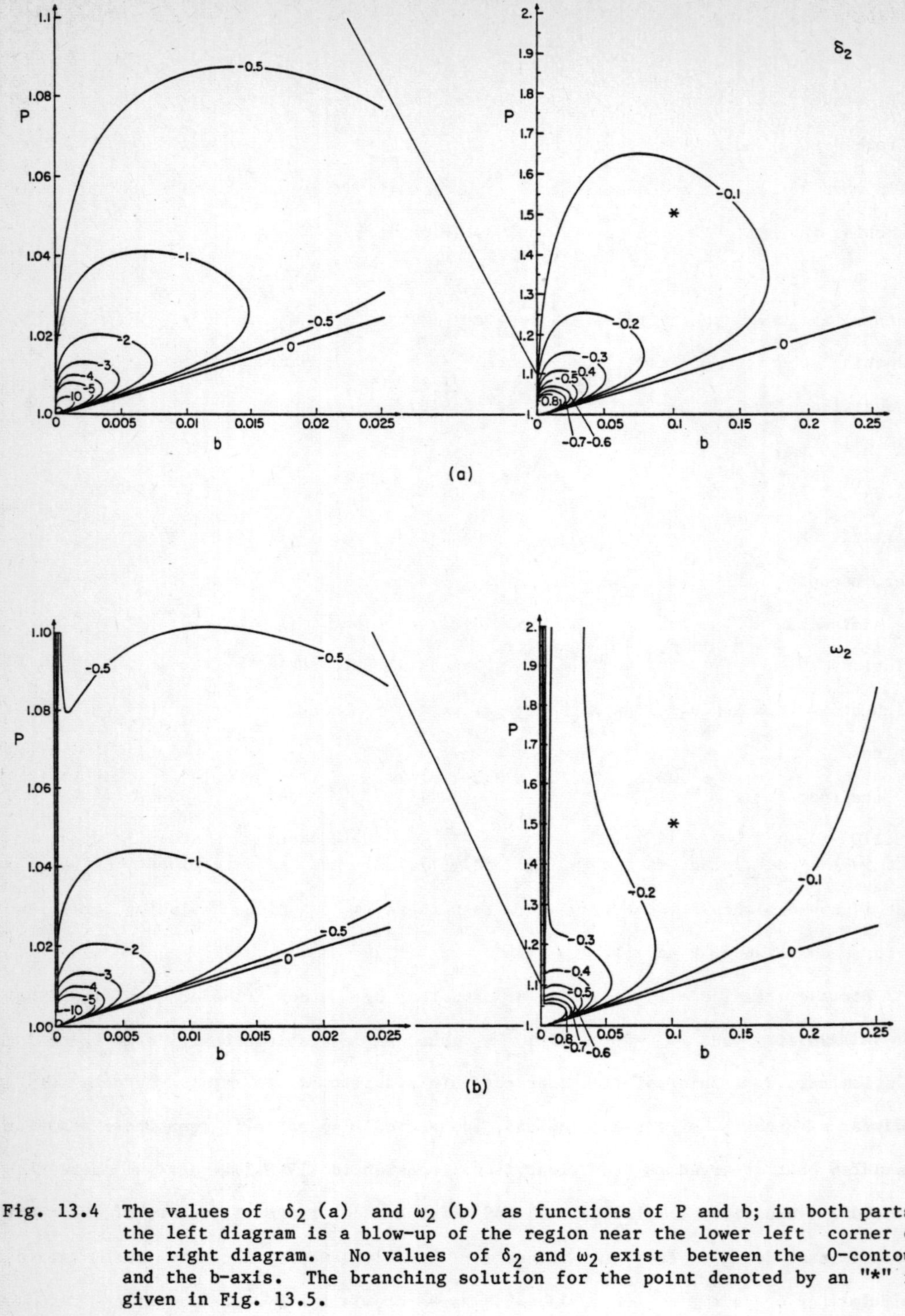

Fig. 13.4 The values of δ_2 (a) and ω_2 (b) as functions of P and b; in both parts, the left diagram is a blow-up of the region near the lower left corner of the right diagram. No values of δ_2 and ω_2 exist between the 0-contour and the b-axis. The branching solution for the point denoted by an "*" is given in Fig. 13.5.

McCracken (1976) with the aid of a different method for calculating the stability of a branching periodic solution, is in error: actually, there are no regions in the (b,P)-plane for which supercritically branching solutions exist. Marsden and McCracken subsequently discovered their error in the final formula on pp. 145-146, which when corrected produces the same result as that found here: only subcritically branching periodic solutions exist in the Lorenz model.

In Figs. 13.4a,b we show how δ_2 and ω_2 vary as functions of P and b. We see that ω_2 is always negative, implying via (13.95) that the period $T = 2\pi/\omega$ of the branching solution increases as the distance along the subcritical branch increases. In addition, the largest magnitudes of both parameters are concentrated near $P = 1$ and $b = 0$ as well as along the P-axis. We recall that, via (13.88)-(13.89) and (13.94), ε associates a particular value of δ_2 with one of r (cf. (13.176) below); similarly, via (13.90) and (13.95), ε associates a value of ω_2 with one of ω. However, because both δ_2 and ω_2 are negative and because both $\delta > 0$ and $\omega > 0$ must hold, the admissible values of ε are limited by $\varepsilon^2 < \delta_o/|\delta_2|$ and $\varepsilon^2 < \omega_o/|\omega_2|$; thus, solutions exist only for $1 < r \leq r_H$. This limitation is illustrated in Fig. 13.5, which shows an example of two representations of the branching periodic solution for the case $P = 1.5$ and $b = 0.1$. The sum $S' = |X'| + |Y'| + |Z'|$ of the absolute values of the perturbation solutions (13.110)-(13.112) of order ε (dashed line) and (13.110)-(13.112), (13.129)-(13.137) of order ε^2 (solid line) are shown as functions of

$$r \cong (\delta_o + \varepsilon^2\delta_2)^2/b + 1 \quad . \tag{13.176}$$

Both solutions have the correct slope as $r \to r_H = 17.25$, and the solutions deviate as the value of ε, or $|r-r_H|$, increases.

Whenever calculations such as those outlined in this chapter reveal that a periodic solution branches supercritically, we expect to find a stable periodic solution. This solution may subsequently lose stability at a larger value of the control parameter, and we need a way to determine this secondary bifurcation point. This determination is the topic of the next chapter, in which we show how to calculate the stability of a known periodic solution and we discover the three principal types of temporal solutions that can bifurcate from the periodic solution when it loses stability.

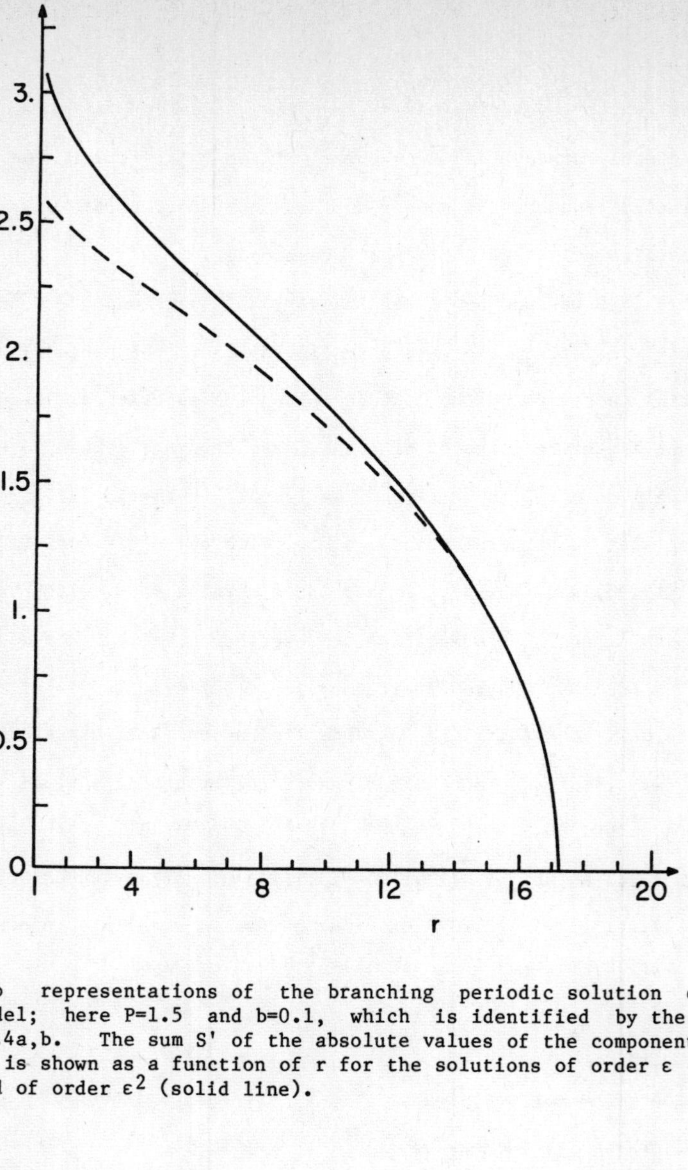

Fig. 13.5 Two representations of the branching periodic solution of the Lorenz model; here P=1.5 and b=0.1, which is identified by the "*" in Fig. 13.4a,b. The sum S' of the absolute values of the components X', Y', and Z' is shown as a function of r for the solutions of order ε (dashed line) and of order ε^2 (solid line).

CHAPTER 14

BIFURCATION ANALYSIS OF PERIODIC SOLUTIONS

STEVEN B. FELDSTEIN

In the previous chapter, we discussed a method for determining the branching direction of a bifurcating periodic solution. We noted that subcritically branching solutions were unstable and supercritically branching ones were stable; that is, small perturbations would amplify away from a subcritical solution but decay toward a supercritical one. In this chapter, we discuss in more detail the notion of stability for a temporal solution having period T; we must modify the concept of stability slightly in order to consider the behavior of perturbations of a time-dependent state.

In analogy to the situation with stationary solutions, we find that stability can be determined by inspecting the eigenvalues of a matrix that contains information about the evolution of nearby trajectories after one period T. There are three qualitatively different ways through which a periodic solution can exchange stability with another temporal solution, and these ways can be identified quantitatively through studying the eigenvalues of this matrix. Here, we review these different types of temporal solutions as a prelude to discussing the transition to turbulence in Chapters 15 and 16.

Although the stability of a periodic solution usually must be determined numerically, in certain special cases we may use an energy method to obtain the results analytically. We begin with a discussion of this approach.

14.1 Evaluating the Stability of a Periodic Solution with the Energy Method

We describe a periodic solution as stable if superimposed perturbations decay and unstable if perturbations amplify. Alternatively, by calculating the rate of change of a positive quantity such as an energy, we can discover whether or not the value of this quantity approaches that of a periodic solution and so determine whether or not the solution is stable. We illustrate this approach by using the simple two-dimensional system we introduced in Section 13.1 to show how to find the branching direction of a bifurcating temporal solution.

The system (13.1)-(13.2) we considered was

$$\dot{y}_1 = y_2 + y_1[\delta - \eta(y_1^2 + y_2^2)] \quad , \tag{14.1}$$

$$\dot{y}_2 = - y_1 + y_2[\delta - \eta(y_1^2 + y_2^2)] \quad . \tag{14.2}$$

This system has the trivial solution $y_1 = y_2 = 0$ and, for $\delta/\eta > 0$, the periodic solution

$$y_1(t) = \sqrt{\delta/\eta}\,\sin(t) \quad , \tag{14.3}$$

$$y_2(t) = \sqrt{\delta/\eta}\,\cos(t) \quad . \tag{14.4}$$

This solution bifurcates from the trivial one at $\delta = 0$; in phase space it appears as a circular orbit of radius $\sqrt{\delta/\eta}$, which we label as P(t) in Fig. 14.1. In Chapter 13, we showed that when $\eta > 0$ the solution is a supercritical one existing only for $\delta > 0$, and so is expected to be stable; when $\eta < 0$ it is a subcritical solution existing only for $\delta < 0$, and so is expected to be unstable. In this section we demonstrate that these expectations are in fact correct.

To develop an energy equation, we simply multiply (14.1) by y_1 and (14.2) by y_2 and sum the results to obtain

$$\dot{E} = \frac{1}{2}\frac{d}{dt}(y_1^2 + y_2^2) = (y_1^2 + y_2^2)[\delta - \eta(y_1^2 + y_2^2)] \quad . \tag{14.5}$$

First, let us consider the supercritical case $\delta > 0$, $\eta > 0$. From (14.5) it is easy to see that if initially $y_1^2 + y_2^2 < \delta/\eta$, then $\dot{E} > 0$ and so the value of $y_1^2 + y_2^2$ becomes larger; thus all such trajectories spiral outward, away from the trivial solution at the origin (Fig. 14.1a). In contrast, if initially $y_1^2 + y_2^2 > \delta/\eta$, then $\dot{E} < 0$ and the value of $y_1^2 + y_2^2$ becomes smaller; here trajectories spiral inward toward the trivial solution. When initially $y_1^2 + y_2^2 = \delta/\eta$ so that the trajectories are beginning on the periodic solution, we have $\dot{E} = 0$ so that they remain on the orbit. From this analysis, we conclude that the supercritically branching periodic solution is stable.

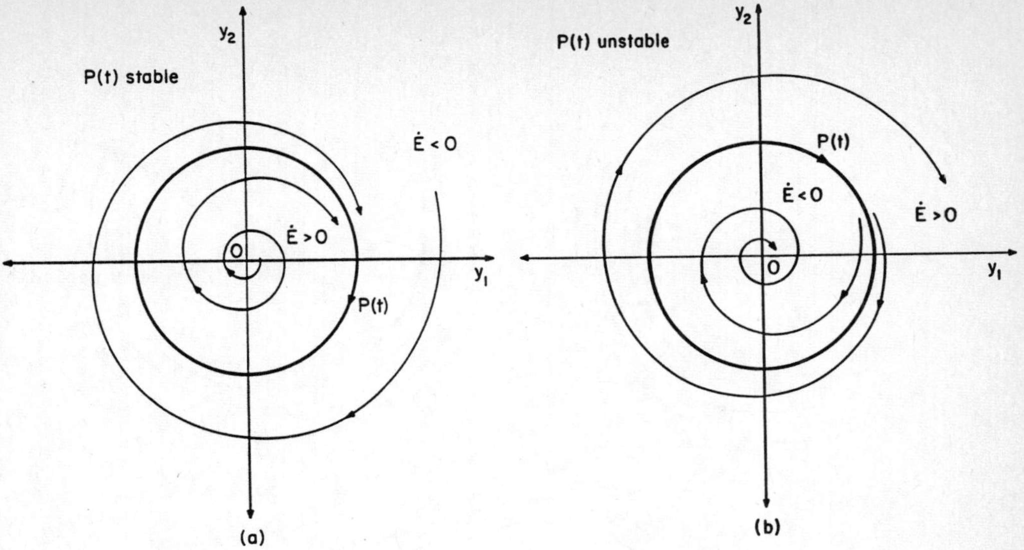

Fig. 14.1 The stabilities of the periodic solution (14.3)-(14.4) to (14.1)-(14.2) as demonstrated by analysis of the energy equation (14.5). For the supercritically branching case in (a), trajectories originating outside the orbit spiral in toward the origin, while those originating near the origin spiral outward; thus all trajectories converge on the periodic solution P(t), which is stable. For the subcritically branching case in (b), all trajectories spiral away from the orbit, and so the periodic solution P(t) is unstable.

For the subcritically branching case, we have $\delta < 0$ and $\eta < 0$. But now when a trajectory originates inside the orbit so that $y_1^2 + y_2^2 < \delta/\eta$, we find that $\dot{E} < 0$; therefore these trajectories spiral away from the periodic solution and toward the origin (Fig. 14.1b). Moreover, when $y_1^2 + y_2^2 > \delta/\eta$, we find that $\dot{E} > 0$ and so these trajectories spiral away from the orbit. Thus we find that subcritically branching solutions are unstable as expected.

Although hydrodynamic systems are rarely simple enough for energy methods to provide such a clear stability result, these methods are useful for determining which portions of phase space that the trajectories traverse (see Section 17.3.3). Usually, then, we must determine the stability of a periodic solution by using numerical methods, and it is this calculation that we discuss in the next section.

14.2 Determining the Stability of Periodic Solutions

In order to motivate the calculations necessary for deducing the stability of a periodic solution, we must introduce the concept of orbital stability (Minorsky,

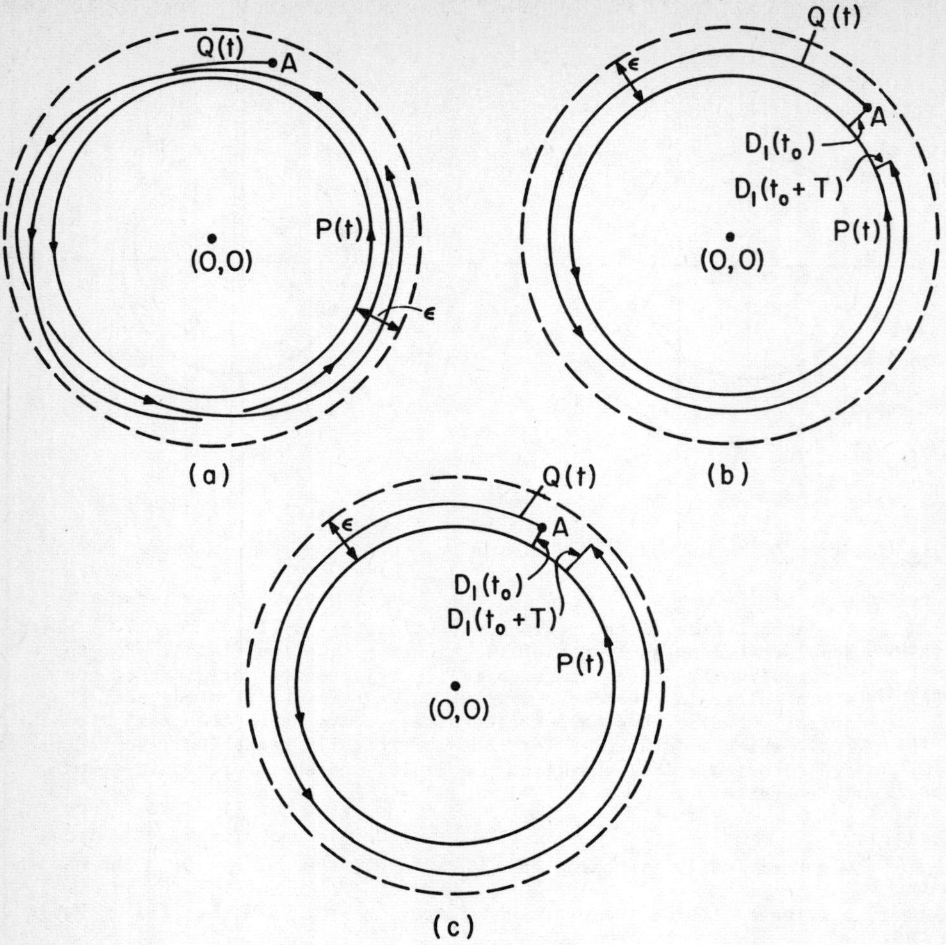

Fig. 14.2 Behavior of perturbation trajectories Q(t) when the periodic solution P(t) is orbitally stable (a), asymptotically orbitally stable (b), and orbitally unstable (c). Here t_o is the initial time, A is the initial value of Q(t), T is the period of the orbit P(t), and D_1 is the distance from P(t) as measured along a line perpendicular to P(t). Note that $D_1(t_o+T) < D_1(t_o)$ in (b), but that $D_1(t_o+T) > D_1(t_o)$ in (c) (after Shirer, 1978).

1962). Suppose we have a periodic solution P(t) as illustrated in Fig. 14.2. Then, we consider a point A in phase space that, at $t = t_o$, is within a small distance ε of P(t); this initial point represents a perturbation about P(t). If for any such point A the resulting trajectory Q(t) stays within ε of P(t), then the periodic solution is <u>orbitally stable</u> (Fig. 14.2a). If all trajectories beginning from such points approach P(t) uniformly, then the periodic solution is <u>asymptotically orbitally stable</u> (Fig. 14.2b). Finally, if for some point A the trajectory departs from P(t), then the periodic solution is <u>orbitally unstable</u> (Fig. 14.2c).

The stability of a periodic solution having period T can also be determined quantitatively in the following way. Let D_1 be the distance from the perturbation to the periodic solution, and let μ_1 be the limiting ratio of D_1 at $t = t_o + T$ to D_1 at $t = t_o$ (Fig. 14.2b,c); that is, we define

$$\mu_1 = \lim_{D_1(t_o)\to 0} [D_1(t_o + T)/D_1(t_o)] \quad . \tag{14.6}$$

Here the values of D_1 are measured along lines perpendicular to the trajectory of the perturbation. If $\mu_1 > 1$, then the periodic solution is unstable (Fig. 14.2c); otherwise it is stable (Fig. 14.2a,b). In general, we find that there are n canonical ratios to consider, where n is the dimension of the phase space, and so in this example there is a ratio μ_2 to calculate as well. However, because one ratio μ_n measures average expansion or contraction along the orbit and because the orbit as a whole does not expand or contract, we must have that $\mu_n = 1$. Here then $\mu_2 = 1$, and so only the value of μ_1 determines the stability of P(t).

For an orbit P(t) in a three-dimensional phase space, there are two canonical ratios μ_1 and μ_2 to calculate in order to find the stability of the orbit (Fig. 14.3a). In this case, the values of <u>both</u> the ratios μ_1 and μ_2 must be less than one for the orbit P(t) to be stable (Fig. 14.3b); if either ratio is greater than one, then P(t) is unstable (Fig. 14.3c). In general, the technique discussed below for determining the stability of periodic solutions requires our finding the values of the n ratios μ_i, i=1, ..., n. In the remainder of this section, we show how to calculate these ratios.

<u>14.2.1 The characteristic multipliers.</u> Suppose we are given the system of n equations

$$\dot{y}_i = f_i(y_1, y_2, \ldots, y_n, R, \xi_1, \xi_2, \ldots, \xi_p) \quad , \quad i=1, \ldots, n \quad , \tag{14.7}$$

which has the periodic solution $y_i(t) = P_i(t)$ of period T. Then we consider perturbations $x_i(t)$ of $P_i(t)$ and write

$$y_i(t) = P_i(t) + x_i(t) \quad , \quad i=1, \ldots, n \quad ; \tag{14.8}$$

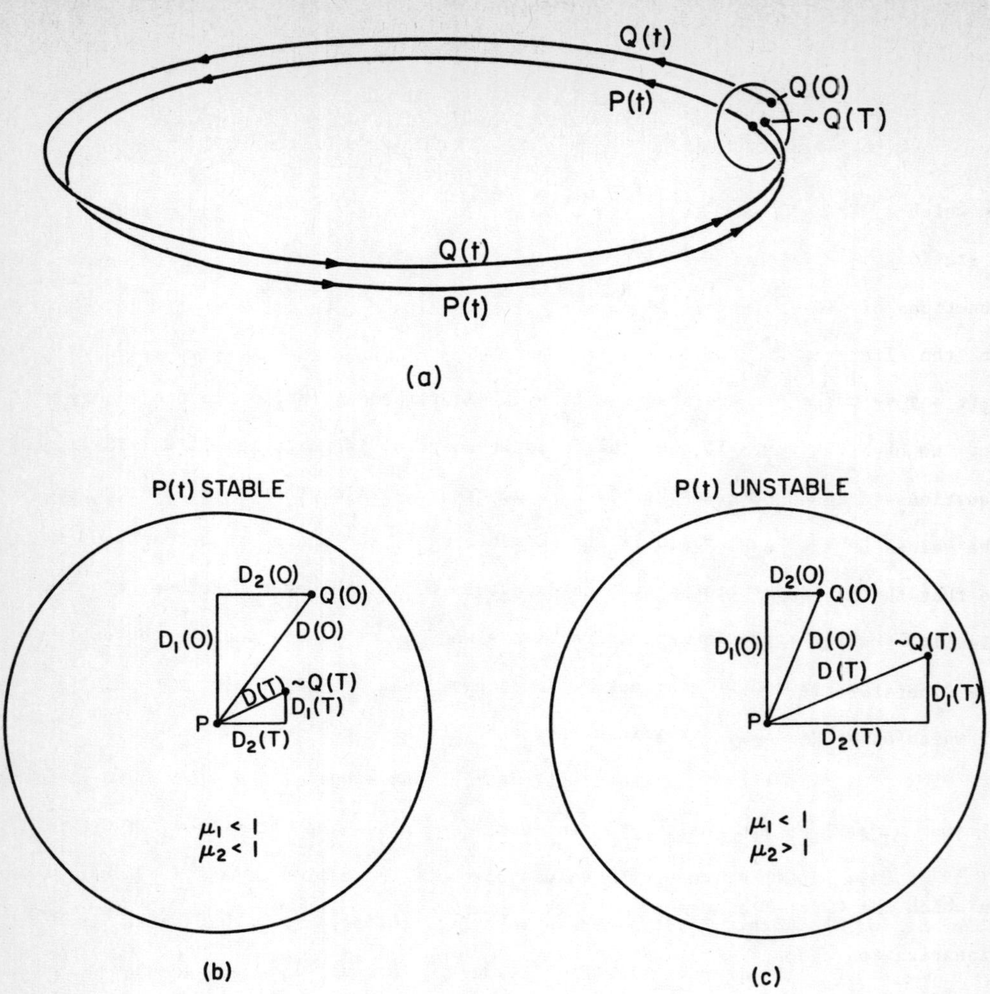

Fig. 14.3 Trajectory of a three-dimensional perturbation Q(t) about an orbit P(t) (a). Note that the distance between P(t) and Q(t) is measured approximately on a disk centered on and perpendicular to the orbit and that there are two components of D to calculate. That is, the limiting values of the ratios $D_1(T)/D_1(0)$ and $D_2(T)/D_2(0)$ are μ_1 and μ_2. Disks for two cases are shown: In (b), $\mu_1 < 1$ and $\mu_2 < 1$ so that P(t) is asymptotically orbitally stable, and in (c) $\mu_1 < 1$ but $\mu_2 > 1$ so that P(t) is orbitally unstable. In (b), continued evolution of the perturbation Q(t) would show a nonspiraling approach of Q(t) to P(t) and in (c) a non-spiraling departure from P(t). In both cases $\mu_3=1$.

thus by knowing whether $|x_i(t)|$ grows or decays, we may determine the stability of the periodic solution $P_i(t)$. We substitute (14.8) into (14.7) and assume that each of the $x_i(t)$ remains small in magnitude so that we may neglect products of perturbations. The resulting linear system of equations for the perturbations $x_i(t)$ has the form

$$\dot{x}_i = \sum_{j=1}^{n} a_{ij}(t)\, x_j \quad , \quad i=1, \ldots, n \quad , \tag{14.9}$$

in which $a_{ij}(t + T) = a_{ij}(t)$. In contrast to the system (4.5) for perturbations of a stationary solution, we find here that at least some of the coefficients a_{ij} are functions of time. This dependence on time results from products of $P_i(t)$ and $x_j(t)$ in the linearization of the nonlinear terms; because the periodic solution obeys $P_i(t + T) = P_i(t)$, it follows that $a_{ij}(t + T) = a_{ij}(t)$ as noted above.

We observe that (14.9) is a system of n first-order ordinary differential equations in n unknowns. Therefore, a solution $x_i(t)$, i=1, ..., n, is determined by the values of its components at some initial time t_o. Furthermore, (14.9) is linear so that the system of functions $x_i(t)$ depends linearly on its initial values $x_i(t_o)$. Finally, the initial conditions $x_i(t_o) \equiv 0$ determine the solution $x_i(t) = 0$ for all t. Therefore, the system (14.9) has n basis solutions $\phi_i^m(t)$, m=1, ..., n, in terms of which any other solution $x_i(t)$ may be written uniquely as

$$x_i(t) = \sum_{m=1}^{n} C_m\, \phi_i^m(t) \quad , \quad i=1, \ldots, n \quad , \tag{14.10}$$

in which the C_m are constants. If the a_{ij} are independent of t, as in the case of linearization about a stationary solution (Section 4.2), then we recall that we have basis solutions given by $\phi_i^m(t) \sim c_i^m \exp[\lambda_m t]$, as in (4.6).

When the a_{ij} are time-dependent, however, the basis functions have a more complicated form (e.g. see (14.35) below); fortunately, we do not have to determine these functions here. Instead, we define

$$\chi_i^\ell(t) = \phi_i^\ell(t + T) \quad , \quad \left\{ \begin{array}{l} i=1, \ldots, n \\ \ell=1, \ldots, n \end{array} \right. \quad , \tag{14.11}$$

and we note that the $\chi_i^\ell(t)$ are also solutions to (14.9) by performing the calculation

$$\begin{aligned} \frac{d\chi_i^\ell(t)}{dt} = \frac{d\phi_i^\ell(t + T)}{dt} &= \sum_{j=1}^{n} a_{ij}(t + T)\, \phi_j^\ell(t + T) \\ &= \sum_{j=1}^{n} a_{ij}(t)\, \chi_j^\ell(t) \end{aligned} \quad , \quad \left\{ \begin{array}{l} i=1, \ldots, n \\ \ell=1, \ldots, n \end{array} \right. \quad , \tag{14.12}$$

in which we have used (14.11) and the fact that $a_{ij}(t) = a_{ij}(t + T)$. Therefore, because the $\phi_i^\ell(t + T)$, i=1, ..., n, are solutions to (14.9) and because any solution can be written as in (14.10) in terms of the n basis functions, we may write

$$\phi_i^\ell(t + T) = \sum_{k=1}^{n} b_{\ell k} \, \phi_i^k(t) \quad , \quad \begin{cases} i=1, \ldots, n \\ \ell=1, \ldots, n \end{cases} \quad , \tag{14.13}$$

in which the $b_{\ell k}$ are constants.

The technique for determining the stability of the periodic solution $P_i(t)$ is based on the supposition that there exist canonical solutions $x_i(t)$ of (14.9) obeying

$$x_i(t + T) = \mu x_i(t) \quad , \quad i=1, \ldots, n \quad , \tag{14.14}$$

where the quantity μ is a generalization of that introduced in (14.6). Clearly, if $\mu > 1$, then amplification of the perturbation occurs and the periodic solution is unstable.

To determine for what values of μ there exists a nontrivial solution $x_i(t)$ satisfying (14.14), we proceed as follows. We can combine (14.10) and (14.13) to show that

$$x_i(t + T) = \sum_{m=1}^{n} C_m \, \phi_i^m(t + T) = \sum_{m=1}^{n} C_m \sum_{k=1}^{n} b_{mk} \, \phi_i^k(t) \quad , \quad i=1, \ldots, n \quad . \tag{14.15}$$

Also, (14.14) can be written as

$$x_i(t + T) = \mu x_i(t) = \mu \sum_{k=1}^{n} C_k \, \phi_i^k(t) = \sum_{m=1}^{n} \sum_{k=1}^{n} \mu \delta_{mk} \, C_m \, \phi_i^k(t) \quad , \quad i=1, \ldots, n \quad , \tag{14.16}$$

where δ_{mk} is the Kronecker delta. Equations (14.15) and (14.16) can be combined to yield

$$\sum_{m=1}^{n} \sum_{k=1}^{n} (C_m b_{mk} - \mu \delta_{mk} C_m) \, \phi_i^k(t) = 0 \quad , \quad i=1, \ldots, n \quad . \tag{14.17}$$

Because the functions $\phi_i^k(t)$ are linearly independent, a nontrivial solution exists if

$$\begin{array}{c} \\ \\ \end{array}\begin{vmatrix} \overset{C_1}{b_{11}-\mu} & \overset{C_2}{b_{12}} & \cdots & \overset{C_n}{b_{1n}} \\ b_{21} & b_{22}-\mu & \cdots & b_{2n} \\ \vdots & \vdots & & \vdots \\ b_{n1} & b_{n2} & \cdots & b_{nn}-\mu \end{vmatrix} = 0 \quad . \qquad (14.18)$$

Inspection of the $n \times n$ determinant in (14.18) reveals that there are n roots or <u>characteristic</u> <u>multipliers</u> $\mu_1, \ldots, \mu_n$ that allow (14.18) to be satisfied.

Next we ask whether, for $\mu = \mu_\ell$, $\ell=1, \ldots, n$, satisfying (14.18), there actually exists a nontrivial system of n functions $x_i^\ell(t)$ of the form (14.10) that obey (14.14). If such a system exists, then we have n solutions of (14.9) and we may use the n values of μ to specify the stability of $P_i(t)$. We begin by recalling from matrix theory (e.g. Kolman, 1970) that for each of the n roots μ_ℓ there exists a nontrivial eigenvector $(C_1^\ell, \ldots, C_n^\ell)^T$ such that

$$\sum_{m=1}^{n} (b_{mk} - \delta_{mk}\mu_\ell)\, C_m^\ell = 0 \quad , \quad \begin{cases} k=1, \ldots, n \\ \ell=1, \ldots, n \end{cases} \quad . \qquad (14.19)$$

We use these eigenvectors to define the functions

$$x_i^\ell(t) = \sum_{m=1}^{n} C_m^\ell\, \phi_i^m(t) \quad , \quad \begin{cases} i=1, \ldots, n \\ \ell=1, \ldots, n \end{cases} \quad , \qquad (14.20)$$

which have the form (14.10), and we ask whether these n functions $x_i^\ell(t)$ satisfy (14.14). To verify that they do, we apply (14.13) to (14.20) and find that

$$x_i^\ell(t+T) = \sum_{m=1}^{n} C_m^\ell\, \phi_i^m(t+T) = \sum_{m=1}^{n} C_m^\ell \sum_{k=1}^{n} b_{mk}\, \phi_i^k(t) \quad , \quad \begin{cases} i=1, \ldots, n \\ \ell=1, \ldots, n \end{cases} \quad . \qquad (14.21)$$

Next we use (14.19) to rewrite (14.21) as

$$x_i^\ell(t+T) = \sum_{m=1}^{n} C_m^\ell \sum_{k=1}^{n} b_{mk}\, \phi_i^k(t) = \sum_{m=1}^{n} \sum_{k=1}^{n} \mu_\ell\, \delta_{mk}\, C_m^\ell\, \phi_i^k(t)$$

$$= \mu_\ell \sum_{m=1}^{n} C_m^\ell\, \phi_i^m(t) = \mu_\ell\, x_i^\ell(t) \quad , \quad \begin{cases} i=1, \ldots, n \\ \ell=1, \ldots, n \end{cases} \quad . \qquad (14.22)$$

Thus we obtain n linearly independent solutions $x_i^\ell(t)$, $\ell=1, \ldots, n$, of (14.9) such that the ℓth solution $x_i^\ell(t)$ satisfies (14.14) with $\mu = \mu_\ell$.

<u>14.2.2 Interpretation of the characteristic multipliers.</u> At this point, it is necessary to observe that some of the characteristic multipliers μ_ℓ may be complex-valued. Since the coefficients b_{mk} in (14.18) are real, the complex roots appear in conjugate pairs. Of course, when μ_ℓ is complex, we see immediately from (14.14) that the corresponding solution $x_i^\ell(t)$ must be complex, and so it too must be one member of a conjugate pair of solutions. But in the case that μ_ℓ is complex-valued, are we still able to relate the occurrence of $|\mu_\ell| > 1$ for some ℓ to the stability of the periodic solution $P_i(t)$ via noting whether $|x_i^\ell(t)|$ grows?

Inspection of (14.14) reveals that, for the case $|\mu_\ell| > 1$, we have

$$|x_i^\ell(t + T)| = |\mu_\ell||x_i^\ell(t)| > |x_i^\ell(t)| \quad , \tag{14.23}$$

so that the distance of the perturbation from the periodic solution increases as time increases. In the case that μ_ℓ is real, we immediately return to the original argument relating the magnitude of μ_ℓ to the stability of $P_i(t)$. But as noted above, in the case that μ_ℓ is complex-valued, the solution $x_i^\ell(t)$ is complex as well, and so it is conceivable that the real, or physically relevant, part of $x_i^\ell(t)$ might decay while the imaginary part might grow sufficiently to account for the relation in (14.23). In this case we would mistakenly conclude that the periodic solution is unstable when in fact it is stable. Fortunately, as we demonstrate below, this mistake cannot be made because the complex-valued characteristic multipliers and their associated solutions $x_i(t)$ occur in conjugate pairs.

Suppose μ and $\bar{\mu}$ are a pair of complex-valued characteristic multipliers and $x_i(t)$ and $\bar{x}_i(t)$ are their corresponding complex solutions. Because (14.9) is linear, we may construct two new solutions

$$\xi_k(t) = [x_k(t) + \bar{x}_k(t)]/2 \quad , \quad k=1, \ldots, n \quad , \tag{14.24}$$

$$\eta_k(t) = [x_k(t) - \bar{x}_k(t)]/2i \quad , \quad k=1, \ldots, n \quad , \tag{14.25}$$

in which now $i = \sqrt{-1}$. We observe two important facts about $\xi_k(t)$ and $\eta_k(t)$: These solutions are real and we may recover the original solutions as linear combinations of them by writing

$$x_k(t) = \xi_k(t) + i\eta_k(t) \quad , \quad k=1, \ldots, n \quad , \tag{14.26}$$

$$\overline{x}_k(t) = \xi_k(t) - i\eta_k(t) \quad , \quad k=1, \ldots, n \quad . \tag{14.27}$$

Thus we have replaced the two complex solutions with two real ones, and we have lost no information. In particular, every real solution that is a combination of $x_k(t)$ and $\overline{x}_k(t)$ is a <u>real</u> combination of $\xi_k(t)$ and $\eta_k(t)$.

Now we are able to express (14.14) in terms of the real solutions $\xi_k(t)$ and $\eta_k(t)$. Let

$$\mu = u + iv = r\exp[i2\pi\theta] \quad , \quad 0 < \theta \leq 1 \quad , \tag{14.28}$$

$$\overline{\mu} = u - iv = r\exp[-i2\pi\theta] \quad , \quad 0 < \theta \leq 1 \quad , \tag{14.29}$$

in which u and v are real numbers. Substitution of (14.26)-(14.29) into (14.14) leads to the matrix equations

$$\begin{bmatrix} \xi_k(t+T) \\ \eta_k(t+T) \end{bmatrix} = \begin{bmatrix} u & -v \\ v & u \end{bmatrix} \begin{bmatrix} \xi_k(t) \\ \eta_k(t) \end{bmatrix} = r \begin{bmatrix} \cos(2\pi\theta) & -\sin(2\pi\theta) \\ \sin(2\pi\theta) & \cos(2\pi\theta) \end{bmatrix} \begin{bmatrix} \xi_k(t) \\ \eta_k(t) \end{bmatrix} \quad . \tag{14.30}$$

Suppose that we follow around the periodic solution P(t), any perturbation Q(t) that is a linear combination of $\xi_k(t)$ and $\eta_k(t)$. First we see from (14.30) that the distance from Q(t) to P(t) is multiplied by the <u>dilatation factor</u> $r = |\mu|$ when time is incremented by one period T. Thus we conclude that, as desired, P(t) is orbitally unstable if $|\mu| > 1$. In contrast, if $\mu_n = 1$ and the remaining μ_ℓ satisfy $|\mu_\ell| < 1$, $\ell=1, \ldots, n-1$, then a theorem states that P(t) is asymptotically orbitally stable (Minorsky, 1962). In addition, we notice from (14.30) that the perturbation twists through an angle $2\pi\theta$ about P(t) as time is increased by one period T. Thus the above interpretation of complex-valued multipliers has led us to new information about the behavior of a periodic solution. We exploit this additional information in Section 14.3 when we classify the possible bifurcations from periodic solutions.

14.2.3 Determination of the characteristic multipliers. To find the values of μ_ℓ, first we must determine the values of the coefficients b_{mk}. Consider the particular basis functions $\phi_i^m(t)$ having the initial conditions

$$\phi_i^m(0) = \delta_{im} \quad , \quad \begin{cases} i=1, \ldots, n \\ m=1, \ldots, n \end{cases} \quad . \tag{14.31}$$

From (14.13) we have

$$\phi_i^m(t+T) = \sum_{k=1}^{n} b_{mk}\, \phi_i^k(t) \quad , \quad \begin{cases} i=1, \ldots, n \\ m=1, \ldots, n \end{cases} \quad ; \tag{14.32}$$

upon evaluating (14.32) at $t = 0$, we discover with the aid of (14.31) that

$$\phi_i^m(T) = b_{mi} \quad , \quad \begin{cases} i=1, \ldots, n \\ m=1, \ldots, n \end{cases} \quad . \tag{14.33}$$

Because they are solutions, the $\phi_i^m(t)$ also satisfy (14.9); that is, they obey

$$\frac{d\phi_i^m}{dt} = \sum_{k=1}^{n} a_{ik}(t)\, \phi_k^m \quad , \quad \begin{cases} i=1, \ldots, n \\ m=1, \ldots, n \end{cases} \quad , \tag{14.34}$$

which is an $n \times n$ system of ordinary differential equations. However, as noted in the example in the following subsection, (14.34) may be regarded as n separate systems in n unknowns.

If (14.34) is integrated numerically from $t=0$ to $t=T$, then the values of the b_{mi} can be found from (14.33). Once the b_{mi} are calculated, the characteristic multipliers μ_ℓ of (14.18) can be found and the stability of $P_i(t)$ determined.

In addition, it can be shown that (14.10) may be written as

$$x_i(t) = \sum_{m=1}^{n} C_m \exp[\ln(\mu_m)t/T]\, g_i^m(t) \quad , \quad i=1, \ldots, n \quad , \tag{14.35}$$

where the $g_i^m(t)$ are some unknown periodic functions of time. Equation (14.35) can also be written as

$$x_i(t) = \sum_{m=1}^{n} C_m \exp(\lambda_m t)\, g_i^m(t) \quad , \quad i=1, \ldots, n \quad , \tag{14.36}$$

where

$$\lambda_m = \frac{\ln(\mu_m)}{T} \quad , \quad m=1, \ldots, n \quad , \tag{14.37}$$

and the λ_m are called characteristic exponents. The perturbation $x_i(t)$ in (14.36) is written in a form very similar to that in (4.8) for the perturbations discussed in Section 4.2, where the stability of time-independent solutions was studied. Corresponding to the fact that $\mu_n = 1$, we have $\lambda_n = 0$; if every other of the n-1 characteristic exponents λ_m satisfies $Re(\lambda_m) < 0$, then the periodic solution is asymptotically orbitally stable. In contrast, if for some λ_m, we have $Re(\lambda_m) > 0$, then the periodic solution is orbitally unstable.

We illustrate the above calculations in the following example.

14.2.4 A sample calculation. Here we show how to carry out the preceding calculations by again considering the stability of the solution (14.3)-(14.4) to (14.1)-(14.2). First, we write solutions to (14.1)-(14.2) in the form (14.8):

$$y_1(t) = \sqrt{\delta/\eta}\,\sin(t) + x_1(t) \quad , \tag{14.38}$$

$$y_2(t) = \sqrt{\delta/\eta}\,\cos(t) + x_2(t) \quad . \tag{14.39}$$

We recall that a supercritically branching solution is given by $\delta > 0$, $\eta > 0$ and a subcritical one by $\delta < 0$ and $\eta < 0$. Noting that (14.3)-(14.4) is a solution to (14.1)-(14.2) and disregarding products of perturbations, we can write the linear equations for the perturbations as

$$\frac{dx_1}{dt} = [-\, 2\delta \sin^2 t]x_1 + [1 - 2\delta \sin(t) \cos(t)]x_2 \quad , \tag{14.40}$$

$$\frac{dx_2}{dt} = - [1 + 2\delta \sin(t) \cos(t)]x_1 - [2\delta \cos^2 t]x_2 \quad . \tag{14.41}$$

Although η does not appear explicitly in the stability problem, it does appear implicitly in the sense that $\delta > 0$ corresponds to supercritical, and presumably stable, solutions and $\delta < 0$ corresponds to subcritical, and unstable, solutions (see Fig. 14.1) provided $\delta/\eta > 0$.

Equations (14.40)-(14.41) are in the same form as (14.9) and they must be integrated numerically over one period T from t=0 to t=2π=T. In matrix form (14.34), (14.40)-(14.41) can be written as

$$\frac{d}{dt}\begin{bmatrix} \phi_{11} & \phi_{12} \\ \phi_{21} & \phi_{22} \end{bmatrix} = \begin{bmatrix} -2\delta \sin^2 t & 1-2\delta \sin(t)\cos(t) \\ -1-2\delta \sin(t)\cos(t) & -2\delta \cos^2 t \end{bmatrix} \begin{bmatrix} \phi_{11} & \phi_{12} \\ \phi_{21} & \phi_{22} \end{bmatrix} , \tag{14.42}$$

where

$$\begin{bmatrix} \phi_{11}(0) & \phi_{12}(0) \\ \phi_{21}(0) & \phi_{22}(0) \end{bmatrix} = \begin{bmatrix} 1 & 0 \\ 0 & 1 \end{bmatrix} , \tag{14.43}$$

are the initial conditions. Equation (14.42) appears to be a system of four equations in four unknowns but really is a pair of separate decoupled systems of equations that are

$$\frac{d}{dt}\begin{bmatrix} \phi_{11} \\ \phi_{21} \end{bmatrix} = \begin{bmatrix} -2\delta \sin^2 t & 1-2\delta \sin(t)\cos(t) \\ -1-2\delta \sin(t)\cos(t) & -2\delta \cos^2 t \end{bmatrix} \begin{bmatrix} \phi_{11} \\ \phi_{21} \end{bmatrix} , \tag{14.44}$$

where

$$\begin{bmatrix} \phi_{11}(0) \\ \phi_{21}(0) \end{bmatrix} = \begin{bmatrix} 1 \\ 0 \end{bmatrix} , \tag{14.45}$$

and

$$\frac{d}{dt}\begin{bmatrix}\phi_{12}\\ \phi_{22}\end{bmatrix} = \begin{bmatrix}-2\delta\sin^2 t & 1-2\delta\sin(t)\cos(t)\\ -1-2\delta\sin(t)\cos(t) & -2\delta\cos^2 t\end{bmatrix}\begin{bmatrix}\phi_{12}\\ \phi_{22}\end{bmatrix}, \quad (14.46)$$

where

$$\begin{bmatrix}\phi_{12}(0)\\ \phi_{22}(0)\end{bmatrix} = \begin{bmatrix}0\\ 1\end{bmatrix}. \quad (14.47)$$

After the matrix

$$[b_{ij}] = \begin{bmatrix}\phi_{11}(t=2\pi) & \phi_{12}(t=2\pi)\\ \phi_{21}(t=2\pi) & \phi_{22}(t=2\pi)\end{bmatrix}, \quad (14.48)$$

is calculated, we can find its two eigenvalues μ_1 and μ_2 and so determine the stability of the periodic solution (14.3)-(14.4) for several different values of δ. For the case $\eta > 0$, the matrix $[b_{ij}]$ was determined by solving (14.44)-(14.47) using a fifth- and sixth-order Runga-Kutta scheme, and the results are given in Table 14.1. The corresponding eigenvalues or characteristic multipliers are shown in Table 14.2. As we expect, the periodic solution is stable for all values of δ because $\mu_1 < 1$, and $\mu_2 = 1$. Since $\mu_2 = 1$, there is no possibility for a pair of conjugate multipliers to appear and thus no possibility for twisting perturbations to appear. A three-dimensional example would have been required to illustrate such twisting behavior.

14.2.5 Checking the accuracy of the computations. Since the above numerical technique depends on accurate calculations of the values of the b_{ij} as determined from possibly lengthy integration of a large system of ordinary differential equations, we must have a means to verify the accuracy of the integration. We can accomplish this by finding analytically the product of the n characteristic

Table 14.1 Calculated values of b_{ij} from (14.48) for determination of the stability of the solution (14.3)-(14.4) to (14.1)-(14.2) for the supercritical case $\eta > 0$. A fifth- and sixth-order Runga-Kutta scheme with an error tolerance of 10^{-4} was used.

δ	b_{11}	b_{21}	b_{12}	b_{22}
0.5	1.0	$1.96 \cdot 10^{-5}$	$5.87 \cdot 10^{-7}$	$1.87 \cdot 10^{-3}$
1.0	1.0	$2.26 \cdot 10^{-5}$	$2.59 \cdot 10^{-5}$	$2.48 \cdot 10^{-6}$
1.5	1.0	$7.99 \cdot 10^{-6}$	$-1.20 \cdot 10^{-5}$	$7.38 \cdot 10^{-5}$
2.0	1.0	$1.70 \cdot 10^{-6}$	$-2.01 \cdot 10^{-5}$	$9.71 \cdot 10^{-8}$
2.5	1.0	$1.15 \cdot 10^{-6}$	$-5.48 \cdot 10^{-6}$	$1.75 \cdot 10^{-5}$
3.0	1.0	$1.26 \cdot 10^{-6}$	$8.18 \cdot 10^{-7}$	$-4.68 \cdot 10^{-9}$
3.5	1.0	$2.56 \cdot 10^{-6}$	$-5.24 \cdot 10^{-6}$	$2.66 \cdot 10^{-7}$
4.0	1.0	$3.38 \cdot 10^{-6}$	$-1.57 \cdot 10^{-6}$	$-4.67 \cdot 10^{-8}$
4.5	1.0	$2.21 \cdot 10^{-6}$	$-3.37 \cdot 10^{-6}$	$-2.75 \cdot 10^{-8}$
5.0	1.0	$6.02 \cdot 10^{-6}$	$-1.61 \cdot 10^{-6}$	$-2.41 \cdot 10^{-6}$

Table 14.2 Magnitudes of the eigenvalues μ_1 and μ_2 of the matrix $[b_{ij}]$ whose components are given in Table 14.1, or characteristic multipliers μ_1 and μ_2 for the determination of the stability of the solution (14.3)-(14.4) when $\eta > 0$.

δ	$\lvert\mu_1\rvert$	$\lvert\mu_2\rvert$
0.5	$1.867 \cdot 10^{-3}$	1.0
1.0	$3.487 \cdot 10^{-6}$	1.0
1.5	$5.828 \cdot 10^{-9}$	1.0
2.0	$8.818 \cdot 10^{-12}$	1.0
2.5	$7.278 \cdot 10^{-14}$	1.0
3.0	$3.082 \cdot 10^{-12}$	1.0
3.5	$5.189 \cdot 10^{-10}$	1.0
4.0	$2.451 \cdot 10^{-11}$	1.0
4.5	$1.558 \cdot 10^{-11}$	1.0
5.0	$1.268 \cdot 10^{-12}$	1.0

multipliers (Friedrichs, 1965). To find this product, we write (14.9) as

$$\frac{dX}{dt} = A(t)\,X \quad , \tag{14.49}$$

where the vector $X = [x_i(t)]^T$ and the matrix $A(t) = [a_{ij}(t)]$. Also we express the characteristic equation (14.18) as

$$\det(B-\mu I_n) = 0 \quad , \tag{14.50}$$

where the matrix $B = [b_{ij}]$ and I_n is the n × n unit or identity matrix. If the matrix $[\phi_i^m(t)]$ having initial conditions $\phi_i^m(0) = \delta_{im}$ is denoted by Z(t), then we find that B = Z(T) as shown earlier in (14.33). The Wronskian W of the matrix Z is defined to be

$$W(t) = \det[Z(t)] \quad . \tag{14.51}$$

It can be shown that W satisfies

$$\frac{dW}{dt} = \left(\mathrm{Tr}(A)\right)\cdot W \quad , \tag{14.52}$$

where $\mathrm{Tr}(A) = \sum_{k=1}^{n} a_{kk}$, the sum of the diagonal elements of A. Therefore, we have

$$W(t) = W(0)\,\exp[\textstyle\int_0^t \mathrm{Tr}[A(\tau)]\,d\tau] \quad . \tag{14.53}$$

Also, since W(0) = 1 and B = Z(T), we find that

$$\det(B) = \exp[\textstyle\int_0^T \mathrm{Tr}[A(\tau)]\,d\tau] \quad ; \tag{14.54}$$

this result is known as <u>Liouville's formula</u> (Hirsch and Smale, 1974). All matrices have the property that the determinant of the matrix equals the product of the eigenvalues, so that

$$\det(B) = \mu_1\mu_2\cdots\mu_n \quad . \tag{14.55}$$

Combining (14.54) and (14.55) gives

$$\mu_1\mu_2\cdots\mu_n = \exp[\textstyle\int_0^T \mathrm{Tr}[A(\tau)]\,d\tau] \quad , \tag{14.56}$$

or

$$\sum_{i=1}^{n} \lambda_i = \frac{1}{T} \int_0^T \mathrm{Tr}[A(\tau)]\, d\tau \quad . \qquad (14.57)$$

If the numerical results obey (14.56) to sufficient accuracy then we can be confident that the stability analysis has produced usable results. The results of this test (14.56) for the example in the previous subsection are shown in Table 14.3. The discrepancy for large values of δ is due to truncation error in the numerical integration and subsequent calculation of the eigenvalues. If anything, the errors show that the magnitudes of μ_1 in Table 14.2 are too large, and so the stability result is not altered. If the numerical results do not pass the test (14.56), then the values of the b_{ij} should be recalculated by performing the integration with a smaller time-step or with a smaller error tolerance. This procedure of decreasing the time-step should be continued until adequate accuracy is achieved.

14.3 Poincaré Maps and Bifurcation of Periodic Solutions

As we have seen, it is helpful in studying orbits and their perturbations to

Table 14.3 Test for accuracy of the eigenvalues μ_1 and μ_2 listed in Table 14.2. The numbers in the two right columns should be equal.

δ	$\lvert\mu_1 \cdot \mu_2\rvert$	$\exp[\int_0^T \mathrm{Tr}[A(\tau)]\, d\tau]$
0.5	$1.867 \cdot 10^{-3}$	$1.867 \cdot 10^{-3}$
1.0	$3.487 \cdot 10^{-6}$	$3.487 \cdot 10^{-6}$
1.5	$5.828 \cdot 10^{-9}$	$6.512 \cdot 10^{-9}$
2.0	$8.818 \cdot 10^{-12}$	$1.217 \cdot 10^{-11}$
2.5	$7.278 \cdot 10^{-14}$	$2.270 \cdot 10^{-14}$
3.0	$3.082 \cdot 10^{-12}$	$4.241 \cdot 10^{-17}$
3.5	$5.189 \cdot 10^{-10}$	$7.290 \cdot 10^{-20}$
4.0	$2.451 \cdot 10^{-10}$	$1.479 \cdot 10^{-22}$
4.5	$1.558 \cdot 10^{-11}$	$2.762 \cdot 10^{-25}$
5.0	$1.268 \cdot 10^{-12}$	$5.158 \cdot 10^{-28}$

note where the perturbation trajectories intersect a plane perpendicular to the periodic solution (Figs. 14.2 and 14.3). We use this idea to introduce the concept of a Poincaré map, which helps us classify the various types of bifurcations from periodic solutions. This classification is important in our discussions of the transition to turbulence in Chapters 15 and 16.

As discussed earlier in this chapter, we can visualize a periodic solution as a closed orbit in phase space. In order to determine the stability of this solution, we place a disk perpendicular to the orbit at some point on it. The periodic solution is perturbed on the disk, and during each successive revolution, the perturbation trajectory passes through the disk. The Poincaré map, or return map, is the map that assigns to each point on the disk the next point where its trajectory meets the disk. For example, if Q(t) is a perturbation of the periodic solution P(t), then the Poincaré map associated with P(t) assigns to Q(0) a point that is approximately the same as the point Q(T) in Figs. 14.3b,c.

To deduce the signature of bifurcation points on periodic solutions, we observe from results given in Section 14.2.2 that the transition from stability to instability of the periodic solution P(t) is given by the transition from $|\mu_\ell| < 1$ to $|\mu_\ell| > 1$ for some $\ell \neq n$. That is, writing μ_ℓ in polar form

$$\mu_\ell = r \exp[i2\pi\theta] \quad , \qquad 0 < \theta \leq 1 \quad , \tag{14.58}$$

or, using (14.37), in the form

$$\lambda_\ell = [\ln(r) + i2\pi\theta]/T \quad , \qquad 0 < \theta \leq 1 \quad , \tag{14.59}$$

we see that stability is lost at r=1 in the transition from ln(r) < 0 to ln(r) > 0.

In our discussion of bifurcation and stability of stationary solutions, we have learned to expect that a new solution emanates from the one losing stability. In this case we link the type of bifurcating solution to the behavior of a perturbation as given by the imaginary part of the characteristic exponent λ -- stationary solutions are signaled by $\mathrm{Im}(\lambda) = 0$ and temporally periodic solutions by $\mathrm{Im}(\lambda) \neq 0$. Furthermore, in the latter case, the limiting period T of the branching solution is given by $T = 2\pi/\mathrm{Im}(\lambda)$.

It is natural to ask whether for periodic solutions the imaginary part of the corresponding characteristic exponent λ plays a similar role in signaling the expected type of bifurcating solution. From (14.59) we notice that

$$\mathrm{Im}(\lambda) = 2\pi\theta/T \quad , \quad 0 < \theta \leq 1 \quad , \tag{14.60}$$

so that here $\mathrm{Im}(\lambda)$ measures the amount of twist that a perturbation $Q(t)$ undergoes in each revolution about a periodic solution $P(t)$. We see that because of the twist, the bifurcating solution $\tilde{P}(t)$ need not be T-periodic, as we show in Fig. 14.4. If the twist angle is positive as shown, then $\tilde{P}(t)$ cannot return to its initial position on the Poincaré disk. However, if $\theta = p/q$, with p and q integers having no common divisors, then θ is rational, and after q returns, $\tilde{P}(t)$ may attain its initial position; if $q = 1$, then the solution $\tilde{P}(t)$ is T-periodic, if $q = 2$, then it is 2T-periodic, etc. Although this expectation is highly plausible, that it actually is correct is very difficult to prove; for further information, see Iooss and Joseph (1980). In the case of rational θ, we are able to deduce that a periodic solution $\tilde{P}(t)$ with limiting period

$$\tilde{T} = qT = \mathrm{Denom}(\theta)\, T \quad , \ \theta \text{ rational} \quad , \tag{14.61}$$

can bifurcate from $P(t)$. As we illustrate in Section 14.3.3, when θ is not rational and hence $\tilde{P}(t)$ cannot ever return to its initial position, then instead $\tilde{P}(t)$ covers the surface of a two-torus.

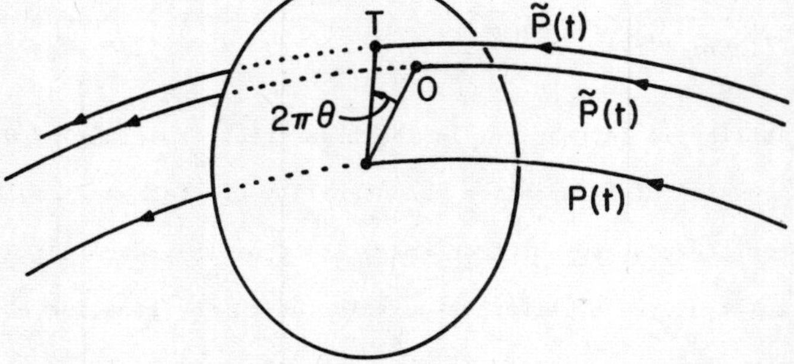

Fig. 14.4 Portions of a periodic solution $P(t)$ and a bifurcating solution $\tilde{P}(t)$ near the Poincaré disk centered at a point on $P(t)$. After one period T of $P(t)$, the new solution $\tilde{P}(t)$ has twisted through the angle $2\pi\theta < 2\pi$ and so $\tilde{P}(t)$ cannot be T-periodic.

Thus the case $|\mu| = 1$ signals bifurcation from a periodic solution P(t). In the simplest and most probable case, either one real characteristic multiplier has magnitude one or a complex conjugate pair of multipliers has magnitude one (Fig. 14.5). Clearly three cases are possible, and these are the only nondegenerate ones:

(i) $\mu = 1$ (harmonic bifurcation) ,

(ii) $\mu = -1$ (subharmonic bifurcation) ,

(iii) $\mu = \exp[\pm i2\pi\theta]$, $0 < \theta < 1$, $\theta \neq 1/2, 1/3, 1/4$

(Hopf bifurcation to a torus).

Three values of θ are excluded in the third case: The value $\theta = 1/2$ produces subharmonic bifurcation and the values $\theta = 1/3$ and $\theta = 1/4$ are discussed in Section 3.5 of Guckenheimer and Holmes (1983). With this information, we are now ready to examine the three branching cases below.

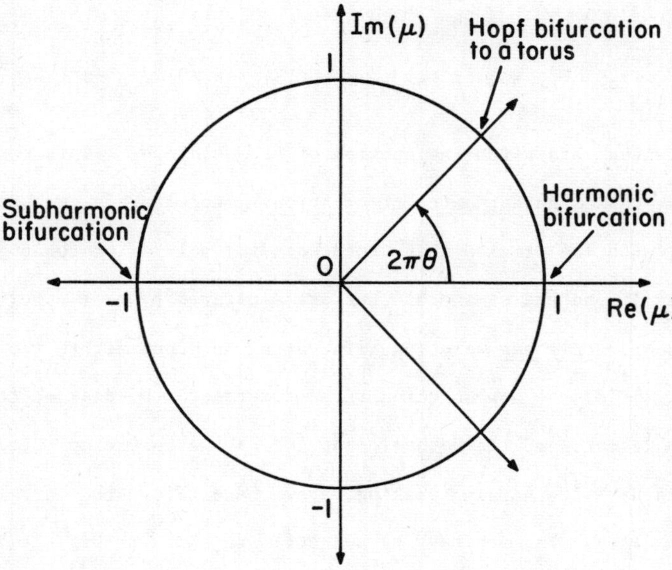

Fig. 14.5 The three nondegenerate cases of bifurcation from a periodic solution P(t) that are signaled by one real or one conjugate pair of characteristic multipliers crossing the unit circle. Harmonic bifurcation is signaled by $\mu=1$, subharmonic bifurcation by $\mu=-1$, and bifurcation to a torus by $|\mu| = |\exp(\pm i2\pi\theta)|=1$ with $0<\theta<1$ and $\theta\neq 1/2, 1/3, 1/4$.

14.3.1 Harmonic bifurcation. First we consider the case $\mu_\ell = 1$ for one of the $n - 1$ characteristic multipliers. Because $q = 1$, we have from (14.61) that

$$T_{new} = T_{old} \quad . \tag{14.62}$$

Thus the period T_{new} of the new solution $\tilde{P}(t)$ is the same as the period T_{old} of the original one $P(t)$; such a bifurcation is called a harmonic bifurcation. In fact, two new solutions $\tilde{P}(t)$ and $\tilde{\tilde{P}}(t)$ having period T_{old} bifurcate from $P(t)$, much in the same way as two new stationary solutions branch from another one to produce a trident bifurcation form (Sparrow, 1982; Guckenheimer and Holmes, 1983). These two new solutions appear as points $\tilde{A}$ and $\tilde{\tilde{A}}$ on the Poincaré disk (Fig. 14.6a). Also, iterates of a Poincaré map for a particular perturbation $Q(t)$ of $P(t)$ are shown approaching $\tilde{P}(t)$. Some other perturbation would approach the second solution $\tilde{\tilde{P}}(t)$ in a similar way. In Fig. 14.6b we show the new stable solutions $\tilde{P}(t)$ and $\tilde{\tilde{P}}(t)$ that occur on both sides of the unstable solution $P(t)$.

14.3.2 Subharmonic bifurcation. When $\mu_\ell = -1$ so that $q = 2$, we have from (14.61) that

$$T_{new} = 2\, T_{old} \quad , \tag{14.63}$$

and the new solution has twice the period of the old one. This period doubling bifurcation is called subharmonic bifurcation. Once again we have a trident branching form, with the proviso that corresponding points of the upper and lower branches actually lie on the same orbit but are separated by half a period of the new orbit. Consequently only one solution bifurcates, in contrast to the harmonic case above. In Fig. 14.7a, the new solution $\tilde{P}(t)$ intersects the disk at the two points labeled $\tilde{A}$. The iterates of the Poincaré map for a perturbation $Q(t)$ of $P(t)$ are shown in Fig. 14.7a alternately passing above and below the original unstable periodic solution $P(t)$. The orbits $P(t)$ and $\tilde{P}(t)$ are shown in Fig. 14.7b.

14.3.3 Hopf bifurcation to a torus. We recall that at a bifurcation point, we have $|\mu_\ell| = 1$ so that

$$|\mu_\ell| = \exp[i2\pi\theta] \quad , \qquad 0 < \theta \leq 1 \quad , \tag{14.64}$$

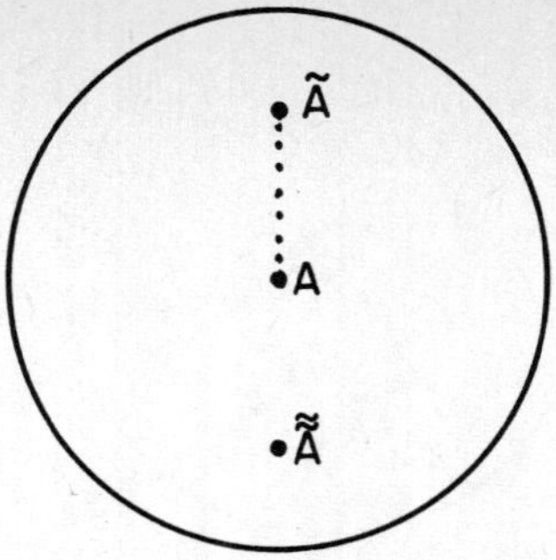

(a)

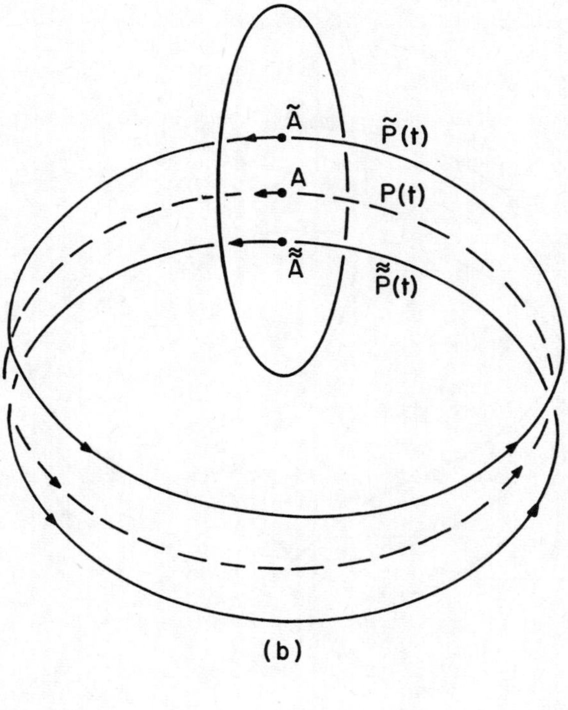

(b)

Fig. 14.6 Poincaré map (a) and periodic solutions (b) for a harmonic bifurcation (q=1) from an old solution P(t) of period T to two new ones $\tilde{P}(t)$ and $\tilde{\tilde{P}}(t)$ of period T. Compare this figure with Fig. 14.8c, in which a T-periodic solution on a torus is shown. Stable solutions are shown by solid curves, unstable ones by dashed curves (after Sparrow, 1982).

in which θ may be rational or irrational. We have already noted that if θ is irrational, then the bifurcating orbit covers the surface of a two-torus (Fig. 14.8a); such an orbit is called <u>quasi-periodic</u>. Thus, instead of a periodic solution

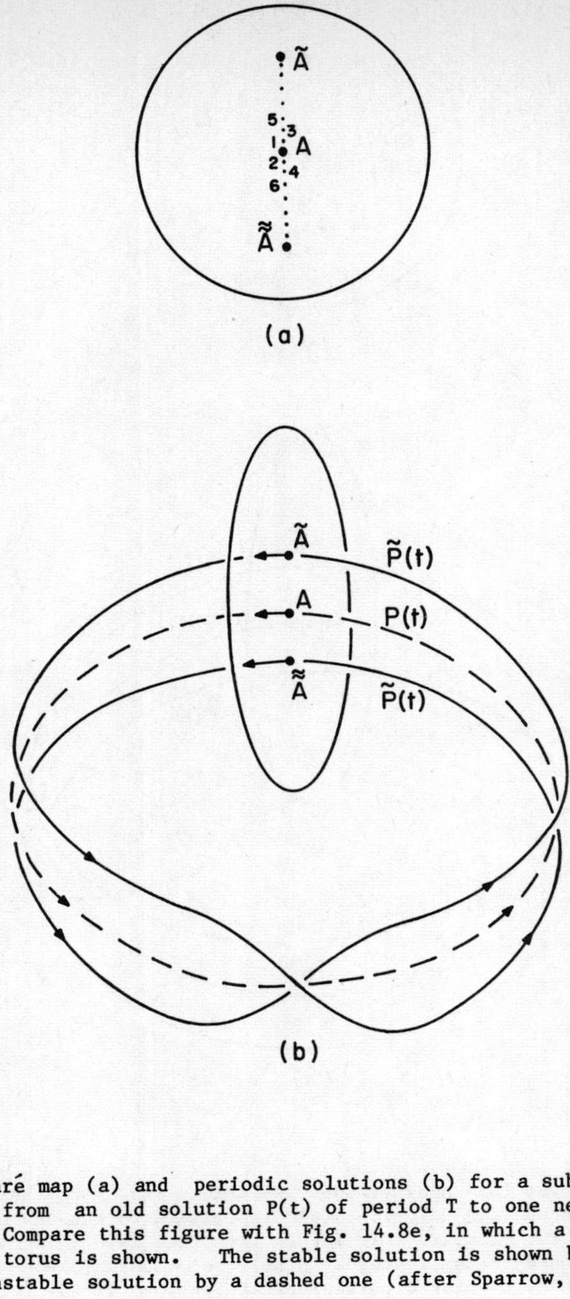

Fig. 14.7 Poincaré map (a) and periodic solutions (b) for a subharmonic bifurcation (q=2) from an old solution P(t) of period T to one new one $\tilde{P}(t)$ of period 2T. Compare this figure with Fig. 14.8e, in which a 2T-periodic solution on a torus is shown. The stable solution is shown by a solid curve and the unstable solution by a dashed one (after Sparrow, 1982).

bifurcating from P(t), we have in this case an invariant two-torus bifurcating from P(t). The surprising fact is that an invariant two-torus bifurcates from P(t) even in the case that θ is rational, provided that $\theta \neq 1, 1/2, 1/3$, or $1/4$ (Iooss and

Joseph, 1980; Guckenheimer and Holmes, 1983). For these four values of θ, a torus may or may not bifurcate, and so the resulting periodic solutions $\tilde{P}(t)$ may or may not be on a torus. The cases illustrated in Figs. 14.6 and 14.7 are examples of periodic solutions that are not on a torus; in Fig. 14.8c we show a period-T solution, and in Fig. 14.8e we show a period-2T solution, on a torus.

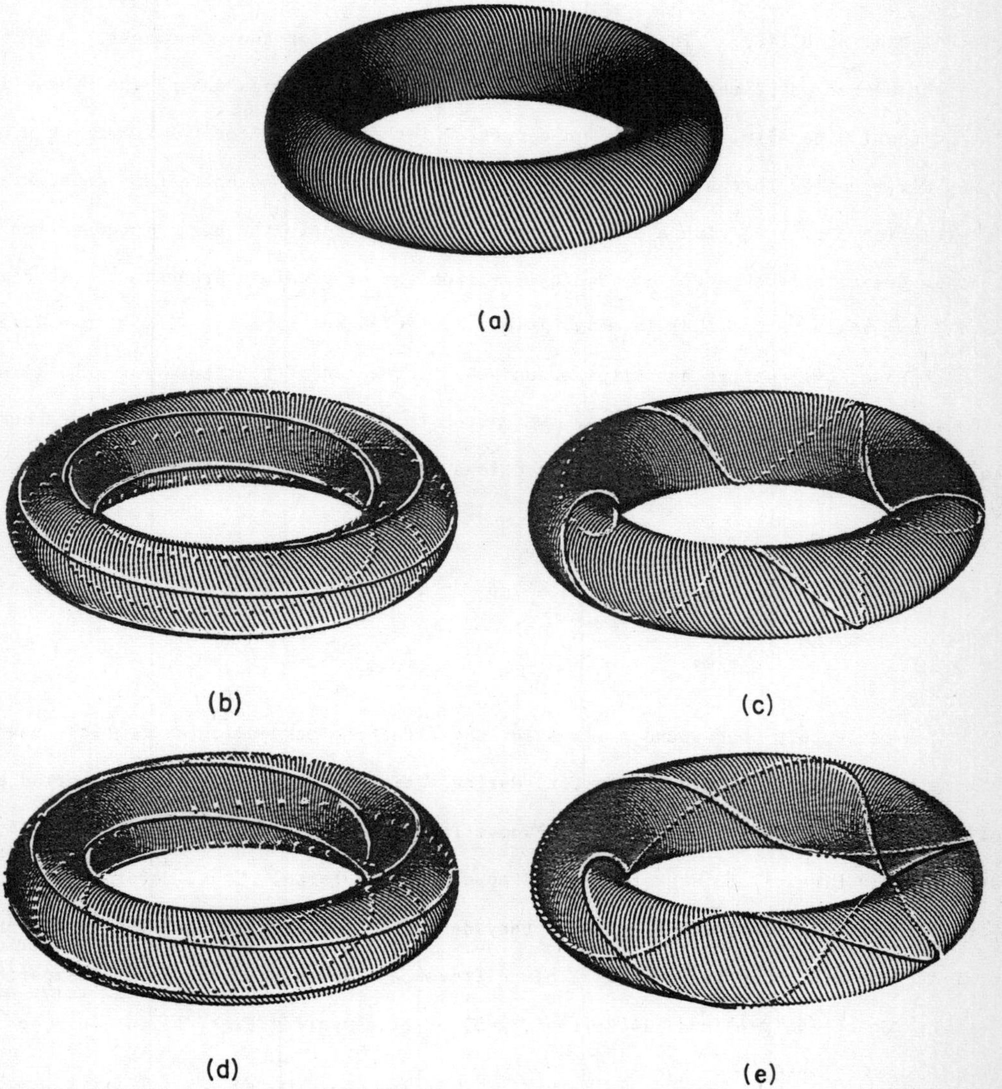

Fig. 14.8 Bifurcation of an invariant two-torus (a) from a periodic solution P(t) and four possible periodic solutions $\tilde{P}(t)$ on the torus (b), (c), (d), (e). In (b) the solution winds q=5 times in the direction parallel to P(t) and p=1 time in the direction perpendicular to P(t), but in (c) q=1 and p=5. In (d) q=5 and p=2, but in (e) q=2 and p=5. The Poincaré maps for the new 5T-periodic solutions shown in (b) and (d) are given in Fig. 14.9.

In the case that $\theta = p/q$ is rational, we considered a bifurcating periodic solution $\tilde{P}(t)$ at the beginning of this section; here p and q are assumed to have no common divisors. This orbit $\tilde{P}(t)$ lies in the bifurcating torus when $\theta \neq 1, 1/2, 1/3$, or $1/4$. The bifurcating torus has two principal directions -- one parallel to the one for the original solution P(t) and the other transverse to that of P(t). We have noted that the period of the new orbit $\tilde{P}(t)$ is qT, where T is the period of the old orbit losing stability. Thus we have an interpretation for the denominator q of θ: q is the number of times that the bifurcating orbit $\tilde{P}(t)$ winds around the torus in the direction parallel to P(t). To deduce an interpretation for the numerator p of θ, we first notice that after one trip around the torus, the Poincaré map carries an intersection $\tilde{A}$ of $\tilde{P}(t)$ with a plane perpendicular to P(t) to the next intersection $\tilde{B}$ that is essentially an angle $\alpha = 2\pi p/q$ away from the original intersection. In Fig. 14.9, the angle α is $\tilde{A}O\tilde{B}$; in Fig. 14.9a, $\alpha = 2\pi/5$ and in Fig. 14.9b, $\alpha = 4\pi/5$. In each case, only after q=5 trips around the torus can $\tilde{P}(t)$ return for the first time to the original intersection $\tilde{A}$. We notice that the total angle described around the origin O by the successive intersections of $\tilde{P}(t)$ with the perpendicular plane is given by

$$\underbrace{2\pi p/q + 2\pi p/q + \cdots + 2\pi p/q}_{q \text{ times}} \sim 2\pi p \quad . \tag{14.65}$$

Thus the trajectory has wound p times in the direction perpendicular to P(t) and q times in the direction parallel to P(t) during a time interval equal to one period qT of $\tilde{P}(t)$. The 5T-periodic solutions whose Poincaré maps are displayed in Fig. 14.9 are shown in Figs. 14.8b,d as they would appear on the torus. Thus, determination of both p and q is significant because they describe quite different aspects of the periodic solutions on the torus. This difference can be seen easily by comparing Figs. 14.8b (q=5, p=1) and 14.8c (q=1, p=5) or by comparing Figs. 14.8d (q=5, p=2) and 14.8e (q=2, p=5).

In the case that θ is irrational, we noted above that the bifurcating quasi-periodic solution covers the torus. The corresponding Poincaré maps produce iterates on the cross section of the torus, but the iterates would only very nearly

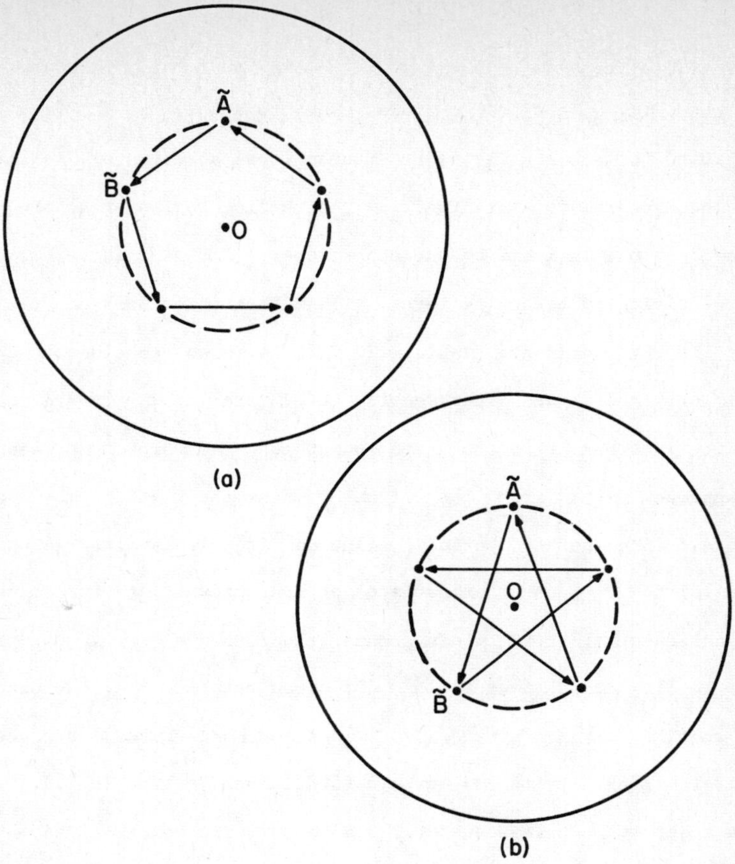

Fig. 14.9 Poincaré maps for two periodic solutions on a torus whose cross section is given schematically by a dashed curve. The orbit beginning at $\tilde{A}$ next crosses the Poincaré disk at $\tilde{B}$, giving an apparent motion as indicated by the arrows. In (a) q=5 and p=1 and each dot is hit successively in p=1 trip around the circle. In (b) q=5 and p=2 so that every other dot is hit requiring p=2 trips around the circle. The periodic solutions are shown in Figs. 14.8b,d as they would appear on the torus.

return to the original point. There is a slow drift around the cross section until that cross section becomes completely filled as time approaches infinity.

Thus we see that if a single real characteristic multiplier crosses the unit circle, then new periodic solutions develop, but if a conjugate pair of multipliers crosses the unit circle, then, except for the few cases noted above, a flow on a torus appears. As with previous examples of bifurcation, supercritical solutions are stable and subcritical ones are unstable. In particular, a supercritically branching torus is asymptotically stable, but on the torus there may be both stable and unstable periodic solutions. To see how these solutions appear, we may represent a torus as a rectangle with opposite sides glued together, as in Fig. 14.10. The bifurcating orbit $\tilde{P}(t)$ appears in such a rectangle as a series of parallel straight lines having the approximate slope $\tan(2\pi\theta)$, each line beginning on the bottom edge where the preceding one left off on the upper edge. For simplicity, we consider the case of a supercritically branching torus. Then both this torus and the bifurcating periodic solution $\tilde{P}(t)$ in it are stable. In Fig. 14.10 we conclude that points near the parallel straight lines representing $\tilde{P}(t)$ are drawn toward these lines. Intuitively, it is clear that there are points on the torus that cannot "decide" whether to approach $\tilde{P}(t)$ from the right or from the left. The set of these decision points define another periodic solution $\tilde{\tilde{P}}(t)$; this other solution $\tilde{\tilde{P}}(t)$ is oriented parallel to $\tilde{P}(t)$ on the surface of the attracting torus, but $\tilde{\tilde{P}}(t)$ is unstable. Consequently, $\tilde{\tilde{P}}(t)$ winds around the torus p times in the direction perpendicular to P(t) and q times in the direction parallel to P(t), exactly as does $\tilde{P}(t)$. These remarks may be expanded to flows on more general surfaces, as discussed in Peixoto (1962), Palis and de Melo (1982), and Section 15.2.4.

In this chapter, we have seen that simple periodic solutions may bifurcate to flows having a second fundamental period. In this way, degrees of freedom are added

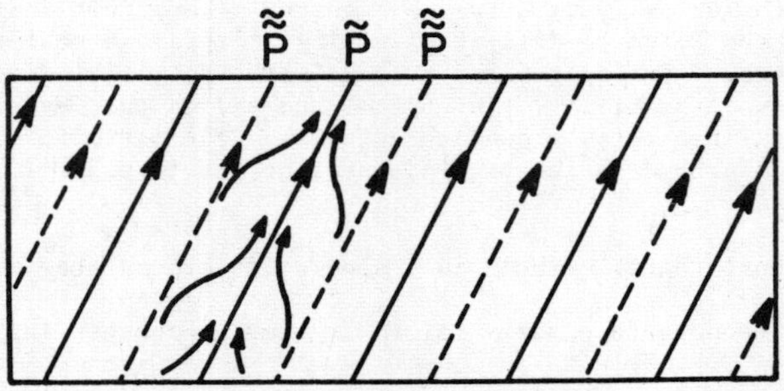

Fig. 14.10 Representation of a torus as a rectangle with opposite sides glued together. When the torus bifurcates supercritically and θ is rational, there is a stable periodic solution $\tilde{P}(t)$ on the torus (solid lines). Perturbation trajectories on the torus approach $\tilde{P}(t)$ from both the right and the left, leaving a dashed bounding set of points. This dashed set is an unstable periodic solution $\tilde{\tilde{P}}(t)$ that is oriented parallel to $\tilde{P}(t)$.

to the flow; further bifurcations might be expected to signal that still more degrees of freedom are becoming available. Thus we expect to see a hierarchy of increasingly more complicated solutions as a control parameter R is increased in value, much as has been observed in laboratory experiments with fluids (see Section 1.1.2). Thus, study of the possible hierarchies provides a basis upon which the different possible routes to turbulence may be discussed. A summary of the proposed routes is one of the topics of the next chapter.

CHAPTER 15

THE TRANSITION TO TURBULENCE

JON M. NESE

We are ready now to turn our attention to more complicated fluid responses than those represented by the stationary and temporally periodic solutions to the equations of motion. As noted in Chapter 1, a hierarchy of transitions is typically seen in forced laboratory fluids, with the steady and periodic flows representing only the initial regimes, and turbulent flows representing the final regime, of motion within the hierarchy. In this and the following chapter, we consider a few mathematical representations of these turbulent flows, as well as a few of the proposed classes of transitions within the hierarchy.

A complete explanation for the origin of turbulence has been sought actively for more than a century. Most explanations have been based on the realization that, in both laboratory experiments and mathematical analysis, one solution may exchange stability with another at certain critical forcing values. The basic, or generic, regimes of flow that are seen as the rate of forcing is increased are

(1) Motionless flows

(2) Steady flows

(3) Temporally periodic flows

(4) Turbulent flows

Flows of types one through three and the transitions between them have been the focus of Chapters 2-14. These regimes are illustrated in Fig. 15.1, which is derived from the experimental work of Krishnamurti (1970a,b; 1973) on Rayleigh-Bénard convection. Two properties that distinguish turbulent flows from the other regimes are a sensitive dependence on the initial state of the system and a complicated spatial or temporal structure.

Unfortunately, the transition to turbulence does not always follow the clearly defined sequence above. For example, periodic flows are not always observed before turbulence develops, and additional temporal regimes may appear between steps three and four. Moreover, laboratory experiments suggest that although we might intuitively expect a turbulent flow to involve an infinite number of frequencies,

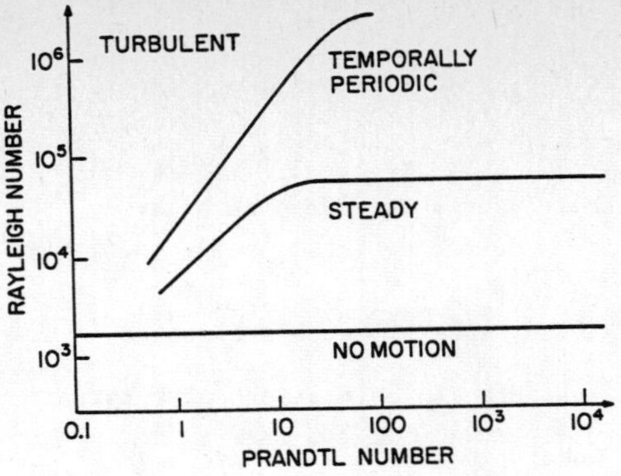

Fig. 15.1 Four regimes of flow observed in Rayleigh-Bénard convection experiments, as functions of the Prandtl and Rayleigh numbers (after Krishnamurti, 1970a,b).

apparently only a finite number of principal frequencies are involved--a fortuitous surprise that simplifies the task of modeling the hierarchy of transitions.

Although only finitely many frequencies appear to be involved in the transition to turbulence, an infinite number of spatial harmonics or modes might be necessary to represent the turbulent flow. As we see later, turbulence having only a complicated temporal structure, known as Ruelle-Takens turbulence, might plausibly be represented in finite truncated models. In contrast, turbulence having a complicated spatial (and temporal) structure appears to be described most plausibly in models by means of Leray's conjecture that the mean square vorticity is infinite at some points (Leray, 1933). The transition to this type of turbulence, known as Leray turbulence, is not well understood, and, because the mean square vorticity in a truncated model is necessarily finite, the study of Leray turbulence requires analysis of the complete partial differential equations. Thus, the generic sequence given at the beginning of this chapter refers to the transition to Ruelle-Takens turbulence (Temam, 1983).

Most theoretical studies of the transition to turbulence are based on partial differential equations such as the Navier-Stokes equations. Solutions representing flows in the first three of the above four steps have been clearly established with use of standard linearization techniques. However, such relatively simple representations do not suffice for turbulent flows and the associated linearization techniques become much more subtle (see Chapter 16). Although there are not yet any solutions of the partial differential equations thought to represent turbulent flows, there are numerous solutions to low-order spectral models that apparently possess some of the salient features of turbulence. These solutions are called chaotic solutions because of their aperiodic temporal behavior (Guckenheimer and Holmes, 1983).

Significantly, the occurrence of such attractors in low-order models does not necessarily mean that a suitable representation of a turbulent flow has been found, but may mean that the model is too small (Marcus, 1981). That is, the chaotic solution may lose stability under model enlargement, leading to the conclusion that the smaller model does not conform to Modeling Principle Seven, which states that a model should preserve structure under extension to more complex forms. We discuss this issue in Section 15.3 after we review in the next two sections some experimental results concerning the transition to turbulence and some theoretical proposals for the routes to chaos.

15.1 Experimental Results

Formulation of a universally accepted operational definition of turbulence remains elusive, and so it is not surprising that experimental conditions necessary for the actual onset of turbulent behavior are not well-defined. Swinney and Gollub (1981) noted that the qualitative appearance of the flow in an experimental fluid as revealed by tracers of the motion is not always a reliable indicator of the true behavior. The introduction of laser Doppler techniques, coupled with the more conventional hot-wire anemometry methods and the application of laboratory computers to the problem, has advanced significantly the experimental study of the transition to turbulence. Power spectrum analysis is used frequently to study the characteristics of laboratory flows. Computers can calculate the power spectra quickly from local velocity and temperature data. Steady and temporally periodic flows are easily identifiable as spikes at specific frequencies; however, quasi-periodic and aperiodic motions, although profoundly different mathematically, are difficult to distinguish by means of a power spectrum analysis.

Swinney and Gollub (1978) studied the transition to turbulence in both circular Couette flow and Rayleigh-Bénard convection. They found that when the steady state becomes unstable, a periodic state having one fundamental frequency ω_1 or ω_3

appears; typical power spectra of the periodic solutions are given in the top diagrams of Fig. 15.2. The spectra contain no frequencies other than the fundamental and its harmonics, and thus the flow is strictly periodic. As the forcing rate is increased, a second time-dependent instability occurs in each system, creating a flow with two irrationally related frequencies: a quasi-periodic flow (see Section 15.2.1). The spectra for this state are shown in the middle diagrams of Fig. 15.2, in which the two fundamental frequencies, ω_1 and ω_2 or ω_3 and ω_4, and their linear combinations can be seen. Further increases in the forcing rate produce the spectra at the bottom of Fig. 15.2, with broad-band noise components appearing while the narrow peaks remain. Eventually, at larger forcing values, the peaks disappear and the flow becomes purely turbulent. It is intriguing that the broad-band spectrum characteristic of turbulence is achieved through a small number of instabilities, with never more than two principal frequencies observed.

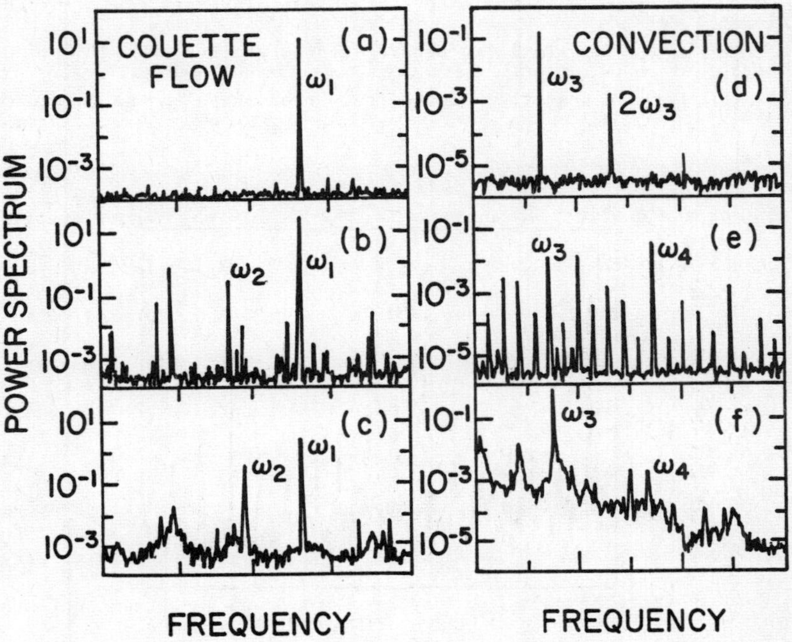

Fig. 15.2 Schematic velocity power spectra illustrating different dynamical regimes observed in experiments on Couette flow and Rayleigh-Bénard convection. The flow is periodic in (a) and (d), quasi-periodic with two fundamental frequencies in (b) and (e), and turbulent in (c) and (f) (after Swinney, 1978).

Another experiment in Rayleigh-Bénard convection was conducted by Maurer and Libchaber (1979) in liquid helium. The first transition they observed is associated with the onset of convection. The second transition produces a frequency ω_1 in the motion, and is associated with waves propagating along the convective rolls. The third transition generates a second incommensurate frequency ω_2, signaling the creation of a quasi-periodic flow. The power spectrum after this third transition is shown in Fig. 15.3. As the rate of forcing is increased further, all the combination frequencies $\omega = m\omega_1 + n\omega_2$, where m and n are integers, appear. This flow is followed by two frequency locking regimes in which first $\omega_1/\omega_2 = 6.5$ and then $\omega_1/\omega_2 = 7.0$. These regimes suggest closed (periodic) motion, rather than quasi-periodic motion, on the surface of a torus (Fig. 14.8a). Turbulence develops from the latter locking state in a sequence of period doubling transitions with the generation of the frequencies $\omega_2/2$, $\omega_2/4$, $\omega_2/8$, and so forth. Again, never more than two fundamental frequencies are observed before turbulence develops.

Two other pathways to turbulence were seen in experiments by Ahlers and Behringer (1978), again for Rayleigh-Bénard convection but in different container geometries. In both cases, they found that broad-band noise characteristic of

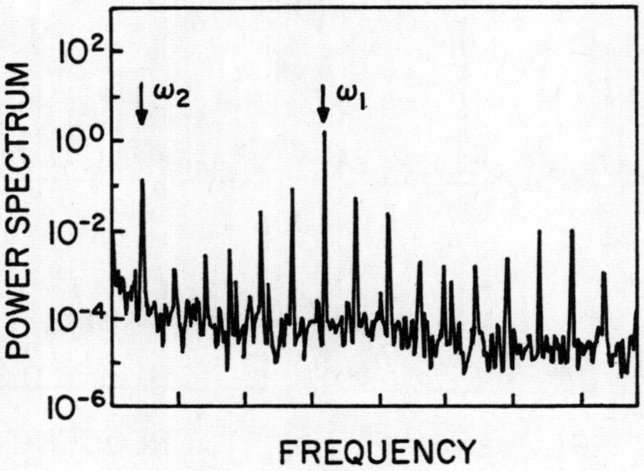

Fig. 15.3 Typical schematic power spectrum after the third transition in Rayleigh-Bénard convection experiments in liquid helium. The frequencies ω_1 and ω_2 are incommensurate, and all other peaks are linear combinations of ω_1 and ω_2 (after Maurer and Libchaber, 1979).

turbulence appears in the power spectra just after the onset of convection, with no intervening periodicity. The intensities of the developing motion vary in the two cases, however, with turbulence developing gradually in relatively shallow containers, but abruptly in deeper containers. Thus, the flows exhibit a direct transition from laminar to turbulent behavior without passing through a series of instabilities, suggesting that yet another factor in determining the transitional behavior is the geometry of the system.

In summary, turbulence has been observed experimentally to develop in several very different ways: from the degeneration of a complicated, two-frequency quasi-periodic flow, from a sequence of period doubling transitions, and directly from the steady convective state. These pathways and their mathematical analogues, which are discussed in the next section, are summarized in Table 15.1. The only significant common aspect of each of these observed mechanisms is the lack of a large number of incommensurate frequencies in the flow preceding the onset of turbulence, providing at least some hope that these transitional mechanisms can be studied with low-order models (see Chapter 16).

15.2 Some Hypothesized Routes

Even in the above brief survey of experimental investigations of the transition to turbulence, a wide variety of pathways and mechanisms is evident, perhaps explaining the difficulties in formulating an all-encompassing mathematical theory describing the routes to chaos. In this section, we review the conjectures that have been advanced, most of which have laboratory analogues. These hypothesized explanations are summarized in Table 15.1.

15.2.1 Landau's hypothesis.

In 1944, Landau suggested that turbulent flow is represented mathematically by a long succession of supercritical Hopf bifurcations, each bifurcation adding a new frequency to the motion (Landau, 1944). Turbulence is then identified with fluid motion consisting of so many frequencies that it is "complicated and confused". Crucial to this hypothesis is the notion of quasi-periodicity, already discussed briefly in Section 14.3.3 in the context of two-frequency motion on a two-torus. A quasi-periodic function of n modes is a function of the form $f(t) = g(\omega_1 t, \omega_2 t, \ldots, \omega_n t)$, $n \geq 2$, where $g(x_1, x_2, \ldots, x_n)$ has period 2π in each variable x_i and the frequencies $\omega_1, \omega_2, \ldots, \omega_n$ are incommensurate.

Table 15.1 A Summary of the Proposed Routes to Chaos

Route	Mathematical Explanation: Name	Mathematical Explanation: Proposers	Mathematical Explanation: Comments	Observational Evidence (Rayleigh-Bénard Convection)
Stationary → Chaos (gradual)	Supercritical bifurcation of three-torus	Newhouse et al. (1978), Shirer and Wells (1985)	Torus containing attractor develops gradually from stationary solution.	Ahlers and Behringer (1978)
Stationary → Chaos (abrupt)	Finite-amplitude transition	Joseph (1976)	Subcritical Hopf bifurcation; no stationary or periodic attractors.	Ahlers and Behringer (1978)
Stationary → Periodic → Quasi-Periodic → Chaos	Bifurcation from two-torus	Ruelle and Takens (1971), Newhouse et al. (1978)	Traditional interpretation; 3 consecutive Hopf bifurcations; last one conjectured to be to strange attractor.	Swinney and Gollub (1978), Ahlers and Behringer (1978)
Stationary → Periodic → Quasi-Periodic → Phase-Locked Periodic → Chaos	Pathological wrinkling of a two-torus	Ostlund et al. (1983)	Two Hopf bifurcations followed by a rapid succession of periodic and quasi-periodic states before transition to strange attractor.	Maurer and Libchaber (1979)
Stationary → Periodic (T) → Periodic (2T) → Periodic (4T) →···→ Periodic (2^nT) →···→ Chaos	Infinite sequence of period doubling bifurcations	Feigenbaum (1978)	Infinite sequence of rationally related, phase-locked frequencies occurs; may be accompanied by noisy periodicity and intermittency in period-three orbits; chaos follows.	Maurer and Libchaber (1979)
Stationary → Periodic (T_1) → Quasi-Periodic (T_1,T_2) → Quasi-Periodic (T_1,T_2,T_3) →···→ Quasi Periodic ($T_1,\ldots,T_n$) →···→ Chaos	Infinite sequence of supercritical Hopf bifurcations	Landau (1944)	Many incommensurate periods (T_i/T_j irrational for all i,j); no sensitivity to initial conditions; no clear onset of turbulence.	None

The function $g(x_1,x_2,\ldots,x_n)$ is defined on the surface of an n-torus, the trajectory given by $x_i(t) = \omega_i t$ for $i = 1,\ldots,n$ fills that torus, and the quasi-periodic function $f(t)$ is the evaluation of $g(x_1,x_2,\ldots,x_n)$ along that trajectory.

Turbulence, then, in Landau's hypothesis, is just the superposition of many quasi-periodic modes. The transition to turbulence is modeled by a hierarchy of Hopf bifurcations as the value of a control parameter is increased, each bifurcation adding a new frequency to the motion. Turbulence is associated with the complicated state that results when the forcing is strong enough to exceed the threshold for many instabilities. In this route, however, there is no well-defined onset of chaos.

One problem with Landau's hypothesis is that quasi-periodic functions do not display sensitive dependence on initial conditions, as seems to be characteristic of turbulent flows (Yorke and Yorke, 1981). Also, quasi-periodic solutions with two frequencies apparently lose stability to aperiodic solutions, as seen in the experiments of Swinney and Gollub (1978) that were discussed in Section 15.1. In fact, it appears that long sequences of bifurcations resulting in quasi-periodic solutions having many dominant incommensurate frequencies do not correspond to any observed situation in fluid dynamics (Swinney and Gollub, 1978). Nonetheless, Landau's conjecture represents one of the earliest attempts to explain the transition to turbulence, and his ideas have stimulated further theoretical development.

15.2.2 The conjecture of Ruelle and Takens. In their now classic 1971 paper "On the Nature of Turbulence", Ruelle and Takens suggested a fundamentally different approach to describing the transition to turbulence. They argued that turbulence can be understood within the framework of the Navier-Stokes equations using the qualitative theory of differential equations. They postulated that the phenomena underlying turbulence are effectively finite-dimensional, with the phenomena being governed by a finite set of "active" modes. Thus, a geometrical analysis of the equations could be undertaken in a fairly small finite-dimensional phase space.

With these assumptions concerning the setting in which turbulence is to be understood, Ruelle and Takens hypothesized that once three or four periods are established in the motion, then a chaotic solution is expected; in Newhouse et al. (1978), the number of periods is fixed at three. This hypothesis is often interpreted to mean that three successive Hopf bifurcations are necessary to produce chaotic solutions. In this view, a stationary solution would lose stability to a temporally periodic solution that in turn loses stability to either closed or quasi-periodic motion on a two-torus. As the forcing rate is increased further, the next bifurcation would produce a chaotic solution on a three-torus. Rigorous theorems are available describing how the first two bifurcations occur, but no such theorem defining the third bifurcation that is to produce the chaotic solution is known.

The Ruelle and Takens postulate was construed slightly differently by Shirer and Wells (1985). They interpreted the Ruelle-Takens conjecture to mean that chaotic behavior is signaled by the appearance of a triple Hopf bifurcation point from which three different supercritically branching periodic solutions emanate simultaneously. However, they explain that the probability of actually observing such a triple point is zero, and so the route to chaos would be expected to occur as three separate bifurcations. The ideas of Shirer and Wells are discussed more thoroughly in Section 15.3.1 in the context of developing a complete classification of the routes to chaos via a method similar to that presented in Chapter 8 for stationary solutions.

Ruelle and Takens claimed that once chaotic solutions develop, then the limit set of these solutions is a mathematical object of finite and reasonably small dimension called a strange attractor. Motion on a strange, or chaotic, attractor is aperiodic, and depends sensitively on the initial data; this motion is fundamentally different from the quasi-periodic motion associated with chaos in Landau's view of turbulence. The structure and properties of strange attractors are discussed in more detail in Section 16.2. It suffices here to say that in the Ruelle-Takens model of the transition to turbulence, the appearance of a strange attractor in the phase space is related to a clearly defined onset of turbulent motion in the fluid.

15.2.3 Infinite sequence of period doubling bifurcations. The passage to chaos has also been hypothesized to occur via an infinite sequence of supercritical period doubling (subharmonic) bifurcations (see Section 14.3.2), a route that was seen in the experiments of Maurer and Libchaber (1979). This mechanism was first studied analytically by Feigenbaum (1978) in the context of one-dimensional maps

$$X_{n+1} = f(X_n) \quad , \tag{15.1}$$

of the unit interval to itself. A specific example that illustrates the relevant properties is the map (Kadanoff, 1983)

$$X_{n+1} = 4\eta X_n(1-X_n) \quad , \quad \text{where } 0 \leq \eta \leq 1 \quad . \tag{15.2}$$

The discussion that follows can be traced on Fig. 15.4. For $\eta < 0.25 = \eta_c$, the solution $X = 0$ is stable and is the only one-cycle of the mapping; by a one-cycle we mean a periodic solution of period one. At $\eta_c = 0.25$, the zero solution loses stability to a new one-cycle $X = 1 - (1/4\eta)$. At $\eta_1 = 0.75$, this one-cycle loses stability to a stable two-cycle; that is, the period of the orbit is now two, and the value of X alternates between the upper and lower branches. As the value of η is increased further, the two-cycle loses stability to a stable four-cycle at $\eta_2 \simeq 0.862$. This four-cycle becomes unstable at $\eta_3 \simeq 0.885$ and a stable eight-cycle appears. This sequence of 2^{n-1}-cycles losing stability to 2^n-cycles at η_n via period doubling bifurcations continues as η increases toward a critical value $\eta_\infty \simeq 0.892$ at which a cycle of infinite length appears. We note that most of the period doubling bifurcations occur in the very limited range of η given approximately by $0.885 < \eta < 0.892$.

The behavior of the system for $\eta_\infty < \eta \leq 1$ is also interesting. At $\eta = 1$, the sequence of X_n's fills the interval [0,1], and the system exhibits chaotic behavior with sensitive dependence on initial conditions. As the value of η decreases from one, the interval of permitted X-values narrows to approximately $[4\eta(1-\eta),\eta]$, but the behavior remains qualitatively the same as that at $\eta = 1$ (Kadanoff, 1983). As η decreases further in magnitude, however, the interval of permitted X-values splits into two bands, then four, then eight, then sixteen, and so forth. At a value of η at which there are 2^n bands, the value of X returns to a given band after 2^n iterations, but the exact point at which it returns within each band is chaotic in the same sense that the map is chaotic at $\eta = 1$. This process of band splitting, called noisy periodicity or semi-periodicity by Lorenz (1980), is seen in the stippled region on the right side of Fig. 15.4. As η approaches η_∞, the bands merge with the above cycle of infinite length.

In the inverval $\eta_\infty < \eta < 1$, the regimes of noisy periodicity are interspersed with regimes containing either n-cycles or solutions having long orderly periods

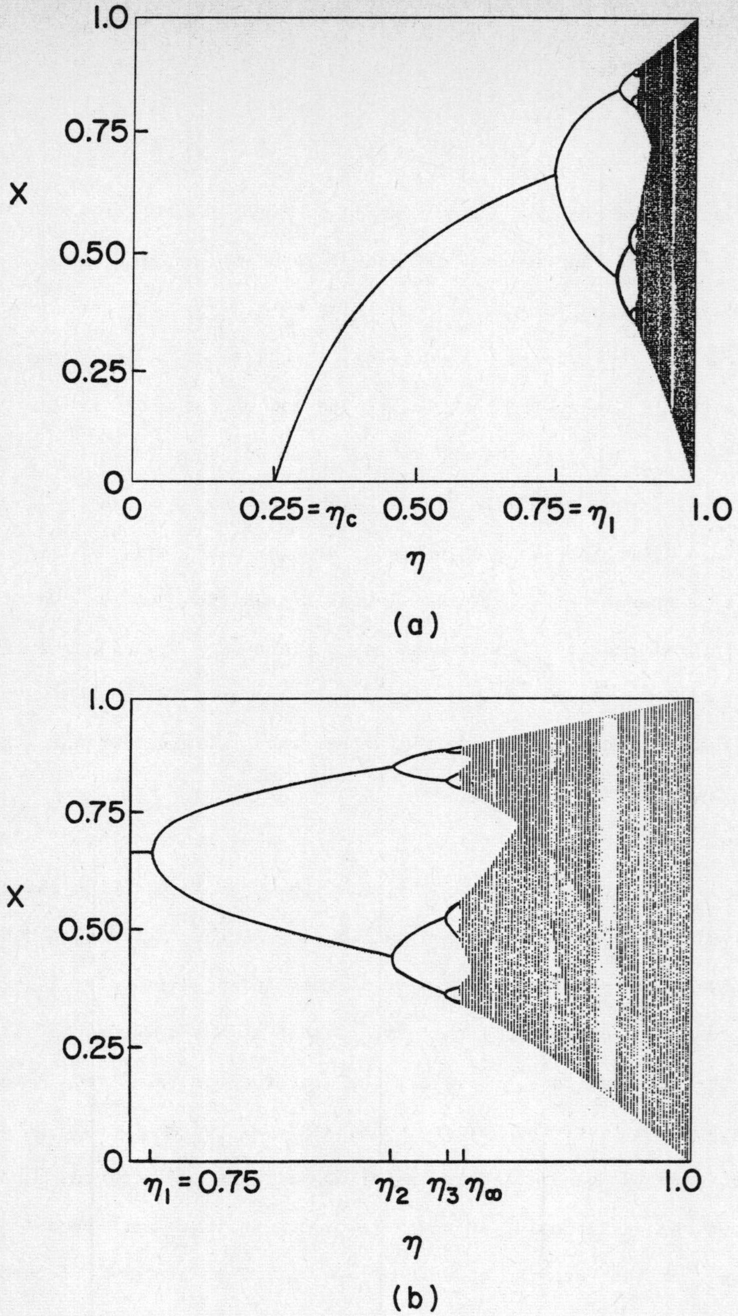

Fig. 15.4 Stably recurring values X of X_n as functions of η for the mapping (15.2). In (a) the solutions for values of η in the entire range $0 \leq \eta \leq 1$ are shown, and in (b) the solutions in the range $0.74 \leq \eta \leq 1$ are shown. In $0 \leq \eta \leq \eta_c$, the iterates approach zero; in $\eta_c \leq \eta \leq \eta_1$, the iterates approach the one-cycle $X=1-(1/4\eta)$; in $\eta_{n-1} \leq \eta \leq \eta_n \leq \eta_\infty$, the iterates approach an n-cycle. For most values of η in $\eta_\infty < \eta \leq 1$, the iterates approach a more complicated invariant set (after Kadanoff, 1983).

resembling three-cycles that are occasionally disturbed by bursts of disorder (May, 1976). This latter type of behavior is called <u>intermittency</u> or <u>intermittent chaos</u>. Interestingly, the general process including period doubling, band splitting, and intermittency seems to be independent of the form of the function $f(X_n)$, as long as $f(X_n)$ satisfies certain conditions--for instance, that it attains a single maximum on the interval [0,1] (Collet and Eckmann, 1980).

The mappings $X_{n+1} = f(X_n)$ possess several other properties of note. Feigenbaum (1978) found that

$$\lim_{n\to\infty} \frac{\eta_n - \eta_{n-1}}{\eta_{n+1} - \eta_n} = \delta \simeq 4.669 \quad , \tag{15.3}$$

where the constant δ is the same for all suitable mappings. In addition, the limiting distance between two new "twins" is proportional to the distance between their parent and its "twin". The limiting proportionality constant is universally $1/\alpha$, where $\alpha \simeq 2.503$, when the two neighboring values of X_n closest to the maximum in the function $f(X_n)$ are chosen (Kadanoff, 1983). The two numbers α and δ are universal constants for any mapping $X_{n+1} = f(X_n)$, provided that $f(X_n)$ satisfies the appropriate conditions.

A motivation for studying these one-dimensional maps is the hope that the processes underlying the transition to turbulent behavior in a fluid system may be mathematically related to the above scenario in which stable n-cycles of some function develop into chaotic solutions. Not only has this mechanism been observed experimentally, but both the three-variable Lorenz (1963) system and a five-coefficient model by Boldrighini and Franceschini (1979) exhibit such period doubling sequences leading to chaos, and the constants δ and α are known to have the same values in these finite models (Franceschini and Tebaldi, 1979; Franceschini, 1980).

<u>15.2.4 The pathological wrinkling of a torus</u>. This pathway to chaos, proposed by Ostlund et al. (1983), is similar to the Ruelle-Takens hypothesis, but the culminating transition to chaos is accomplished through the "wrinkling" of the surface of a stable two-torus. In this route, a stable stationary solution loses stability via a Hopf bifurcation to a stable limit cycle that subsequently bifurcates

to a solution on a torus. As this torus grows, it alternately contains a sequence of quasi-periodic and periodic solutions. In Section 14.3.3 we noted that a periodic solution on a torus is expected if the ratio of the periods is rational; otherwise, a quasi-periodic solution would appear. However, that ratio is defined only in special cases; more generally, a number called the rotation number plays the role of the above ratio of periods.

The <u>rotation number</u> is the magnitude of the average angular velocity under the return map of a point on the Poincaré section. To make the notion of rotation number more precise, we consider the motion on the two-torus displayed in Fig. 15.5a. A trajectory beginning at the point ξ on the circle C of circumference ℓ returns to the point $\phi(\xi)$ and so we obtain a Poincaré map ϕ: C $\to$ C. We introduce coordinates in C by choosing arbitrarily an origin ξ_o and assigning to a point ξ the arc length $s(\xi)$ (in a fixed direction) from ξ_o. In terms of the coordinate $s(\xi)$, we may represent ϕ by means of a smooth function Φ as follows (see Fig. 15.5b):

$$s\big(\phi(\xi)\big) = \Phi\big(s(\xi)\big) \quad . \tag{15.4}$$

From Fig. 15.5b we see that $\Phi\big(s(\xi)\big) - s(\xi)$ measures how far along C the map ϕ carries the point ξ. Iterating ϕ n times, we see that the point ξ moves a total distance

$$\Phi(s) - s + \Phi\big(\Phi(s)\big) - \Phi(s) + \cdots + \Phi^n(s) - \Phi^{n-1}(s) = \Phi^n(s) - s \quad , \tag{15.5}$$

where $s = s(\xi)$, $\Phi\big(\Phi(s)\big) = \Phi^2(s)$, $\Phi\big(\Phi(\Phi(s))\big) = \Phi^3(s)$, and $\Phi^n(s)$ follows accordingly. The average distance a point ξ moves per iteration of ϕ is given by $\big[\Phi^n(s) - s\big]/n$. A remarkable theorem of Denjoy (Nitecki, 1971) ensures that for almost every point ξ, the limit

$$\rho_\phi(\xi) = \frac{1}{\ell} \lim_{n\to\infty} \left[\frac{\Phi^n(s)-s}{n}\right] = \frac{1}{\ell} \lim_{n\to\infty} \left[\frac{\Phi^n(s)}{n}\right] \quad , \tag{15.6}$$

exists and is independent of ξ. We define the <u>rotation number</u> ρ_ϕ to be the common value of the limits of $\rho_\phi(\xi)$. Moreover, the theorem states that the Poincaré map ϕ has a q-cycle if and only if $\rho_\phi = m/q < 1$ for integers m and q and that ϕ is topologically equivalent to rigid rotation through an angle $2\pi\rho_\phi$ when ρ_ϕ is irrational. In Fig. 15.5a, m = 1 and q = 2 so that $\rho_\phi = 1/2$ and the motion has period 2T. For

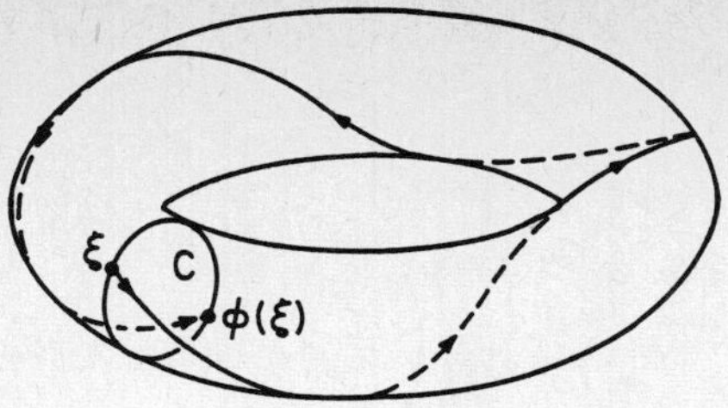

(a)

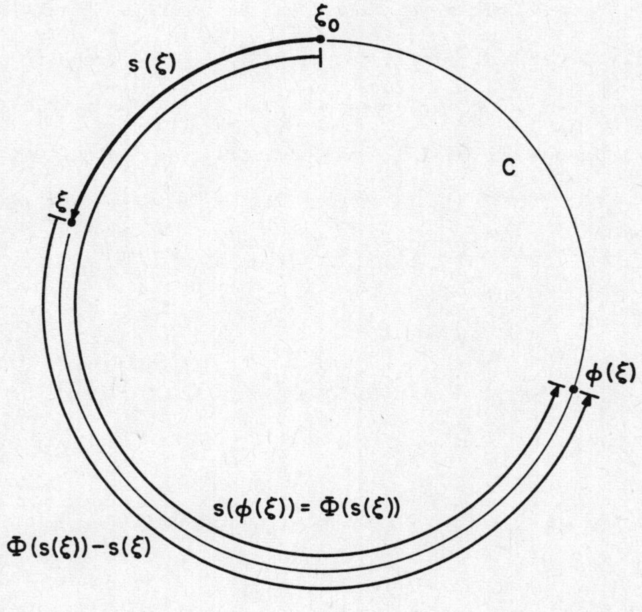

(b)

Fig. 15.5 Functions used to define the rotation number of a flow on a two-torus. The Poincaré map ϕ of a point ξ on the circle C given by a cross section through the torus is shown in (a). The arc length $s(\xi)$, the function $\Phi\big(s(\xi)\big)$, and the first iterate in the limit given in (15.6) are shown on C in (b). The 2T-periodic solution in (a), for which $\rho_\phi=1/2$, is also shown in Fig. 14.8e.

rational values m/q of the rotation number, a further important theorem of Peixoto (Palis and de Melo, 1982) refines the theorem of Denjoy to state that generically, ϕ has an even number of q-cycles, half of them attracting and the other half repelling. These q-cycles determine finitely many robust periodic solutions on the two-torus, half of them stable and the other half unstable, as shown schematically in

Fig. 14.10. Also, when the rotation number is irrational, the motion on the torus is essentially the same as the simple quasi-periodic motion discussed in Section 14.3.

It is in the context of such rotation numbers and Poincaré sections that Ostlund et al. (1983) described the development of chaos. As the forcing is increased in magnitude, the rotation number abruptly becomes sensitive to initial conditions. They observed that the points of the Poincaré map begin to clump, or bunch together in patterns resembling a Cantor set (Fig. 15.6). This clumping of points is illustrated schematically in Fig. 15.7a. Theoretically, this clumping has often been interpreted to mean that "wrinkles" or "curls" develop on the surface of the torus between the clumps, as shown in Fig. 15.7b. Eventually, a wrinkle occurs between every pair of points. One such wrinkle is shown at three levels of magnification in Fig. 15.7c, in which it is seen that even the wrinkles have folds. Thus, what was once a simple surface--a two torus--has become a complicated sheeted structure. In

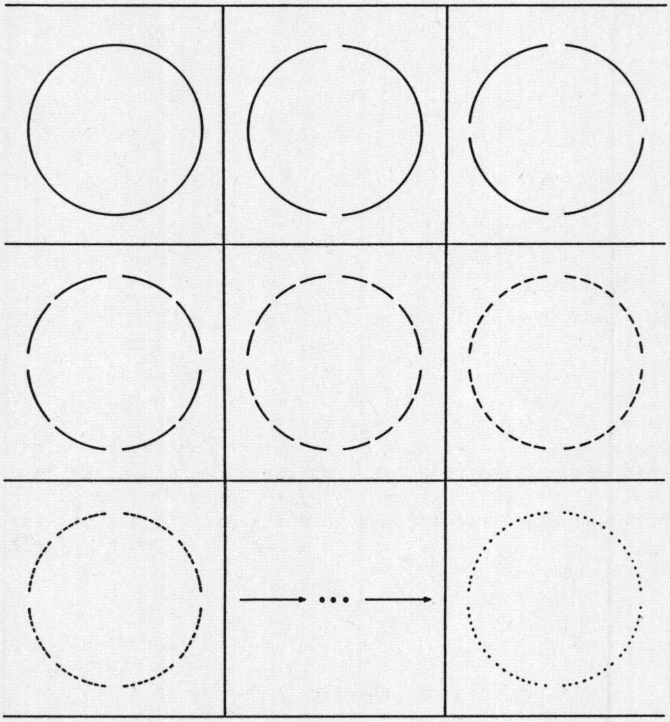

Fig. 15.6 Construction of a Cantor set on a circle. In the first step, one-ninth of each semicircle is deleted. At each subsequent step, the middle ninth of each remaining curve is removed. The process is repeated an infinite number of times. The classic Cantor set is formed by the infinite process of deleting the middle third of an original line segment of unit length.

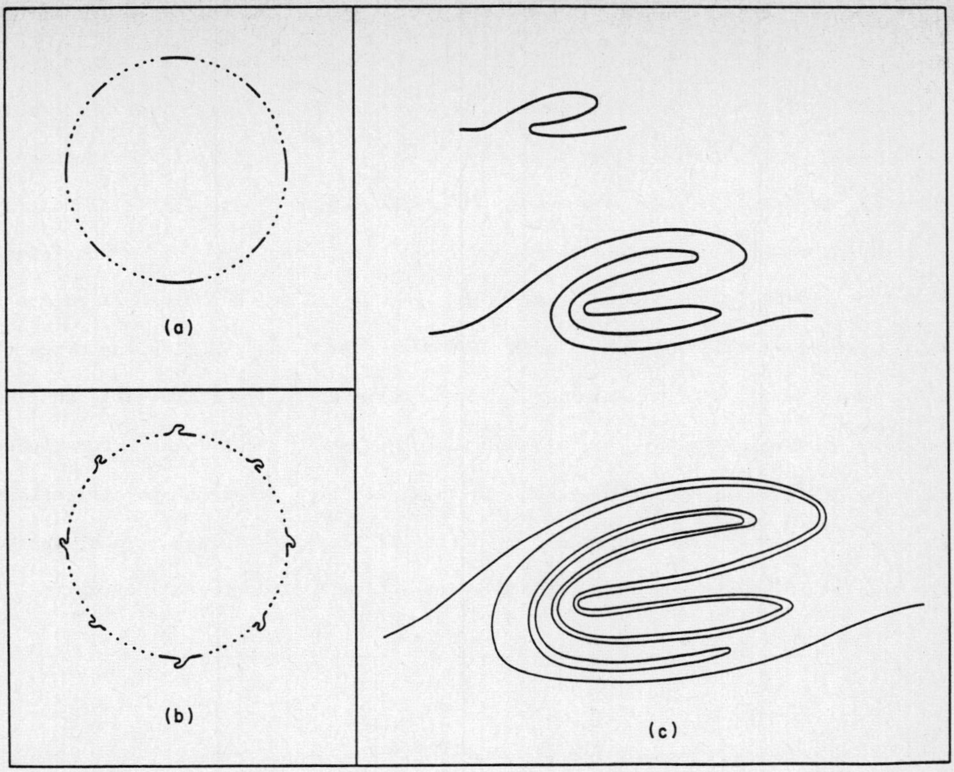

Fig. 15.7 Conjectured Poincaré sections through a two-torus at several steps in the route to chaos via the Ostlund et al. route: Points on the Poincaré map begin to "clump" (a), "wrinkles" or "curls" form between the clumps (b), and a particular wrinkle is shown at three levels of magnification (c).

fact, this wrinkled torus is not topologically equivalent to a torus, implying that the complicated flow developing from the two-torus provides an example of a strange attractor. Consequently, in this hypothesized route, a small number of Hopf bifurcations leads to stable two-frequency motion on a two-torus; the surface of the torus then wrinkles owing to another bifurcation or series of bifurcations, eventually producing chaotic solutions.

15.2.5 Subcritical bifurcation. The passage to chaos has also been hypothesized to occur via an abrupt transition from a stationary solution to a chaotic one without any intervening periodicity (Joseph, 1976). Mathematically, this transition is seen as a subcritical Hopf bifurcation that results in a direct transition to chaos without any additional bifurcations. Above the critical Hopf bifurcation value, phase space trajectories become asymptotically aperiodic and approach a strange attractor. This type of sudden transition to chaos has been seen in the laboratory in the experiments of Ahlers and Behringer (see Section 15.1), and also has been detected numerically in the three-variable Lorenz (1963) model. Nese et al. (1987) found that such behavior also seems likely to account for the development of chaos in the seven-variable model of Chang and Shirer (1984), which was introduced in Section 9.2 and which is discussed further in Section 16.3.1.

From the above discussion, we conclude that there are two prominent classes--gradual and abrupt--of hypothesized routes to chaos (Shirer and Wells, 1985). As we reviewed in Section 15.1, experimental evidence for all the routes except the one of Landau exists. In addition, numerical evidence for several of these routes has been reported in many studies of low-order models of Rayleigh-Bénard convection (e.g. McLaughlin and Martin, 1975; Curry, 1978; Sparrow, 1982; Nese et al., 1987). However, not all the numerical results are universally accepted as modeling actual turbulent flow, as we discuss in the following section.

15.3 Some Comments on Modeling Issues

There is both experimental and mathematical evidence suggesting that turbulence develops in a fluid after only a small number of transitions have occurred within a restricted range of parameter values. In most cases, orderly flow seems to be expected when two irrationally related periods characterize the flow, but disorderly flow is expected when there are three periods. Unfortunately, several apparently independent routes to chaos have been proposed, and so identification of a unifying characteristic has been unresolved. Recently, Shirer and Wells (1985) have proposed a means for classifying the routes by identifying them with paths in a parameter space whose coordinates can be determined by unfolding about a certain singularity; these ideas extend those introduced in Chapter 8, and they are the topic of the first part of this section. Complicating the classification problem is the fact that not all chaotic solutions to low-order models are physically acceptable, as we explain in the remainder of the chapter.

15.3.1 Possible classification of the routes.

We noted in Chapter 8 that in many cases, transitions between stationary solutions occur in a small number of qualitatively different ways, and that we can classify these transitions via identification of the controlling parameters of the problem. We accomplish this classification by locating a bifurcation point, or singularity, at which the polynomial equation governing the stationary solutions has the high-order form $x^n = 0$. We unfold about the singularity by adding parameters multiplying the lower-order terms of the polynomial function x^n, and in so doing, we separate multiple solutions into individual ones. For example, a triple zero root of $x^3 = 0$ becomes three separate roots once we add the two parameters β_1 and β_2 to create the polynomial equation $x^3 + \beta_2 x + \beta_1 = 0$. Knowing the values of β_1 and β_2, we can determine whether one or three real roots exist as well as whether smooth or sudden transitions are expected as the values of β_1 and β_2 are varied.

In addition, we saw in Chapter 9 that the existence of double bifurcation points signals the appearance of secondary branches once a parameter such as the aspect ratio a is varied from a singular value a_{mj} at which two primary bifurcation points coalesce. If $a < a_{mj}$ for $m > j$ and $Ra_m < Ra_j$, then we find that a secondary branch joining the two primary branches P_m and P_j appears, and stability is transferred from a stationary solution having horizontal wavenumber m to one having horizontal wavenumber j. However, if $a > a_{mj}$ and $Ra_j < Ra_m$, then no secondary transitions occur and P_m remains stable.

The above observations suggest that a similar classification of the routes to chaos might be possible, at least near an appropriate controlling singularity on a stationary solution. The existence of such a singular point follows from Ruelle and Takens (1971), who showed how three successive Hopf bifurcations can give rise to stable attracting three-tori. This result can be interpreted to mean that an attracting three-torus grows gradually from a triple Hopf bifurcation point on a stationary solution. With three independent periods available to the flow, Newhouse et al. (1978) showed that there is a finite probability that on this three-torus there is a chaotic attractor.

Shirer and Wells (1985) hypothesized that the existence of such a triple Hopf bifurcation point is the key to classifying many of the routes to chaos. Because perturbations exist in any physical system, the occurrence of a triple Hopf bifurcation point is impossible to observe. As a consequence, the development of a three-torus would be expected to occur via a sequence of three consecutive, but nearly simultaneous bifurcations of temporal flows near the Hopf bifurcation points R_{H1}, R_{H2}, R_{H3} on the stationary solution. In analogy to the case of stationary solutions discussed in Chapter 9, the hierarchy of transitions between the stationary and temporal solutions would vary depending on the ordering of these bifurcation points. At the very least, one route would be expected if $R_{H1} < R_{H2} < R_{H3}$, another if $R_{H2} < R_{H1} < R_{H3}$, and a third if $R_{H3} < R_{H1} < R_{H2}$.

Thus, at least three parameters α_1, α_2, α_3 would be needed to classify all exchanges of stability near a triple Hopf bifurcation point. The values of these parameters determine which of the three bifurcation points R_{H1}, R_{H2}, R_{H3} occur first and the subsequent variations in the values of α_1, α_2, α_3 determine which route to chaos would be seen. For the case $\alpha_3 = 0$, three such routes are shown schematically in Fig. 15.8, which is taken from Shirer and Wells (1985). Here 0 represents the triple Hopf bifurcation point, and route number three corresponds to the gradual growth of a chaotic attractor on the three-torus that emanates from the stationary solution. If $\alpha_2 < 0$ and the value of α_1 is increased past zero, then the Hopf bifurcation linked to α_1 occurs first and the first periodic solution develops at $R = R_{H1}$. Via a secondary bifurcation, this solution loses stability to a flow on a two-torus; if that flow is periodic, then, for example, a sequence of period doubling bifurcations occurs until chaos develops once the curve C_∞ is crossed (path number one in Fig. 15.8). In contrast, if $\alpha_1 < 0$ and the value of α_2 is increased past zero then the second periodic solution develops at $R = R_{H2}$. This solution would be expected to exchange stability with a different set of two-tori than occurred in path number one, because, as we found in Chapter 9, secondary branching is an asymmetric process. As the values of α_1 and α_2 vary along path number two in Fig. 15.8, the attracting torus might begin to wrinkle, for example, indicating that chaos would develop via the Ostlund et al. (1983) route.

Thus, we see that extensions of the typical behavior of stationary solutions to temporal flows provides a basis for possible classification of the routes to chaos. However, this classification depends on the presence of a very special situation--occurrence of a triple Hopf bifurcation point on a stationary solution. Unfortunately, no hydrodynamic examples of such a singularity are known to us,

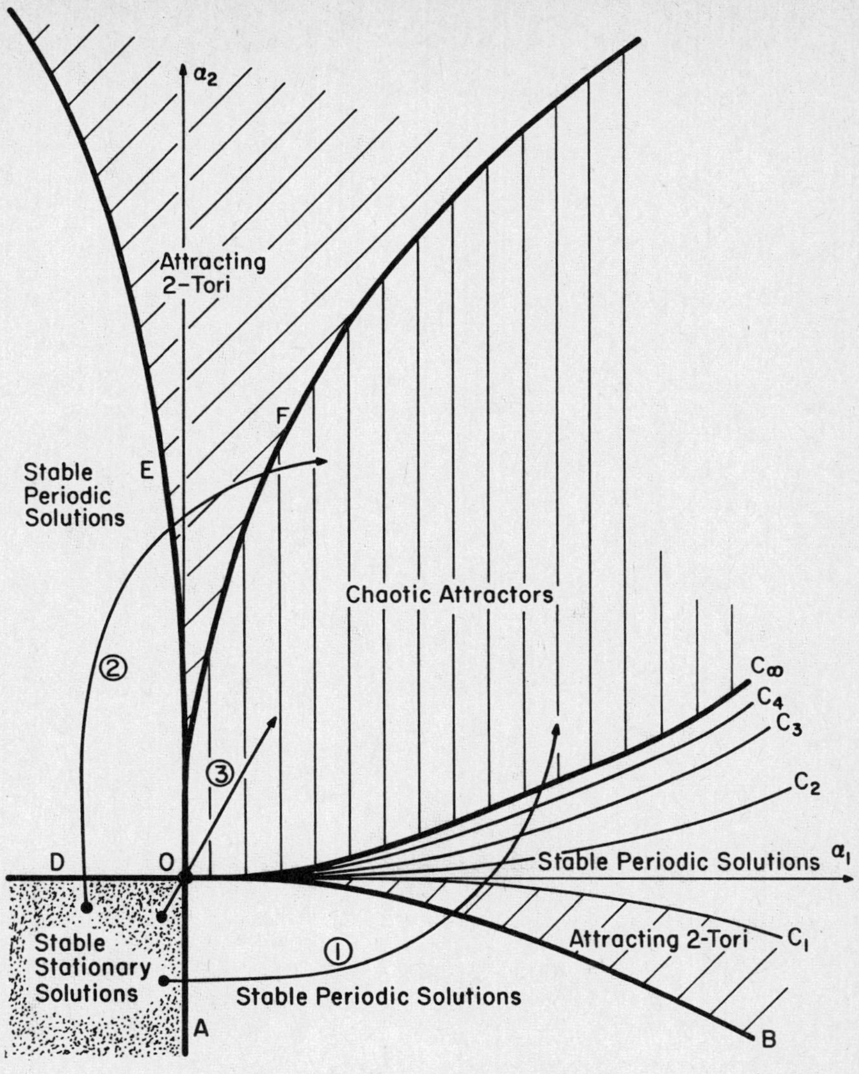

Fig. 15.8 A schematic representation of three possible routes to chaos that might exist near a triple Hopf bifurcation at 0. In Route 1, a transition of the Feigenbaum type is shown via the transitions A, B, C_1, C_2,...,C_∞, where A is a Hopf bifurcation at α_1=0 to a stable periodic solution, B is an associated Hopf bifurcation (related to α_2=0) to an attracting torus containing phase-locked periodic solutions, C_1, C_2,... is a sequence of period doubling bifurcations, and C_∞ is the culminating transition to a chaotic attractor. In Route 2, a transition of the Ostlund et al. type is shown via the transitions D, E, F, where D is a Hopf bifurcation (related to α_2=0) to a stable periodic solution, E is an associated Hopf bifurcation (related to α_1=0) to an attracting torus containing unstable quasi-periodic solutions, and F is the culminating torus-wrinkling transition to a chaotic attractor. In Route 3, a transition of Ruelle-Takens type is shown via the transition at 0 directly from a stable stationary solution to a chaotic attractor (after Shirer and Wells, 1985).

although they are easy to develop in an ad hoc manner. At this point, it remains an open question whether this classification strategy is a fruitful one.

Nevertheless, chaotic solutions to low-order hydrodynamic models are quite commonly produced numerically, and one of the first was discovered by Lorenz (1963) in the three-coefficient model that we discuss throughout this monograph. We show some examples of this chaotic attractor in the next subsection; in the following subsection, we discuss the apparent dependence of the attractor on the truncation level of the model.

15.3.2 The Lorenz attractor and predictability. We saw in Chapter 2 that the Lorenz system (2.80)-(2.82) very faithfully and efficaciously models the first developing convective state. Although we know from Chapter 9 that missing representations of the Jacobian $J(\psi^*,\tilde{\nabla}^2\psi^*)$ become active for sufficiently large values of the forcing, we are nevertheless tempted to investigate the temporal behavior of the solutions in the entire range of $r > r_c$. Indeed, many investigators have sought to determine what types of flow are possible, and the most important results are summarized in a monograph by Sparrow (1982).

Surprisingly, the temporal behavior of solutions to this small system of ordinary differential equations is extremely complicated for some values of the forcing in the range $r_H \simeq 24.7 < r < \simeq 215$ (when $P = 10$ and $a^2 = 1/2$). As first discovered by Lorenz (1963), the details of the evolving solutions are very sensitive to initial conditions, and this discovery has implications for predictability. We briefly summarize some of these implications here.

Lorenz examined solutions for $r = 28 > r_H$, $P = 10$, and $a^2 = 1/2$. An example of the oscillations he found is given in Fig. 15.9. From the discussion in Sections 4.2.2 and 11.1, we expect a temporally periodic solution to appear at $r = r_H$, and indeed we see regular oscillations in the initial portion of the time series. As expected, these oscillations occur about one of the stationary solutions. However, these oscillations amplify until they become quite irregular, involving some circuits around one stationary solution, and then some circuits around the other. No long-term periodicity is apparent and indeed none exists. The attractor is chaotic, or using the terminology of Ruelle and Takens (1971), "strange"; for the Lorenz model the attractor is called, quite appropriately, the Lorenz attractor.

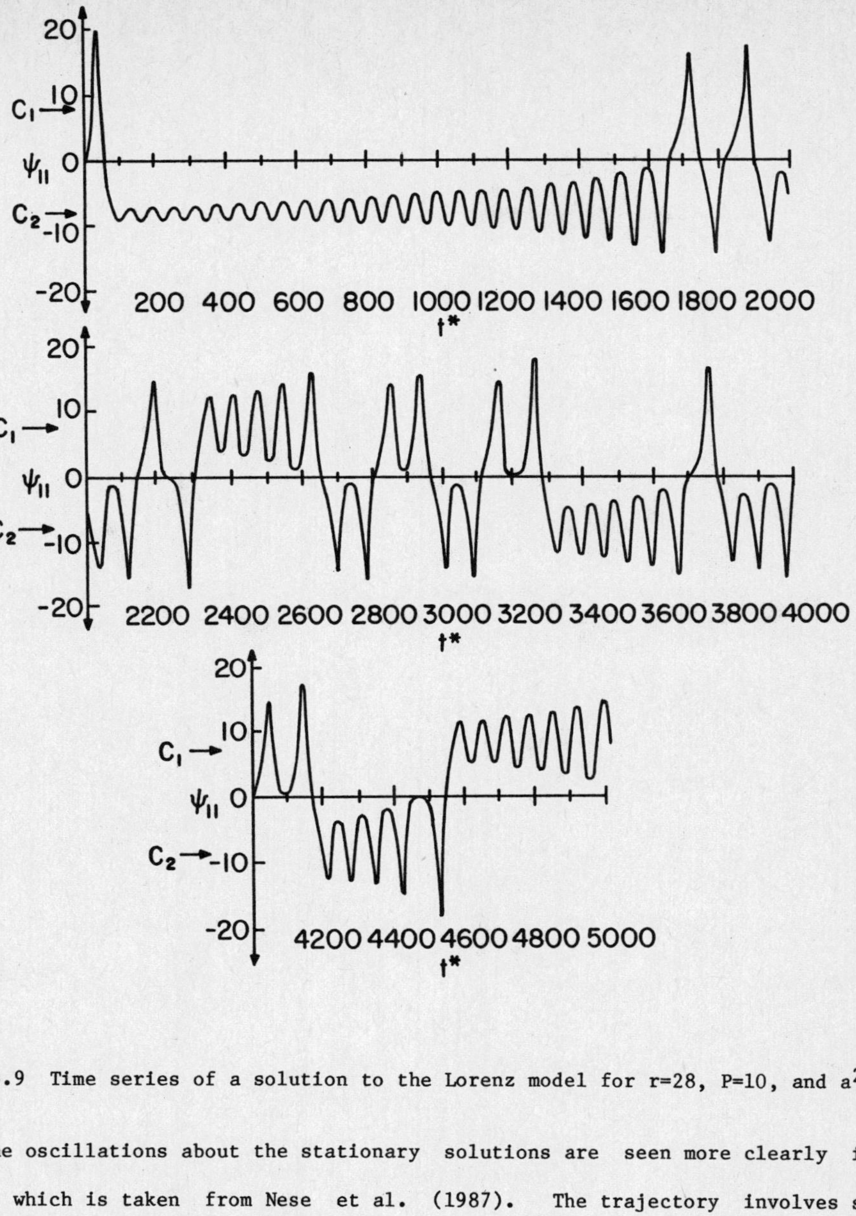

Fig. 15.9 Time series of a solution to the Lorenz model for r=28, P=10, and a^2=1/2.

The oscillations about the stationary solutions are seen more clearly in Fig. 15.10, which is taken from Nese et al. (1987). The trajectory involves spirals around one stationary solution, denoted by C_1, followed by circuits about C_2. The trajectory is recurrent, that is it returns near to itself, but does not approach an individual orbit. Also, the intersection of a line with the attractor resembles a Cantor set. A rather surprising feature of the trajectory is that it occasionally appears near the origin, in agreement with the type of behavior introduced during the discussion of stable and unstable manifolds in Section 4.3.

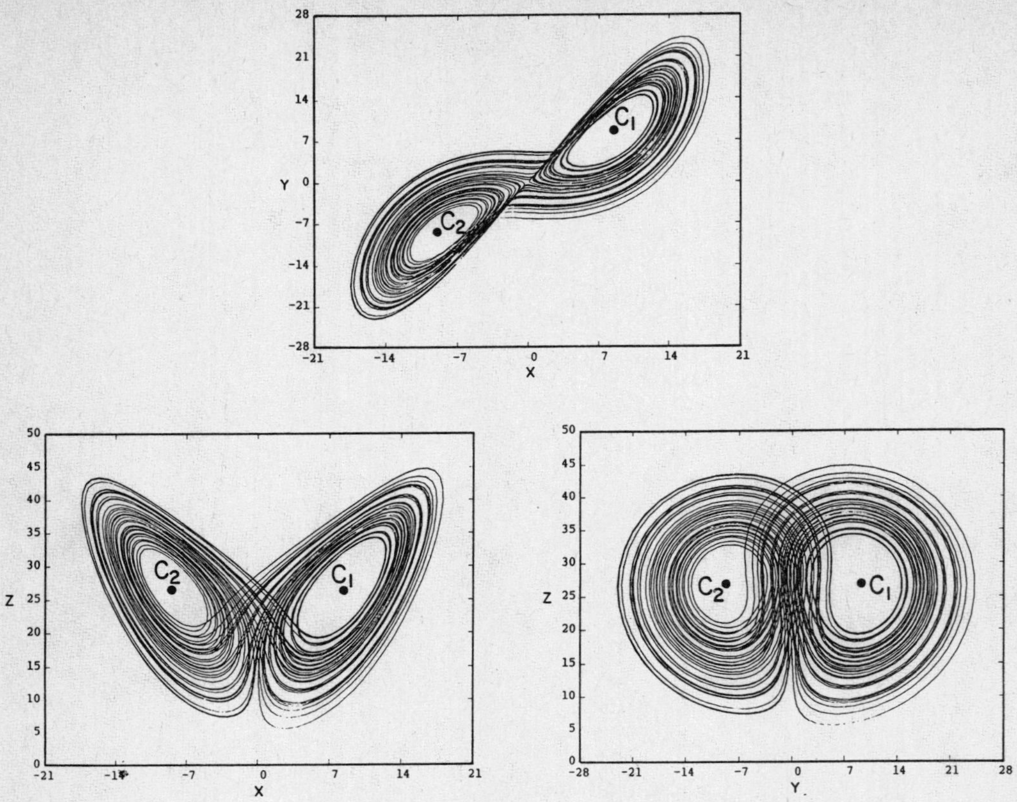

Fig. 15.10 Projections of a solution trajectory of the Lorenz model onto the XY-plane, XZ-plane, and the YZ-plane, for r=28, P=10, and $a^2=1/2$ (from Nese et al., 1987).

The apparent mix of short-scale, regular oscillations with ones having no long-term periodicity has some implications for the sensitivity of the solutions to initial conditions and so for the predictability of the flow. Dutton and Wells (1984) illustrated the effects of initial errors by examining the variations in the size and shape of triangles connecting points on three trajectories that are initially close to one another. In both cases illustrated in Fig. 15.11, projections of the trajectories onto the XY-plane are shown. Thus, the origin at the center of the stippled region in the figure corresponds to the Z-axis in the phase space. As the triplets of trajectories wind around C_1, the associated triangles initially stretch but remarkably shrink as they approach the origin. This stretching implies that the growth of errors primarily involves phase or timing errors rather than amplitude errors. In the circuit around C_2 shown in Fig. 15.11a, all three trajectories leave the origin together, again stretching for a time, and then shrinking again. In Fig. 15.11b, the triangles grow significantly because one of the three trajectories circles C_1 while the others circle C_2; consequently, large errors not due to phasing are possible. We see that once a trajectory begins a circuit around a stationary solution, it proceeds along a rather predictable path. The change in circuit occurs when a trajectory is near the origin. Thus, there are certain decision points along the path. For trajectories near these decision points, there is a high degree of sensitivity to initial conditions. However, once the directions have been determined at a decision point, the further evolution of the trajectories is easy to predict for one circuit around C_1 or C_2. Thus, examination of predictability problems involves determining the number of decision points that are encountered by the trajectories and ascertaining how accurately the location of a trajectory must be known before the correct decision can be predicted.

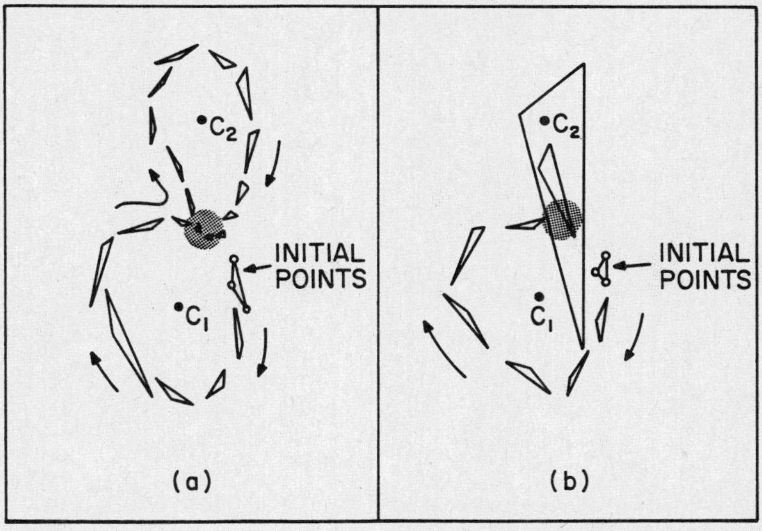

Fig. 15.11 Projections onto the XY-plane of triangles formed by connecting points on three trajectories beginning at slightly different triplets of initial points. In (a) the triangles circle C_1, approach the origin in the stippled region, and then circle C_2 in a rather predictable manner. In (b), the triangles circle C_1 in an orderly way but then enlarge as two trajectories circle C_2 while the other one circles C_1, leading to a loss of predictability (after Dutton and Wells, 1984).

15.3.3 The Lorenz attractor and modal truncations. The question that must be addressed when interpreting results from a low-order model such as the Lorenz system is whether the stationary and temporal solutions are a consequence of the chosen truncation or of the physical properties of the fluid. A properly designed hierarchy of models should produce solutions that form a sequence converging to the actual one; the higher the resolution in a model, the more accurate the solution should be. In the context of Modeling Principle Seven, a solution to a low-order model gains acceptability as it is identified in increasingly larger models. For example, the stationary solutions to the three-component Lorenz model form the primary branches in the goal form of the seven-component Saltzman (1962) and Chang and Shirer (1984) models; thus we conclude that the stationary solutions to the Lorenz model become more plausible representatives of a physical system.

We recall that Lorenz (1963) found that there is a sudden transition from a stationary solution to a strange attractor as the value of a Hopf bifurcation point is exceeded. However, Curry (1978) found different results for the same values of r and P in his fourteen-component system. The flow exhibits a normal bifurcation from a stationary convective solution to a periodic solution and this branching is followed by a subharmonic bifurcation to a period doubled solution. The flow then bifurcates to one on an attracting torus that finally is replaced by a strange attractor. In addition, Tommre et al. (1977) and Marcus (1978) found that if the vertical structure is finely resolved by the spectral truncation, but only one mode is retained in the horizontal, then no bifurcations occur and a stationary solution is seen regardless of the value of the Rayleigh number. This conclusion led Marcus to investigate the origin of the Lorenz attractor.

Following the modeling principles set forth in Chapter 1, we would require that the Lorenz attractor be seen in a larger model in order to accept its temporal behavior as possibly being physically relevant, and Marcus (1981) studied this question. He examined the convective solutions in a spherical Rayleigh-Bénard problem and determined which qualitative features of the solutions might represent actual physical processes and which are due solely to the effects of truncation. He studied a hierarchy of models, the largest having twelve wavenumbers in the horizontal and sixteen in the vertical. Notably, he was able to compute stable stationary solutions to both a model of Lorenz type and to the largest model for moderate supercritical values of the Rayleigh number Ra. However, after Marcus compared the temporal behavior of the solutions to the models in the hierarchy, he concluded that the chaotic behavior seen in the Lorenz model is not accurate for large values of the Rayleigh number, and he linked this inaccuracy to the insufficient number of degrees of freedom in the Lorenz model.

We know from Chapter 9 that there is a transition between stationary solutions as the value of the Rayleigh number increases in low-order systems that include amplitude coefficients for more than one horizontal wavelength. However, the solutions eventually become aperiodic for large enough forcing rates. Marcus found that for a large value of the Rayleigh number, his least severe truncation produces a stable stationary solution. Furthermore, when both the value of Ra and the degree of the vertical resolution are held fixed, and the number of horizontal modes is decreased, there is a transition from a stationary to a temporally periodic solution. As the number of horizontal modes is decreased still further, the solution becomes aperiodic. Thus, we conclude that aperiodicity seen in low-order models may be an artifact linked to the severity of the truncation.

These results can be combined with those of Lorenz (1963) and Chang and Shirer (1984) to develop a probable branching diagram for the Marcus models. To see how the aperiodic solutions could be replaced by either periodic or stationary ones as more horizontal modes are added to the truncation, we consider in Fig. 15.12 three schematic branching diagrams. In a smaller model (Fig. 15.12a), there is a Hopf bifurcation at some Rayleigh number Ra_{H1}, and at a value $Ra_1 > Ra_{H1}$, aperiodic motion is observed. If the results of Marcus have been interpreted correctly, then we should be able to extend the smaller system to a larger one and for the same value Ra_1 find a stationary solution. This behavior is shown in Fig. 15.12b, in which the secondary bifurcation point at which the stationary connecting branch appears occurs at a smaller value of Ra than Ra_{H1}. Thus, an exchange of stability to a different stationary solution occurs rather than an exchange to a chaotic solution. It is significant that the Hopf bifurcation point Ra_{H1} remains on the primary branch, and so the aperiodic motion is a solution to the system; this solution is no longer an attractor, however, because the new characteristic exponent associated with the new secondary bifurcation point has changed sign.

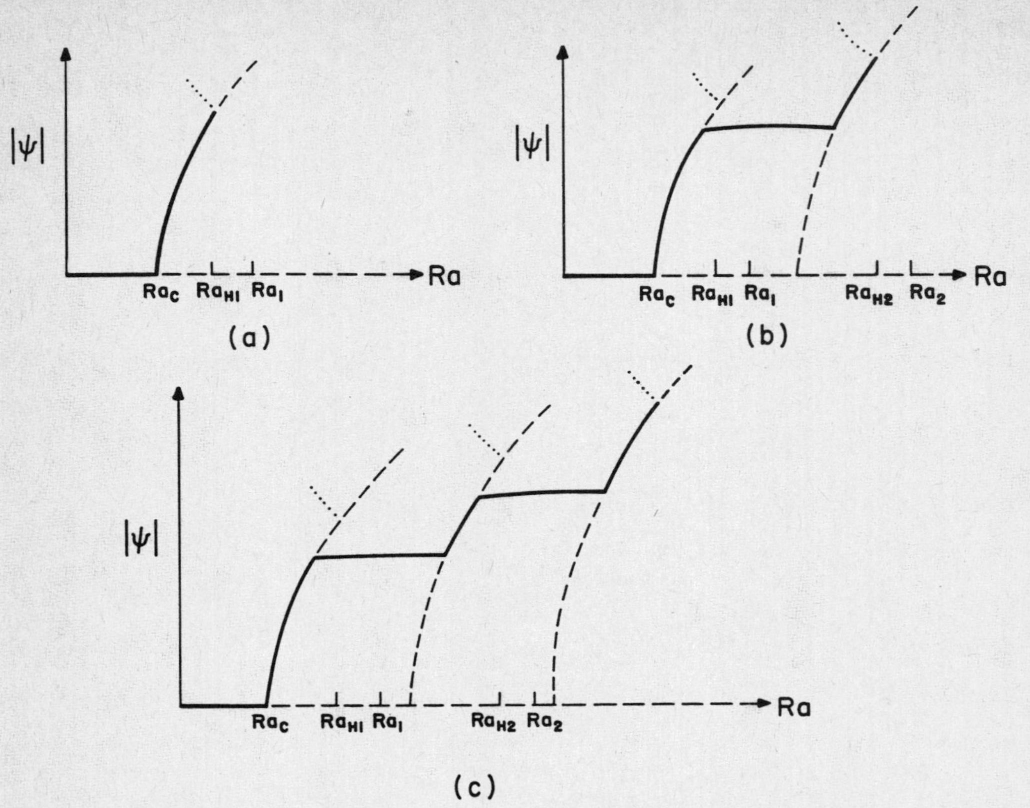

Fig. 15.12 Three schematic branching diagrams showing how changes in the branching hierarchy can cause chaotic attractors to disappear. The solid lines indicate stable stationary solutions and the dashed lines indicate unstable ones. The dotted lines indicate subcritical Hopf bifurcations to unstable periodic solutions and the associated occurrences of chaotic attractors. The symbols Ra_{H1} and Ra_{H2} indicate the critical values of Ra at which Hopf bifurcations occur in the systems. The points Ra_1 and Ra_2 are used in the text. In (a) a Lorenz-type model having one primary branch is considered, in (b) a Chang and Shirer-type model having two primary branches is illustrated, and in (c) a larger model having three primary branches is given.

Finally, if the horizontal resolution in the second model is held fixed and the value of the Rayleigh number is increased to $Ra_2 > Ra_{H2}$, then aperiodic motion is again possible. A subcritical Hopf bifurcation of the type found previously on the first primary branch might be expected to occur from the second primary branch; however, in the second model the value of the Hopf bifurcation point is greater. If the second model is extended to a third larger one, then a transition to another secondary branch would be expected before the second Hopf bifurcation point is reached (Fig. 15.12c); as before, a stationary solution rather than a temporal solution is observed. Extending this technique indefinitely, we may be able to confirm analytically the numerical results of Marcus: For a very large value of the Rayleigh number, the model should possess a stable stationary solution if sufficient horizontal resolution is chosen in the truncation.

Thus, we encounter a major problem in the physical interpretation of chaotic solutions to low-order models. As discussed here, experimental evidence suggests that turbulent states develop after a small number of distinct transitions have occurred, implying that only a few modes control the process. Nevertheless, the chaotic solutions displayed by some low-order models are found to be artifacts of the truncation level. Consequently, we need methods for distinguishing between realistic and spurious chaotic attractors, so that we can judge whether or not our models are designed properly. If chaos is discovered to be spurious, then we would conclude that either crucial parameters or fundamental modes are absent from the problem. For example, it has been proposed that convective turbulence is a three-dimensional problem (e.g., Deardorff, 1964) and so any two-dimensional model should contain only stationary solutions. This observation suggests that the necessary additional modes would involve variations in the third spatial dimension, rather than additional wavelengths in either of the other two.

In recent years, some means for examining the characteristics of a particular solution have been proposed using various measures of the sizes of the attractors. As hypothesized by Shirer and Wells (1985), an eventual theory allowing for the separation of acceptable from unrealistic chaotic solutions may require the qualitative information provided by these measures. A discussion of two of them, the Lyapunov dimension and the correlation dimension, is presented in the following chapter.

CHAPTER 16

DIAGNOSING THE STRUCTURES OF ATTRACTORS

JON M. NESE

We have seen briefly in the previous chapter how tori and so-called "strange attractors" in phase space may provide the underlying mathematical representations of the processes involved in the creation of turbulence. Stationary and temporally periodic solutions, which we have covered in depth in Chapters 2 to 14, provide the simplest examples of <u>attractors</u>--the phase space limits of model trajectories--and their properties are relatively easy to describe analytically. However, with the need to consider more complicated temporal flows when modeling the transition to turbulence, it becomes essential to define quantitative measures for characterizing and categorizing the various types of attractors.

In this chapter we introduce the Lyapunov exponents (Oseledec, 1968), the Lyapunov dimension (Kaplan and Yorke, 1979), and the correlation dimension (Grassberger and Procaccia, 1983a,b). These quantities give information about the attractor structure, solution transitions, and predictability characteristics of nonlinear models. We investigate how these quantitative measures of attractor dynamics might be helpful in distinguishing different types of chaotic attractors, and thereby possibly distinguishing some of the different routes to chaos. Moreover, because the seventh modeling principle suggests that a model must have sufficient complexity to represent a phenomenon in adequate detail, these quantitative measures may help us evaluate the adequacy of a particular model. Specifically, we illustrate the utility of the Lyapunov and correlation dimensions in characterizing attractors in several low-order spectral models, including the Lorenz (1963) model, the seven-coefficient generalized Lorenz system of Chang and Shirer (1984), and a related eleven-coefficient model.

16.1 Notions of Dimension

Perhaps the most basic characterization of an attractor is its geometric dimension, which measures the amount of information needed to specify an arbitrary point on the attractor. The dimension is also a lower bound on the number of variables necessary for modeling the system dynamics (Farmer et al., 1983). Of course, the dimension of an attractor is no greater than the dimension of the phase space in which the attractor resides; that is, the attractor dimension is less than N, the number of coefficients in the spectral model.

Assigning a dimension to simple attractors is relatively easy. Using any reasonable definition, we find that a fixed point is zero-dimensional while a temporally periodic solution or limit cycle is one-dimensional. Determining a relevant dimension for a strange attractor, however, is not as straightforward, because its structure is often fractured and highly irregular. The Poincaré map (see Section 14.3) for a simple attractor such as a limit cycle fixes a single point or retraces a set of points at regular intervals. The Poincaré map for a typical strange attractor, however, shows an irregularly arranged, apparently random set of points resembling a Cantor set (see Fig. 15.6). Such a fractured, chaotic structure suggests that the dimension of a strange attractor may be best described by a non-integer.

A dimension relevant to our work is the fractal dimension d_F, which was originally defined by Kolmogorov (1958). If the attractor resides in a phase space of dimension N, and if $M(\varepsilon)$ is the minimum number of N-dimensional hypercubes of side ε needed to cover the attractor, then the fractal dimension or geometric dimension is defined as

$$d_F = \lim_{\varepsilon \to 0} \frac{\log[M(\varepsilon)]}{\log(1/\varepsilon)} \quad . \tag{16.1}$$

We prefix "cube", which is generally assumed to be a three-dimensional object, with "hyper" to emphasize that the volume takes on the dimension N of the phase space in question. Using (16.1), we see that if the attractor is a fixed point, then $M(\varepsilon) = 1$ and $d_F = 0$. If the attractor is the unit interval [0,1], then $M(\varepsilon) = 1/\varepsilon$ and $d_F = 1$. For these simple attractors, the fractal dimension gives the intuitive answer.

What about the fractal dimension of a more complicated set? The classic Cantor set described in the caption of Fig. 15.6 provides an interesting example. For this set, if $\varepsilon = 1/3$, then $M(\varepsilon) = 2$; if $\varepsilon = 1/9$, then $M(\varepsilon) = 4$; and if $\varepsilon = (1/3)^p$, then $M(\varepsilon) = 2^p$. Therefore, we have $d_F = \log(2^p)/\log(3^p) \simeq 0.631$, and thus the Cantor set has a non-integer fractal dimension. Although we have not arrived at this set as an attractor of a dynamical system, this result is nonetheless important to our work because Cantor set-like structure is common in the Poincaré maps of strange attractors.

The information dimension d_I is a generalization of the fractal dimension that takes into account the relative probability of a trajectory visiting each of the N-dimensional hypercubes. The information dimension is defined as

$$d_I = \lim_{\varepsilon \to 0} \frac{I(\varepsilon)}{\log(1/\varepsilon)} \quad , \tag{16.2}$$

in which

$$I(\varepsilon) = \sum_{i=1}^{M(\varepsilon)} P_i \log(1/P_i) \quad , \tag{16.3}$$

and P_i is the relative probability that the trajectory visits the ith hypercube. The sum of all the P_i's is one. Notice that if all hypercubes are equally probable, then $P_i = 1/M(\varepsilon)$ and $d_F = d_I$. In general, however, for unequal probabilities, $d_F > d_I$ (Farmer et al., 1983; Grassberger and Procaccia, 1983a,b).

Owing to computational limitations, use of the above original definitions to calculate d_F and d_I is impractical for attractors residing in phase spaces larger than three dimensions (Greenside et al., 1982). However, more efficient algorithms for estimating d_F have been devised (e.g. Takens, 1981). Nevertheless, because the Lyapunov dimension d_L and correlation dimension ν are often easier to calculate than d_F and d_I, and because ν and d_L are likely to be lower and upper bounds, respectively, on d_F, we concentrate on them here.

16.1.1 Lyapunov exponents and dimension. The fractal and information dimensions are often referred to as "box-counting" dimensions because their calculation requires covering the attractor with N-dimensional hypercubes and then counting the number of hypercubes needed to enclose the attractor completely. The system dynamics does not enter into the computation.

Kaplan and Yorke (1979) created the Lyapunov dimension in an attempt to incorporate the dynamics of the system into the definition of a dimension. It is the Lyapunov dimension, d_L, and the quantities from which it is derived, the Lyapunov exponents, that we introduce in this subsection.

Consider an N-dimensional dynamical system $\dot{\underset{\sim}{X}}(t) = \underset{\sim}{F}(\underset{\sim}{X}(t))$ and let J(t) be the $N \times N$ Jacobian matrix of partial derivatives of the system variables with respect to the initial conditions:

$$J(t) = \left[\frac{\partial X_i(\underset{\sim}{X}^o, t)}{\partial X_j^o} \right] , \quad \left\{ \begin{array}{l} i = 1, \ldots, N \\ j = 1, \ldots, N \end{array} \right. . \tag{16.4}$$

Differentiation of (16.4) with respect to time yields

$$\dot{J}(t) = \left[\frac{\partial \dot{X}_i(\underset{\sim}{X}^o, t)}{\partial X_j^o} \right] = \left[\frac{\partial F_i}{\partial X_j^o} \right] , \quad \left\{ \begin{array}{l} i = 1, \ldots, N \\ j = 1, \ldots, N \end{array} \right. . \tag{16.5}$$

Then because

$$\left[\frac{\partial F_i}{\partial X_j^o} \right] = \left[\sum_{k=1}^{N} \frac{\partial F_i}{\partial X_k} \frac{\partial X_k}{\partial X_j^o} \right] , \quad \left\{ \begin{array}{l} i = 1, \ldots, N \\ j = 1, \ldots, N \end{array} \right. , \tag{16.6}$$

we have, combining (16.4)-(16.6)

$$\dot{J}(t) = \Lambda(t)\, J(t) \quad , \tag{16.7}$$

where

$$\Lambda(t) = \left[\frac{\partial F_i}{\partial X_k} \right] , \quad \left\{ \begin{array}{l} i = 1, \ldots, N \\ k = 1, \ldots, N \end{array} \right. , \tag{16.8}$$

is the $N \times N$ matrix of partial derivatives of the functions $\underset{\sim}{F}(\underset{\sim}{X}(t))$. Equation (16.7) is a matrix differential equation for the evolution of the Jacobian J(t). Liouville's formula (Hirsch and Smale, 1974) then gives (see Section 14.2.5)

$$\det[J(t)] = \det[J(0)] \exp\left\{ \int_0^t \mathrm{Tr}[\Lambda(s)]ds \right\} \quad , \tag{16.9}$$

where $\mathrm{Tr}[\Lambda(t)]$ is the divergence of the system. Because we consider dissipative systems in which $Tr[\Lambda(t)]$ is always a negative constant, we conclude that $\det[J(t)] \to 0$ as $t \to \infty$.

Alternatively, the columns of the Jacobian can be viewed as representing vectors that span an N-dimensional hypercube in the phase space. We encountered a simple example of this situation in Section 4.3 when we discussed the stable and unstable manifolds of a fixed point. The axes in Fig. 4.1 would be the two vectors for the stationary solution in the two-dimensional phase space; along the x_1-axis, there is expansion and along the x_2-axis, contraction. Here we have a much more general case; the evolving Jacobian matrix contains information about how the volume V of an arbitrary region of phase space behaves under the action of the system. By considering how the volume can change, we are led to the relation (e.g. Section 5.2 in Dutton, 1976, 1986)

$$\frac{1}{V}\frac{dV}{dt} = \sum_{i=1}^{N} \frac{\partial \dot{X}_i}{\partial X_i} = Tr(\Lambda) \quad , \qquad (16.10)$$

and so we find that

$$V(t) = V(0)\, \exp\{[Tr(\Lambda)]t\} \quad . \qquad (16.11)$$

If I_N is the $N \times N$ identity matrix, then for $J(0) = I_N$ with $\det[J(0)] = V(0) = 1$, and for constant values of $Tr(\Lambda)$, we see from (16.9) and (16.11) that $\det[J(t)]$ is the "volume" of the N-dimensional hypercube that has evolved according to (16.7). This relationship between the evolving Jacobian matrix and the asymptotic behavior of phase space volumes is exploited below in the definition of the Lyapunov exponents.

Let $j_1(t) \geq j_2(t) \geq \cdots \geq j_N(t)$ be the magnitudes of the eigenvalues of $J(t)$. Then the <u>Lyapunov exponents</u> are defined as

$$\gamma_i = \lim_{t\to\infty} \{\ln[j_i(t)]^{1/t}\} \quad , i = 1, \ldots, N \quad . \qquad (16.12)$$

The usual numbering convention is that $\gamma_1 \geq \gamma_2 \geq \cdots \geq \gamma_N$. An attractor of an N-dimensional dynamical system necessarily has N Lyapunov exponents.

The Lyapunov exponents give a quantitative description of the average stability properties of an orbit on the phase space attractor of a dynamical system. Negative

Lyapunov exponents measure the average rate of exponential convergence of trajectories onto the attractor, while positive exponents measure the average exponential divergence of nearby trajectories. For the example depicted in Fig. 4.1, $\gamma_1 > 0$ for trajectories near the expanding x_1-axis, while $\gamma_2 < 0$ for trajectories near the contracting x_2-axis. The relevance of the Lyapunov exponents to predictability is clear. Trajectories with similar initial conditions diverge in directions associated with positive Lyapunov exponents, leading to a loss of predictability. Even a small error in specifying the initial data grows with time. Thus, positive Lyapunov exponents quantify the degree of sensitive dependence on initial conditions of the system.

The Lyapunov exponents can be determined more directly (that is, without first finding the eigenvalues of J(t)) by following N pairs of initially nearby trajectories and calculating their average rates of convergence or divergence. A method for carrying out this calculation, complete with Fortran code, is found in Wolf et al. (1985). Nese (1985) presents a different method for calculating the Lyapunov exponents that is practical for use with systems containing up to about eight variables. With this latter procedure, differential equations for the Lyapunov exponents can be derived.

As a check on the accuracy of computed Lyapunov exponents, it can be shown that

$$\sum_{k=1}^{N} \gamma_k = \sum_{i=1}^{N} \frac{\partial \dot{X}_i}{\partial X_i} = \mathrm{Tr}(\Lambda) \quad . \tag{16.13}$$

Since $\mathrm{Tr}(\Lambda)$ is a specific constant for each of the dissipative systems that we study, this relationship is obviously very useful. In Section 14.2.5, we used a similar relationship to check the accuracy of the numerically obtained characteristic multipliers. (Of course, (16.13) does <u>not</u> imply that $\gamma_i = \partial\dot{X}_i/\partial X_i$ for any i.)

We note that for almost any pair of points $\underset{\sim}{X}_o$ and $\underset{\sim}{X}'_o$ in the basin of a given attractor (see Section 4.3), a theorem of Oseledec (1968) states that the Lyapunov exponents calculated along the trajectory through $\underset{\sim}{X}_o$ are equal to the corresponding Lyapunov exponents calculated along the trajectory through $\underset{\sim}{X}'_o$. Thus these exponents are determined uniquely by the attractor. An important implication of Oseledec's theorem is that the spectrum of Lyapunov exponents can be used as a means for detecting and classifying attractors. Consider a three-dimensional phase space. A stable attracting fixed point would have only negative exponents giving a (-,-,-) spectrum, since locally all trajectories are converging. The evolution of a phase space volume when the attractor is a stable fixed point is illustrated in Fig. 16.1a. A stable limit cycle would have a (0,-,-) spectrum, indicating convergence of trajectories in two principal directions and neutrality in the third. Fig. 16.1b is similar to Fig. 16.1a except now the attractor is a stable limit cycle. For these simple attractors, the dimension is just the number of zero Lyapunov exponents.

A strange attractor in a three-dimensional phase space, however, has a (+,0,-) Lyapunov exponent spectrum. The positive exponent, which measures the rate at which initially nearby solution trajectories diverge, introduces structural complications and accounts for the "strangeness" of the attractors. In a closed and bounded phase space (see Section 17.3.3 for a discussion of the consequences of this typical case), the divergence of trajectories implied by a positive exponent means that phase space volumes must evolve into sheets that are infinitely folded by the flow (Fig. 16.1c). The condition $\gamma_1 > 0$ is often specified as a necessary condition for chaos.

Kaplan and Yorke (1979) conjectured a relationship between the Lyapunov exponents and the dimension of the system attractor. They define the <u>Lyapunov dimension</u> d_L as

$$d_L = K - \frac{\gamma_1 + \gamma_2 + \cdots + \gamma_K}{\gamma_{K+1}} , \qquad (16.14)$$

in which $K \leq N$ is the largest integer for which $\gamma_1 + \gamma_2 + \cdots + \gamma_K \geq 0$. If $\gamma_1 < 0$, then $d_L = 0$. If $\gamma_1 + \gamma_2 + \cdots + \gamma_N \geq 0$, then $d_L = N$. Note that when it is not a pure integer, d_L is an integer <u>plus</u> some fractional part since $\gamma_{K+1} < 0$. For a three-dimensional system with one positive Lyapunov exponent, this fractional part is related to the complexity of the sheeting of the strange attractor. In higher-dimensional phase spaces, the interpretation of the fractional part of the Lyapunov dimension is not altogether clear.

The form of (16.14) can be motivated with the following argument, which is similar to one presented by Farmer et al. (1983). As we noted above, a Lyapunov exponent γ_j, $1 \leq j \leq N$, measures the rate of exponential expansion, if $\exp(\gamma_j) > 1$,

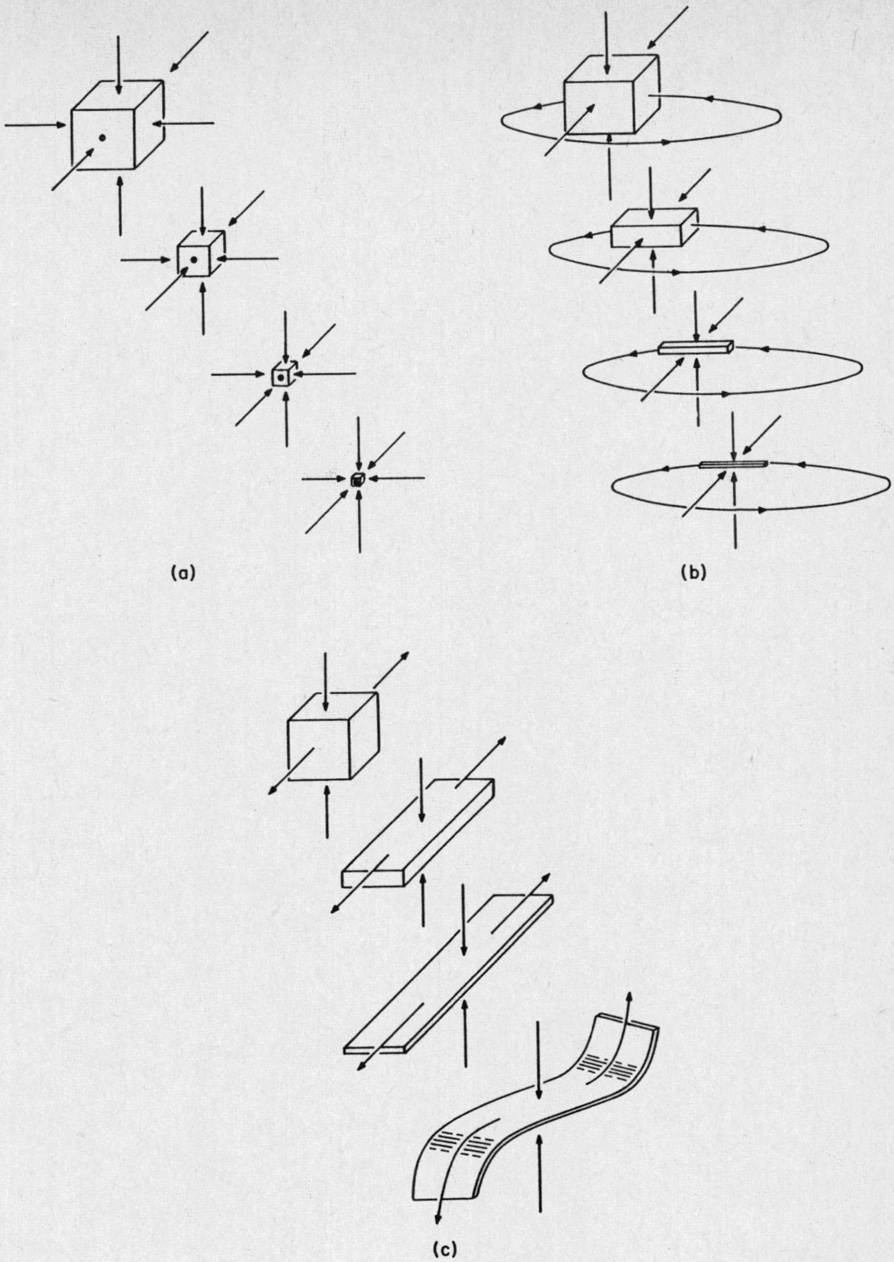

Fig. 16.1 The evolution of a three-dimensional phase space volume for three types of attractors: (a) For a stable fixed point, denoted by the dot, all three Lyapunov exponents are negative and the volume contracts in all three principal directions. (b) For a stable periodic attractor, two Lyapunov exponents are negative and the third is zero, so the volume contracts in two principal directions and remains unchanged in the third. (c) For a strange attractor, one Lyapunov exponent is positive, so the volume evolves into a sheet that, owing to the bounded nature of the phase space, is folded and refolded infinitely by the flow.

or contraction, if $\exp(\gamma_j) < 1$, in the direction associated with it. We seek a function of the exponents that gives an upper limit for the dimension of the typical portions of phase space that undergo expansion. Certainly, an attractor contains entirely any expanding portion of space that itself contains a point of the attractor. Set $\mu_j = \exp(\gamma_j)$, $j = 1,\ldots,N$, and then consider the products $\omega_1 = \mu_1$, $\omega_2 = \mu_1\mu_2$, ..., $\omega_N = \mu_1\mu_2\cdots\mu_N$. Whenever $\omega_1 > 1$, we expect the expanding portions of phase space to be at least one-dimensional; whenever $\omega_2 > 1$, we expect them to be at least two-dimensional. In general, if $\omega_\ell > 1$, then we expect them to be at least ℓ-dimensional. We choose K to be the integer for which $\omega_K > 1$ but $\omega_{K+1} < 1$. A reasonable conjecture is that the dimension of the expanding regions would be K+s, for $0 < s < 1$. To estimate this dimension, we define a generalized geometric average of ω_K and ω_{K+1} by $\omega_K^{1-s}\omega_{K+1}^{s}$, $0 < s < 1$, and then find the value of s for which $\omega_K^{1-s}\omega_{K+1}^{s} = 1$. We may plausibly expect that $K + s$ is then the least upper bound for the dimension of the expanding portions of phase space: There are expanding portions of nearly that dimension, but none of greater dimension. The expression we obtain for $K + s$ is given by the right side of (16.14), and so d_L is a plausible upper limit for the geometric dimension of the attractor.

We note that the exponents $\gamma_1,\ldots,\gamma_{K+1}$ constitute a measurement of the degree of sensitive dependence on initial conditions near the attractor; thus, the Lyapunov dimension d_L is a dimension defined in terms of that dependence alone. In particular, the Lyapunov dimension also makes sense for trajectories that escape to infinity and hence are nonrecurrent; therefore, it is clear that d_L is independent of the recurrence properties of the trajectories. For example, d_L does not measure explicitly the frequency with which various regions on the attractor are visited by a typical trajectory. However, there is a dimension, the correlation dimension, that explicitly incorporates such information, as we discuss in the following subsection.

The Lyapunov dimension is a discontinuous function of its data, the Lyapunov exponents, but the discontinuities occur where actual bifurcations of solutions occur. Kaplan and Yorke (1979) originally hypothesized that the Lyapunov dimension d_L would equal the fractal dimension d_F. Frederickson et al. (1983) suggested that d_L is more probabilistic in nature and actually equals the information dimension d_I. Recently, Constantin and Foias (1985) have proved that if "global" Lyapunov exponents, which they define, are used in the Kaplan and Yorke formula (16.14), then the resulting dimension is an upper bound for the fractal dimension. Here we use the classical Lyapunov exponents in our calculations of d_L; Constantin et al. (1985) prove that for the classical exponents, K + 1 is an upper bound for the fractal dimension d_F.

Certainly with simple attractors such as fixed points and limit cycles, we have $d_L = d_F = d_I$. The conjectured equalities relating d_L, d_F, and d_I have also been verified experimentally for the chaotic attractors in some low-dimensional systems (Russell et al., 1980). Grassberger and Procaccia (1983b) have shown heuristically that both the original conjecture $d_L = d_F$ and the more recent claim that $d_L = d_I$ would not necessarily hold if the attractor resembles a Cantor set in more than one principal direction, a situation that would be likely to occur if the attractor has more than one positive Lyapunov exponent. We investigate several such strange attractors in Section 16.3.

Apparently, the Lyapunov dimension overestimates the geometric or fractal dimension of the attractor because d_L also contains some information about the strength of the attractor. To see how this information may distort the estimate of the Lyapunov dimension, we consider a simple, structurally stable situation: Suppose that a dynamical system is given by the equation $\dot{\underset{\sim}{x}} = \underset{\sim}{f}(\underset{\sim}{x})$, with $\underset{\sim}{x} = (x_1,\ldots,x_N)$. Suppose further that this system contains an attractor A having geometric dimension d_F and Lyapunov exponents $\gamma_1,\ldots,\gamma_N$. Finally, suppose that $\gamma_1 + \cdots + \gamma_K > 0$ and $\gamma_1 + \cdots + \gamma_{K+1} < 0$. We extend the dynamical system by introducing M new temporally decaying variables $\underset{\sim}{y} = (y_1,\ldots,y_M)$, uncoupled from the variables $x_1,\ldots,x_N$ and governed by the equation $\dot{\underset{\sim}{y}} = \exp(\gamma)\underset{\sim}{y}$; we choose γ by requiring that $\gamma_{K+1} < \gamma < 0$, $\gamma < \gamma_K$, and $\gamma_1 + \cdots + \gamma_K + M\gamma > 0$. (A structurally stable version of the above example is clearly possible.) In the extended dynamical system given by both $\dot{\underset{\sim}{x}} = \underset{\sim}{f}(\underset{\sim}{x})$ and $\dot{\underset{\sim}{y}} = \exp(\gamma)\underset{\sim}{y}$, the set A is still an attractor, and of course its intrinsic geometric dimension d_F is still the same. However, in the new system, the Lyapunov exponents of A are given by $\gamma_1,\ldots,\gamma_K,\gamma,\ldots,\gamma,\gamma_{K+1},\ldots,\gamma_N$, where there are M repetitions of $\gamma < 0$ in the list of new exponents. It follows that the Lyapunov dimension of A in the new system is at least M whole numbers greater than that of A in the old system. Clearly, this anomaly arises because $|\gamma|$ is not large enough to prevent an increase in the value of K, even though γ itself is negative; that is, A is not a sufficiently strong attractor in the extended system for the Lyapunov dimension to be "correct." In this way, d_L might overestimate the effects of the negative exponents on increasing the dimension of the attractor. However, if the attractor A is strong enough for $\gamma < \gamma_{K+1}$ to hold instead, then the dimensions of A in the two systems agree.

16.1.2 Correlation dimension. Recently, Grassberger and Procaccia (1983a,b) introduced the correlation dimension ν as a measure of the local structure of an attractor. They argue that ν is a lower bound on the fractal and information dimensions. However, computer estimates of ν may be larger than computer estimates of d_F when the data coverage is nonuniform (Henderson and Wells, 1987). Grassberger and Procaccia (1983b) also show heuristically that for the number L^+ of positive Lyapunov exponents we have

$$L^+ \leq \nu \leq d_L \quad , \tag{16.15}$$

further motivating the calculation of ν. The results of Nese (1985) support the validity of (16.15). Significantly, the correlation dimension can be determined from observed or experimental data, as well as model-generated output. Our use of ν involves only the latter, although Fraedrich (1986) provides a recent example involving the former.

The correlation dimension is calculated as follows. Let Y_j, $j = 1,\ldots, n$, be n points on an attractor residing in an N-dimensional phase space. The points may be obtained, for example, as a time series $Y_j = Y(t + j\tau)$ where τ is a fixed time increment. A point, Y_k, is selected from these data and the distances $||Y_j - Y_k||$ between this point and the remaining n - 1 points are computed; any norm can be used to define these distances. The number of points within a distance ℓ of the point Y_k are then tabulated, for a range of values of ℓ. This procedure is repeated for all points Y_k on the attractor and a correlation integral $C(\ell)$ is computed as

$$C(\ell) = \lim_{n\to\infty} \left[\frac{1}{n^2} \sum_{\substack{j,k=1 \\ j\neq k}}^{n} H(\ell - ||Y_j - Y_k||) \right] \quad , \tag{16.16}$$

where the Heaviside function $H(x) = 1$ if $x \geq 0$, and $H(x) = 0$ otherwise.

Equation (16.16) is essentially equivalent to calculating the density of points on an attractor within a range of distances ℓ from a given point Y_k, and then finding the average of this density over all n points. If the attractor is a line, then for small values of ℓ we would expect that this average density of points within a distance ℓ would increase in proportion to ℓ. The constant of proportionality should not be sensitive to the number n of data points if n is sufficiently large. A similar argument in two dimensions would suggest that if the attractor is a surface, then $C(\ell) \propto \ell^2$. In general, if the attractor is ν-dimensional, then we would expect, for small enough ℓ, that

$$C(\ell) \propto \ell^{\nu} \quad , \tag{16.17}$$

in which the power ν is the <u>correlation</u> <u>dimension</u>. Equation (16.17) is useful in distinguishing between deterministic chaos and purely random noise in an N-component system, because if the data points are totally uncorrelated, then $C(\ell) \propto \ell^N$.

In contrast to the Lyapunov dimension, the correlation dimension depends on the recurrence characteristics of the flow--that is, on the amount of phase space continually revisited by a typical trajectory. For example, when $\nu = 2$, a single trajectory essentially fills a two-dimensional object within the N-dimensional phase space. No information concerning contraction or expansion appears explicitly in the definition of ν, and so no explicit information regarding sensitivity to initial conditions is included.

In applying (16.16) and (16.17), it is important that the points used are actually on the attractor and are not on transient parts of trajectories. Enough points must be included to capture the entire structure; the more "clumped" the data points, the more slowly the algorithm converges. In our experiments, we eliminate the first 10^5 to 2×10^5 iterations of the integration and then choose 10^4 to 2×10^4 points at equally spaced intervals in time from the next 10^6 iterations. Even with these precautions, the correlation dimension is often difficult to estimate accurately. Once the correlation integral $C(\ell)$ is tabulated, the correlation dimension ν is determined from the slope of the graph of $\ln[C(\ell)]$ - vs - $\ln(\ell)$ in the range of ℓ for which (16.17) appears to hold. For chaotic attractors, we find that the correlation dimension as well as the Lyapunov dimension are easiest to calculate when the chaos is well-developed, that is, for forcing parameters whose values are distant from those that produce bifurcations (Nese et al., 1987).

16.2 Some Properties of the Measures

The Lyapunov exponents, Lyapunov dimension, and correlation dimension give quantitative descriptions of the characteristics of the attractors and solution regimes of nonlinear models. Thus, they may provide us with a quantitative means for studying the transition to turbulence with finite models and for determining which transitional processes are occurring.

16.2.1 Applications to the transition to turbulence. For each of the hypothesized routes to chaos discussed in Section 15.2, we conjecture what changes would be observed in the Lyapunov quantities and the correlation dimension as the forcing rate in an N-dimensional dynamical system is increased. The attractor dimensions given in the tables below refer to both d_L and ν.

In the Landau (1944) scenario, the dimension of the torus on which the flow resides would increase by one as each new instability is added, since the quasi-periodic motion fills the surface of the torus. At each bifurcation, another Lyapunov exponent would increase to zero, as shown in Table 16.1. From the point of view of the Lyapunov exponents, chaos would have to be associated with M-frequency quasi-periodic motion on an M-torus, where $3 \leq M \leq N - 1$, with M Lyapunov exponents

Table 16.1 Conjectured signs of the Lyapunov exponents, and values of the Lyapunov and correlation dimensions for each solution regime that appears as the forcing rate is increased, for the route to chaos proposed by Landau (1944).

Landau Hypothesis

N Lyapunov exponents	Dimension (d_L or ν)	Attractor
(−,−,−, ... ,−,−)	0	fixed point
(0,−,−, ... ,−,−)	1	limit cycle
(0,0,−, ... ,−,−)	2	quasi-periodic two-torus
⋮	⋮	⋮
(0,0,0, ... ,0,−)	N-1	quasi-periodic (N-1)-torus

equal to zero. Having no positive Lyapunov exponents violates the usual specification that chaotic motion depends sensitively on initial conditions, thereby rendering the Landau scenario implausible.

Another interpretation of the Landau hypothesis is that turbulence involves infinitely many frequencies in a quasi-periodic way. To model turbulence under this interpretation requires the use of the full system of partial differential equations, with the M-torus now replaced by an attracting ∞-torus in the phase space of the partial differential equations, and now $d_F = d_L = \infty$. However, Constantin et al. (1985) show that under very general assumptions, attractors in the phase space of the Navier-Stokes equations have finite Lyapunov dimensions. Thus this second interpretation of the Landau hypothesis is also rendered implausible.

The revised Ruelle and Takens route to chaos (Newhouse et al., 1978) would produce significantly different changes in the Lyapunov exponents and thus in the dimensions of the attractors, as shown in Table 16.2. We have chosen to illustrate this route to chaotic flow on a three-torus using the most common interpretation of the theory. If the bifurcation from a stable limit cycle is to periodic motion on a two-torus, then there would be no apparent change in the dimension because the motion is still periodic. However, as illustrated in our tests with the Lorenz model (Nese, 1985), magnitude changes in the Lyapunov exponents can help identify the singular bifurcation value. If the bifurcation produces two-frequency quasi-periodic motion,

Table 16.2 Conjectured signs of the Lyapunov exponents, and values of the Lyapunov and correlation dimensions for each solution regime that appears as the forcing rate is increased, for the route to chaos originally proposed by Ruelle and Takens (1971) and revised by Newhouse et al. (1978).

Ruelle and Takens Hypothesis

N Lyapunov exponents	Dimension (d_L or ν)	Attractor
(-,-,-, ... ,-,-)	0	fixed point
(0,-,-, ... ,-,-)	1	limit cycle
(0,-,-, ... ,-,-)	1	closed orbit on two-torus
(0,0,-, ... ,-,-)	2	quasi-periodic two-torus
(+, ... ,0, ... ,-,-)	non-integer > 2	strange

then an additional Lyapunov exponent would increase to zero and the dimension of the attractor would be two. The next conjectured bifurcation would produce chaos and at least one exponent would become positive.

The changes in the Lyapunov quantities and the correlation dimension as chaos develops via an infinite sequence of period doubling bifurcations are shown in Table 16.3. As the forcing rate is increased in magnitude, only fixed point and periodic behavior would be observed prior to chaos. The attractor after the first Hopf bifurcation but before the system becomes chaotic is always a limit cycle, no matter how many period doublings may have occurred. However, as we show in Section 16.2.2, the exact parameter values at which these subharmonic bifurcations occur can be detected using the Lyapunov exponents.

The Ostlund et al. (1983), or torus-wrinkling, route to chaos is similar to that of Ruelle and Takens, except for the culminating mechanism that produces chaos. Thus, as seen in Table 16.4, the representation in terms of the Lyapunov quantities and the correlation dimension is similar to that in Table 16.2. In this route, however, we include several occurrences of both periodic and quasi-periodic motion on a two-torus because the ratios of the two frequencies apparently pass from rational to irrational numbers several times before chaos is seen.

Table 16.3 Conjectured signs of the Lyapunov exponents, and values of the Lyapunov and correlation dimensions for each solution regime that appears as the forcing rate is increased, for the route to chaos via an infinite sequence of period doubling bifurcations.

Infinite Sequence of Period Doubling Bifurcations

N Lyapunov exponents	Dimension (d_L or ν)	Attractor
(-,-,-, ... ,-,-)	0	fixed point
(0,-,-, ... ,-,-)	1	limit cycle, period T
(0,-,-, ... ,-,-)	1	limit cycle, period 2T
(0,-,-, ... ,-,-)	1	limit cycle, period 4T
⋮	⋮	⋮
(+, ... ,0, ... ,-,-)	non-integer > 2	strange

Table 16.4 Conjectured signs of the Lyapunov exponents, and values of the Lyapunov and correlation dimensions for each solution regime that appears as the forcing rate is increased, for the Ostlund et al. (1983) torus wrinkling route to chaos.

Ostlund et al. Hypothesis

N Lyapunov exponents	Dimension (d_L or ν)	Attractor
(-,-,-, ... ,-,-)	0	fixed point
(0,-,-, ... ,-,-)	1	limit cycle
(0,-,-, ... ,-,-)	1	closed orbit on two-torus
(0,0,-, ... ,-,-)	2	quasi-periodic two-torus
(0,-,-, ... ,-,-)	1	closed orbit on two-torus
(0,0,-, ... ,-,-)	2	quasi-periodic two-torus
⋮	⋮	⋮
(0,0,-, ... ,-,-)	2	quasi-periodic two-torus
(0,-,-, ... ,-,-)	1	closed orbit on two-torus
(+, ... ,0, ... ,-,-)	non-integer > 2	strange

The subcritical bifurcation route to chaos has an even simpler representation, as is shown in Table 16.5. This representation also fits the simultaneous triple Hopf bifurcation interpretation that Shirer and Wells (1985) proposed based on the theory of Ruelle, Takens, and Newhouse. As the Hopf bifurcation value is exceeded, at least one Lyapunov exponent becomes positive and the dimension jumps from zero to the dimension of the chaotic attractor. However, the attractor would be fully developed in the subcritical bifurcation route, while it would grow from the unstable fixed point in the triple Hopf bifurcation route. Such an abrupt transition to chaos is detected quantitatively in the Lorenz (1963) and Chang and Shirer (1984) models studied in the next two subsections.

16.2.2 Applications to the Lorenz system. We first investigate the three-coefficient Lorenz system to show that the Lyapunov quantities and the correlation dimension yield information about the phase space structure that is similar to known analytical and numerical results. Although the system is very low-dimensional, the Lorenz model exhibits a variety of solution regimes and also several of the

Table 16.5 Conjectured signs of the Lyapunov exponents, and values of the Lyapunov and correlation dimensions for each solution regime that appears as the forcing rate is increased, for the route to chaos via a subcritical bifurcation.

	Subcritical Bifurcation	
N Lyapunov exponents	Dimension (d_L or ν)	Attractor
(-,-,-, ... ,-,-)	0	fixed point
(+, ... ,0, ... ,-,-)	non-integer > 2	strange

hypothesized routes to chaos discussed in Section 15.2. We set P = 10 and $a^2 = 1/2$ (b = 8/3), Lorenz's original values, and then vary the value of r, the normalized Rayleigh number. Many of the results we present are also found in Nese et al. (1987).

We use Fig. 16.2 to summarize in schematic form the solution regimes of the models that we study in this and the next section. The solution regimes of the Lorenz model are shown in Fig. 16.2a. We know that for r < 1, the origin is a hyperbolic sink and the only attractor. At r = 1, two new stable fixed points, C_1 and C_2, appear at $\left(\pm[b(r-1)]^{1/2}, \pm[b(r-1)]^{1/2}, r-1\right)$ as the origin loses stability in a supercritical bifurcation. These fixed points are stable until $r = r_H \simeq 24.74$, where a subcritical Hopf bifurcation occurs. For $r_H < r < \simeq 215$, aperiodic motion on what is believed to be a strange attractor dominates (Section 15.3.2), with regimes of periodic motion interspersed. For $r > \simeq 215$, the system exhibits stable periodic behavior (Robbins, 1979; Lorenz, 1980).

Since at least one stable fixed point exists for all $r < r_H$, we might expect a Lyapunov exponent spectrum of (-,-,-) for values of r in this range. An exception to this occurs at r = 1, where the largest Lyapunov exponent increases to zero. This result should not be interpreted as indicating the instantaneous appearance of a stable (finite-amplitude) periodic orbit, since the largest Lyapunov exponent is negative for all values of r close to r = 1. Rather, the variation in γ_1 signals the exchange of stability associated with the simple bifurcation at r = 1.

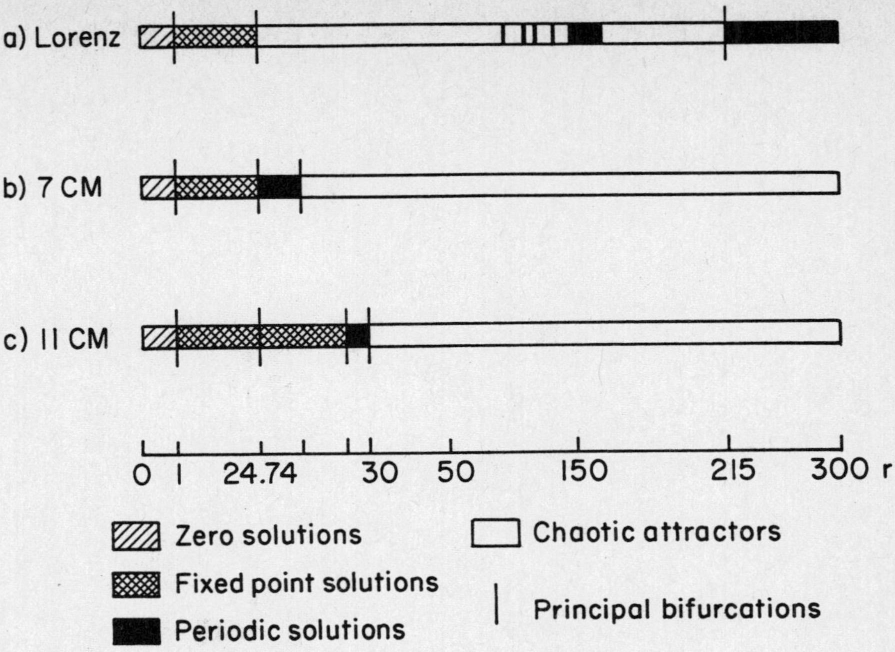

Fig. 16.2 Set of schematics illustrating the solution regimes and transitions between solutions in the Lorenz (1963) model (a), the Chang and Shirer (1984) model (b), and the eleven-coefficient model (c), as the forcing rate represented by the Rayleigh number r is varied (adapted from Nese et al., 1987).

For $r > r_H$, all three fixed points of the system are unstable. At $r = 28$ (a case studied originally by Lorenz), we find Lyapunov exponents of (0.93, 0, -14.60) and a Lyapunov dimension of 2.06. Tests using a set of fifty initial points confirm that these values are independent of the initial data. This value for d_L agrees with previous calculations of the fractal dimension by Mori (1980) and of the correlation dimension by Grassberger and Procaccia (1983b). The non-integer dimension further supports the conclusion that a strange attractor is what we are seeing in the projections in Fig. 15.10.

In addition to providing quantitative information about the stationary and chaotic solutions, the Lyapunov exponents and dimension also quantify the behavior near the periodic regimes scattered throughout $r_H < r < \simeq 215$. Within these periodic subranges are three types of behavior associated with the passage to chaos exhibited by one-dimensional maps of the unit interval to itself (Feigenbaum, 1978; Kadanoff, 1983): noisy periodicity, intermittency, and an infinite sequence of period doubling bifurcations. The largest periodic subrange in $r_H < r < \simeq 215$ is $\simeq 146 < r < \simeq 166$, and we use this window of periodicity to illustrate the usefulness of the Lyapunov quantities in studying such a regime.

For a value of r slightly less than 166.06, a stable periodic orbit, whose X-Z planar projection is symmetric about the Z-axis (Sparrow, 1982), exists as the system attractor. As the value of r decreases past approximately 154.4, the single symmetric orbit loses stability to a pair of asymmetric periodic orbits (Sparrow, 1982). This bifurcation is a harmonic one in which the new periodic solutions have the same period as the old one. As the value of r is decreased further, a period doubling (subharmonic) bifurcation occurs near r = 148.4, and a second occurs at $r \simeq 147.2$. This succession of period doubling bifurcations continues as the value of r decreases, accumulating at $r_M \simeq 145.9$ (Manneville and Pomeau, 1979, 1980).

Although the attractor for $r_M < r < \simeq 166.06$ remains a stable periodic orbit, the above bifurcations can be detected using the Lyapunov quantities. Fig. 16.3

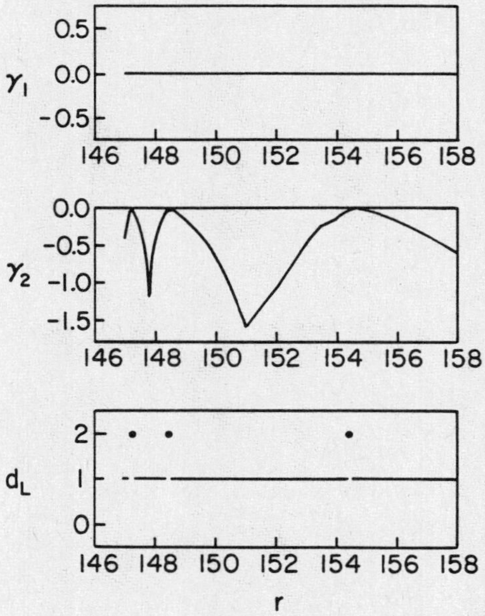

Fig. 16.3 The two largest Lyapunov exponents and the Lyapunov dimension of the attractor of the Lorenz (1963) system for the range of Rayleigh numbers $147 \leq r \leq 158$. To avoid a cluttered depiction, we have not shown the additional period doubling behavior in the range $146 \leq r \leq 147$ (from Nese et al., 1987).

shows the two largest Lyapunov exponents and the Lyapunov dimension for $147 \leq r \leq 158$. While γ_1 remains zero in this range, $\gamma_2 \to 0$ as the value of r approaches a bifurcation value. At the bifurcation points, $\gamma_2 = 0$, and thus exactly at those critical values of r, $d_L = 2$. This behavior of the Lyapunov exponents was also noted by Frøyland and Alfsen (1984), and is analogous to the pattern exhibited by γ_1 for $r = 1$. Since $\gamma_2 < 0$ for Rayleigh numbers near the bifurcation values, the Lyapunov dimension of two computed at these critical values of r does not signal the instantaneous appearance of a quasi-periodic two-torus, which would be an attractor likely to produce a dimension of two. The Lyapunov quantities simply detect a structural change in the attractor rather than a change in the type of attractor; thus there is no permanent change in the dimension.

For values of r just below the period doubling accumulation value r_M, a stable periodic orbit no longer exists, but an infinite number of unstable orbits remains--the product of the infinite succession of bifurcations that took place at $r > r_M$. Lorenz (1980) explains the behavior at values of r just below r_M using Poincaré maps and the properties of "band splitting" observed in one-dimensional maps (see Section 15.2.3). Lorenz found that as the value of r increases toward r_M, the pattern of chaotic motion as viewed on a Poincaré section becomes more orderly, or predictable. Although the motion remains aperiodic, the trajectories intersect the Poincaré section in two, then four, then eight, then sixteen, and so forth, distinct regions, with the 2^k regions entirely contained within the 2^{k-1} regions. Trajectories move from region to region regularly but fill each individual region chaotically. As noted in Section 15.2.3, Lorenz calls this phenomenon noisy (or semi-) periodicity.

At the upper limit of the periodic regime, just above $r \simeq 166.06$, intermittent chaos, or intermittency, has been observed (Manneville and Pomeau, 1979, 1980). A stable limit cycle no longer exists, but for long periods of time, trajectories move in a laminar pattern, occasionally interrupted by "bursts" in which the trajectories wander chaotically. As the magnitude of r increases, the length of the laminar intervals decreases and the intermittency gradually yields to a purely chaotic state (Sparrow, 1982).

The Lyapunov exponents detect the variations in the degree of predictability associated with both noisy periodicity and intermittency. In Table 16.6 we list the largest Lyapunov exponent and the Lyapunov dimension for several values of r near $r_M \simeq 145.9$, where noisy periodicity occurs, and near r = 166.06, where intermittency occurs. It appears that γ_1 decreases monotonically and continuously to zero at the transitions to laminar behavior, signaling a gain in predictability. Unfortunately, the Lyapunov quantities do not differentiate between noisy periodicity and intermittent chaos, since in both cases the transition to a higher degree of chaos appears as an increase in the largest exponent and dimension. However, noisy periodicity, in the Lorenz system at least, is confined to Rayleigh numbers just beyond the accumulation point of a monotonic sequence of period doubling bifurcations, while intermittency occurs just beyond the end of a stable periodic regime.

Table 16.6 The largest Lyapunov exponent and the Lyapunov dimension of the attractor of the Lorenz system for a range of values of the Rayleigh number containing a periodic regime.

r	γ_1	d_L	Solution Characteristics
142.	1.28	2.086	noisy periodicity
144.	0.67	2.047	
145.	0.58	2.041	
145.85	0.37	2.026	
145.9	0.12	2.009	
145.95	0.	1.	periodic regime
.	.	.	
.	.	.	
.	.	.	
166.06	0.	1.	
166.063	0.05	2.004	intermittency
166.065	0.18	2.013	
166.085	0.38	2.027	
166.2	0.97	2.066	
166.5	1.66	2.108	

An additional insight into the nature of Lyapunov exponents is found from calculating them on the stationary points of the system. Then, $\dot{X} = \dot{Y} = \dot{Z} = 0$ and the Lyapunov exponents are simply the real parts of the eigenvalues of the constant matrix Λ of partial derivatives--that is, they are simply the real parts of the characteristic exponents λ. As we saw in Section 4.3 this linearization calculation yields valuable information about the directions and rates of expansion and contraction of the phase space near the fixed points. When a fixed point loses stability, the largest characteristic (or Lyapunov) exponent becomes positive and locally measures the exponential rate of divergence of adjacent trajectories while they remain close to the fixed point.

Table 16.7 shows the largest Lyapunov exponents calculated at the origin and at the stationary points C_1 and C_2 for selected values of the Rayleigh number. When the fixed points are stable, which is the case for $r < 1$ for the origin and $1 < r < r_H$ for C_1 and C_2, the largest exponent is negative. The calculation of γ_1 at the origin shows the loss of stability at $r = 1$ and an increase in the strength of the one-dimensional unstable manifold as the value of r increases. In addition, since $\gamma_1 + \gamma_2 + \gamma_3 = -(P + b + 1) = -41/3$, and $\gamma_2 = -8/3$ at the origin, γ_3 becomes increasingly negative as γ_1 becomes more positive. Thus, trajectories are strongly attracted toward the origin, and therefore toward each other, parallel to the two-dimensional stable manifold; however, the large positive exponent indicates that once near the origin, nearby trajectories diverge from each other at a large exponential rate. This behavior supports the observation by Dutton and Wells (1984) and Shirer (1984) that unstable points are <u>decision points</u> (see also Section 4.3). Thus, trajectories passing in the vicinity of the origin are susceptible to large prediction errors in a finite time and an explosive sensitivity to initial data, even if the stable fixed points C_1 and C_2 are reached asymptotically (cf. Fig. 4.3).

The calculation of the Lyapunov exponents at C_1 and C_2 shows the loss of stability between $r = 24$ and $r = 25$, but the positive exponents suggest a much weaker "potential instability" in this region as compared with that near the origin. The Λ matrix at C_1 and C_2 has a complex conjugate pair of eigenvalues for $r > 1.346$, so at those points, $\gamma_1 = \gamma_2$ for all values of $r > 1.346$. Thus, near C_1 and C_2 for $r > r_H$, phase space volumes expand very weakly in two principal directions and

Table 16.7 The largest Lyapunov exponent calculated at the origin and at the stationary points C_1 and C_2 of the Lorenz system for various values of the Rayleigh number.

	(0,0,0)	C_1, C_2
r	γ_1	γ_1
0	-1.	points do not exist
$1 = r_c$	0.	0.
2	0.84	-1.21
5	2.88	-0.93
10	5.47	-0.60
15	7.55	-0.35
22	10.00	-0.09
$24 < r_H$	10.63	-0.02
$25 > r_H$	10.94	0.01
30	12.40	0.15
50	17.31	0.56
80	23.14	0.97

contract strongly in the third. The combined effect of this two-dimensional expansion, however, is still about two orders of magnitude smaller than the one-dimensional expansion associated with the positive exponent at the origin. In the sense of locating areas in the phase space susceptible to predictability problems, the Lyapunov exponents differentiate between the extremely difficult neighborhood near the origin and the less troublesome regions surrounding C_1 and C_2.

16.3 Comments on Larger Systems

We now use the Lyapunov quantities and correlation dimension to investigate the solution regimes of two larger models whose temporal attractors have not been studied previously in any detail. Both larger systems contain several three-coefficient Lorenz-type submodels, and both preserve all the bifurcation points involving the stationary solutions that occur in the Lorenz model. We use this hierarchy of models to ascertain how increasing the number of coefficients changes the nature of the attractors and solution transitions. A more thorough study of the properties of the temporal attractors of these models is given in Nese et al. (1987).

16.3.1 Seven-coefficient model (7CM). This generalized Lorenz model (Chang and Shirer, 1984) was introduced in Section 9.2. The model contains two submodels of Lorenz type, which we denote as $LS_m = (\psi_{m1},0,0,T_{m1},0,0,T_{02})$ and $LS_n = (0,\psi_{n1},0,0,T_{n1},0,T_{02})$. These Lorenz submodels are three-dimensional manifolds in the seven-dimensional phase space, and are represented as primary branches on the system bifurcation diagram. Stationary solutions P_m and P_n branch from the trivial solution at critical Rayleigh numbers Ra_m and Ra_n, respectively. As we saw in Section 9.2.3, the choices of wavenumbers m, n and aspect ratio a determine which branch appears first, and thus which convective solution is initially stable.

We choose m = 4, n = 2, $a = \sqrt{2}/8$, and P = 10, which gives $Ra_c = Ra_4 = 6.75$ and $Ra_2 = 11.390625$. For these choices of parameter values, the seven-variable model is a solution to the eleven-coefficient system that we investigate later in this section. To facilitate comparisons with the solutions to the Lorenz model, we give our results in terms of r, where $Ra = Ra_c r = 6.75r$.

Fig. 16.2b shows the solution regimes that appear as the value of r is varied. The origin loses stability at r = 1 to P_4^+ and P_4^-, the two stationary points of the P_4 branch. These points remain stable for $1 < r < r_H \simeq 24.74$. As in the Lorenz system, there is a Hopf bifurcation at $r = r_H$; of course, in the 7CM, this Hopf bifurcation is still subcritical. However, the stationary solution loses stability to a stable periodic solution of finite amplitude rather than to a strange attractor. The largest Lyapunov exponent increases to zero at $r = r_H$, signaling this transition, and remains zero for $r_H < r < \simeq 26.10 = r_{H2}$. Our calculations of the second largest exponent do not reveal any bifurcations, such as period doublings, associated with this periodic regime.

At $r \simeq r_{H2}$, the periodic regime becomes unstable and a chaotic solution appears. In Table 16.8 we list the five largest Lyapunov exponents, the Lyapunov dimension, and some correlation dimensions for several values of r in this chaotic regime. If we were able to compute the Lyapunov quantities exactly at $r = r_{H2}$, then we would expect to find $\gamma_1 = \gamma_2 = 0$ and $d_L = 2$. We see from Table 16.8 that by r = 26.25, $\gamma_1 > |\gamma_3 + \gamma_4|$ and so already $d_L > 4$. Thus, in the small Rayleigh number range

Table 16.8 The five largest Lyapunov exponents, the Lyapunov dimension, and some correlation dimensions of the attractor of the 7CM for various values of the Rayleigh number, for m = 4, n = 2, $a = \sqrt{2}/8$, and P = 10.

$r = Ra/Ra_4$	γ_1	γ_2	γ_3	γ_4	γ_5	d_L	ν
26.20	0.25	0.	-0.09	-0.22	-14.4	3.73	
26.23	0.40	0.	-0.09	-0.34	-14.5	3.91	2.0 ± 0.2
26.25	0.53	0.	-0.07	-0.38	-14.6	4.005	
26.40	0.85	0.	-0.04	-0.43	-14.6	4.026	2.4 ± 0.1
26.65	0.95	0.03	0.	-0.51	-14.7	4.03	
28	1.31	0.12	0.	-0.53	-14.8	4.06	3.1 ± 0.1
37	1.70	0.48	0.	-0.28	-14.7	4.13	
56	2.21	0.96	0.	-0.40	-14.3	4.19	4.1 ± 0.1
200	4.52	1.92	0.	-0.80	-12.0	4.47	4.3 ± 0.1

$r_{H2} < r < 26.25$, $\Delta d_L/\Delta r$ is very large, and it remains an open question as to whether $d_L = 3$ is possible. Since $|\gamma_5|$ is large, $\Delta d_L/\Delta r$ is very small once $d_L > 4$. At $r \approx 26.60$, a second Lyapunov exponent becomes positive, and the Lyapunov dimension remains slightly above four.

Although changes in d_L are concentrated near the bifurcation point r_{H2}, changes in ν are more uniformly distributed over the entire supercritical range of r. Eventually, for large enough values of r, both d_L and ν approach similar values greater than four. We recall that the expected relation among ν, d_F, and d_L is $\nu \leq d_F \leq d_L$, and so ν is in general a lower bound and d_L is an upper bound for the dimension of the attractor. This relation between ν and d_L is clearly seen in Table 16.8, but for only well-developed chaos are ν and d_L close in value, thereby providing good bounds for the attractor dimension. In contrast, for weakly developed chaos near r_{H2}, the bounds ν and d_L are far apart, leading to uncertainty in the estimate for the dimension of the attractor. Although we cannot tell which of the two estimates is closer, we know that d_L overestimates the effects of the negative exponents among $\gamma_1,\ldots,\gamma_K$ on increasing the dimension of the attractor.

In Figs. 16.4a and 16.4b we show projections for r = 28 of a chaotic seven-dimensional solution trajectory onto triples of two-dimensional planes spanning

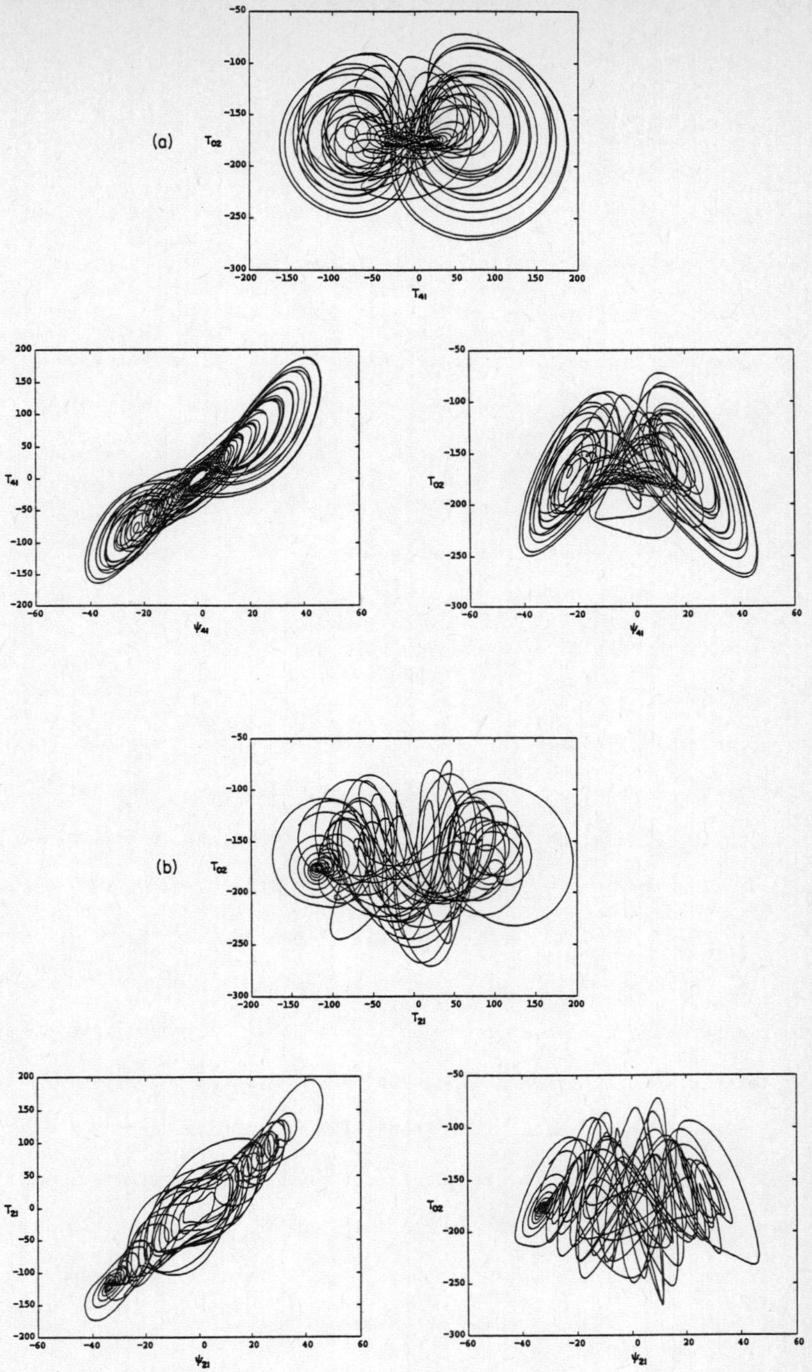

Fig. 16.4 Projections of a seven-dimensional chaotic solution trajectory of the Chang and Shirer (1984) model onto the planes spanning the LS_4 subspace (a) and the LS_2 subspace (b), for r=28, P=10, and $a=\sqrt{2}/8$.

the LS_4 and LS_2 solutions, respectively. The first 20,000 iterations have been removed to eliminate transient portions of the trajectory. Even though the chaotic motion of the solution to the 7CM is not confined to either the LS_4 or LS_2 subspace, the projections onto the LS_4 subspace are remarkably similar to those of the Lorenz attractor in Fig. 15.10. So, given four additional degrees of freedom, trajectories still exhibit what appears to be deterministic chaos, but on a strange attractor having geometric dimension between three and four (Table 16.8).

An interesting distinction between the Lyapunov and correlation dimensions can be illustrated by following a trajectory emanating from an initial condition on one of the three-dimensional Lorenz subspaces. The three-dimensional subspaces LS_4 and LS_2 are invariant, and thus trajectories on either manifold remain on that manifold for all time. Once the stationary solutions P_4^+ and P_4^- lose stability at $r = r_H$, a trajectory originating on the three-dimensional LS_4 subspace is forced to wander chaotically on a "restricted" strange attractor. Intuitively, we might expect that the geometric dimension of this restricted attractor would be less than three since the attractor resides completely on a three-dimensional manifold within the full seven-dimensional phase space. However, for the initial condition (-6, 0, 0, 10, 0, 0, 16), on LS_4, and $r = 56$, a forcing value for which P_4^+ and P_4^- are unstable, we find Lyapunov exponents of (3.9, 1.9, 0.0, -2.0, -15.5, -22.5, -44.1), and thus $d_L = 4.25$. Such an unrealistic Lyapunov dimension is not surprising since (16.14) is supposed to apply only when the Lyapunov exponents are those for the system attractor and not some restricted attractor. This large value of d_L results from the definition of the Lyapunov exponents as measures of the exponential rates of stretching or contraction of an infinitesimal N-dimensional ball in all N principal directions. Even though the attractor is confined to three dimensions, the evolution of the seven-dimensional volume reveals information about the four remaining phase space directions, some of which are unstable. (Even if the remaining phase space directions are contracting, then the value of the Lyapunov dimension may be too large, provided that some of the directions are sufficiently weakly contracting.) The correlation dimension, however, detects the characteristics of flows restricted to the manifold on which the attractor resides. We find $\nu = 2.1 \pm 0.1$, which confirms that the geometrical structure of this "restricted" chaotic attractor resembles that of the original Lorenz attractor, which has both a Lyapunov dimension and a correlation dimension near 2.06.

16.3.2 Eleven-coefficient model (11CM). This 11CM, developed in unpublished work by Dr. Hai-Ru Chang, contains as a solution the 7CM with $m = 4$, $n = 2$, and $a = \sqrt{2}/8$, and also contains three Lorenz-type submodels. The evolution of the Fourier coefficients of convection is governed by

$$\dot{\psi}_{21} = A_1A_6\psi_{31}\psi_{12}/A_5 + A_2A_7\psi_{41}\psi_{22}/A_5 + 2aPT_{21}/A_5 - PA_5\psi_{21} \quad , \tag{16.18}$$

$$\dot{\psi}_{31} = A_1A_3\psi_{21}\psi_{12}/A_4 + A_{11}A_8\psi_{41}\psi_{12}/A_4 + 3aPT_{31}/A_4 - PA_4\psi_{31} \quad , \tag{16.19}$$

$$\dot{\psi}_{41} = 3A_2\psi_{21}\psi_{22}/A_{10} - A_{11}A_6\psi_{31}\psi_{12}/A_{10} + 4aPT_{41}/A_{10} - PA_{10}\psi_{41} \quad , \tag{16.20}$$

$$\dot{\psi}_{12} = A_1A_{15}\psi_{21}\psi_{31}/A_9 + A_{11}A_{13}\psi_{31}\psi_{41}/A_9 + aPT_{12}/A_9 - PA_9\psi_{12} \quad , \tag{16.21}$$

$$\dot{\psi}_{22} = A_2A_{14}\psi_{21}\psi_{41}/A_{12} + 2aPT_{22}/A_{12} - PA_{12}\psi_{22} \quad , \tag{16.22}$$

$$\dot{T}_{21} = A_1\psi_{31}T_{12} + A_2\psi_{41}T_{22} + A_1\psi_{12}T_{31} + A_2\psi_{22}T_{41} + 2a\psi_{21}(T_{02} + Ra) - A_5T_{21} \quad , \tag{16.23}$$

$$\dot{T}_{31} = A_1\psi_{21}T_{12} + A_{11}\psi_{41}T_{12} - A_1\psi_{12}T_{21} + A_{11}\psi_{12}T_{41} + 3a\psi_{31}(T_{02} + Ra) - A_4T_{31} \quad , \tag{16.24}$$

$$\dot{T}_{41} = A_2\psi_{21}T_{22} + A_{11}\psi_{31}T_{12} - A_{11}\psi_{12}T_{31} - A_2\psi_{22}T_{21} + 4a\psi_{41}(T_{02} + Ra) - A_{10}T_{41} \quad , \tag{16.25}$$

$$\dot{T}_{02} = - a\psi_{21}T_{21} - A_2\psi_{31}T_{31} - 2a\psi_{41}T_{41} - 4T_{02} \quad , \tag{16.26}$$

$$\dot{T}_{12} = - A_1\psi_{21}T_{31} - A_1\psi_{31}T_{21} - A_{11}\psi_{31}T_{41} - A_{11}\psi_{41}T_{31} + a\, Ra\, \psi_{12} - A_9T_{12} \quad , \tag{16.27}$$

$$\dot{T}_{22} = - A_2\psi_{21}T_{41} - A_2\psi_{41}T_{21} + 2a\, Ra\, \psi_{22} - A_{12}T_{22} \quad , \tag{16.28}$$

in which the parameters a, P, and Ra are as in the 7CM. Again we give our results in terms of r, where $Ra = 6.75r$. The constants A_1 to A_{15} are functions of the aspect ratio a and are defined by

$$A_1 = 5a/4 \quad , \tag{16.29}$$

$$A_2 = 3a/2 \quad , \tag{16.30}$$

$$A_3 = 3-3a^2 \quad , \tag{16.31}$$

$$A_4 = 1+9a^2 \quad , \tag{16.32}$$

$$A_5 = 1+4a^2 \quad , \qquad (16.33)$$

$$A_6 = 8a^2-3 \quad , \qquad (16.34)$$

$$A_7 = 12a^2-3 \quad , \qquad (16.35)$$

$$A_8 = 15a^2-3 \quad , \qquad (16.36)$$

$$A_9 = 4+a^2 \quad , \qquad (16.37)$$

$$A_{10} = 1+16a^2 \quad , \qquad (16.38)$$

$$A_{11} = 7a/4 \quad , \qquad (16.39)$$

$$A_{12} = 4+4a^2 \quad , \qquad (16.40)$$

$$A_{13} = -7a^2 \quad , \qquad (16.41)$$

$$A_{14} = -12a^2 \quad , \qquad (16.42)$$

$$A_{15} = -5a^2 \quad . \qquad (16.43)$$

On a bifurcation diagram, this eleven-coefficient system has three primary branches P_4, P_3, P_2, each representing the stationary solutions to a three-dimensional Lorenz submodel. Horizontal wavenumbers two, three, and four are included, and thus the Lorenz-type submodels are $LS_4 = (0,0,\psi_{41},0,0,0,0,T_{41},T_{02},0,0)$, $LS_3 = (0,\psi_{31},0,0,0,0,T_{31},0,T_{02},0,0)$, and $LS_2 = (\psi_{21},0,0,0,0,T_{21},0,0,T_{02},0,0)$. The seven-coefficient Chang and Shirer submodel is denoted as $CS_{42} = (\psi_{21},0,\psi_{41},0,\psi_{22},T_{21},0,T_{41},T_{02},0,T_{22})$.

Fig. 16.2c shows the solution regimes of the 11CM in schematic form. Just as in the 7CM, the conductive solution loses stability at $r = 1$ to the primary branch P_4. These points subsequently lose stability at $r = r_H \simeq 24.74$. However, instead of a periodic solution appearing, as in the 7CM, stability is transferred at finite amplitude to the primary branch P_3. This transfer occurs because the Hopf bifurcation at $r = r_H$ is subcritical and the primary branch has regained stability (see Section 9.2). The inclusion of four coefficients and an additional horizontal wavenumber allows a second primary branch P_3 to become active, and defers the appearance of the stable periodic regime. This observation substantiates the results of Marcus (1981) and Curry et al. (1984) regarding the truncation dependency of finite-model attractors (see Section 15.3.3). Not until $r \simeq 29.98$ does P_3 lose stability via a Hopf bifurcation and a stable periodic solution develop.

The Rayleigh number range for which the 11CM remains periodic is small, only $\simeq 29.98 < r < \simeq 30.25$, and at $r \simeq 30.25$, chaos develops. It appears that three Lyapunov exponents become positive simultaneously at the transition to chaos in the 11CM, and thus we expect $\gamma_1 = \gamma_2 = \gamma_3 = \gamma_4 = 0$ and $d_L = 4$ at the bifurcation value. All eleven coefficients are active in the chaos. Table 16.9 is similar to Table 16.8, except that we list the seven largest Lyapunov exponents. For $r = 30.30$, the Lyapunov dimension is already nearly six, but the correlation dimension is still less than four. Recall that just above the bifurcation to chaos in the 7CM, we found $d_L \simeq 3.7$ and $\nu \simeq 2.0$. As the value of r is increased and the attractor becomes more chaotic, the Lyapunov dimension becomes slightly greater than six, while the correlation dimension is 5.7 ± 0.1 by $r = 56$. Thus, increases in the degree of chaos of the system suggested by increases in the values of γ_1, γ_2, and γ_3 are more dramatically realized by the correlation dimension, while the large magnitude of γ_7 restricts the variation of d_L. Interestingly, as the value of r approaches 200, both dimensions of the chaotic attractor decrease in value, even though the

Table 16.9 The seven largest Lyapunov exponents, the Lyapunov dimension, and some correlation dimensions of the attractor of the 11CM for several values of the Rayleigh number.

$r = Ra/Ra_4$	γ_1	γ_2	γ_3	γ_4	γ_5	γ_6	γ_7	d_L	ν
30.27	0.98	0.54	0.08	0.	-0.60	-1.48	-13.9	5.68	
30.30	1.08	0.57	0.10	0.	-0.65	-1.45	-13.9	5.76	3.4 ± 0.2
30.37	1.12	0.61	0.11	0.	-0.66	-1.38	-13.9	5.86	
30.70	1.21	0.65	0.12	0.	-0.67	-1.36	-13.8	5.96	
37	1.90	1.10	0.28	0.	-0.50	-1.43	-13.8	6.10	
56	2.72	1.65	0.73	0.	-0.35	-1.67	-13.8	6.22	5.7 ± 0.1
200	3.80	1.65	0.42	0.	-2.30	-4.20	-10.1	5.85	4.3 ± 0.2

magnitude of the largest Lyapunov exponent increases. Moreover, the value of ν becomes nearly identical to that obtained in the 7CM (see Table 16.8). These observations are partly explained by additional numerical integrations that indicate that trajectories approach the seven-dimensional CS_{42} subspace at larger forcing values.

Thus, in comparing the solution regimes of the three-, seven- and eleven-coefficient models, we see evidence that the observed chaos is aphysical; that is, the product of insufficient spatial resolution in the model. As coefficients are added to the three-coefficient Lorenz system to create a hierarchical set of models, the appearance of chaos is delayed until larger forcing values. These results are consistent with those of Marcus (1981) and Curry et al. (1984) concerning the truncation dependency of finite model attractors.

We have shown that the Lyapunov exponents, the Lyapunov dimension and the correlation dimension act to detect, distinguish, and resolve complex characteristics of the structure and predictability of the solutions to nonlinear low-order spectral models. Transitions from one solution regime to another occur at forcing values at which one or more Lyapunov exponents either become zero and remain zero, increase or decrease from zero, or change sign. At these values of the forcing, a Hopf bifurcation occurs and the dimension of the system attractor changes. More subtle bifurcations, such as period doublings, in which stability is transferred but the attractor dimension is unchanged, are signaled by one Lyapunov exponent increasing to zero exactly at the bifurcation value but remaining negative for nearby forcing values.

As measures of chaos in higher-dimensional models, the Lyapunov and correlation dimensions differ significantly, particularly at values of the forcing just above the transition to aperiodicity. Smooth variations in ν appear to be strongly tied to smooth variations in the magnitudes of the positive Lyapunov exponents. However, in all experiments, for L^+ the number of positive Lyapunov exponents, we find $L^+ \leq \nu \leq d_L$, supporting the argument of Grassberger and Procaccia (1983b). For well-developed chaos, d_L follows a simple rule: the integer part K of the Lyapunov dimension is just twice the number L^+ of positive Lyapunov exponents. This result suggests that the value of d_L is very sensitive to the number of expanding directions in the phase space. Intriguingly, for such well-developed chaos, L^+ is also the number of primary branches emanating from the conductive solution, and exactly the number of Lorenz submodels (two in the 7CM, three in the 11CM). These observations suggest not only that the relationships between a model and its low-order submodels are complex, but also that these dimensions may have important roles in resolving this complexity. It is just such roles that we hope these measures will play in guiding development of suitable models for the study of chaotic behavior.

CHAPTER 17

INTRODUCTION TO TOPOLOGICAL HYDRODYNAMICS

JOHN A. DUTTON AND ROBERT WELLS

The development and utilization of models depends, as indicated in Chapter 1, on the maturity of the discipline. Once the discipline has evolved sufficiently that an axiomatic mathematical model is available to specify the evolution of the state variables of a system, then our attempt to develop theories involves proving theorems about the behavior of the solutions to the system. We may use the conclusions of the theorems to suggest how to apply the models to a wide variety of practical problems. Examples of such applications in the atmospheric sciences range from numerical weather forecasting to studies of possible climate changes.

The investigation of the implications of a model is thus a mathematical endeavor, in two related senses. The first is that the conventions of mathematics provide a language with which to describe the physical behavior. State variables are viewed on a four-dimensional domain, and operations such as differentiation and integration can produce new relevant quantities. The second is that the formalisms of mathematics provide an objective mechanism for obtaining inferences about the behavior of the modeled system. Upon verifying that the hypotheses of theorems hold, we may use the conclusions to describe the structure of the solutions, even if the solutions are not known explicitly. In effect, we treat a model as a collection of axioms together with rules of inference, and we then use the axioms to derive theorems.

Thus, the strategy for studying a particular system is to attach an appropriate mathematical structure to a model of the system. In this chapter, we illustrate this process by reviewing some fundamental theorems concerning atmospheric behavior. Some of the discussion here is drawn from Dutton (1982, 1986).

17.1 Molecules to Models

The most fundamental model of the atmosphere represents it as a finite collection of molecules of various gases that interact with each other through well-known physical processes such as collision. In principle, we could write a set of ordinary differential equations that describes the behavior of this collection of molecules, and upon showing that the system has finite energy, we would know that a solution exists for all time (Lumley, 1970). However, this result is of little practical value because of the excessively large number of equations (at least 10^{24}) that we would have to integrate to find this solution.

Therefore, we turn instead to a statistical representation of the behavior of the molecules and introduce relatively few state variables such as pressure, density, temperature, and macroscopic velocity. These variables are averages of well-defined quantities describing molecular properties and motion. Either through the methods of statistical mechanics or through extensions to continua of the classical macroscopic physical conservation equations and Newton's law, we produce partial differential equations that express the local rates of change of the new state variables as functionals of the state variables themselves.

While this process has created an apparently more tractable representation of the atmosphere, it has transformed a finite-dimensional problem into an infinite-dimensional one. The apparent simplicity of representation of local rates of change of state variables is gained through the introduction of the quadratic nonlinearity in the advective terms of the equations of atmospheric motion. The new model also stimulates questions, which are under continuing investigation, about the existence and uniqueness of solutions to the associated boundary value problem.

The equations of motion that have been produced by this process are remarkably successful. In appropriate forms, they describe a great variety of atmospheric processes, ranging from the instability properties of the long waves in the westerlies to the dynamics of turbulence and the propagation of sound waves. They are, so far as we know, a faithful model of processes occurring across an immense range of temporal and spatial scales, ranges so wide that they eliminate the possibility of accurate direct simulation even with modern computers.

The use of the equations of motion to examine scientific questions or to solve practical problems related to atmospheric evolution requires that the equations be reduced to appropriate approximate forms. This reduction involves two related activities. First, we determine the essential temporal and spatial features of the phenomena to be studied. Second, we seek appropriate alterations of the equations of motion that capture the essential processes while excluding others that are not believed to be important at the scales of interest.

Creation of these approximate models is described schematically in Fig. 17.1. We begin in the upper left corner with a specific fluid system such as the entire atmosphere. Usually in studying this fluid system, we restrict attention to distinct flow regimes or to phenomena that appear within reduced ranges of spatial or temporal scales. We thus attempt, in some sense, to isolate those features of the flow that are essential to the issues at hand. This selection is denoted by the double arrow on the left of Fig. 17.1, and the resulting reduced physical system is represented at the lower left. On the upper right, the original system is modeled by a complete set

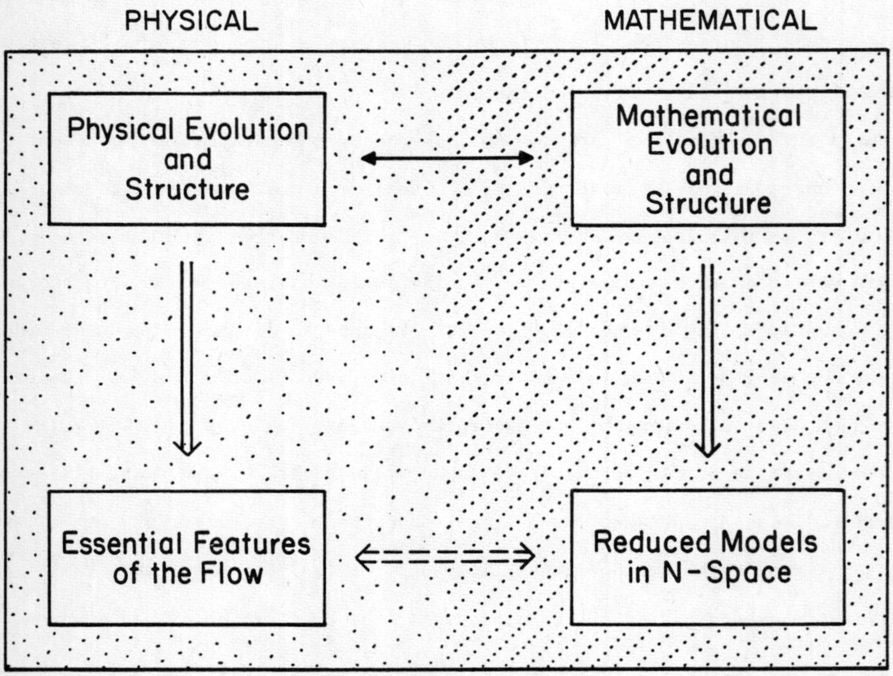

Fig. 17.1 The process of creating a suitable N-dimensional approximate model of hydrodynamic flow. The box in the upper left represents a specific fluid system such as the atmosphere, the box in the lower left a reduced physical system, the box in the upper right the set of partial differential equations for the complete system, and the box in the lower right an N-dimensional approximate model of the system. The two-headed arrow signifies that the atmosphere and the complete model of it are equivalent, the double arrow that a reduction in the scope of the problem occurs by either scale selection (left) or projection on N-space (right), and the dashed arrow that verification of the solutions to the reduced model is carried out by comparison of their properties with those of the hypothesized essential features of the flow.

of partial differential equations whose solutions would represent the evolution of the physical system. We cannot find these solutions analytically, and so we must approximate them finite-dimensionally. As denoted by the double arrow on the right of the diagram, we therefore obtain an N-dimensional approximation of the solution to the complete partial differential equations. It remains to compare the implications of the approximate model with the physical structures obtained by formal or subjective identification of the essential features. The process of verifying the model, as denoted by the dashed arrow, may lead to changes in its formulation, or in some cases, to revisions in our perception of what really are the essential features of the flow.

This notion of projection on N-space is fundamental to any theoretical or practical application of a model. Two standard methods of projection are often used. One is representation on a grid of points, with the evolution specified by finite-difference equations. The other is conversion to a spectral model that specifies the evolution of Fourier coefficients via representation of the field with a finite set of basis functions.

The latter process seems to offer a variety of advantages, and both theoretical and practical applications are turning in this direction. It is this approach that we have adopted throughout the monograph. In this chapter we show that both the complete solutions and the finite-dimensional ones satisfy similar theorems, thus supporting our contention that the finite models are properly specified.

17.2 Canonical Differential Equations

Models of atmospheric, oceanic, or laboratory flows are almost always based on the Navier-Stokes equations along with the First Law of Thermodynamics, although these equations are often modified for application to specific problems. From a mathematical viewpoint, we are interested in the existence and uniqueness of the solutions to the associated boundary value problem and in finding effective procedures for characterizing the topological behavior of the solutions. From the viewpoint of elucidating the properties of the solutions for practical applications, we are concerned with solution regimes, stability properties of solutions, and issues related to the efficacy of approximation. Particular concern centers on questions associated with the predictability of flows.

In this section, we present a canonical version of the equations of atmospheric motion along with a simplified dynamical model, and develop some results related to uniqueness, instability and predictability. After exploring some of the properties of the equations directly, we turn in the next section to eigenvalue problems that provide a basis for Galerkin methods that reduce the complexity of problems associated with the original equations.

<u>17.2.1 The atmospheric boundary value problem</u>. It is advantageous for a variety of reasons to reduce the equations of atmospheric motion to a dimensionless form that incorporates the Boussinesq approximation. Scaling both horizontal and vertical distances with a single length scale L (perhaps the radius of the planet) and scaling time with the planetary rotation rate Ω produces the dimensionless set of equations (Dutton, 1982, 1986):

$$\frac{\partial \underset{\sim}{v}^*}{\partial t^*} + \underset{\sim}{v}^* \cdot \nabla \underset{\sim}{v}^* = -\nabla \Pi^* + \Gamma \tau^* \underset{\sim}{k} - \underset{\sim}{\omega}^* \times \underset{\sim}{v}^* + \alpha_o \nabla \cdot \rho_o \nu \nabla \underset{\sim}{v}^* \quad , \tag{17.1}$$

$$\frac{\partial \tau^*}{\partial t^*} + \underset{\sim}{v}^* \cdot \nabla \tau^* = -\Gamma w^* + \Lambda q + P^{-1} \alpha_o \nabla \cdot \rho_o \nu \nabla \tau^* \quad , \tag{17.2}$$

$$\nabla \cdot \rho_o \underset{\sim}{v}^* = 0 \quad . \tag{17.3}$$

The equations are assumed to be defined on a finite three-dimensional spatial domain D (perhaps contained between spherical shells at $z^* = 0$ and $z^* = z_T^*$). The vector $\underset{\sim}{v}^* = (v_1^*, v_2^*, v_3^*) = (u^*, v^*, w^*)$ is a dimensionless velocity, τ^* is a scaled representation of the fractional potential temperature perturbation θ'/θ_o, and Π^* is a scaled version of the product of the dimensionless pressure p^* and ρ_o. The variables $\rho_o = 1/\alpha_o$ and θ_o represent the vertical stratification in an isothermal state with the maximum entropy that can be obtained in an atmosphere with the same mass and total energy as the state of interest (see Dutton 1973, 1986). The heating is prescribed by q, and the parameters in the equation are $\Gamma = N/\Omega$, where $N^2 = g\, \partial[\ln(\theta_o)]/\partial z$, $\Lambda = g/(N\Omega L)$, the Prandtl number $P = \nu/\kappa$, and the dimensionless rotation rate $\underset{\sim}{\omega}^*$.

A standard set of boundary conditions are that

$$\underset{\sim}{v}^* = 0 \text{ at } z^* = 0,\ z_T^* \quad , \tag{17.4}$$

$$\frac{\partial\tau^*}{\partial z^*} = 0 \text{ at } z^* = 0 \quad , \tag{17.5}$$

$$\tau^* = 0 \text{ at } z^* = z_T^* \quad , \tag{17.6}$$

where z_T^* is the scaled top of the atmosphere and can be any finite value. A consequence of these boundary conditions is that the model loses energy at the boundaries. The choice $\partial\tau^*/\partial z^* = 0$ at $z^* = 0$ eliminates conductive heating, and as a consequence, all of the thermal forcing appears in q. A more realistic description of surface heating patterns imposed by the distribution of land, sea, and ice might be obtained by prescribing a boundary temperature $\tau_B^* = \tau^*(x^*,y^*)$ at $z^* = 0$. A convenient approach then is to set $\tau^* = \tau_B^* + \tau'$ with $\tau' = 0$ at $z^* = 0$; the function τ_B^* and its horizontal derivatives would then appear in the equations as forcing terms (e.g., Yost and Shirer, 1982).

We have, in making these choices in (17.4)-(17.6), isolated the atmosphere from thermal interaction with the ocean or the land surface since the boundary conditions are temporally invariant. We must also face the issue of whether or not to use the molecular value of viscosity; parametric values representing the effects of small scale phenomena become necessary when we truncate spectral expansions. For the present purposes, we take the heating function as fixed in time but spatially variable, perhaps representing the present values of net atmospheric heating from radiative, sensible, and latent sources. Alternatively, the heating can be scaled by a parameter or given in a Newtonian formulation.

The equations (17.1)-(17.3) admit of an energy conservation principle obtained by taking the dot product of the first equation with $\rho_o \underset{\sim}{v}^*$ and the scalar product of the second with $\rho_o\tau^*$, and then integrating the results over the model domain. Use of the Divergence Theorem, the boundary conditions, and the incompressibility condition (17.3) produces the results

$$\dot{KE} = \frac{\partial}{\partial t^*}\int_D \frac{\rho_o|\underset{\sim}{v}^*|^2}{2}\, d\underset{\sim}{x}^* = \Gamma\int_D \rho_o w^*\tau^*\, d\underset{\sim}{x}^* - \int_D \rho_o\nu|\nabla\underset{\sim}{v}^*|^2 d\underset{\sim}{x}^* - B_v \quad , \tag{17.7}$$

$$\dot{AE} = \frac{\partial}{\partial t^*}\int_D \frac{\rho_o\tau^{*2}}{2}\, d\underset{\sim}{x}^* = -\Gamma\int_D \rho_o w^*\tau^*\, d\underset{\sim}{x}^* + \Lambda\int_D \rho_o\tau^* q\, d\underset{\sim}{x}^* - P^{-1}\int_D \rho_o\nu|\nabla\tau^*|^2 d\underset{\sim}{x}^* - B_\tau \quad , \tag{17.8}$$

in which B_v and B_τ are nonnegative boundary dissipation terms and the total energy $E = KE + AE$. As is usual in Boussinesq models, the available energy generated by the heating is transferred to kinetic energy through the vertical heat flux $\rho_o w^* \tau^*$.

Mathematical study of the equations (17.1)-(17.3) is often facilitated by further reduction. We take the density ρ_o to be constant, eliminate the Coriolis force, ignore the First Law, and set Γ to zero. In order to provide an analog of the thermal forcing in the original model, we add a term $\underset{\sim}{F}$, scaled by a parameter μ, to the equation. Thus we have the Navier-Stokes equations

$$\frac{\partial \underset{\sim}{v}^*}{\partial t^*} + \underset{\sim}{v}^* \cdot \nabla \underset{\sim}{v}^* = -\nabla \Pi^* + \nu \nabla^2 \underset{\sim}{v}^* + \mu \underset{\sim}{F} \quad , \tag{17.9}$$

$$\nabla \cdot \underset{\sim}{v}^* = 0 \quad , \tag{17.10}$$

subject to the boundary condition that $\underset{\sim}{v}^* = 0$ on the boundary ∂D.

<u>17.2.2 Fundamental theorems of atmospheric science</u>. On the assumption that solutions to the boundary value problem posed in (17.1)-(17.3) and (17.4)-(17.6) exist in an appropriate sense (for otherwise we have nothing to talk about), we can proceed to discuss two basic theorems about this model of atmospheric flow.

Let us refer to a situation in which both $\underset{\sim}{v}^*$ and $\partial \underset{\sim}{v}^*/\partial t^*$ vanish everywhere in D in a nonempty interval I of time as steady and motionless. Then for steady motionless conditions, the equations (17.1)-(17.3) become

$$\nabla \Pi^* - \Gamma \tau^* \underset{\sim}{k} = 0 \quad , \tag{17.11}$$

$$\frac{\partial \tau^*}{\partial t^*} = \Lambda q + P^{-1} \alpha_o \nabla \cdot \rho_o \nu \nabla \tau^* \quad , \tag{17.12}$$

where the first implies that in $D \times I$

$$\nabla_H \Pi^* = 0 \quad , \tag{17.13}$$

$$\frac{\partial \Pi^*}{\partial z^*} = \Gamma \tau^* \quad , \tag{17.14}$$

and hence that

$$\nabla_H \tau^* = 0 \quad . \tag{17.15}$$

But now (17.12) implies that in $D \times I$, we have

$$\nabla_H q = 0 \quad . \tag{17.16}$$

Stating the contrapositive result, we see that steady and motionless solutions are impossible if the heating field varies on spherical horizontal surfaces in the model atmosphere. In its original form, this theorem is due to Jeffreys; it has been discussed at length by Dutton (1976, 1986). Because of its global implications, we shall refer to it as the First Fundamental Theorem of Atmospheric Science. We note that a similar theorem holds for flows confined to the cyclic rectangular domains discussed in earlier chapters of the monograph.

We turn to the second global result, which is proved using the energy method. We shall use the two Poisson inequalities that

$$\int_D \rho_o \nu |\nabla \underset{\sim}{v}^*|^2 d\underset{\sim}{x}^* \geq \gamma_1 \int_D \rho_o |\underset{\sim}{v}^*|^2 d\underset{\sim}{x}^* \quad , \tag{17.17}$$

$$\int_D \rho_o \nu |\nabla \tau^*|^2 d\underset{\sim}{x}^* \geq \eta_1 \int_D \rho_o \tau^{*2} d\underset{\sim}{x}^* \quad , \tag{17.18}$$

in which γ_1 and η_1 are positive, finite numbers that depend on ν. With these, the energy equations (17.7)-(17.8) may be stated as

$$\begin{aligned}
\dot{E} &= \dot{KE} + \dot{AE} \\
&= \Lambda \int_D \rho_o \tau^* q \, d\underset{\sim}{x}^* - \int_D \rho_o \nu [\,|\nabla \underset{\sim}{v}^*|^2 + P^{-1}|\nabla \tau^*|^2]\, d\underset{\sim}{x}^* - B_v - B_\tau \\
&\leq \Lambda \left(\int_D \rho_o \tau^{*2} d\underset{\sim}{x}^* \int_D \rho_o q^2 d\underset{\sim}{x}^*\right)^{1/2} - \int_D \rho_o [\gamma_1 |\underset{\sim}{v}^*|^2 + P^{-1}\eta_1 \tau^{*2}]\, d\underset{\sim}{x}^* \\
&\leq \sqrt{2}\, \Lambda\, E^{1/2} Q - 2\eta E \quad ,
\end{aligned} \tag{17.19}$$

where we have used the facts that $B_v > 0$ and $B_\tau > 0$, we have introduced the parameters

$$Q^2 = \int_D \rho_o q^2 d\underset{\sim}{x}^* \quad , \tag{17.20}$$

$$\eta = \frac{\min(\gamma_1, \eta_1)}{\max(1, P)} \quad , \tag{17.21}$$

and we have used the Schwarz inequality

$$\int_D |fg| \, d\underset{\sim}{x}^* \leq \left(\int_D f^2 d\underset{\sim}{x}^* \int_D g^2 d\underset{\sim}{x}^*\right)^{1/2} \quad . \tag{17.22}$$

From the differential inequality (17.19), we conclude that

$$E^{1/2}(t^*) \leq e^{-\eta t^*} E^{1/2}(0) + \frac{\Lambda Q}{\sqrt{2}\eta}\left[1 - e^{-\eta t^*}\right] \quad . \tag{17.23}$$

As a first interpretation, we see that the energy of any solution is uniformly bounded by the maximum of the quantity on the right and hence is bounded as $t^* \to \infty$ by a multiple of the mean-square heating rate Q.

This result has a deeper meaning, however. Let $V = (\underset{\sim}{v}^*, \tau^*)$ denote the solution to the boundary value problem of (17.1)-(17.3) and (17.4)-(17.6) as

$$V(\underset{\sim}{x}^*, t^*) = S_{t^*} V(\underset{\sim}{x}^*, 0) \quad . \tag{17.24}$$

Let U_T be the set of all initial conditions $V(\underset{\sim}{x}^*,0)$ with finite energy E that produce solutions that exist for $0 \leq t^* \leq T$. Then all initial fields $V(\underset{\sim}{x}^*,0)$ are mapped by S_{t^*} at $t^* = T$ into the ball of square integrable functions specified by the right of (17.23) evaluated at $t^* = T$. More significantly, all functions in U_∞ (if there are any) are mapped into the ball specified by (17.23) as functions only of the mean square heating and dissipation rates. Thus, the interaction of the heating and the dissipation control the asymptotic variation permitted in the flow.

This result, as well as its more specific version that holds in a spectral version of this model (see Section 17.3.3), is known as the <u>Trapping Theorem</u>. It too has global implications, and we refer to it as the <u>Second Fundamental Theorem of Atmospheric Science</u>.

The reduced model (17.9)-(17.10) also yields these two theorems. In most cases of interest, the forcing vector $\underset{\sim}{F}$ has both solenoidal and irrotational components. The assumption of steady, motionless conditions implies that the irrotational component of $\underset{\sim}{F}$ vanishes. Hence Jeffreys' Theorem, in this case, is that there must be motion if the curl of $\underset{\sim}{F}$ does not vanish. The Trapping Theorem is obtained from (17.9)-(17.10) with the method used in (17.19), only obvious modifications being necessary.

17.2.3 Uniqueness, instability, and predictability. Examination of issues related to uniqueness of solutions, to the instability process that leads to determination of the dominant regime, and to limitations on predictability all involve comparison of two solutions to the boundary value problem (17.1)-(17.3) and (17.4)-(17.6) or to the problem (17.9)-(17.10). Various approaches can be taken, but the most direct is an extension of the energy method of the previous subsection.

We let $\underset{\sim}{v}^* = \underset{\sim}{U}^*$, $\tau^* = \Phi^*$ and $\Pi^* = \Theta^*$ be a solution, either steady or evolutionary, to the first boundary value problem. Then we define another solution as $\underset{\sim}{v}^* = \underset{\sim}{U}^* + \underset{\sim}{u}^*$, $\tau^* = \Phi^* + \phi^*$, and $\Pi^* = \Theta^* + \theta^*$. The fields $\underset{\sim}{u}^*$, ϕ^*, and θ^* are thus the difference of two solutions and the equations governing their evolution are obtained by subtracting (17.1)-(17.3) applied to the two solutions. The result obtained when the same forcing q is applied to both cases is

$$\frac{\partial \underset{\sim}{u}^*}{\partial t^*} + \underset{\sim}{U}^*\cdot\nabla\underset{\sim}{u}^* + \underset{\sim}{u}^*\cdot\nabla\underset{\sim}{U}^* + \underset{\sim}{u}^*\cdot\nabla\underset{\sim}{u}^* = -\nabla\theta^* + \Gamma\phi^*\underset{\sim}{k} - \underset{\sim}{\omega}^* \times \underset{\sim}{u}^* + \alpha_o\nabla\cdot\rho_o\nu\nabla\underset{\sim}{u}^* \quad , \tag{17.25}$$

$$\frac{\partial \phi^*}{\partial t^*} + \underset{\sim}{U}^*\cdot\nabla\phi^* + \underset{\sim}{u}^*\cdot\nabla\Phi^* + \underset{\sim}{u}^*\cdot\nabla\phi^* = -\Gamma u_3^* + P^{-1}\alpha_o\nabla\cdot\rho_o\nu\nabla\phi^* \quad , \tag{17.26}$$

$$\nabla\cdot\rho_o\underset{\sim}{u}^* = 0 \quad . \tag{17.27}$$

The energy equation for the difference fields in (17.25)-(17.27) is found, by the same techniques we used earlier, to be

$$\dot{E}' = \frac{\partial}{\partial t^*}\int_D \frac{\rho_o}{2}\left(|\underset{\sim}{u}^*|^2 + \phi^{*2}\right) d\underset{\sim}{x}^*$$

$$= -\int_D \rho_o\left[\underset{\sim}{u}^*\cdot(\underset{\sim}{u}^*\cdot\nabla\underset{\sim}{U}^*) + \phi^*\underset{\sim}{u}^*\cdot\nabla\Phi^*\right] d\underset{\sim}{x}^*$$

$$-\int_D \rho_o\nu\left[|\nabla\underset{\sim}{u}^*|^2 + P^{-1}|\nabla\phi^*|^2\right] d\underset{\sim}{x}^* - B_u - B_\phi \quad . \tag{17.28}$$

We can refer to the solution $(\underset{\sim}{U}^*,\Phi^*,\Theta^*)$ as stable if the perturbation energy E' decreases for all perturbations (u^*,ϕ^*,θ^*). Instability, then, must arise from the processes represented in the first term on the right, in which we have the Reynolds stresses $u_i^*u_j^*$ operating on the shear $\partial U_i^*/\partial x_j^*$ and the heat flux $u_i^*\phi^*$ operating on the temperature gradient $\partial\Phi^*/\partial x_i^*$. Simple examples show that this integral can be expected to be negative for many flow configurations and thus force the growth of perturbations, but it clearly can have widely varying values depending on the precise arrangements of the perturbation variables relative to the shear and temperature gradients. It is, therefore, difficult to establish sufficient conditions for instability to occur, even though we can identify the physical processes that drives it.

Now suppose that the fields $(\underset{\sim}{u}^*,\phi^*,\theta^*)$ represent the differences between two solutions that evolve from slightly different initial conditions. Experience with simulating or predicting the evolution of fluid flows has demonstrated that slight or even negligible differences in initial conditions can lead to strikingly different flow fields, thus stimulating interest in the theoretical and practical limits of predictability. We see from (17.28) that the growth of differences is caused by the same mechanisms that create instability and that predictability problems are solely a consequence of the nonlinearity of the flow.

Upon assuming for convenience that classical solutions to the boundary value problem exist, we can proceed to investigate the possible uniqueness of solutions with the aid of the two inequalities

$$\int_D \rho_o \underset{\sim}{u}^* \cdot (\underset{\sim}{u}^* \cdot \nabla \underset{\sim}{U}^*)\, d\underset{\sim}{x}^* \leq \int_D \rho_o \sum_{i,j=1}^{3} |u_i^*||u_j^*| \left|\frac{\partial U_i^*}{\partial x_j^*}\right| d\underset{\sim}{x}^*$$

$$\leq \max_{D,i,j} \left|\frac{\partial U_i^*}{\partial x_j^*}\right| \int_D \rho_o \sum_{i,j=1}^{3} |u_i^*||u_j^*|\, d\underset{\sim}{x}^*$$

$$\leq 3 \max_{D,i,j} \left|\frac{\partial U_i^*}{\partial x_j^*}\right| \int_D \rho_o |\underset{\sim}{u}^*|^2 d\underset{\sim}{x}^* \quad , \qquad (17.29)$$

$$\int_D \rho_o \phi^* \underset{\sim}{u}^* \cdot \nabla \Phi^*\, d\underset{\sim}{x}^* \leq \int_D \rho_o |\phi^*||\underset{\sim}{u}^*||\nabla \Phi^*|\, d\underset{\sim}{x}^*$$

$$\leq \max_D |\nabla \Phi^*| \left(\int_D \rho_o |\phi^*|^2 d\underset{\sim}{x}^* \int_D \rho_o |\underset{\sim}{u}^*|^2 d\underset{\sim}{x}^*\right)^{1/2}$$

$$\leq \max_D |\nabla \Phi^*|\, \frac{1}{2} \int_D \rho_o (\phi^{*2} + |\underset{\sim}{u}^*|^2)\, d\underset{\sim}{x}^* \quad , \qquad (17.30)$$

which permit us, using (17.17)-(17.18), to put (17.28) in the form

$$\dot{E}' \leq [7M(t^*) - 2\eta]\, E' \quad , \tag{17.31}$$

where

$$M(t^*) = \max_{D,i,j} \left[\left|\frac{\partial U_i^*}{\partial x_j^*}\right|, \left|\frac{\partial \Phi^*}{\partial x_j^*}\right| \right] \quad , \tag{17.32}$$

$$\eta = \frac{\min(\gamma_1, \eta_1)}{\max(1,P)} \quad , \tag{17.33}$$

and thus to arrive at (cf. (17.23))

$$\dot{E}'(t^*) \leq E'(0)\, \exp[\, 7 \int_0^{t^*} M(s)\, ds - 2\eta t^*] \quad . \tag{17.34}$$

This result has a number of implications. First, a steady solution $(\underset{\sim}{U}^*, \Phi^*, \Theta^*)$ is stable to all perturbations provided that the Reynolds number

$$3.5 \max_{t^*}[M(t^*)]/\eta < 1 \quad . \tag{17.35}$$

Second, if the two flows $(\underset{\sim}{U}^*, \Phi^*, \Theta^*)$ and $(\underset{\sim}{v}^*, \tau^*, \Pi^*)$ evolve from initial conditions that are identical except on a set of zero volume, then $E' = 0$ and so uniqueness is established for any Reynolds number for classical solutions. Finally, (17.34) shows that the solutions are continuous with respect to initial conditions in any finite interval [0,T] in which the evolving solution $(\underset{\sim}{U}^*, \Phi^*, \Theta^*)$ has bounded gradients $|\nabla \underset{\sim}{U}^*|$ and $|\nabla \Phi^*|$.

We use a different set of inequalities to examine these issues for the system (17.9)-(17.10). The energy equation equivalent to (17.28) is now

$$\dot{E}' = - \int_D \underset{\sim}{u}^* \cdot (\underset{\sim}{u}^* \cdot \nabla \underset{\sim}{U}^*)\, d\underset{\sim}{x}^* - \int_D \nu |\nabla \underset{\sim}{u}^*|^2 d\underset{\sim}{x}^* - B_u \quad . \tag{17.36}$$

We introduce the embedding inequality for three dimensions (Ladyzhenskaya, 1969)

$$\int_D |u^*|^4 d\underset{\sim}{x}^* \leq C^2 (\int_D |\underset{\sim}{u}^*|^2 d\underset{\sim}{x}^*)^{1/2} (\int_D |\nabla \underset{\sim}{u}^*|^2 d\underset{\sim}{x}^*)^{3/2} \quad , \tag{17.37}$$

where C is a constant, and we define the norm

$$||\underset{\sim}{u}^*||_p = (\int_D |\underset{\sim}{u}^*|^p\, d\underset{\sim}{x}^*)^{1/p} \quad ; \tag{17.38}$$

then with (17.17) for $\rho_o = 1$ we may conclude that

$$||\underset{\sim}{u}^*||_4^2 \leq C||\nabla\underset{\sim}{u}^*||_2^2 \nu^{1/4}\gamma_1^{-1/4} \quad . \tag{17.39}$$

Now with the Schwarz inequality (17.22) we can write

$$\begin{aligned}\int_D \underset{\sim}{u}^*\cdot(\underset{\sim}{u}^*\cdot\nabla\underset{\sim}{U}^*)\, d\underset{\sim}{x}^* &\leq \int_D |\underset{\sim}{u}^*|^2|\nabla\underset{\sim}{U}^*|\, d\underset{\sim}{x}^* \\ &\leq (\int_D |\underset{\sim}{u}^*|^4 d\underset{\sim}{x}^* \int_D |\nabla\underset{\sim}{U}^*|^2 d\underset{\sim}{x}^*)^{1/2} \\ &= ||\underset{\sim}{u}^*||_4^2\ ||\nabla\underset{\sim}{U}^*||_2 \\ &\leq C||\nabla\underset{\sim}{u}^*||_2^2 \nu^{1/4}\gamma_1^{-1/4}||\nabla\underset{\sim}{U}^*||_2 \quad ,\end{aligned} \tag{17.40}$$

and so, recalling that $B_u \geq 0$, we have

$$\dot{E}' \leq \left(\frac{C||\nabla\underset{\sim}{U}^*||_2}{\gamma_1^{1/4}\nu^{-1/4}} - \nu\right) ||\nabla\underset{\sim}{u}^*||_2^2 \quad . \tag{17.41}$$

If $\underset{\sim}{U}^*$ is a steady solution, then integrating the inner product of (17.9) with $\underset{\sim}{U}^*$ and using the inequality (17.17) with $\rho_o = 1$, we find that

$$\begin{aligned}\nu||\nabla\underset{\sim}{U}^*||_2^2 = \nu \int_D |\nabla\underset{\sim}{U}^*|^2 d\underset{\sim}{x}^* &= \mu \int_D \underset{\sim}{U}^*\cdot\underset{\sim}{F}\, d\underset{\sim}{x}^* - B_U \\ &\leq \mu||\underset{\sim}{U}^*||_2\ ||\underset{\sim}{F}||_2 \\ &\leq \mu||\nabla\underset{\sim}{U}^*||_2\ ||\underset{\sim}{F}||_2 \nu^{1/2}/\sqrt{\gamma_1} \quad .\end{aligned} \tag{17.42}$$

This inequality implies that

$$||\nabla\underset{\sim}{U}^*||_2 \leq \mu||\underset{\sim}{F}||_2/(\sqrt{\nu\gamma_1}) \quad , \tag{17.43}$$

and so now the condition for stability implied by (17.41) is that

$$Gr = \frac{\mu C||\underset{\sim}{F}||_2}{\nu^2 \lambda_1^{3/4}} < 1 \quad . \tag{17.44}$$

In (17.44), we have introduced the parameter $\lambda_1 = \gamma_1/\nu$ that, owing to (17.17), is independent of ν. The quantity Gr is the Grashof number; it has emerged recently (e.g., for two-dimensional flows in Constantin and Foias, 1985) as a controlling factor in the dimensionality of hydrodynamic attractors. Its significance in (17.44) is that the stability criterion is expressed in terms of system and control parameters, even though the criterion is only a sufficient, and probably not precise, estimate of the stability boundary.

17.3 Reduction of Dimension, Reduction of Complexity

The essential difficulty with the model of fluid flow presented by the nonlinear partial differential equations is that only indirect methods of inference about the nature of the solutions are currently available. Thus despite the intuitively attractive form of the model, the development of specific information about the evolution of the flow or numerical simulation of its properties requires a reduction in complexity. We have the choice of eliminating nonlinearity or reducing the dimensionality of the problem.

Since the nonlinearity is responsible for the most interesting aspects of fluid flow, including instability, regime selection, and difficulties with predictability, we evidently attempt to retain reasonably faithful portrayals of its dynamical consequences. In contrast, reduction of dimensionality might prove efficacious since the physical flows we seek to model and comprehend are, as mentioned earlier, inherently finite-dimensional themselves.

17.3.1 Eigenvalue problems and basis functions. A basic strategy in mathematics is to represent complicated objects as combinations of simpler components. Thus the familiar representation of a vector in Euclidean space R^3 as a linear combination of unit vectors leads to the general notion of a vector space and a set of basis functions. The dimension of the space is determined by the number of independent basis functions necessary to represent its members as linear combinations.

The research of J. B. Fourier on heat transfer and on solutions of the heat conduction equation led to the discovery that differential equations of certain types generate infinite families of functions that can serve as bases for infinite-dimensional spaces in which the solutions reside. These ideas and techniques thus provide us with an explicit representation of solutions as linear combinations of known functions and give us the option of choosing to work within the confines of a finite-dimensional subspace, a choice that offers the availability of explicit mathematical methods.

Fourier's technique, which we discussed in detail in Section 3.2, leads to a differential equation $y'' + \sigma y = 0$ defined on the interval [0,1]. Solutions exist only for certain values of σ, and the boundary conditions that $y(0) = y(1) = 0$ generate the functions $\sin(\sqrt{\sigma}x)$ for $\sigma = (n\pi)^2$, $n = 1,2, \ldots$, while the conditions that $y(0) = y(1) = 1$ generate $\cos(\sqrt{\sigma}x)$ for $\sigma = (n\pi)^2$; $n = 0,1,2, \ldots$. These functions are orthogonal, upon integration over the interval, and thus can serve as basis functions, or upon normalization, as the analogue of unit vectors. The linear combinations of such functions, which can, subject to technical restrictions, represent any function defined on [0,1], are known as Fourier series.

As we noted in Section 3.2, a common approach to developing a set of basis functions for physical problems is to solve Laplace's equation on the domain of interest, subject to the boundary conditions to be applied to the problem. The resulting eigenfunctions provide a Fourier expansion of the variables that may be used to create a spectral model. For hydrodynamic problems, this approach can be successful but complicated for various reasons.

As a superior alternative, we can attempt to choose basis functions that incorporate some of the dynamics of the flow itself. Thus for vectors $\underset{\sim}{v}(\underset{\sim}{x}^*,t^*)$ we might extract the linear uncoupled part of the equation of motion (17.1) and pose the Stokes eigenvalue problem

$$\nabla\cdot\rho_o\nu\nabla\underset{\sim}{\Psi}^* = -\gamma\nu\rho_o\underset{\sim}{\Psi}^* + \rho_o\nabla\Theta^* \quad , \tag{17.45}$$

$$\nabla\cdot\rho_o\underset{\sim}{\Psi}^* = 0 \quad , \tag{17.46}$$

where Θ^* is a scalar function; this problem gives a set of positive eigenvalues γ_m and a set of vector eigenfunctions $\underset{\sim}{\Psi}^*_m$ that can be normalized to produce the expansion

$$\underset{\sim}{v}^*(\underset{\sim}{x}^*,t^*) = \sum_{m=1}^{\infty} a_m(t^*)\underset{\sim m}{\Psi}^*(\underset{\sim}{x}^*) \quad . \tag{17.47}$$

The problem

$$\nabla \cdot \rho_o \nu \nabla \phi^* = - \xi \nu \rho_o \phi^* \quad , \tag{17.48}$$

obtained from the First Law is a slight modification of Laplace's equation and gives the expansion

$$\tau^*(\underset{\sim}{x}^*,t^*) = \sum_{m=1}^{\infty} b_m(t^*)\phi_m(\underset{\sim}{x}^*) \quad . \tag{17.49}$$

These procedures are more general than might be indicated by the boundary conditions specified above. For example, the first eigenvalue problem above can be solved relative to boundary conditions of the form $a\partial\underset{\sim}{\Psi}^*/\partial z^* + b\underset{\sim}{\Psi}^* = 0$ at $z^* = 0$ and $z^* = z_T^*$ (with certain desirable properties depending on the choice of sign of the constants a and b). Moreover, temporally or spatially varying boundary values $\underset{\sim B}{v}^*(\underset{\sim}{x}^*,t^*)$ may be accommodated, as mentioned earlier, by setting $\underset{\sim}{v}^* = \underset{\sim B}{v}^* + \underset{\sim}{u}^*(\underset{\sim}{x}^*,t^*)$, where now $\underset{\sim}{u}^*$ satisfies the condition (17.4) and the Fourier coefficients of $\underset{\sim B}{v}^*$ would appear in the spectral equations as forcing terms.

The eigenvalue problem (17.45)-(17.46), we note, produces basis functions (for ρ_o constant and, usually, $\nu = 1$) that can be used to develop spectral versions of the reduced equations (17.9)-(17.10) (see Section 17.3.4).

<u>17.3.2 Canonical spectral equations and the flow in phase space</u>. Spectral equations associated with the equations (17.1)-(17.3) are obtained by substituting the expansions (17.47) and (17.49) into (17.1)-(17.3) and using the orthonormality relations

$$\int_D \rho_o \underset{\sim m}{\Psi}^* \cdot \underset{\sim n}{\Psi}^* \, d\underset{\sim}{x}^* = \delta_{mn} = \begin{cases} 1, & m=n \\ 0, & m\neq n \end{cases} \quad , \tag{17.50}$$

$$\int_D \rho_o \phi_m^* \phi_n^* \, d\underset{\sim}{x}^* = \delta_{mn} \quad , \tag{17.51}$$

implied by the eigenvalue problems (17.45)-(17.46) and (17.48) to isolate the rate of change of the individual Fourier coefficients; here δ_{mn} is the Kronecker delta. We make the substitution, form the dot product of (17.1) and $\rho_o \underset{\sim}{\Psi}^*_n$ and multiply (17.2) by $\rho_o \phi^*_n$, integrate over D using the Divergence Theorem and the incompressibility condition (17.3) as appropriate, and obtain

$$\dot{a}_n + \sum_{\ell,m=1}^{\infty} D_{\ell mn} a_\ell a_m = \sum_{m=1}^{\infty} \Gamma E_{mn} b_m - \sum_{m=1}^{\infty} C_{mn} a_m - \nu\gamma_n a_n \quad , \quad n = 1, \ldots \quad ,(17.52)$$

$$\dot{b}_n + \sum_{\ell,m=1}^{\infty} F_{\ell mn} a_\ell b_m = -\sum_{m=1}^{\infty} \Gamma E_{nm} a_m + \Lambda \hat{q}_n - P^{-1}\nu\xi_n b_n \quad , \quad n = 1, \ldots \quad , (17.53)$$

in which ℓ and m are positive integers and we have taken ν to be constant. The interaction coefficients produced by the integrations used to obtain (17.52)-(17.53) are defined by

$$D_{\ell mn} = \int_D \rho_o \underset{\sim}{\Psi}^*_n \cdot (\underset{\sim}{\Psi}^*_\ell \cdot \nabla)\underset{\sim}{\Psi}^*_m \, d\underset{\sim}{x}^* = -D_{\ell nm} \quad , \tag{17.54}$$

$$F_{\ell mn} = \int_D \rho_o \phi^*_n (\underset{\sim}{\Psi}^*_\ell \cdot \nabla)\phi^*_m \, d\underset{\sim}{x}^* = -F_{\ell nm} \quad , \tag{17.55}$$

$$C_{mn} = \int_D \rho_o \underset{\sim}{\omega}^* \cdot (\underset{\sim}{\Psi}^*_m \times \underset{\sim}{\Psi}^*_n) \, d\underset{\sim}{x}^* = - C_{nm} \quad , \tag{17.56}$$

$$E_{mn} = \int_D \rho_o (\underset{\sim}{\Psi}^*_n \cdot \underset{\sim}{k})\phi^*_m \, d\underset{\sim}{x}^* \quad , \tag{17.57}$$

$$\hat{q}_n = \int_D \rho_o \phi^*_n q \, d\underset{\sim}{x}^* \quad . \tag{17.58}$$

The antisymmetry of the coefficients displayed in the first three definitions allows us, in the next subsection, to develop energy relations analogous to those that derive from the original equations and to prove that solutions exist to truncated versions of the equations (17.52)-(17.53).

The spectral equations (17.52)-(17.53) provide a transformation of the properties of the flow from the physical space in which it occurs to a phase space in which the behavior of the Fourier coefficients is portrayed. This transformation is an efficacious one that provides more information than we might have expected.

To study this transformation further, let us truncate the system (17.52)-(17.53) so that $\ell,m,n = 1, 2, \ldots, N$, where N is any finite positive integer. Then the resulting autonomous differential system may be represented as

$$\dot{\tilde{y}} = \tilde{Y}(\tilde{y}) \quad , \tag{17.59}$$

in which the 2N-vector $\tilde{y} = (a_1, \ldots, a_N, b_1, \ldots, b_N)$ represents a point in the phase space R^{2N}. Each such point corresponds to velocity and temperature fields represented at a time t^* by

$$\tilde{v}^N(\tilde{x}^*,t^*) = \sum_{m=1}^{N} a_m(t^*)\tilde{\Psi}_m^*(\tilde{x}^*) \quad , \tag{17.60}$$

$$\tau^N(\tilde{x}^*,t^*) = \sum_{m=1}^{N} b_m(t^*)\phi_m^*(\tilde{x}^*) \quad . \tag{17.61}$$

Conversely, the evolution of the fields (17.60)-(17.61) in physical space is represented by the motion of the point $\tilde{y}$ in phase space. Thus a specific pattern of evolution in physical space corresponds to the motion of $\tilde{y}$ along a trajectory in phase space (see also Section 3.1).

If we use the notation $S_{t*}\tilde{y}_o$ to denote the solution $\tilde{y}(t^*)$ emanating from the initial point $\tilde{y}_o$, then the operator S_{t*} generates a mapping or a flow

$$\tilde{y}(t^*) = S_{t*}\tilde{y}_o, \qquad S_{t*}: \ R^{2N} \to R^{2N} \quad , \tag{17.62}$$

that describes a transformation of R^{2N} into itself. This transformation can be applied to the set in phase space of all initial conditions in an appropriate subspace (one that has finite energy, for example) and thus generates an evolution of phase space that simultaneously represents the evolution of all physical flows with those initial conditions. We have advanced from studying the evolution of one flow in physical space or one trajectory in phase space to studying, conceptually, the evolution of a large collection of flows by observing the deformation or motion of the phase space itself. A particular objective, then, is to ascertain the limiting properties of classes of flows by observing the characteristics of the phase space in the limit.

17.3.3 The fundamental theorems--in phase space. If transformations from physical space to finite-dimensional phase spaces are to be truly effective in studying the behavior of fluid flows, then evidently the essential characteristics of the flow must be correctly transformed and accessible in either space.

Before turning to the fundamental theorems, we show that solutions to the truncated spectral equations always exist. To do so, we use the well-known result that ordinary differential systems that are analytic in their variables have solutions that exist for all time if the solutions are bounded (an expanded version of the outline presented below is available in Dutton, 1982). Since the Fourier coefficients a_n and b_n appear linearly and quadratically, the spectral equations are certainly analytic in their variables. Boundedness of solutions follows from finite energy. We multiply (17.52) by a_n and (17.53) by b_n and then sum over $\ell,m,n = 1, 2, \ldots, N$ to obtain the energy equation

$$\dot{E}_N = \frac{1}{2}\frac{d}{dt*}\Big(\sum_{n=1}^{N}(a_n^2 + b_n^2)\Big)$$

$$= \Lambda \sum_{n=1}^{N} b_n \hat{q}_n - \nu \sum_{n=1}^{N}(\gamma_n a_n^2 + P^{-1}\xi_n b_n^2) \quad , \tag{17.63}$$

analogous to the first two lines of (17.19) because the eigenvalues γ_n and ξ_n increase with n. With the aid of the Schwarz inequality for sums (cf. (17.22)), we may convert (17.63) into the inequality, valid for every $N < \infty$,

$$\dot{E}_N \leq \Lambda\Big(\sum_{n=1}^{N} b_n^2 \sum_{n=1}^{N} \hat{q}_n^2\Big)^{1/2} - \nu \min(\gamma_1,\xi_1)\sum_{n=1}^{N}(a_n^2 + P^{-1}b_n^2)$$

$$\leq \sqrt{2}\,\Lambda\, E_N^{1/2}\, Q_N - 2\eta\, E_N \quad , \tag{17.64}$$

where

$$\eta = \nu\,\frac{\min(\gamma_1,\xi_1)}{\max(1,P)} \quad . \tag{17.65}$$

Here we have written

$$Q_N = \Big(\sum_{n=1}^{N} \hat{q}_n^2\Big)^{1/2} \quad , \tag{17.66}$$

and hence Q in (17.20) is Q_∞. As before, the inequality implies that

$$E_N^{1/2}(t^*) \leq e^{-\eta t^*} E_N^{1/2}(0) + \frac{\Lambda Q_N}{\sqrt{2}\eta}\left[1 - e^{-\eta t^*}\right] \quad , \tag{17.67}$$

and thus $E_N(t^*)$ is uniformly bounded in t^* when $E_N(0)$ and Q_N are finite. Thus solutions to the truncated spectral system exist for all $N < \infty$ provided only that the initial energy and the mean square heating rate Q are finite.

The energy equation (17.63) can be transformed to give a more revealing result, as first shown by Lorenz (1963). Upon completing the square, we find that

$$\dot{E}_N = -\nu \sum_{n=1}^{N} \gamma_n a_n^2 - P^{-1} \nu \sum_{n=1}^{N} \xi_n \left[b_n - \frac{\Lambda \hat{q}_n P}{2\xi_n \nu}\right]^2 + P\Lambda^2 \sum_{n=1}^{N} \frac{\hat{q}_n^2}{4\xi_n \nu} \quad , \tag{17.68}$$

which expresses the rate of change of the energy as the difference of positive definite expressions. Setting $\dot{E}_N$ equal to zero in (17.68) produces the equation of a hyperellipse C_N that divides the phase space R^{2N} into two distinct regions; the boundary of the hyperellipse includes the origin ($\underset{\sim}{a},\underset{\sim}{b} = 0$) and the point $\underset{\sim}{a} = 0$, $\underset{\sim}{b} = \Lambda\underset{\sim}{\hat{q}}P/(\xi\nu)$. In the interior of the domain bounded by C_N, we find that $\dot{E}_N > 0$ holds by evaluating (17.68) at $a_n = 0$ and $b_n = \Lambda\hat{q}_n P/(2\xi_n\nu)$ for $n = 1, \ldots, N$. Because the two negative terms dominate when the magnitudes of $\underset{\sim}{a}$ and $\underset{\sim}{b}$ are large enough, we find that $\dot{E}_N < 0$ throughout the rest of phase space.

The energy E_N is a measure of the square of the distance of a point on the phase space trajectory from the point B given by $a_n = 0$, $b_n = \Lambda\hat{q}_n P/(2\xi_n\nu)$, $n = 1, \ldots, N$. Thus in the region in which $\dot{E}_N < 0$, trajectories must be moving monotonically toward B, even though they may have complex motion tangent to surfaces of constant energy. If we let E_N^* be a constant-energy surface that intersects $\dot{E}_N = 0$ tangentially at just one point, then E_N^* encloses the entire region in which $\dot{E}_N > 0$ and includes the entire surface $\dot{E}_N = 0$ along with part of the region in which $\dot{E}_N < 0$. The consequence is that every trajectory moving inward from initial values with large energy eventually penetrates the surface E_N^* and then is forever trapped inside. Similarly, a trajectory with an initial point inside E_N^* can never escape, since it must become tangential to a surface of constant energy as it approaches the surface $\dot{E}_N = 0$. Because all trajectories are eventually trapped inside the closed ball A_N with exterior boundary E_N^*, A_N is a global attractor as $t \to \infty$ for any bounded region of phase space.

This result has a number of important consequences (discussed in detail by Dutton, 1982, 1986): (1) The truncated version of the system of equations (17.52)-(17.53) has at least one stationary solution; (2) Every trajectory whose initial point has finite energy has at least one limit point in A_N and thus has at least one recurrent point; (3) There is in A_N a collection of trajectories composed entirely of limit points.

Since all trajectories are eventually trapped in the attractor A_N, the asymptotic behavior of all flows is determined by the dynamical properties of the system inside this global attractor. The volume A_N is not a minimal attractor, however, because almost all trajectories cross the boundary of A_N in an inward direction, never to return. Minimal attractors in phase space can be fixed points, closed orbits, or such strange sets as the Lorenz attractor (see Section 15.3.2). As we have seen throughout the monograph, it is the properties of such minimal attractors in phase space that are the key to resolving important issues in hydrodynamics.

The validity of Jeffreys' Theorem for the truncated form of the spectral model (17.52)-(17.53) follows from the observation that unaccelerated, motionless flow is equivalent to all a_n being zero, which requires that the b_n vanish and hence that the $\hat{q}_n$ vanish. For the reduced model formed from (17.9)-(17.10), the same conclusion is reached since the Fourier coefficients f_n resolve the rotational, not the solenoidal, part of $\underset{\sim}{F}$ because the eigenfunctions are solenoidal.

<u>17.3.4 Instability at a stationary point revisited</u>. A fluid forced into motion typically exhibits responses of increasing complexity as the forcing is intensified, with dramatic transitions to regimes ranging from smooth steady flows to turbulent ones (Chapter 15). As we have seen throughout the monograph, the instability process responsible for these transitions and the topology of the phase space structure characterizing the distinct regimes have their origins in nonlinear interactions. During a regime transition, a stationary solution or fixed point $\underset{\sim}{A}_o$ loses stability to a new one $\underset{\sim}{A}_1$ that lies on an extension of the unstable manifold of $\underset{\sim}{A}_o$ (cf. points 0 and C_1 in Fig. 4.3). When a series of bifurcations between stationary solutions occurs, the resulting hierarchy of transitions may be organized

initially by locating the appropriate stable and unstable manifolds of the solutions (cf. Fig. 4.4). In this subsection, we develop formally the concepts of stable and unstable manifolds of a fixed point as a prelude to generalizing these concepts in the following subsection to apply to points on a nonstationary trajectory.

To review the instability process discussed in detail in Chapter 4, let us consider the spectral equation derived from (17.9)-(17.10):

$$\dot{a}_n + \sum_{\ell,m=1}^{N} D_{\ell mn} a_\ell a_m + \nu\gamma_n a_n = \mu f_n \quad , \quad n = 1, \ldots, N \quad , \tag{17.69}$$

in which the intensity of the forcing is controlled by the parameter μ. Let $\underset{\sim}{A}(t) = \{A_n(t)\}$ be a solution to (17.69) and define a perturbed solution by $a_n(t) = A_n(t) + \alpha_n(t)$, $n = 1, \ldots, N$. Then we have

$$\dot{\alpha}_n + \sum_{\ell,m=1}^{N} D_{\ell mn}(A_\ell \alpha_m + A_m \alpha_\ell + \alpha_\ell \alpha_m) + \nu\gamma_n \alpha_n = 0 \quad , \quad n = 1, \ldots, N \quad . \tag{17.70}$$

Utilizing the antisymmetry of $D_{\ell mn}$ in m and n (cf. (17.54)), we find that the energy of the perturbation varies according to

$$\frac{1}{2}\frac{d}{dt^*}\sum_{n=1}^{N} \alpha_n^2 + \sum_{\ell,m,n=1}^{N} D_{\ell mn} A_m \alpha_\ell \alpha_n = -\nu \sum_{n=1}^{N} \gamma_n \alpha_n^2 \quad , \tag{17.71}$$

and hence the perturbation energy can increase only if the nonlinear terms are sufficiently large to overwhelm the dissipation of perturbation energy. The spectral representation thus leads to the same conclusion we reached in the discussion of (17.36); as a consequence, the formulation of the series of equations (17.69)-(17.71) applies equally well to the predictability issue as did our discussion in Section 17.2.3 of the partial differential equations.

To obtain more detailed information, let us concentrate on the behavior of the spectral model near a stationary solution $\underset{\sim}{A} = \{A_n\}$, whose existence is assured by the Trapping Theorem. We fix the truncation level N and observe that for $\mu = 0$, we have a trivial solution $\underset{\sim}{A} = 0$. Writing (17.69) as

$$\dot{a}_n = F_n(\underset{\sim}{a},\mu) \quad , \quad n = 1, \ldots, N \quad , \tag{17.72}$$

we may calculate the differential matrix

$$DF = \left[\frac{\partial \dot{a}_n}{\partial a_k}\right] = -\left[\sum_{\ell,m=1}^{N} D_{\ell mn}(a_\ell \delta_{mk} + a_m \delta_{\ell k}) + \nu\gamma_n \delta_{nk}\right] \quad , \quad k,n = 1, \ldots, N \, , \tag{17.73}$$

and then observe that

$$\det[DF]\Big|_{\underset{\sim}{a}=0} = (-1)^N \nu \prod_{n=1}^{N} \gamma_n \neq 0 \quad . \tag{17.74}$$

As discussed in Section 5.1, we may use the Implicit Function Theorem to show that there is a unique stationary solution $\underset{\sim}{A} = \underset{\sim}{A}(\mu)$ to $\underset{\sim}{F}(\underset{\sim}{A},\mu) = 0$ emanating from $\underset{\sim}{A} = 0$ at $\mu = 0$. By continuation, we can trace this solution as long as det[DF] does not vanish. If we define the eigenvalues, or characteristic exponents, λ of DF by

$$\det[DF - \lambda I_N] = 0 \quad , \tag{17.75}$$

where I_N is the $N \times N$ identity matrix, then we see that det[DF] can vanish if and only if at least one eigenvalue λ vanishes. Now it is clear from (17.73) and (17.74) that at $\underset{\sim}{A} = 0$ and $\mu = 0$, (17.75) becomes

$$\prod_{n=1}^{N} (\nu\gamma_n + \lambda) = 0 \quad , \tag{17.76}$$

and so in the case of no forcing, all characteristic exponents are initially real and negative. As the magnitude of μ increases, some exponents may become complex pairs, some of which may move toward the imaginary axis. If at a critical value $\mu = \mu_c$ an exponent crosses through the origin, then the original stationary solution need no longer be unique because det[DF] has vanished (Section 5.1). If a complex pair crosses the imaginary axis, then a Hopf bifurcation occurs, as discussed in Section 11.1, and the stationary solution is still uniquely continuable as $\underset{\sim}{a} = \underset{\sim}{a}(\mu)$, but is no longer stable.

As in Chapter 5, we connect this loss of uniqueness to instability by linearizing (17.70) about the stationary solution $\underset{\sim}{A}$; to do so, we discard the nonlinear term with $\alpha_\ell \alpha_m$. We write the result in the form

$$\dot{\underset{\sim}{\alpha}} = M\underset{\sim}{\alpha} \quad , \tag{17.77}$$

where from (17.73) we have

$$M = DF(\underset{\sim}{A}) = - \left[\sum_{\ell,m=1}^{N} D_{\ell mn}(A_\ell \delta_{mk} + A_m \delta_{\ell k}) + \nu\gamma_n \delta_{nk} \right] \quad , \quad k,n = 1, \ldots, N \quad . \tag{17.78}$$

Thus if we define, in analogy with the definition of an exponential of a numerical argument, the expression

$$e^{t^*M} = I_N + t^*M + \frac{t^{*2}}{2} MM + \cdots \quad , \tag{17.79}$$

then we have

$$\frac{d}{dt^*} e^{t^*M} = Me^{t^*M} \quad . \tag{17.80}$$

A solution to (17.77) is therefore

$$\underset{\sim}{\alpha}(t^*) = e^{t^*M}\underset{\sim}{\alpha}(0) \quad , \tag{17.81}$$

for the initial condition $\underset{\sim}{\alpha}(0)$. This calculation illustrates the fact that the matrix M contains all the information necessary to characterize the solution to the linear equation (17.77).

To extract that information in another form, let us again use an analogy with the case of a single first-order differential equation and substitute into (17.77) a trial solution

$$\underset{\sim}{\alpha} = \underset{\sim}{v}e^{\lambda t^*} \quad , \tag{17.82}$$

where $\underset{\sim}{v}$ is an N-vector and λ is a number. The result is

$$\lambda e^{\lambda t^*}\underset{\sim}{v} = Me^{\lambda t^*}\underset{\sim}{v} \quad , \tag{17.83}$$

or

$$[M - \lambda I_N]\, \underset{\sim}{v} = 0 \quad . \tag{17.84}$$

This trial solution thus generates the eigenvalues λ_n and associated eigenvectors $\underset{\sim}{v}_n$, n = 1, ..., N, of the matrix M. Henceforth we adopt the simplifying assumption that the eigenvalues are distinct. Then the individual solutions to the linear equation may be combined to give the general linear solution

$$\underset{\sim}{\alpha}_L(t^*) = \sum_{i=1}^{N} c_i \underset{\sim}{v}_i e^{\lambda_i t^*} \quad , \tag{17.85}$$

in which the initial value $\underset{\sim}{\alpha}(0)$ and the linear independence of the eigenvectors determine the constants c_i (see Section 4.2).

The components of the solution fall into three classes. Those for which the eigenvalues λ satisfy $\mathrm{Re}(\lambda) < 0$ diminish in time, those for which $\mathrm{Re}(\lambda) > 0$ grow, and those for which $\mathrm{Re}(\lambda) = 0$ oscillate. We thus define three spaces E^s, E^c, and E^u as shown in Table 17.1. The <u>stable subspace</u> E^s is composed of components that vanish exponentially; the <u>unstable subspace</u> E^u is composed of components that grow exponentially, and the <u>center</u> or <u>neutral subspace</u> E^c has components that oscillate sinusoidally.

It is clear from the representation (17.85) that these subspaces are invariant

Table 17.1 Specification of the three spaces E^s, E^c, and E^u. Here $n^- + n^0 + n^+ = N$ because of the assumption of distinct eigenvalues. When n^-, n^0, or n^+ is equal to zero, then there are no associated eigenvalues in that particular category.

Condition	Eigenvectors	Space Spanned by Eigenvectors
$\mathrm{Re}(\lambda_j^-) < 0,\ j = 1, \ldots, n^-$	$\underset{\sim}{v}_j^-$	E^s
$\mathrm{Re}(\lambda_j^0) = 0,\ j = 1, \ldots, n^0$	$\underset{\sim}{v}_j^0$	E^c
$\mathrm{Re}(\lambda_j^+) > 0,\ j = 1, \ldots, n^+$	$\underset{\sim}{v}_j^+$	E^u

to the flow in the sense that the components in each subspace evolve independently of the components in the other subspaces. Put another way, a solution vector for the linear equation initially in one of these three subspaces will remain forever in that subspace.

The case in which an eigenvalue or characteristic exponent is zero or in which a complex pair has zero real parts signals a bifurcation to another stationary solution or to a temporally periodic solution. These bifurcations indicate that the solutions are passing from one regime to another. Within a solution regime, the eigenvalues have non-zero real parts, the solutions are referred to as hyperbolic, and their linear equivalents are clearly composed of the stable and unstable components.

The stable subspace E^s consists of the points on solution trajectories to the linearized equation that approach the fixed point $\underset{\sim}{A}$ as time approaches infinity. The unstable subspace E^u similarly consists of points on trajectories that depart from $\underset{\sim}{A}$ as time increases. In neighborhoods of the fixed point, the nonlinear solutions approaching or departing from the fixed point can be separated into surfaces or manifolds analogous to the linear stable and unstable subspaces (see Section 4.3). In fact, the Stable Manifold Theorem (Chillingworth, 1976; Irwin, 1980) asserts the existence near $\underset{\sim}{A}$ of manifolds $W^s_{loc}(\underset{\sim}{A})$ and $W^u_{loc}(\underset{\sim}{A})$ (called S and U, respectively, in Section 4.3). Moreover, this theorem asserts that they have the same dimensions as E^s and E^u and have E^s and E^u as tangent spaces at $\underset{\sim}{A}$. In Fig. 4.1, the tangent spaces at 0 are given by the x_1- and x_2-axes, respectively.

If we were to let all the points in the local unstable manifold be mapped into solution trajectories as time increased, then they would sweep out a global unstable manifold $W^u(\underset{\sim}{A})$. Similarly, if we reverse time and take points in the local stable manifold as initial conditions for trajectories going backwards, then they would sweep out the global stable manifold $W^s(\underset{\sim}{A})$ of all trajectories that approach $\underset{\sim}{A}$ as time increases.

We may regard a solution $\underset{\sim}{a}(t)$ as being composed of a component $\underset{\sim}{a}^u(t)$ in the unstable manifold $W^u(\underset{\sim}{A})$ and a transverse component $\underset{\sim}{a}^\tau(t)$. For $\underset{\sim}{a}(t)$ near $\underset{\sim}{A}$, the transverse component $\underset{\sim}{a}^\tau(t)$ may be regarded as lying in the stable manifold $W^s(\underset{\sim}{A})$, and so then $\underset{\sim}{a}^\tau(t) = \underset{\sim}{a}^s(t)$ for $\underset{\sim}{a}^s(t)$ the component in $W^s(\underset{\sim}{A})$. Thus, in a suitable sense, we may write $\underset{\sim}{a}(t) = \underset{\sim}{a}^s(t) + \underset{\sim}{a}^u(t)$, and as $t \to \infty$, $\underset{\sim}{a}^s(t)$ approaches zero so that

$\tilde{a}(t)$ is asymptotic to $\tilde{a}^u(t)$. In this way the attractors of the system and the asymptotic behavior of $\tilde{a}(t)$ are characterized by the structure of the unstable manifolds associated with the stationary solutions.

The notions of this section are illustrated by an example presented by Guckenheimer and Holmes (1983). Let the system of equations be given by

$$\dot{x} = x \quad , \tag{17.86}$$

$$\dot{y} = -y + \frac{3}{2}x^2 \quad . \tag{17.87}$$

Then $(\tilde{x},\tilde{y}) = (0,0)$ is the only fixed point. The differential matrix at this point is

$$DF\Big|_{(0,0)} = \begin{bmatrix} 1 & 0 \\ 0 & -1 \end{bmatrix} \quad , \tag{17.88}$$

and thus has eigenvalues $\lambda_1 = 1$ and $\lambda_2 = -1$ along with associated normalized eigenvectors $\tilde{v}_1 = (1,0)$ and $\tilde{v}_2 = (0,1)$. In this case, E^u is the x-axis and E^s is the y-axis (Fig. 17.2). The solution to (17.86)-(17.87) is readily computed to be

$$x(t) = x_o e^t \quad , \tag{17.89}$$

$$y(t) = e^{-t}\left[\int_0^t \frac{3}{2} x_o^2 e^{3\tau} d\tau + y_o\right] = y_o e^{-t} + \frac{x_o^2}{2}(e^{2t} - e^{-t}) \quad , \tag{17.90}$$

for the initial point (x_o,y_o). We find an explicit expression for an invariant curve through the point (x_o,y_o) by combining (17.89) and (17.90) to yield

$$y = \frac{x^2}{2} + \left(y_o - \frac{x_o^2}{2}\right)\frac{x_o}{x} \quad . \tag{17.91}$$

The invariant curve through $(x_o,y_o) = (0,0)$ is tangent to the x-axis there and so must be the unstable manifold

$$W^u = \left\{(x,y) \mid y = \frac{x^2}{2}\right\} \quad , \tag{17.92}$$

as illustrated in Fig. 17.2.

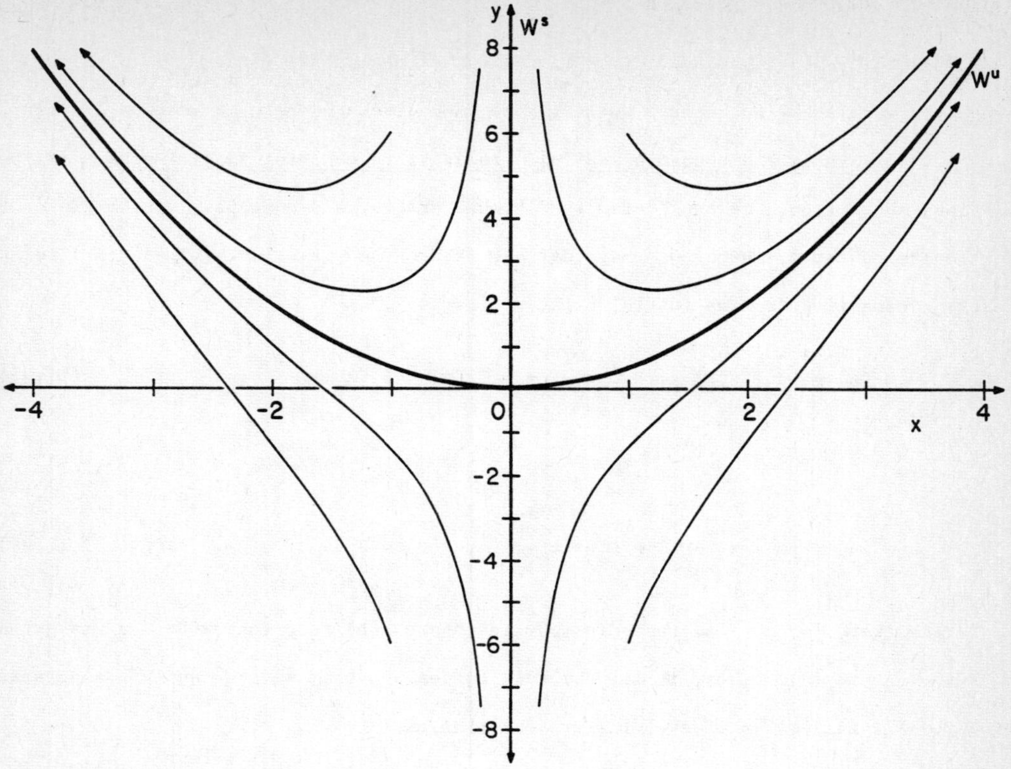

Fig. 17.2 A few trajectories (17.89)-(17.90) of the system (17.86)-(17.87). Clearly the trajectories depart from the stable manifold W^s and approach the unstable manifold W^u. The spaces E^u and E^s are the x- and y-axes, respectively.

To find the stable manifold W^s, we rewrite (17.91) as

$$xy = \frac{x^3}{2} + \left(y_o - \frac{x_o^2}{2}\right) x_o \quad . \tag{17.93}$$

We notice that the family of curves determined by (17.93) differs from the family determined by (17.91) only in that it includes one more curve -- the trajectory $x = 0$ emanating from $x_o = 0$. It is easy to check that this curve is the stable manifold (Fig. 17.2) given by

$$W^s = \{(x,y) \mid x = 0\} \quad . \tag{17.94}$$

The structures of interest would thus seem to lie in the unstable manifolds; the trajectories that determine the long-term statistics of the solutions and the dynamics of the attractors are confined there. Optimum spectral models might be constructed in coordinate systems designed to emphasize the unstable manifolds, as suggested earlier by Dutton and Wells (1984), and discussed here in Section 17.4.1.

17.3.5 Stable and unstable manifolds relative to evolving trajectories. In the previous subsection, we considered the global stable and unstable manifolds of a stationary point $\underset{\sim}{A}$, which we may define, using the notation $\underset{\sim}{x}(t) = \underset{\sim}{S}_t(\underset{\sim}{x}_o)$ for a solution emanating from an initial point $\underset{\sim}{x}_o$, as

$$W^s(\underset{\sim}{A}) = \{\underset{\sim}{x}_o \,\big|\, |\underset{\sim}{x}(t)-\underset{\sim}{A}| \to 0 \text{ as } t \to \infty,\ \underset{\sim}{x}(t) = \underset{\sim}{S}_t(\underset{\sim}{x}_o)\} \quad , \tag{17.95}$$

and

$$W^u(\underset{\sim}{A}) = \{\underset{\sim}{x}_o \,\big|\, |\underset{\sim}{x}(t)-\underset{\sim}{A}| \to 0 \text{ as } t \to -\infty,\ \underset{\sim}{x}(t) = \underset{\sim}{S}_t(\underset{\sim}{x}_o)\} \quad . \tag{17.96}$$

We notice that, for $\underset{\sim}{x}_o = \underset{\sim}{A}$, the solution trajectory $\underset{\sim}{x}(t)$ such that $\underset{\sim}{x}(0) = \underset{\sim}{x}_o$ is given by $\underset{\sim}{x}(t) = \underset{\sim}{A} = \underset{\sim}{S}_t(\underset{\sim}{A})$. Thus, it is natural to define the sets W^s and W^u associated with the initial points of evolving trajectories as

$$W^s(\underset{\sim}{x}_o) = \{\underset{\sim}{y}_o \,\big|\, |\underset{\sim}{x}(t) - \underset{\sim}{y}(t)| \to 0 \text{ as } t \to \infty,\ \underset{\sim}{x}(t) = \underset{\sim}{S}_t(\underset{\sim}{x}_o),\ \underset{\sim}{y}(t) = \underset{\sim}{S}_t(\underset{\sim}{y}_o)\} \quad , \tag{17.97}$$

and

$$W^u(\underset{\sim}{x}_o) = \{\underset{\sim}{y}_o \,\big|\, |\underset{\sim}{x}(t) - \underset{\sim}{y}(t)| \to 0 \text{ as } t \to -\infty,\ \underset{\sim}{x}(t) = \underset{\sim}{S}_t(\underset{\sim}{x}_o),\ \underset{\sim}{y}(t) = \underset{\sim}{S}_t(\underset{\sim}{y}_o)\} \quad . \tag{17.98}$$

In Chapter 16, we introduced the Lyapunov exponents in order to describe in part the stability and instability properties of an arbitrary trajectory. The sets $W^s(\underset{\sim}{x}_o)$ and $W^u(\underset{\sim}{x}_o)$ are clearly relevant to such a description of these properties, and we see below that there is a close connection between the Lyapunov exponents of the trajectory $\underset{\sim}{x}(t)$ emanating from $\underset{\sim}{x}_o$ and these sets.

It is thus important to find ways to determine the location and properties of both $W^u(\underset{\sim}{x}_o)$ and $W^s(\underset{\sim}{x}_o)$ in order to resolve the structure of the attractors and to attempt the development of optimum models based on the dynamical implications of that structure. To accomplish this objective, it is necessary to have an explicit procedure that yields the requisite information about these sets. We consider the N-dimensional dynamical system

$$\dot{\underset{\sim}{x}} = \underset{\sim}{F}(\underset{\sim}{x}) \quad , \tag{17.99}$$

with differential matrix DF and Jacobian matrix (see Section 16.1.1)

$$J(\underset{\sim}{x}_o;t) = \left[\frac{\partial x_i(t)}{\partial x_j(0)}\right] \quad , \qquad i,j = 1, \ldots, N \quad , \tag{17.100}$$

in which $\underset{\sim}{x}(0) = \underset{\sim}{x}_o$ and

$$\dot{J} = (DF)J \quad . \tag{17.101}$$

The matrix $J^T J$ is symmetric and has positive eigenvalues. Ruelle (1979) has shown that

1. The limit

$$\Gamma_+ = \lim_{t\to\infty} \left[J(t)^T \; J(t)\right]^{1/2t} \quad , \tag{17.102}$$

exists for J(t) evolved from almost any initial point $\underset{\sim}{x}_o$,

2. The set $W^s(\underset{\sim}{x}_o)$ is a smooth manifold, and
3. The eigenvectors of Γ_+ associated with the negative exponents (the logarithms of the eigenvalues) span the tangent space of $W^s(\underset{\sim}{x}_o)$.

We are now entitled to call $W^s(\underset{\sim}{x}_o)$ the stable <u>manifold</u> of $\underset{\sim}{x}_o$. Let $k = \dim[E^s(\underset{\sim}{x}_o)]$; then there exists a collection of continuously r-differentiable homeomorphisms, or coordinate maps,

$$\psi_\alpha : V_\alpha \to U_\alpha \quad , \tag{17.103}$$

mapping a family of open sets $\{V_\alpha\}$ of R^k to an open covering $\{U_\alpha\}$ of $W^s(\underset{\sim}{x}_o)$. A manifold is locally homeomorphic to R^k, and so k coordinates are required to describe position within a k-dimensional submanifold. For k-dimensional submanifolds of R^N, N-k coordinates are required to describe the position of the submanifold within R^N.

Therefore, we expect that locally, the structure of the flow along the unstable manifolds would be determined by the k longitudinal coordinates locating points within each unstable manifold, while the structure of the flow across the unstable manifolds would be determined by the N-k transverse coordinates locating the unstable manifolds themselves. We note that for $\underset{\sim}{x}_o$ a hyperbolic stationary solution, we now have two definitions for the stable manifolds of this point: the definition resulting from the classical Stable Manifold Theorem (Chillingworth, 1976; Irwin, 1980) and the definition resulting from Ruelle's Theorem; these two definitions agree.

In order to use Ruelle's Theorem to find the unstable manifold $W^u(\underset{\sim}{x}_o)$, we must reverse time, since the stable manifold as $t \to -\infty$ is the unstable manifold as $t \to \infty$. This time reversal is somewhat delicate and care is required. To begin, we utilize the notion introduced in Chapter 16 concerning a perturbed trajectory. Thus, if

$$\underset{\sim}{x}(t) = \underset{\sim}{S}_t(\underset{\sim}{x}_o) \quad , \tag{17.104}$$

and

$$\underset{\sim}{x}^*(t) = \underset{\sim}{S}_t(\underset{\sim}{x}_o + \underset{\sim}{\xi}_o) \quad , \tag{17.105}$$

then

$$\begin{aligned} \underset{\sim}{\xi}(t) = \underset{\sim}{x}^*(t) - \underset{\sim}{x}(t) &= \underset{\sim}{S}_t(\underset{\sim}{x}_o + \underset{\sim}{\xi}_o) - \underset{\sim}{S}_t(\underset{\sim}{x}_o) \\ &= \underset{\sim}{S}_t(\underset{\sim}{x}_o) + D\underset{\sim}{S}_t(\underset{\sim}{x}_o)\underset{\sim}{\xi}_o + \cdots - \underset{\sim}{S}_t(\underset{\sim}{x}_o) \\ &= D\underset{\sim}{S}_t(\underset{\sim}{x}_o)\underset{\sim}{\xi}_o + \cdots \quad , \end{aligned} \tag{17.106}$$

and so the linear evolution of a perturbed trajectory is specified by (Fig. 17.3b)

$$\underset{\sim}{\xi}(t) = D\underset{\sim}{S}_t(\underset{\sim}{x}_o)\underset{\sim}{\xi}_o \quad , \tag{17.107}$$

where $D\underset{\sim}{S}_t(\underset{\sim}{x}_o)$ is the Jacobian matrix $J(\underset{\sim}{x}_o;t)$.

Under time reversal, the solution beginning at $\underset{\sim}{x}_1$ is given by $\underset{\sim}{S}_{-t}(\underset{\sim}{x}_1)$ and the linear evolution of a perturbation is given by (Fig. 17.3c)

$$\underset{\sim}{\eta}(t) = \left(D\underset{\sim}{S}_{-t}(\underset{\sim}{x}_1)\right)\underset{\sim}{\eta}_o \quad . \tag{17.108}$$

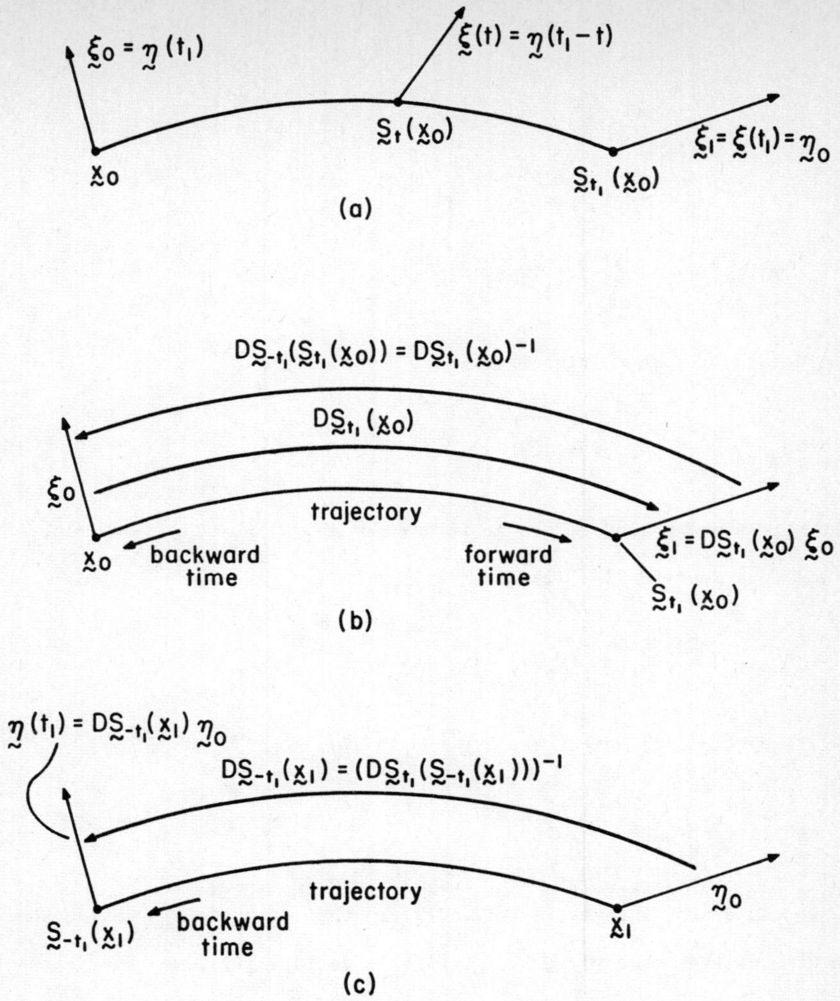

Fig. 17.3 Maps for defining the reverse Jacobian matrix. In (a) the linearized perturbations $\xi(t)$ for forward time and $\eta(t)$ for backward time are labeled. In (b) the reverse-time linear map $t \to DS_{-t}$ is shown to be the inverse of the forward-time linear map $t \to DS_t$ when suitably evaluated. In (c) the reverse-time linear map is depicted with the initial condition relabeled as x_1.

Now suppose we evolve an initial point x_o and a perturbation ξ_o to $x_1 = x(t_1)$ and $\xi_1 = \xi(t_1)$ at t_1 (Fig. 17.3b), label the results as η_o, x_1 (Fig. 17.3c), and then evolve η_o backwards to $\eta(t_1)$. Because $\eta(t_1)$ must be identical to ξ_o (Fig. 17.3a), we see that

$$\eta_o = \xi_1 = DS_{t_1}(x_o)\xi_o \quad , \tag{17.109}$$

and therefore that

$$\underset{\sim}{\xi}_o = \underset{\sim}{\eta}(t_1) = \left(D\underset{\sim}{S}_{-t_1}(\underset{\sim}{x}_1)\right)\left(D\underset{\sim}{S}_{t_1}(\underset{\sim}{x}_o)\right)\underset{\sim}{\xi}_o \quad , \tag{17.110}$$

where $\underset{\sim}{x}_1 = \underset{\sim}{S}_{t_1}(\underset{\sim}{x}_o)$ implies that $\underset{\sim}{x}_o = \underset{\sim}{S}_{-t_1}(\underset{\sim}{x}_1)$. Hence, we have

$$\left\{I_N - \left(D\underset{\sim}{S}_{-t_1}(\underset{\sim}{x}_1)\right)\left(D\underset{\sim}{S}_{t_1}\left(\underset{\sim}{S}_{-t_1}(\underset{\sim}{x}_1)\right)\right)\right\}\underset{\sim}{\xi}_o = 0 \text{ for all } \underset{\sim}{\xi}_o \quad , \tag{17.111}$$

and this fact implies that (Fig. 17.3c)

$$D\underset{\sim}{S}_{-t_1}(\underset{\sim}{x}_1) = \left(D\underset{\sim}{S}_{t_1}\left(\underset{\sim}{S}_{-t_1}(\underset{\sim}{x}_1)\right)\right)^{-1} \quad ; \tag{17.112}$$

alternatively, since $\underset{\sim}{x}_1$ and t_1 are arbitrary, we may start at $\underset{\sim}{x}_o$ and proceed t units in time and thus rewrite (17.112) as

$$D\underset{\sim}{S}_{-t}(\underset{\sim}{x}_o) = \left(D\underset{\sim}{S}_{t}\left(\underset{\sim}{S}_{-t}(\underset{\sim}{x}_o)\right)\right)^{-1} \quad . \tag{17.113}$$

It is equivalent to write

$$J(\underset{\sim}{x}_o;-t) = \left(J\left(\underset{\sim}{S}_{-t}(\underset{\sim}{x}_o);t\right)\right)^{-1} \quad , \tag{17.114}$$

and thus we can avoid integrating (17.101) in both directions. Since phase space volume V(t) evolves according to $V(t)/V_o = \det[J(\underset{\sim}{x}_o;t)]$, we see that (17.114) confirms our intuition that the change in volume in reversed evolution is the inverse of volume change in forward evolution.

For clarity we now augment $J(\underset{\sim}{x}_o;t) = D\underset{\sim}{S}_t(\underset{\sim}{x}_o)$ with

$$K(\underset{\sim}{x}_o;t) = D\underset{\sim}{S}_{-t}(\underset{\sim}{x}_o) = J(\underset{\sim}{x}_o;-t) \quad , \tag{17.115}$$

and thus Ruelle's Theorem assures us that the matrix

$$\Gamma_- = \lim_{t\to\infty} (K^TK)^{1/2t} \quad , \tag{17.116}$$

exists and that its eigenvectors corresponding to the eigenvalues with negative exponents span the tangent space of $W^u(\underset{\sim}{x}_o)$.

Next, we observe that the eigenvectors of K^TK are the same as the eigenvectors of $(K^TK)^{-1}$, while the eigenvalues of the two matrices are mutually inverse. Therefore, to calculate the eigenvectors of K^TK, we need only calculate the eigenvectors of

$$(K^TK)^{-1} = K^{-1}(K^T)^{-1} = \left(D\underset{\sim}{S}_{-t}(\underset{\sim}{x}_o)\right)^{-1}\left(D\underset{\sim}{S}_{-t}(\underset{\sim}{x}_o)^T\right)^{-1}$$

$$= \left(J(\underset{\sim}{x}_o;-t)\right)^{-1}\left(J(\underset{\sim}{x}_o;-t)^T\right)^{-1}$$

$$= J\left(\underset{\sim}{S}_{-t}(\underset{\sim}{x}_o);t\right)\, J\left(\underset{\sim}{S}_{-t}(\underset{\sim}{x}_o);t\right)^T \quad , \tag{17.117}$$

according to (17.114). Below we use the limits of the eigenvectors of $\left(K^TK\right)^{-1}$ to span the unstable manifold $W^u(\underset{\sim}{x}_o)$.

Now we show that the limiting eigenvectors of J^TJ and $\left(K^TK\right)^{-1}$ are the eigenvectors of Γ_+ and Γ_-, respectively. Let μ_n be the eigenvalues and $\underset{\sim}{\phi}^{(n)}$, n=1, ..., N, be the corresponding normalized eigenvectors of J^TJ. Then we have

$$(J^TJ)[\underset{\sim}{\phi}^{(1)},\ldots,\underset{\sim}{\phi}^{(N)}] = [\mu_1\underset{\sim}{\phi}^{(1)},\mu_2\underset{\sim}{\phi}^{(2)},\ldots,\mu_N\underset{\sim}{\phi}^{(N)}]$$

$$= [\underset{\sim}{\phi}^{(1)},\underset{\sim}{\phi}^{(2)},\ldots,\underset{\sim}{\phi}^{(N)}]\begin{bmatrix} \mu_1 & 0 & \cdots & 0 \\ 0 & \mu_2 & \cdots & 0 \\ & & \vdots & \\ 0 & 0 & \cdots & \mu_N \end{bmatrix} \quad . \tag{17.118}$$

For $E_+ = [\underset{\sim}{\phi}^{(1)},\underset{\sim}{\phi}^{(2)},\ldots,\underset{\sim}{\phi}^{(N)}]$ and D_+ the matrix in (17.118) having eigenvalues on its diagonal, we may write

$$J^TJE_+ = E_+D_+ \quad , \tag{17.119}$$

or

$$J^TJ = E_+D_+E_+^{-1} \quad . \tag{17.120}$$

Using the identity

$$(J^TJ)^m = (E_+D_+E_+^{-1})^m = \underbrace{(E_+D_+E_+^{-1})\cdots(E_+D_+E_+^{-1})}_{\text{m times}} = E_+D_+^mE_+^{-1} \quad , \tag{17.121}$$

we may write (17.120) as

$$J^TJ = \left(E_+D_+^{1/p}E_+^{-1}\right)^p \quad , \tag{17.122}$$

or

$$\left(J^TJ\right)^{1/p} = E_+D_+^{1/p}E_+^{-1} \quad . \tag{17.123}$$

Thus, we find that

$$\Gamma_+ = \lim_{t\to\infty}\left(J^TJ\right)^{1/2t} = \lim_{t\to\infty}\left[E_+D_+^{1/2t}E_+^{-1}\right]$$

$$= E_\infty \lim_{t\to\infty} \begin{bmatrix} \mu_1^{1/2t} & 0 & \cdots & 0 \\ 0 & \mu_2^{1/2t} & \cdots & 0 \\ & & \vdots & \\ 0 & 0 & \cdots & \mu_N^{1/2t} \end{bmatrix} E_\infty^{-1} \quad , \tag{17.124}$$

in which

$$E_\infty = \lim_{t\to\infty} E_+ \quad . \tag{17.125}$$

Therefore, we have

$$\Gamma_+E_\infty = \begin{bmatrix} \rho_1^+ & 0 & \cdots & 0 \\ 0 & \rho_2^+ & \cdots & 0 \\ & & \vdots & \\ 0 & 0 & \cdots & \rho_N^+ \end{bmatrix} E_\infty \quad , \tag{17.126}$$

in which the ρ_n^+ are the limits of the $\mu_n^{1/2t}$. Thus, we have shown that, by virtue of (17.125), the eigenvectors of Γ_+ are the limits of the eigenvectors of J^TJ. As a consequence, to find the limit eigenvectors we need only find the eigenvectors associated with the limits of the (1/2t)-powers of the eigenvalues of J^TJ. Moreover, the connection with the Lyapunov exponents γ_n, n=1, ..., N, of J was shown by Ruelle (1979) to be given by $\gamma_n = \ln(\rho_n^+)$.

In the same way, we may write (cf. (17.120))

$$K^T K = E_- D_- E_-^{-1} \quad , \tag{17.127}$$

and we obtain

$$\Gamma_- = \lim_{t\to\infty} \left(K^T K\right)^{1/2t} = E_{-\infty} \begin{bmatrix} \rho_1^- & 0 & \cdots & 0 \\ 0 & \rho_2^- & \cdots & 0 \\ & & \vdots & \\ 0 & 0 & \cdots & \rho_N^- \end{bmatrix} (E_{-\infty})^{-1} \quad , \tag{17.128}$$

in which

$$E_{-\infty} = \lim_{t\to\infty} E_- \quad , \tag{17.129}$$

and where the N eigenvalues ρ_n^- , which are the negative logarithms of the Lyapunov exponents γ_n of J, are the entries in the matrix given by $\lim_{t\to\infty}(D_-)^{1/2t}$. By inverting both sides of (17.128), we see that

$$\Gamma_-^{-1} = \lim_{t\to\infty} \left(K^{-1}(K^T)^{-1}\right)^{1/2t}$$

$$= E_{-\infty} \begin{bmatrix} (\rho_1^-)^{-1} & 0 & \cdots & 0 \\ 0 & (\rho_2^-)^{-1} & \cdots & 0 \\ & & \vdots & \\ 0 & 0 & \cdots & (\rho_N^-)^{-1} \end{bmatrix} (E_{-\infty})^{-1} \quad . \tag{17.130}$$

Of course, the eigenvectors of Γ_- are the same as those of $(\Gamma_-)^{-1}$ and are the columns of $E_{-\infty}$. From (17.130), we see that these eigenvectors are approximated as closely as desired by those of $K^{-1}(K^T)^{-1}$, again without our needing to take the (1/2t)-power of a matrix.

To illustrate these notions, we use the example introduced at the end of Section 17.3.4, for which the solution (17.89)-(17.90) of the system (17.86)-(17.87) emanating from $\underset{\sim}{x}_1 = (x_1, y_1)$ may be expressed as

$$\underset{\sim}{S}_t(x_1,y_1) = \left(x_1 e^t,\ y_1 e^{-t} + x_1^2\ \theta(t)/2\right) \quad , \tag{17.131}$$

where

$$\theta(t) = e^{2t} - e^{-t} \quad . \tag{17.132}$$

Then from (17.131) we have for $J(\underset{\sim}{x}_1;t)$ evolved from the initial point $\underset{\sim}{x}_1 = (x_1,y_1)$:

$$J(x_1,y_1;t) = \begin{bmatrix} e^t & 0 \\ x_1\theta(t) & e^{-t} \end{bmatrix} \quad , \tag{17.133}$$

and so for the initial point (x_o,y_o) we have

$$J^T J(x_o,y_o;t) = \begin{bmatrix} e^{2t} + x_o^2\theta^2(t) & x_o e^{-t}\theta(t) \\ x_o e^{-t}\theta(t) & e^{-2t} \end{bmatrix} \quad . \tag{17.134}$$

We see that $\det[J^T J] = 1$ for all t and thus $\mu_1 = \mu_2^{-1}$. The eigenvalues are easily found to be

$$\mu_{1,2} = \frac{e^{2t} + e^{-2t} + x_o^2\theta^2(t)}{2}\left\{1 \pm \left(1 - \frac{4}{[e^{2t} + e^{-2t} + x_o^2\theta^2(t)]^2}\right)^{1/2}\right\} \quad . \tag{17.135}$$

Thus as $t \to \infty$, the larger eigenvalue μ_1 is approximately

$$\mu_1(t) = e^{2t} + e^{-2t} + x_o^2(e^{2t}-e^{-t})^2 \quad , \tag{17.136}$$

which gives

$$\lim_{t\to\infty} [\mu_1(t)]^{1/2t} = \rho_1^+ = \begin{cases} e^2 \text{ for } x_o \neq 0 \\ e \ \text{ for } x_o = 0 \end{cases} \quad . \tag{17.137}$$

To determine the vector $\underset{\sim}{\tau}^s$ tangent to the stable manifold $W^s(x_o,y_o)$ of (x_o,y_o), we note that Ruelle's Theorem asserts that this vector is the limit as t approaches infinity of $\underset{\sim}{\phi}^{(2)}$, the eigenvector of the matrix J^TJ (17.134) corresponding to the smaller eigenvalue $\mu_2 = \mu_1^{-1}$ whose limiting value is $\rho_2^+ = e^{-2}$. In the present example, we have the form

$$\begin{bmatrix} a-\mu_2 & b \\ b & c-\mu_2 \end{bmatrix} \begin{bmatrix} \phi_1 \\ \phi_2 \end{bmatrix} = 0 \quad , \text{ where } \underset{\sim}{\phi}^{(2)} = \begin{bmatrix} \phi_1 \\ \phi_2 \end{bmatrix} \quad , \tag{17.138}$$

and so

$$\underset{\sim}{\phi}^{(2)} = \begin{bmatrix} c-\mu_2 \\ -b \end{bmatrix} = \begin{bmatrix} c-\mu_1^{-1} \\ -b \end{bmatrix} \quad , \tag{17.139}$$

or in scaled form

$$\underset{\sim}{\phi}^{(2)} = \begin{bmatrix} (c-\mu_1^{-1})/(-b) \\ 1 \end{bmatrix} \quad . \tag{17.140}$$

Thus, with (17.132), (17.134) and (17.136) we find that, for $x_o \neq 0$,

$$\underset{\sim}{\tau}^s = \lim_{t\to\infty} \begin{bmatrix} \dfrac{\left(e^{-2t} - \dfrac{1}{e^{2t} + e^{-2t} + x_o^2\,\theta^2(t)}\right)}{-x_o(e^t - e^{-2t})} \\ 1 \end{bmatrix} = \begin{bmatrix} 0 \\ 1 \end{bmatrix} \quad ; \tag{17.141}$$

the same result holds when $x_o = 0$.

To determine the vector $\underset{\sim}{\tau}^u$ tangent to the unstable manifold $W^u(\underset{\sim}{x}_o)$, we have two choices. First, we can find the smallest eigenvalue of $J(\underset{\sim}{x}_o;-t)^TJ(\underset{\sim}{x}_o;-t)$ and the associated eigenvector directly, which is easy in this case because we have an analytical solution. Alternatively, we can employ (17.128) and (17.117) to find the largest eigenvalue and associated eigenvector of $J\big(\underset{\sim}{S}_{-t}(\underset{\sim}{x}_o);t\big)J\big(\underset{\sim}{S}_{-t}(\underset{\sim}{x}_o);t\big)^T = (K^TK)^{-1}$, where we see from (17.131) that

$$\underset{\sim}{S}_{-t}(\underset{\sim}{x}_o) = \{x_o e^{-t},\ y_o e^t + x_o^2\ \theta(-t)/2\} \qquad ; \tag{17.142}$$

hence in (17.133) we substitute $x_1 = x_o e^{-t}$, which gives (17.117) as

$$JJ^T(\underset{\sim}{S}_{-t}(x_o,y_o);t) = \begin{bmatrix} e^{2t} & x_o\theta(t) \\ x_o\theta(t) & e^{-2t} + x_o^2 e^{-2t}\theta^2(t) \end{bmatrix} \ . \tag{17.143}$$

The larger eigenvalue υ_1 of this matrix is given by the equation

$$\upsilon_1 = \frac{e^{2t} + e^{-2t} + x_o^2 e^{-2t}\ \theta^2(t) + [(e^{2t}+e^{-2t}+x_o^2 e^{-2t}\theta^2(t))^2-4]^{1/2}}{2} \ . \tag{17.144}$$

We substitute (17.143) in the defining equation

$$[JJ^T - \upsilon_1]\underset{\sim}{\psi}^{(1)} = 0 \qquad , \tag{17.145}$$

and using the scaled form (as in (17.138)-(17.140))

$$\underset{\sim}{\psi}^{(1)}(t) = \begin{bmatrix} 1 \\ -b/(c-\upsilon_1) \end{bmatrix} \qquad , \tag{17.146}$$

obtain,

$$\underset{\sim}{\tau}^u = \lim_{t\to\infty} \left(\underset{\sim}{\psi}^{(1)}(t)\right) = \begin{bmatrix} 1 \\ x_o \end{bmatrix} \qquad , \tag{17.147}$$

for all x_o.

The vectors $\underset{\sim}{\tau}^s$ and $\underset{\sim}{\tau}^u$ and the associated stable and unstable manifolds are shown in Fig. 17.4. The stable manifolds $W^s(\underset{\sim}{z})$ are vertical lines

$$x = \xi^{(1)} \qquad , \tag{17.148}$$

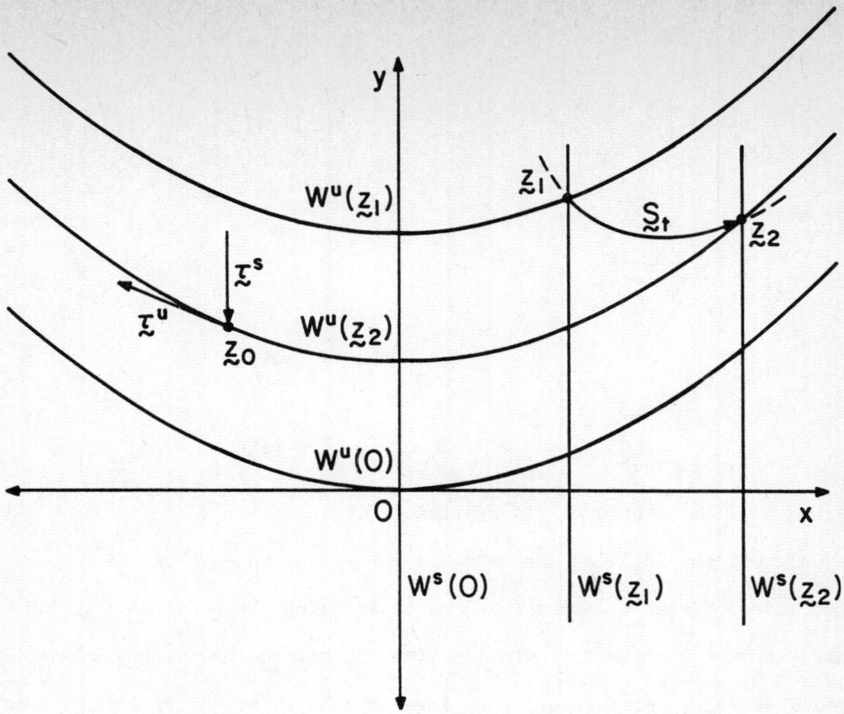

Fig. 17.4 Stable and unstable manifolds for the points 0, z_1, and z_2. The trajectory S_t from z_1 to z_2 carries the stable manifold $W^s(z_1)$ to the stable manifold $W^s(z_2)$, and similarly it carries $W^u(z_1)$ to $W^u(z_2)$. Typical tangent vectors τ^s and τ^u at the point z_0 are also shown.

specified by the values $\xi^{(1)}$ because the tangent vectors τ^s are always vertical. From (17.147), we see that the tangent vector τ^u depends on the coordinate x_0, but not on the coordinate y_0, and has the same slope as $y = x^2/2$ at $x = x_0$.

Thus for fixed x_0, all τ^u are parallel to the vector τ^u tangent to the unstable manifold $W^u(0)$ of the origin, which is given by $y = x^2/2$. Accordingly, a typical unstable manifold $W^u(z)$ is a curve parallel to $W^u(0)$, and it is given by

$$y = \frac{x^2}{2} + \xi^{(2)} \quad , \tag{17.149}$$

for specified $\xi^{(2)}$. Thus we have introduced a new, curvilinear coordinate system $(\xi^{(1)}, \xi^{(2)})$ in R^2. Furthermore, the trajectories of any system such as (17.86)-

(17.87) carry stable manifolds to stable manifolds and unstable manifolds to unstable manifolds. It follows that the equations of motion in the new coordinate system decouple; in fact, it is easy to verify in this case that they are given by the equations

$$\dot{\xi}^{(1)} = \xi^{(1)} \quad , \tag{17.150}$$

$$\dot{\xi}^{(2)} = -\xi^{(2)} \quad . \tag{17.151}$$

Therefore, the solutions $\xi^{(1)}(t) = \xi^{(1)}(0)e^{t}$ and $\xi^{(2)}(t) = \xi^{(2)}(0)e^{-t}$ along with (17.148) and (17.149) reproduce (17.86) and (17.87).

The decoupling in the above example strongly suggests that a similar decoupling based on stable and unstable manifolds might be possible for more general dynamical systems. In the following section, we examine how such a decoupling might be accomplished by exploiting Ruelle's Theorem, the theory of Pfaffian systems, the Frobenius Theorem, and modern, large-scale computing machinery.

17.4 Toward Optimum Spectral Models

An appropriate goal for the study of hydrodynamical systems is to obtain a theoretical resolution of the nonlinear processes and their consequences as reflected in the sequence of transformations of solution structure in phase space as the forcing increases in intensity. It is quite clear that very low-order models cannot portray the full complexity of fluid motions, and yet it has been shown that a finite number of degrees of freedom is sufficient to resolve the structure of the attractors of infinite-dimensional flows (e.g., Constantin et al., 1984; Foias et al., 1983; Kloeden, 1986b; Wells and Dutton, 1986). Initially, we might suspect that this number is very large. However, experience with low-order spectral models suggests that these in turn may be truncated to even lower-order models that can recover adequately the information in certain flow regimes. For example, the Chang and Shirer (1984) model of Section 9.2 contains two Lorenz-type systems as submodels and actually recovers some aspects of the steady flow regime of Rayleigh-Bénard convection. The example discussed in Section 16.3.2 strongly suggests that for large enough Rayleigh numbers, the chaotic flows of an 11-coefficient model may be represented by a suitable lower-order one. In fact, it was precisely this type of observation that led Lorenz (1963) to define and explore his reduced three-coefficient form of the Saltzman (1962) seven-coefficient model.

The available spectral models generally have been developed with essentially ad hoc families of basis functions that reflect either domain geometry or linear forms of the original model. As described by Modeling Principle Four (Section 1.3), optimum models would, in some sense, provide a maximum amount of information about the solution characteristics of topological structure with a fixed number of basis functions. If families of basis functions could be found that portrayed critical physical structures or reflected the interactions between flow components in the stable and unstable manifolds, then they might provide models far more effective than those now in use.

The development of such models will require either striking new theoretical progress or new approaches to the simulation and observation of flows. Theoretical or analytical approaches cannot yet produce detailed information about topological structure from examination of the governing equations, in either partial differential or spectral form. Direct numerical integration and simulation can reveal statistical or structural characteristics, as shown in Chapter 16, but obscures the interaction of physical processes in models complex enough to represent physical flows adequately.

In this section, we examine two quite different ways to use numerical simulations or methods to produce optimum spectral models. The first method is based on developing coordinate systems that decouple the original spectral equations into components residing along the stable and unstable manifolds. The second uses the empirical orthogonal functions of the Proper Orthogonal Decomposition Theorem to produce a model that, at each truncation level, resolves a maximum fraction of ensemble variance. The objective in both approaches is to use the power of modern computational methods and facilities to develop the information necessary to create optimum models that might be of order low enough to permit theoretical resolution of important issues.

17.4.1 Optimum reduction using unstable manifolds. Two critical issues of abstract hydrodynamical modeling are whether adequate finite models exist and, supposing they do exist, how to develop explicit algorithms for constructing optimum models that have a minimum number of components.

We suppose that an adequate, but presumably large, finite model exists and that we have an implementation of it in both analytical and numerical form. In this subsection, we propose a method for reducing such a model to a much smaller and therefore more nearly optimum one by finding new coordinates that decouple the stable and unstable components of the solutions of the larger model. This method of reduction is suggested by the decomposition of the phase space near a stationary solution $\underset{\sim}{A}$ of a hydrodynamical spectral system into the sum of the tangent spaces E^s and E^u to the stable and unstable manifolds $W^s(\underset{\sim}{A})$ and $W^u(\underset{\sim}{A})$ relative to $\underset{\sim}{A}$, as described at the end of Section 17.3.4. For weak forcing, all of the eigenvalues of the associated linear matrix are negative and all of the spectral components are stable. As the forcing rate increases, a finite number of eigenvalues with positive real part appear along with the unstable manifold W^u and its tangent space E^u. In a large model, we might therefore expect the dimension of the unstable manifold to be small relative to the dimension of the phase space for weak forcing, and to increase moderately as the forcing reaches the intensity necessary to produce chaotic responses. As described earlier, the solution trajectories then collapse asymptotically onto their unstable components and approach attractors in the limit set of the unstable manifold.

It is thus worthwhile to attempt to find effective methods for determining the location and structure of the unstable manifold, as outlined in Section 17.3.5. Moreover, Galerkin representations based on the geometry of the physical domain or on the linear characteristics of the model usually do not resolve the unstable manifold effectively, because it generally lies in an arbitrary position with respect to the phase space coordinates and so might appear to have a bizarre limit set. The search for representations having components parallel and transverse to the unstable manifold might provide the most natural basis functions for creating optimum spectral models. An example with such parallel and transverse components in phase space is given in Section 17.3.5. We note that in this example, only one unstable manifold, that passing through the origin, is invariant under the flow; nonetheless, the stable and unstable portions of the flow may be decoupled and all trajectories approach the invariant manifold. We may hope to replicate this phenomenon more generally by decoupling the unstable part of the flow, which is represented by relatively few equations, from the stable part.

As with the example in Section 17.3.5, the essential concept is Ruelle's Theorem, which ensures the existence of stable and unstable manifolds passing through almost every point $\underset{\sim}{x}$ with respect to an invariant volume and which provides a method for calculating the basis vectors of E^s and E^u at each such $\underset{\sim}{x}$. In this discussion, we restrict attention to those spectral models for which the manifolds exist at every point $\underset{\sim}{x}$ in the phase space and for which the manifolds have constant and complementary dimensions.

The stable and unstable manifolds may be regarded locally as the level sets of a certain new system of coordinates in the phase space; we assume that this system of coordinates is smooth. We caution that it is precisely in making this assumption that we may well exclude many cases of interest. However, the assumption is satisfied at least by some ordinary differential systems, such as the example (17.86)-(17.87) discussed in Sections 17.3.4 and 17.3.5. Moreover, it is a natural hypothesis to pursue because it has the important consequence that the system decouples locally into separate stable and unstable differential systems: The geometric fact that the solutions of the model carry stable manifolds to stable manifolds and unstable manifolds to unstable manifolds implies that the differential equations for the coordinates determining position on the unstable manifolds are decoupled from the differential equations for the coordinates determining position on the stable manifolds.

To examine the implication of this fact, let the coordinates $\underset{\sim}{\alpha} = \underset{\sim}{\alpha}(\underset{\sim}{x})$ be locally given by $\underset{\sim}{\alpha} = (\alpha_1, \ldots, \alpha_m)$ and $\underset{\sim}{\beta} = \underset{\sim}{\beta}(\underset{\sim}{x}) = (\beta_1, \ldots, \beta_{N-m})$ so that the level manifolds defined by holding the coordinates β_i constant are the m-dimensional unstable manifolds, while the level manifolds defined by holding the α_i constant are the (N-m)-dimensional stable manifolds. In these new coordinates, the dynamical system (17.99) may be written as

$$\dot{\underset{\sim}{\alpha}} = \underset{\sim}{G}(\underset{\sim}{\alpha},\underset{\sim}{\beta}) \quad , \tag{17.152}$$

$$\dot{\underset{\sim}{\beta}} = H(\underset{\sim}{\alpha},\underset{\sim}{\beta}) \quad . \tag{17.153}$$

The geometric fact that any level manifold given by $\alpha_i = k_i$, $i = 1, \ldots, m$, where the k_i are constants, is carried to another may be expressed by writing

$$\underset{\sim}{\alpha}\left(\underset{\sim}{S}_t(\underset{\sim}{x}_o)\right) = \underset{\sim}{f}\left(\underset{\sim}{\alpha}(\underset{\sim}{x}_o),t\right) \quad , \tag{17.154}$$

where $\underset{\sim}{S}_t(\underset{\sim}{x}_o)$ is the solution trajectory of (17.99) with initial condition $\underset{\sim}{x}_o$ and $\underset{\sim}{f}$ is a vector function of $\underset{\sim}{\alpha}$ and t. The equation (17.154) simply expresses the fact that the $\underset{\sim}{\alpha}$-coordinates of $\underset{\sim}{S}_t(\underset{\sim}{x}_o)$ depend only on the $\underset{\sim}{\alpha}$-coordinates $\underset{\sim}{\alpha}_o$ of $\underset{\sim}{x}_o$ and not on the $\underset{\sim}{\beta}$-coordinates $\underset{\sim}{\beta}_o$ of $\underset{\sim}{x}_o$. Consequently, we have

$$\dot{\underset{\sim}{\alpha}}\Big|_{t=0} = \frac{\partial}{\partial t}\,\underset{\sim}{f}(\underset{\sim}{\alpha}_o,t)\Big|_{t=0} = \underset{\sim}{G}(\underset{\sim}{\alpha}_o,\underset{\sim}{\beta}_o) \quad ; \tag{17.155}$$

thus $\underset{\sim}{G}(\underset{\sim}{\alpha}_o,\underset{\sim}{\beta}_o)$ is independent of $\underset{\sim}{\beta}_o$ and we may write in general

$$\dot{\underset{\sim}{\alpha}} = \underset{\sim}{G}(\underset{\sim}{\alpha}) \quad . \tag{17.156}$$

In the same way, we may write

$$\dot{\underset{\sim}{\beta}} = \underset{\sim}{H}(\underset{\sim}{\beta}) \quad , \tag{17.157}$$

thereby expressing the original dynamical system in the decoupled form (17.156)-(17.157).

Having established the existence of a decoupled coordinate system, we turn to the problems of constructing this new coordinate system and of writing the evolutionary equations for the spectral model in that system. With the hypothesis that Ruelle's Theorem applies to <u>every point</u> $\underset{\sim}{x}$ in the phase space, we may use the limit matrix equation (17.130) with time reversal to generate m tangent vector fields $\underset{\sim}{\tau}_1(\underset{\sim}{x}), \ldots, \underset{\sim}{\tau}_m(\underset{\sim}{x})$ that span the tangent spaces of the unstable manifolds. In the same way, we may use the forward limit (17.126) to generate N-m tangent vector fields $\underset{\sim}{\tau}_{m+1}(\underset{\sim}{x}), \ldots, \underset{\sim}{\tau}_N(\underset{\sim}{x})$ that span the tangent spaces of the stable manifolds; these are the fields that we assume to be smooth. In general, these N vectors do not form an orthogonal basis, but by applying the concepts of tensor analysis, we can readily find a set of dual vectors $\underset{\sim}{\eta}^{(i)}$ defined by

$$\underset{\sim}{\eta}^{(i)} \cdot \underset{\sim}{\tau}_j = \delta^i_j \quad , \quad i,j = 1, \ldots, N \quad , \tag{17.158}$$

where δ^i_j is the Kronecker delta.

We may now utilize the coordinate system $(\underset{\sim}{\alpha},\underset{\sim}{\beta})$ introduced above to define locally the tangent space of the stable manifold $W^s(\underset{\sim}{x})$ through a given point $\underset{\sim}{x}$ in two ways: First, as the set of all vectors $\underset{\sim}{v} \in R^N$ for which

$$\underset{\sim}{v} \cdot \nabla\alpha_1(\underset{\sim}{x}) = \cdots = \underset{\sim}{v} \cdot \nabla\alpha_m(\underset{\sim}{x}) = 0 \quad , \tag{17.159}$$

where the α_i are each defined only locally, and second as the set of all vectors $\underset{\sim}{v}$ for which

$$\underset{\sim}{v} \cdot \underset{\sim}{\eta}^{(1)}(\underset{\sim}{x}) = \cdots = \underset{\sim}{v} \cdot \underset{\sim}{\eta}^{(m)}(\underset{\sim}{x}) = 0 \quad . \tag{17.160}$$

The orthogonal complement of the tangent space of the stable manifold through a given point $\underset{\sim}{x}$ is spanned by the vectors $\underset{\sim}{\eta}^{(i)}$, $i = 1, \ldots, m$. The directional derivatives $\nabla\alpha_i$, $i = 1, \ldots, m$ must lie in that orthogonal complement since the coordinates α_i vary only along the unstable manifold. Hence $\nabla\alpha_i$ is a linear combination of the $\underset{\sim}{\eta}^{(i)}$ and we may write the Pfaffian system

$$\nabla\alpha_i = \sum_{j=1}^{m} a_{ij}(\underset{\sim}{x})\, \underset{\sim}{\eta}^{(j)}(\underset{\sim}{x}) \quad , \quad i=1, \ldots, m \quad . \tag{17.161}$$

Recognizing that $\underset{\sim}{\alpha} = \underset{\sim}{\alpha}(\underset{\sim}{x})$ and recalling that $\dot{\underset{\sim}{x}} = \underset{\sim}{F}(\underset{\sim}{x})$, we now have

$$\frac{d\alpha_i}{dt} = (\nabla\alpha_i) \cdot \frac{d\underset{\sim}{x}}{dt} = (\nabla\alpha_i) \cdot \underset{\sim}{F} = \sum_{j=1}^{m} \sum_{k=1}^{N} a_{ij}\, \eta^{(j)}_k\, F_k \quad , \quad i=1, \ldots, m \quad . \tag{17.162}$$

Thus we have found a form of the differential equation (17.152), or equivalently (17.156). Notice that $\alpha_1, \ldots, \alpha_m$ are coordinates <u>along</u> the unstable manifold. Consequently, the equation (17.156), or equivalently (17.162), expresses the unstable part of the dynamical system (17.99). The right side of (17.162) is given as a function of $\underset{\sim}{x}$, but eventually we must know the right side as a function of $\underset{\sim}{\alpha}$. Ruelle's Theorem provides a way to generate the basis vectors $\underset{\sim}{\eta}^{(j)}$ from knowledge of

$F(x)$ using (17.124), (17.130), and (17.158). The limit calculations can only be approximate; they must be carried out at sufficiently many points x to provide a reasonable approximation for the vectors $\eta^{(j)}(x)$. Similarly intensive computation is required to determine the matrix $[a_{ij}(x)]$. With modern supercomputers, these computations might be feasible.

Ruelle's Theorem assures us that the functions $\alpha_1(x), \ldots, \alpha_m(x)$ and the matrix function $[a_{ij}(x)]$ exist satisfying the defining equation (17.161). To find these functions given the assurance that they exist, we turn to the classical Frobenius Theorem, (Chevalley, 1946), which not only states precisely the necessary and sufficient conditions for the functions $\alpha_1, \ldots, \alpha_m$ to exist, but also prescribes an algorithm, albeit computationally very expensive, for constructing them from the given data.

We note that it suffices to find the functions $\alpha_1, \ldots, \alpha_m$ in (17.161), because then the independence of the vectors $\eta^{(j)}(x)$ and the gradients $\nabla\alpha_i(x)$ allows us to find the matrix $[a_{ij}]$ directly. The Frobenius Theorem describes a situation in which a system $X_1, \ldots, X_k$ of linearly independent, smooth vector fields near the point x_o in R^N is given. In our case $k = N-m$ and the vector fields are specified by the equation $X_1(x), \ldots, X_k(x) = \tau_{m+1}(x), \ldots, \tau_N(x)$. Then we may seek conditions on this system ensuring the existence of a family I of disjoint k-dimensional manifolds M covering a neighborhood of x_o in R^N, such that the tangent space T_xM at x of the manifold M is the vector space spanned by the vectors $X_1(x), \ldots, X_k(x)$. In our case these manifolds are the stable manifolds of the system (17.99); such a manifold M is called an <u>integral manifold</u> of the system $X_1, \ldots, X_k$ and the family I is called the <u>integral foliation</u> of the system in the terminology of Chevalley (1946).

Instead of seeking conditions ensuring the existence of an integral foliation, equivalently we may seek conditions ensuring the existence of an (N-k)-tuple $\alpha_1, \ldots, \alpha_{N-k}$ of functions defined with linearly independent gradients at each point near x_o, such that, for x near x_o,

$$X_i(x)\cdot\nabla\alpha_\ell(x) \equiv 0 \quad , \quad \begin{cases} i = 1, \ldots, k \\ \ell = 1, \ldots, N-k = m \end{cases} \quad . \tag{17.163}$$

In our case then, these functions are clearly the ones we hope to find.

We notice that the independence of the gradients implies that their orthogonal complement is k-dimensional. The condition (17.163) states that $\underset{\sim}{X}_i(\underset{\sim}{x})$ is in that orthogonal complement for i = 1, ..., k, and then the independence of $\underset{\sim}{X}_1(\underset{\sim}{x}), \ldots, \underset{\sim}{X}_k(\underset{\sim}{x})$ implies that these vectors span that orthogonal complement and thus form a basis for it. That is, if $\underset{\sim}{\zeta}$ is any vector such that $\underset{\sim}{\zeta}\cdot\nabla\alpha_\ell(\underset{\sim}{x}) = 0$ for $\ell = 1, \ldots, N-k$, then there exist unique numbers $c_1, \ldots, c_k$ such that

$$\underset{\sim}{\zeta} = c_1\underset{\sim}{X}_1(\underset{\sim}{x}) + \cdots + c_k\underset{\sim}{X}_k(\underset{\sim}{x}) \quad . \tag{17.164}$$

To determine a necessary condition for (17.163) to hold, we associate with any two vector fields $\underset{\sim}{X}$ and $\underset{\sim}{Y}$ a new vector field, the <u>Lie bracket</u> $[\underset{\sim}{X},\underset{\sim}{Y}]$ (Chevalley, 1946) by defining

$$[\underset{\sim}{X},\underset{\sim}{Y}] = (\underset{\sim}{X}\cdot\nabla)\underset{\sim}{Y} - (\underset{\sim}{Y}\cdot\nabla)\underset{\sim}{X} \quad . \tag{17.165}$$

It is easy to check (with an expansion into scalars) that

$$[\underset{\sim}{X},\underset{\sim}{Y}]\cdot\nabla f = (\underset{\sim}{X}\cdot\nabla)(\underset{\sim}{Y}\cdot\nabla f) - (\underset{\sim}{Y}\cdot\nabla)(\underset{\sim}{X}\cdot\nabla f) \quad , \tag{17.166}$$

for any function f.

Now we assume that the functions $\alpha_1, \ldots, \alpha_{N-k}$ exist. Then (17.166) and (17.163) combine to show that

$$[\underset{\sim}{X}_i,\underset{\sim}{X}_j]\cdot\nabla\alpha_\ell = 0 \quad , \quad \begin{cases} i,j = 1, \ldots, k \\ \ell = 1, \ldots, N-k \end{cases} \quad , \tag{17.167}$$

and so the Lie bracket $[\underset{\sim}{X}_i,\underset{\sim}{X}_j]$ is in the orthogonal complement of $\nabla\alpha_1, \ldots, \nabla\alpha_{N-k}$. However, because $\underset{\sim}{X}_1, \ldots, \underset{\sim}{X}_k$ form a basis for the complement, unique functions $c_{ijp}(\underset{\sim}{x})$ exist such that

$$[\underset{\sim}{X}_i,\underset{\sim}{X}_j](\underset{\sim}{x}) = \sum_{p=1}^{k} c_{ijp}(\underset{\sim}{x})\,\underset{\sim}{X}_p(\underset{\sim}{x}) \quad , \quad i,j = 1, \ldots, k \quad ; \tag{17.168}$$

thus we have found a necessary condition for the existence of the functions $\alpha_1(\underset{\sim}{x}), \ldots, \alpha_{N-k}(\underset{\sim}{x})$. This observation leads us to the formal statement:

<u>Theorem (Frobenius)</u>: Functions $\alpha_1, \ldots, \alpha_{N-k}$ exist satisfying (17.163) near $\underset{\sim}{x}_o$ if and only if the system of vector fields $\underset{\sim}{X}_1, \ldots, \underset{\sim}{X}_k$ satisfies (17.168) near $\underset{\sim}{x}_o$.

The classical proof of this theorem (Chevalley, 1946) may be interpreted as an algorithm for constructing the functions $\alpha_1, \ldots, \alpha_{N-k}$. We begin with the case $k = 1$, for which we may assume that $\underset{\sim}{x}_o = 0$ and that $\underset{\sim}{X}_1(0)$ is transverse to R^{N-1}. It follows from the standard Picard Existence and Uniqueness Theorem for ordinary differential equations (e.g., Coddington and Levinson, 1955) that, near $\underset{\sim}{x} = 0$, each trajectory of the differential equation

$$\dot{\underset{\sim}{x}} = \underset{\sim}{X}_1(\underset{\sim}{x}) \quad , \tag{17.169}$$

intersects R^{N-1} exactly once, enabling us to assign to any point $\underset{\sim}{x}$ near 0 the time $T_1(\underset{\sim}{x})$ that it takes for a trajectory of (17.169) to travel from an initial point in R^{N-1} to $\underset{\sim}{x}$. We denote the initial value of a trajectory $\underset{\sim}{x}(t)$ crossing through R^{N-1} by $\underset{\sim}{x}_o$ and write $\underset{\sim}{x}(t) = \underset{\sim}{S}_t(\underset{\sim}{x}_o)$. Then the point $\underset{\sim}{q}_1(\underset{\sim}{x})$ of intersection with R^{N-1} is given by $\underset{\sim}{q}_1(\underset{\sim}{x}) = \underset{\sim}{S}_{-T_1}(\underset{\sim}{x}) = \underset{\sim}{S}_{-T_1}\big(\underset{\sim}{S}_t(\underset{\sim}{x}_o)\big)$ and is constant along each trajectory. With the function $\underset{\sim}{q}_1(\underset{\sim}{x})$, we define the functions $\alpha_1, \ldots, \alpha_{N-1}$ by setting

$$\big(\alpha_1(\underset{\sim}{x}), \ldots, \alpha_{N-1}(\underset{\sim}{x})\big) = \underset{\sim}{q}_1(\underset{\sim}{x}) \in R^{N-1} \quad . \tag{17.170}$$

If, as above, $\underset{\sim}{S}_t(\underset{\sim}{x})$ is the solution of (17.169) with initial value $\underset{\sim}{x}$, then, by definition, $\underset{\sim}{q}_1\big(\underset{\sim}{S}_t(\underset{\sim}{x})\big) = \underset{\sim}{q}_1(\underset{\sim}{x})$ so that $\alpha_i\big(\underset{\sim}{S}_t(\underset{\sim}{x})\big)$ is constant. Thus for the directional derivative, we have

$$X_1\big(\underset{\sim}{S}_t(\underset{\sim}{x})\big)\cdot\nabla\alpha_i\big(\underset{\sim}{S}_t(\underset{\sim}{x})\big) = \frac{d}{dt}\,\alpha_i\big(\underset{\sim}{S}_t(\underset{\sim}{x})\big) = 0 \quad , \quad i = 1, \ldots, N-1 \quad , \tag{17.171}$$

and hence for the special case $t = 0$, we have $\underset{\sim}{X}_1(\underset{\sim}{x})\cdot\nabla\alpha_i(\underset{\sim}{x}) = 0$ for $i = 1, \ldots, N-1$.

To proceed by induction to the case $k > 1$, we suppose that the theorem has been proved for any system of (k-1)-vector fields satisfying (17.168). Using $\underset{\sim}{X}_1$, we construct the <u>time function</u> T_1 and the <u>initial value function</u> $\underset{\sim}{q}_1$ as above, and we note that $\underset{\sim}{X}_1(\underset{\sim}{x})\cdot\nabla T_1(\underset{\sim}{x}) \equiv 1$, because $(\underset{\sim}{X}_1\cdot\nabla)$ differentiates along the trajectory, and that $T_1(\tilde{x}) = 0$ precisely for $\tilde{x}$ in R^{N-1} near 0. Next, we define the linearly independent vectors

$$\tilde{X}'_\ell = \tilde{X}_\ell - (\tilde{X}_\ell \cdot \nabla T_1)\tilde{X}_1 \quad , \quad \ell = 2, \ldots, k \quad . \tag{17.172}$$

It is easy to show that $\tilde{X}'_\ell \cdot \nabla T_1 \equiv 0$. It follows that the restrictions of the vector fields $\tilde{X}'_2(\tilde{x}), \ldots, \tilde{X}'_k(\tilde{x})$ to $\tilde{x}$ near $\tilde{x} = 0$ in R^{N-1} are tangent to the hypersurface defined by setting $T_1 = 0$, which is R^{N-1} itself. That is, $\tilde{X}'_2(\tilde{x}), \ldots, X'_k(\tilde{x})$ are vectors in R^{N-1} when $\tilde{x}$ is in R^{N-1}. Furthermore, it is easy to verify that the vector fields $\tilde{X}'_2, \ldots, \tilde{X}'_k$ satisfy condition (17.168). Noticing that $N - 1 - (k - 1) = N - k$, we see that the inductive hypothesis thereby produces functions $\alpha_1^{(k-1)}, \ldots, \alpha_{N-k}^{(k-1)}$ on R^{N-1} near 0, with linearly independent gradients normal to the fields $\tilde{X}'_2, \ldots, \tilde{X}'_k$. Finally, we define the functions $\alpha_1, \ldots, \alpha_{N-k}$ on R^N near 0 by setting

$$\alpha_j(\tilde{x}) = \alpha_j^{(k-1)}\big(\tilde{q}_1(\tilde{x})\big) \quad , \quad j = 1, \ldots, N-k \quad , \tag{17.173}$$

for $\tilde{x}$ near 0. Now it is a straightforward calculation to verify that the gradients of the functions $\alpha_1, \ldots, \alpha_{N-k}$ are independent and normal to the fields $\tilde{X}'_2, \ldots, \tilde{X}'_k$ near 0. In addition, the definition (17.173) implies that $\alpha_j\big(\tilde{S}_t(\tilde{x})\big)$ is independent of t so that

$$\tilde{X}_1(\tilde{x}) \cdot \nabla \alpha_j(\tilde{x}) = \frac{d}{dt}\bigg|_0 \alpha_j\big(\tilde{S}_t(\tilde{x})\big) = 0 \quad , \quad j = 1, \ldots, N-k \quad . \tag{17.174}$$

Therefore the gradients of the functions $\alpha_1, \ldots, \alpha_{N-k}$ are normal to the fields $\tilde{X}_1, \tilde{X}'_2, \ldots, \tilde{X}'_k$, and so finally, to the fields $\tilde{X}_1, \tilde{X}_2, \ldots, \tilde{X}_k$, thus concluding the proof of sufficiency in the Frobenius Theorem.

Sufficiency in the Frobenius Theorem also may be proved in terms of integral manifolds (Chevalley, 1946). From that point of view, the integral (m-1)-manifolds of $\tilde{X}'_2, \ldots, \tilde{X}'_m$ in R^{N-1} sweep out the m-dimensional integral manifolds of $\tilde{X}_1, \ldots, \tilde{X}_m$ under the motion $\tilde{x} \to \tilde{S}_t(\tilde{x})$.

With the Frobenius Theorem now available, we may return to the central concern of this section. Using Ruelle's Theorem, subject to certain subsidiary hypotheses, we have produced $k = N - m$ vector fields $\tilde{X}_1(\tilde{x}), \ldots, \tilde{X}_k(\tilde{x}) = \tilde{\tau}_{m+1}(\tilde{x}), \ldots, \tilde{\tau}_N(\tilde{x})$ that are linearly independent at every point x and that span the tangent space at x of the stable manifold through x. Thus, the stable manifolds are the integral manifolds of the system $\tau_{m+1}(x), \ldots, \tau_N(x)$. Using the necessary part of the Frobenius Theorem, we see that these fields must satisfy condition (17.168). Then, using the sufficiency proof of the Frobenius Theorem sketched above, we may attempt to construct the functions $\alpha_1, \ldots, \alpha_m$ whose level manifolds are the (stable) integral manifolds. It follows that these are the coordinate functions we seek <u>along</u> the <u>unstable</u> manifolds; a similar construction could be used, starting with the unstable manifolds, to produce coordinate functions $\beta_1, \ldots, \beta_{N-m}$ along the stable manifolds.

The construction of the functions $\alpha_1, \ldots, \alpha_m$ is based on fairly extensive integrations, as well as on other lengthy maneuvers, which we now describe near a point $x_o = 0$. We initialize our procedure by introducing linear coordinates in R^N so that $X_1(0)$ is transverse to R^{N-1}; $X_1(0)$ and $X_2(0)$ are transverse to R^{N-2}; and so on, down to R^{N-k}. We define the function T_1 on R^N near 0 by integrating the equation $\dot{x} = X_1(x)$ with initial values in R^{N-1}, as in the proof of the Frobenius Theorem; we also require and may obtain from these integrations the initial value function $q_1(x)$ as above, with values in R^{N-1}.

Next, for x in R^{N-1}, we decompose the fields $X_2(x), \ldots, X_k(x)$ into components $X_2^{(1)}(x) = X_2'(x), \ldots, X_k^{(1)}(x) = X_k'(x)$ in R^{N-1} and a component proportional to $X_1(x)$. As before, we define the function $T_2(x)$ on R^{N-1} near 0 by integrating the equation $\dot{x} = X_2^{(1)}(x)$ in R^{N-1} with initial values in R^{N-2}; we obtain also the corresponding initial value function $q_2(x)$ with values in R^{N-2}.

In exactly the same way, for x in R^{N-2}, we find the components $X_3^{(2)}(x), \ldots, X_k^{(2)}(x)$ in R^{N-2} of $X_3^{(1)}(x), \ldots, X_k^{(1)}(x)$ respectively. Using $\dot{x} = X_3^{(2)}(x)$ in R^{N-2} with initial values in R^{N-3}, we find the corresponding time function $T_3(x)$, as well as the initial value function $q_3(x)$ with values in R^{N-3}.

Continuing in this way for $i = 1, 2, \ldots, k-1$ and U_i a suitable open neighborhood of 0 in R^{N-i}, we construct functions $q_i(x)$ defined for x in U_i that take values in U_{i+1}. Thus, the composition $Q(x) = q_k(q_{k-1}(\cdots (q_1(x)) \cdots))$ of these functions q_i is defined for x near 0 in R^N, taking values in R^{N-k}. It follows from the proof of the Frobenius Theorem that a system of functions $\alpha_1(\underset{\sim}{x}), \ldots, \alpha_{N-k}(\underset{\sim}{x})$ of the type we seek may be defined by setting

$$\alpha_i(\underset{\sim}{x}) = Q_i(\underset{\sim}{x}) \quad , \quad i = 1, \ldots, N\text{-}k \quad , \tag{17.175}$$

where $Q_i(\underset{\sim}{x})$ is the ith component of $\underset{\sim}{Q}(\underset{\sim}{x})$ in R^{N-k}.

Clearly, if N is large, the number of numerical integrations and linear operations necessary to carry out the construction of the functions $\alpha_1(\underset{\sim}{x}), \ldots, \alpha_m(\underset{\sim}{x})$ is prohibitively large, even with the aid of supercomputers. However, the number of necessary operations may be drastically reduced when the dimension m of the unstable manifold is of moderate size, as is frequently the case in spectral models such as those discussed in this monograph. Then, the function $\underset{\sim}{Q}(\underset{\sim}{x})$ need be computed only for $\underset{\sim}{x}$ in the tangent space to the unstable manifold near the point $\underset{\sim}{x}_o = 0$, and thus the pseudo-program proposed here may well be feasible. In such a case, the resulting information would suffice to approximate the form of the differential equation (17.156) with a degree of accuracy compatible with the level of resolution associated with the integrations.

Finally we remark that Ruelle's Theorem produces even more information than we have sought to exploit thus far. Specifically, we may define more refined unstable manifolds of a point $\underset{\sim}{x}_o$ by setting for $\gamma > 0$

$$W^u(\underset{\sim}{x}_o;\gamma) = \{\underset{\sim}{x} \,\big|\, |\underset{\sim}{S}_{-t}(\underset{\sim}{x}) - \underset{\sim}{S}_{-t}(\underset{\sim}{x}_o)|\, e^{\gamma t} \to 0 \text{ as } t \to \infty\} \quad . \tag{17.176}$$

Then Ruelle's Theorem makes the stronger statement that $W^u(\underset{\sim}{x}_o;\gamma)$ is a smooth manifold provided that $\gamma \neq \gamma_i$ for $i = 1, \ldots, N$, where $\gamma_1, \gamma_2, \ldots, \gamma_N$ are the Lyapunov exponents at $\underset{\sim}{x}_o$. Furthermore, for any $\underset{\sim}{x}_1 \in W^u(\underset{\sim}{x}_o;\gamma)$ we have $W^u(\underset{\sim}{x}_o;\gamma) = W^u(\underset{\sim}{x}_1;\gamma)$. And finally, the tangent space of $W^u(\underset{\sim}{x}_o;\gamma)$ at $\underset{\sim}{x}_o$ is spanned by the eigenvectors $\underset{\sim}{\tau}_1(\underset{\sim}{x}_o), \ldots, \underset{\sim}{\tau}_r(\underset{\sim}{x}_o)$ with $r \leq m$, for which the corresponding logarithms of the eigenvalues $\gamma_1, \ldots, \gamma_r > \gamma$. Thus, in place of the system of differential equations

$$\dot{\underset{\sim}{\alpha}} = \underset{\sim}{G}(\underset{\sim}{\alpha}) \quad , \tag{17.177}$$

we may obtain a more refined hierarchical system

$$\left.\begin{aligned} \dot{\underset{\sim}{\alpha}}^{(1)} &= G_1\left(\underset{\sim}{\alpha}^{(1)}\right) \\ \dot{\underset{\sim}{\alpha}}^{(2)} &= G_2\left(\underset{\sim}{\alpha}^{(1)},\underset{\sim}{\alpha}^{(2)}\right) \\ &\vdots \\ \dot{\underset{\sim}{\alpha}}^{(q)} &= G_m\left(\underset{\sim}{\alpha}^{(1)},\ldots,\underset{\sim}{\alpha}^{(q)}\right) \end{aligned}\right\} , \qquad (17.178)$$

where each $\underset{\sim}{\alpha}^{(i)}$ is a vector with n_i components, so that the original coordinate system $\underset{\sim}{\alpha}$ is given by $\underset{\sim}{\alpha} = \left(\underset{\sim}{\alpha}^{(1)}, \ldots, \underset{\sim}{\alpha}^{(q)}\right)$, and where $\sum_{i=1}^{q} n_i = m$. With the system in this form, we are able to distinguish and to treat independently the different natural time scales associated with the system (17.99).

17.4.2 A numerically optimized Galerkin representation. Galerkin representations based on families of orthogonal basis functions all possess in some form the Parseval property that the variance or mean square is given by the sum of the squared moduli of the Fourier coefficients. The set of basis functions produced by the Proper Orthogonal Decomposition Theorem (Loeve, 1963), which is sketched below, has the attractive property of concentrating the explanation of variance in the lower-order functions. An expansion within a specified ensemble is optimum if the linear combinations of a finite set of these functions explain more variance than would the linear combinations of any other set with the same number of functions. The empirical orthogonal functions produced by this method usually are determined by observations and have proved effective in numerous applications. Detailed information and references may be found in Loeve (1963), Lumley (1970), and Panofsky and Dutton (1984).

Empirical orthogonal functions developed from a specific flow regime might be expected to provide an optimum spectral model. Dutton and Henderson (1982) calculated such functions from atmospheric observations and showed how they might be used to develop a spectral model of quasi-geostrophic flow. Here we propose a new approach for determining empirical orthogonal functions that would be expected to extract an optimum spectral model from numerical simulations of a higher-order model. Presumably, the process would be effective when boundary or forcing effects or attractor dynamics produce characteristic structures in the physical flow realizations. A similar approach based on observed motion fields has been pursued over a number of years by Professor John L. Lumley; most recent results and references are given in Aubrey et al. (1986).

Suppose that from observation or simulation of a flow regime, we have an ensemble $\{\underset{\sim}{v}(\underset{\sim}{x},t)\}$ of flow realizations on a domain D. We would like to find a vector function $\underset{\sim}{\phi}(\underset{\sim}{x})$ that represents the characteristic structure of these velocity fields, and so we seek a function $\underset{\sim}{\phi}$ that maximizes the normalized scalar product

$$\sigma = \frac{\overline{\langle (\int_D \underset{\sim}{\phi} \cdot \underset{\sim}{v} \, d\underset{\sim}{x})^2 \rangle}}{\int_D \underset{\sim}{\phi} \cdot \underset{\sim}{\phi} \, d\underset{\sim}{x}} \quad , \tag{17.179}$$

in which < > is the probabilistic expectation over the ensemble or an average over a finite number of realizations, and the overbar denotes a time average over an appropriate interval. We assume first that $\underset{\sim}{\phi}$ exists and that it is a member of a complete orthonormal set of functions whose properties we describe here. Then the problem of maximizing σ in (17.179) is equivalent to that of maximizing the numerator subject to the constraint that the value of the denominator be held equal to one. Denoting a solution $\underset{\sim}{\phi}$ as $\underset{\sim}{\phi}^{(1)}$, the first element in the set of a vector functions, we see that $\sigma = \sigma_1$ is the temporal average of the expected value squared of the $\underset{\sim}{\phi}^{(1)}$-coefficients of the vector functions $\underset{\sim}{v}(\underset{\sim}{x},t)$ in the ensemble. Thus, the solution $\underset{\sim}{\phi}^{(1)}(\underset{\sim}{x})$ is the unit vector that, with respect to the double average, carries the dominant part of any Fourier expansion of the functions $\underset{\sim}{v}(\underset{\sim}{x},t)$. The next step is to find the second element $\underset{\sim}{\phi}^{(2)}(\underset{\sim}{x})$ in the optimum orthonormal set; such a function must be orthogonal to $\underset{\sim}{\phi}^{(1)}(\underset{\sim}{x})$. We assume that $\underset{\sim}{\phi}^{(2)}(\underset{\sim}{x})$ exists and then observe that it is the solution obtained by maximizing

$$\sigma_2 = \overline{\langle (\int_D \underset{\sim}{\phi}^{(2)} \cdot \underset{\sim}{v} \, d\underset{\sim}{x})^2 \rangle} \quad , \tag{17.180}$$

subject to the constraints

$$\int_D [\underset{\sim}{\phi}^{(2)}(\underset{\sim}{x})]^2 \, d\underset{\sim}{x} = 1 \quad , \tag{17.181}$$

$$\int_D \underset{\sim}{\phi}^{(2)}(\underset{\sim}{x}) \cdot \underset{\sim}{\phi}^{(1)}(\underset{\sim}{x}) \, d\underset{\sim}{x} = 0 \quad . \tag{17.182}$$

Because $\underset{\sim}{\phi}^{(2)}$ is subject to more constraints than $\underset{\sim}{\phi}^{(1)}$, we see that $\sigma_2 \leq \sigma_1$. Moreover, it is clear that the next function $\underset{\sim}{\phi}^{(3)}(x)$ in the orthonormal basis is subject to the constraints that it have unit norm and that it be orthogonal to both $\underset{\sim}{\phi}^{(1)}$ and $\underset{\sim}{\phi}^{(2)}$. Continuing in the way thus established for σ_2, we obtain an orthonormal set $\underset{\sim}{\phi}^{(1)}, \underset{\sim}{\phi}^{(2)}, \underset{\sim}{\phi}^{(3)}, \ldots$ and associated maxima $\sigma_1 \geq \sigma_2 \geq \sigma_3 \geq \cdots$ with all $\sigma_n > 0$. In addition, it may be shown that the functions $\underset{\sim}{\phi}^{(n)}$ exist, that the corresponding eigenvalues $\sigma_n \to 0$ as $n \to \infty$, and that the system $\{\underset{\sim}{\phi}^{(n)}\}$ is complete in the space of square integrable vector functions on the domain D (see Chapter 3 in Courant and Hilbert, 1953).

The above results are summarized in the Proper Orthogonal Decomposition Theorem. Here we sketch a proof of this theorem in order to outline an effective procedure for actually finding the functions $\underset{\sim}{\phi}^{(1)}(\underset{\sim}{x}), \underset{\sim}{\phi}^{(2)}(\underset{\sim}{x}), \ldots$, upon which we base the optimum model. Let $\underset{\sim}{\phi}$ be a maximizing function for (17.179), let $\delta\underset{\sim}{\phi}$ be an arbitrary vector, and insert $\underset{\sim}{\phi} + \varepsilon\delta\underset{\sim}{\phi}$ into (17.179). Then, because $\underset{\sim}{\phi}$ is the maximizing vector, we would have

$$\left.\frac{\partial\sigma(\varepsilon)}{\partial\varepsilon}\right|_{\varepsilon=0} = 0 \quad . \tag{17.183}$$

Performing this operation on (17.179) produces the requirement that

$$\sum_{i=1}^{3} \int_D R_{ij}(\underset{\sim}{x},\underset{\sim}{y})\, \phi_i(\underset{\sim}{x})\, d\underset{\sim}{x} = \sigma\, \phi_j(\underset{\sim}{y}) \quad , \qquad j = 1, 2, 3 \quad , \tag{17.184}$$

in which the correlation tensor is given by

$$R_{ij}(\underset{\sim}{x},\underset{\sim}{y}) = \overline{\langle\, v_i(\underset{\sim}{x},t)\; v_j(\underset{\sim}{y},t)\,\rangle} \quad , \qquad i,j = 1, 2, 3 \quad , \tag{17.185}$$

and $\underset{\sim}{\phi} = (\phi_1, \phi_2, \phi_3)$.

Such an optimum vector $\underset{\sim}{\phi}$ would be an eigenfunction of the eigenvalue problem

$$\sum_{i=1}^{3} \int_D R_{ij}(\underset{\sim}{x},\underset{\sim}{y})\, \phi_i^{(n)}(\underset{\sim}{x})\, d\underset{\sim}{x} = \sigma_n\, \phi_j^{(n)}(\underset{\sim}{y}) \quad , \quad \begin{cases} j = 1, 2, 3 \\ n = 1, \ldots, N \end{cases} \quad . \tag{17.186}$$

It is easy to see that its eigenvalue would be σ, and that it would be the largest eigenvalue. Conversely, if the eigenvalue problem had a largest eigenvalue, then it would be the σ we seek and its corresponding eigenfunction would be the optimum vector function $\underset{\sim}{\phi}$. In fact, the eigenvalue problem (17.186) does have such a solution $\underset{\sim}{\phi}^{(1)}(\underset{\sim}{x})$ (see Section 97 of Riesz and Nagy, 1955) because the problem is defined by an integral equation with bounded symmetric kernel $R_{ij}(\underset{\sim}{x},\underset{\sim}{y})$. In (17.186) the number of eigenvalues is N, a value that in practice is limited by the size of the ensemble $\{\underset{\sim}{v}(\underset{\sim}{x},t)\}$ (e.g., van Storch and Hannoschöck, 1985) since we cannot form more than N functions $\underset{\sim}{\phi}^{(n)}$ as linearly independent combinations of N functions in $\{\underset{\sim}{v}(\underset{\sim}{x},t)\}$. If the tensor $R_{ij}(\underset{\sim}{x},\underset{\sim}{y})$ were known as an analytic function, then such a restriction would not apply and N would be replaced by infinity.

Significantly, the eigenvalue problem (17.186) yields a collection $\underset{\sim}{\phi}^{(n)}$ of functions each of whose contribution to the total ensemble of variance is proportional to σ_n. To see this fact, we observe that the symmetry

$$R_{ij}(\underset{\sim}{x},\underset{\sim}{y}) = R_{ji}(\underset{\sim}{y},\underset{\sim}{x}) \quad , \quad i,j = 1, 2, 3 \quad , \tag{17.187}$$

allows us to establish orthonormality in the form

$$\int_D \underset{\sim}{\phi}^{(\ell)}(\underset{\sim}{y})\cdot\underset{\sim}{\phi}^{(m)}(\underset{\sim}{y})\, d\underset{\sim}{y} = \delta_{\ell m} \quad , \quad \ell,m = 1, \ldots, N \quad , \tag{17.188}$$

for normalized functions $\underset{\sim}{\phi}^{(n)}$. Now the expansion

$$\underset{\sim}{v}(\underset{\sim}{x},t) = \sum_{n=1}^{N} b_n(t)\, \underset{\sim}{\phi}^{(n)}(\underset{\sim}{x}) \quad , \tag{17.189}$$

in which

$$b_n(t) = \int_D \underset{\sim}{\phi}^{(n)}(\underset{\sim}{x})\cdot\underset{\sim}{v}(\underset{\sim}{x},t)\, d\underset{\sim}{x} \quad , \quad n = 1, \ldots, N \quad , \tag{17.190}$$

leads to

$$\overline{< b_\ell b_m >} = \int_D \int_D \phi_i^{(\ell)}(\underset{\sim}{x})\, \phi_j^{(m)}(\underset{\sim}{y})\, R_{ij}(\underset{\sim}{x},\underset{\sim}{y})\, d\underset{\sim}{x}\, d\underset{\sim}{y} = \sigma_\ell \delta_{\ell m} \quad , \ell,m = 1, \ldots, N, \tag{17.191}$$

by virtue of (17.186). To carry out this derivation, we need only note the fact that the operations of expectation and integration may be interchanged when the correlation function of the process has nice properties. Thus from (17.189) we have

$$\int_D \overline{< \underset{\sim}{v}(\underset{\sim}{x},t)\cdot\underset{\sim}{v}(\underset{\sim}{x},t) >}\, d\underset{\sim}{x} = \sum_{n=1}^{N} \sigma_n \quad . \tag{17.192}$$

Clearly, then, we may arrange the positive eigenvalues σ_n in decreasing order and select the functions $\underset{\sim}{\phi}^{(n)}$ to be used in an expansion in the same order.

Next we turn to the role of simulation in determining the empirical orthogonal functions that would provide the optimum basis for a finite model of a certain flow regime. We begin with an original N-coefficient spectral model having orthogonal basis functions $\underset{\sim}{\psi}^{(n)}(\underset{\sim}{x})$ of the type we have considered throughout this monograph. We employ numerical integration of the model to develop an ensemble $\{\underset{\sim}{v}(\underset{\sim}{x},t)\}$ of realizations of the form

$$\underset{\sim}{v}(\underset{\sim}{x},t) = \sum_{n=1}^{N} a_n(t)\, \underset{\sim}{\psi}^{(n)}(\underset{\sim}{x}) \quad . \tag{17.193}$$

To obtain the optimum basis $\underset{\sim}{\phi}^{(n)}(\underset{\sim}{x})$ for which

$$\underset{\sim}{v}(\underset{\sim}{x},t) = \sum_{n=1}^{N} b_n(t)\, \underset{\sim}{\phi}^{(n)}(\underset{\sim}{x}) \quad , \tag{17.194}$$

we first compute

$$R_{ij}(\underset{\sim}{x},\underset{\sim}{y}) = \sum_{r,s=1}^{N} A_{rs}\, \psi_i^{(r)}(\underset{\sim}{x})\, \psi_j^{(s)}(\underset{\sim}{y}) \quad , \qquad i,j = 1, \ldots, N \quad , \tag{17.195}$$

in which

$$A_{rs} = \overline{\langle\, a_r(t)\, a_s(t)\, \rangle} \quad , \qquad r,s = 1, \ldots, N \quad . \tag{17.196}$$

Then we observe that we can write

$$\underset{\sim}{\phi}^{(n)}(\underset{\sim}{x}) = \sum_{k=1}^{N} C_k^{(n)}\, \underset{\sim}{\psi}^{(k)}(\underset{\sim}{x}) \quad , \qquad n = 1, \ldots, N \quad , \tag{17.197}$$

because the $\underset{\sim}{\psi}^{(n)}$ are a basis. Therefore, the construction of the $\underset{\sim}{\phi}^{(n)}$ is equivalent to finding the values of the constants $C_k^{(n)}$. To find these constants, we substitute (17.195) and (17.197) into (17.186) to obtain

$$\sum_{r,s=1}^{N} A_{rs}\, C_r^{(n)}\, \underset{\sim}{\psi}^{(s)}(\underset{\sim}{y}) = \sigma_n\, \underset{\sim}{\phi}^{(n)}(\underset{\sim}{y}) \quad , \qquad n = 1, \ldots, N \quad . \tag{17.198}$$

After using (17.197) on the right of (17.198), we take the inner product of the result with $\underset{\sim}{\psi}^{(s)}(\underset{\sim}{y})$ to reduce the problem to matrix form

$$\sum_{r=1}^{N} A_{rs}\, C_r^{(n)} = \sigma_n\, C_s^{(n)} \quad , \qquad n,s = 1, \ldots, N \quad . \tag{17.199}$$

It is now routine to determine the eigenvalues σ_n and the eigenvector coefficients $C_k^{(n)}$ from the known values (17.196) of A_{rs}, and thus complete the specification of $\underset{\sim}{\phi}^{(n)}$.

Now that we have the functions $\phi^{(n)}(\underset{\sim}{x})$, we may use them to produce a new truncated spectral model from the original partial differential equations. This new model is equivalent to the old one generated by (17.193) using as basis the functions $\underset{\sim}{\psi}^{(1)}(\underset{\sim}{x}), \ldots, \underset{\sim}{\psi}^{(N)}(\underset{\sim}{x})$. To see why the new model is optimum, we recall that the eigenvalues σ_n are positive and decrease in magnitude with increasing n. We may interpret this fact to conclude that the corresponding eigenfunctions $\underset{\sim}{\phi}^{(n)}$ carry decreasing amounts of information about the trajectories in the N-dimensional model determined by (17.193). The model generated by (17.194) using $\underset{\sim}{\phi}^{(1)}(\underset{\sim}{x}), \ldots, \underset{\sim}{\phi}^{(K)}(\underset{\sim}{x})$, with $K \leq N$ recovers at least as much of the ensemble variance as any other K-coefficient model. It is in this sense that the new model is the optimum K-coefficient truncation of the original partial differential equations.

The N-coefficient model obtained by substituting (17.194) into (17.9)-(17.10) and performing the usual calculations is given by

$$\dot{b}_n + \sum_{\ell,m=1}^{N} \Delta_{\ell mn} b_\ell b_m + \nu \sum_{\ell=1}^{N} \Lambda_{n\ell} b_\ell = \mu \hat{f}_n \quad , \qquad n = 1, \ldots, N \quad , \tag{17.200}$$

where

$$\Delta_{\ell mn} = \int_D \underset{\sim}{\phi}^{(n)} \cdot [\underset{\sim}{\phi}^{(\ell)} \cdot \nabla \underset{\sim}{\phi}^{(m)}]\, d\underset{\sim}{x}^* \quad , \qquad \ell,m,n = 1, \ldots, N \quad , \tag{17.201}$$

$$\Lambda_{\ell n} = - \int_D \underset{\sim}{\phi}^{(n)} \cdot \nabla^2 \underset{\sim}{\phi}^{(\ell)}\, d\underset{\sim}{x}^* \quad , \qquad \ell,n = 1, \ldots, N \quad , \tag{17.202}$$

$$\hat{f}_n = \int_D \underset{\sim}{\phi}^{(n)} \cdot \underset{\sim}{F}\, d\underset{\sim}{x}^* \quad , \qquad n = 1, \ldots, N \quad . \tag{17.203}$$

Because we generated the basis functions $\underset{\sim}{\phi}^{(n)}$ from the ensemble of solutions of the spectral model

$$\dot{a}_n + \sum_{\ell,m=1}^{N} D_{\ell mn} a_\ell a_m + \nu\gamma_n a_n = \mu f_n \quad , \qquad n = 1, \ldots, N \quad , \tag{17.204}$$

and because we may express via (17.197) the new basis functions $\underset{\sim}{\phi}^{(n)}(\underset{\sim}{x}^*)$ in terms of the original ones $\underset{\sim}{\psi}^{(n)}(\underset{\sim}{x}^*)$, we may rewrite (17.201)-(17.203) in terms of the already calculated coefficients in (17.204). We begin by recalling that the $\underset{\sim}{\psi}^{(n)}(\underset{\sim}{x}^*)$ are the functions in the orthogonal basis obtained from the Stokes problem

$$\nu\nabla^2\underset{\sim}{\Psi}^* = -\gamma\nu\underset{\sim}{\Psi}^* + \nabla\Theta^* \quad , \tag{17.205}$$

$$\nabla\cdot\underset{\sim}{\Psi}^* = 0 \quad . \tag{17.206}$$

Because the $\underset{\sim}{\psi}^{(n)}(\underset{\sim}{x}^*)$ are nondivergent, we see from (17.197) that the basis $\underset{\sim}{\phi}^{(n)}(\underset{\sim}{x}^*)$ is also; that is, we have

$$\nabla\cdot\underset{\sim}{\phi}^{(n)} = \sum_{k=1}^{N} C_k^{(n)}\, \nabla\cdot\underset{\sim}{\psi}^{(k)} = 0 \quad , \qquad n = 1, \ldots, N \quad . \tag{17.207}$$

Thus, we may rewrite (17.202) by combining (17.197) and (17.205) to obtain

$$\begin{aligned}\Lambda_{\ell n} &= -\int_D \underset{\sim}{\phi}^{(n)}\cdot\nabla^2\underset{\sim}{\phi}^{(\ell)}\, d\underset{\sim}{x}^* = -\int_D \underset{\sim}{\phi}^{(n)}\cdot \sum_{k=1}^{N} C_k^{(\ell)}\, \nabla^2\underset{\sim}{\psi}^{(k)}\, d\underset{\sim}{x}^* \\ &= -\sum_{k=1}^{N} C_k^{(\ell)} \int_D \underset{\sim}{\phi}^{(n)}\cdot[-\gamma_k\, \underset{\sim}{\psi}^{(k)} + \nu^{-1}\nabla\theta^{(k)}]\, d\underset{\sim}{x}^* \\ &= \sum_{k=1}^{N} C_k^{(\ell)} \int_D \underset{\sim}{\phi}^{(n)}\cdot\gamma_k\, \underset{\sim}{\psi}^{(k)}\, d\underset{\sim}{x}^* \quad , \qquad \ell,n = 1, \ldots, N \quad .\end{aligned} \tag{17.208}$$

In (17.208) we have used (17.206), the Divergence Theorem, and the boundary conditions (17.4) to show that $\int_D \underset{\sim}{\phi}^{(n)}\cdot\nabla\theta^{(k)}\, d\underset{\sim}{x}^* = 0$. Substituting (17.197) into (17.208), we arrive at

$$\Lambda_{\ell n} = \sum_{k=1}^{N} \gamma_k\, C_k^{(\ell)}\, C_k^{(n)} = \Lambda_{n\ell} \quad , \qquad \ell,n = 1, \ldots, N \quad . \tag{17.209}$$

Moreover, we observe that $\Lambda = [\Lambda_{\ell n}]$ is a positive definite matrix. To show this, we choose an arbitrary vector $\underset{\sim}{\xi} = (\xi_1, \ldots, \xi_N)$ and calculate

$$\sum_{\ell,n=1}^{N} \Lambda_{\ell n}\, \xi_\ell\, \xi_n = \sum_{k=1}^{N} \gamma_k \left[\sum_{\ell=1}^{N} C_k^{(\ell)}\, \xi_\ell \sum_{n=1}^{N} C_k^{(n)}\, \xi_n \right]$$

$$= \sum_{k=1}^{N} \gamma_k \left[\sum_{\ell=1}^{N} C_k^{(\ell)}\, \xi_\ell \right]^2 \quad , \qquad (17.210)$$

in which we have used the fact that ℓ and n are dummy indices. To rewrite (17.201) and (17.203), we substitute (17.197) into them to find with (17.54) that

$$\Delta_{\ell mn} = \sum_{p,q,r=1}^{N} C_p^{(n)}\, C_q^{(\ell)}\, C_r^{(m)} \int_D \underset{\sim}{\psi}^{(p)} \cdot [\underset{\sim}{\psi}^{(q)} \cdot \nabla \underset{\sim}{\psi}^{(r)}]\, d\underset{\sim}{x}^*$$

$$= \sum_{p,q,r=1}^{N} C_p^{(n)}\, C_q^{(\ell)}\, C_r^{(m)}\, D_{qrp} \quad , \quad \ell, m, n = 1, \ldots, N \quad , \qquad (17.211)$$

and

$$\hat{f}_n = \sum_{p=1}^{N} C_p^{(n)}\, f_p \quad , \qquad n = 1, \ldots, N \quad . \qquad (17.212)$$

The model (17.200) has the associated energy equation

$$\dot{E}_N = \frac{1}{2}\frac{d}{dt^*} \sum_{n=1}^{N} b_n^2 = \sum_{n=1}^{N} b_n \left(\mu \hat{f}_n - \nu \sum_{\ell=1}^{N} \Lambda_{n\ell}\, b_\ell\right) \quad . \qquad (17.213)$$

To see that (17.200) obeys the Trapping Theorem, we observe that the rate of change of energy vanishes at $\underset{\sim}{b} = 0$ and at

$$b_m = \frac{\mu}{\nu} \sum_{n=1}^{N} \Lambda_{mn}^{-1}\, \hat{f}_n \quad , \qquad m = 1, \ldots, N \quad . \qquad (17.214)$$

Because the matrix $\Lambda = [\Lambda_{mn}]$ is positive definite, the surface defined by

$$\dot{E}_N = -\nu \sum_{n,\ell=1}^{N} \Lambda_{n\ell}\, b_n b_\ell + \mu \sum_{n=1}^{N} b_n \hat{f}_n = 0 \quad , \qquad (17.215)$$

is a hyperellipsoid (except for certain degenerate possibilities associated with singular values of the $\hat{f}_n$). We can select points on the ray from the origin through the point on the hyperellipsoid specified by (17.214) by setting

$$b_m = \frac{\alpha\mu}{\nu} \sum_{n=1}^{N} \Lambda_{mn}^{-1} \hat{f}_n \quad , \qquad m = 1, \ldots, N \quad , \tag{17.216}$$

for constant α in the range $0 \leq \alpha < \infty$. Then we observe that the rate of change of energy

$$\dot{E}_N(\alpha) = \alpha(1 - \alpha) \frac{\mu^2}{\nu} \sum_{n,p=1}^{N} \Lambda_{np}^{-1} \hat{f}_n \hat{f}_p \quad , \tag{17.217}$$

is positive inside the hyperellipsoid ($0 < \alpha < 1$) and negative outside ($\alpha > 1$), since Λ^{-1} is positive definite when Λ is. Clearly, $\dot{E}_N$ can change sign only on the hyperellipsoidal surface given by $\dot{E}_N = 0$. By establishing the above facts that for certain interior points $\dot{E}_N > 0$ and for certain exterior points $\dot{E}_N < 0$, it follows immediately that $\dot{E}_N > 0$ for <u>all</u> interior points and that $\dot{E}_N < 0$ for <u>all</u> exterior points. This argument, which does not rely on completing the square in (17.215) (cf. (17.68)) establishes the Trapping Theorem.

The method proposed here for determining optimum low-order models from the empirical orthogonal functions describing ensembles of solutions to larger spectral models remains to be tested. If the eigenvalues σ_n decrease rapidly with increasing n so that the variance is resolved by a limited number of functions, then an optimum model will have been produced. In contrast, if the σ_n decrease slowly, then the variance will be distributed across a much larger set of functions and the model, while more effective than the original, may not be sufficiently reduced to achieve our objective.

The theoretical simplicity of this procedure and its conceptual appeal masks the numerical and computational difficulties that may be encountered in implementing it. Nevertheless, the available computational facilities are rapidly achieving sufficient power to make numerical simulation of complex flow an acceptable alternative to observation. Empirical orthogonal expansions based on the results of such simulation may produce models that will stimulate important theoretical advances.

CHAPTER 18

MODELING AND METAMODELING

JOHN A. DUTTON

Models, we said in Chapter 1, are devices that mirror Nature. Our concerns until now have centered on mathematical models and how they may be used to provide information about physical processes and the evolution of hydrodynamic flow. Now we turn to a preliminary examination of the process of modeling and to some of the issues raised in an attempt to clarify and perhaps codify this activity.

Mathematical modeling is concerned with representing physical phenomena or processes in forms that stimulate and foster logical and quantitative deductions. It clearly involves abstractions of reality; in such abstractions we create higher-level concepts and techniques whose efficacy derives from their association with formal procedures for reaching both inductive and deductive conclusions. In a similar spirit, we can envision an attempt to abstract the crucial elements in the process of modeling and to create a formal system of inference that deals with the structure and implications of models, and with the modeling process itself.

Metamodeling is an appropriate name for such a study. In metamodeling we study the process of modeling, just as metamathematics examines mathematics and the processes of mathematics. In studying modeling, as in studying physical systems, we shall presumably find it useful to construct abstract versions of the elements of models and of the processes of modeling. An aim of metamodeling, then, is to construct a model of the modeling process.

To do so, we shall have to develop formal linguistic and logical structures for discussing and examining the process of modeling. The history of mathematics demonstrates the power and advantages of creating abstract structures to represent the objects of interest and to obtain specific information about them as applications of broader theorems rather than as direct deductions. The same development of an abstract framework for understanding how to use computers effectively is now underway in computer science. The further abstraction represented by metamathematics has provided striking and surprising information about the nature of mathematics.

Metamodeling similarly might be expected to illuminate the logical processes of modeling, reveal methods for constructing approximations with desirable or optimum limiting properties, and to suggest generic forms of models and generic properties that certain forms of models would possess.

Clearly, metamodeling and the mathematics of modeling are closely entwined and the deductions of metamodeling will be reached by transforming metamodeling issues into forms that can be resolved mathematically. Determination of the structure of the attractor of a model provides an example. As a mathematical question, the issue is to deduce from the form of the equation the topological structure--for example the dimension--of the attractor. As a metamodeling question, the issue is to determine a mapping from model form to attractor structure that applies across a wide range of models. Since hydrodynamic models have an intrinsically complicating quadratic nonlinearity that arises from the nonlinear advection term, it is imperative that we inquire whether such an attractor exists at all.

The same association of mathematical and metamodeling issues arises with other concerns, including generic properties and structural stability of hydrodynamic models. The transition from steady flow to turbulence as the intensity of the forcing is increased would seem to be generic (see Chapter 15). An important question is whether a generic sequence of events can be identified as constituting this transition, or whether the sequence changes in response to model forms. To establish the link between metamodeling and mathematics, we first must resolve some standard problems of dynamics, including the possibility of developing a theorem that describes stable, center, and unstable manifolds relative to an evolving solution, the possibility of identifying ergodically long-term temporal averages with averages over attractors or parts of attractors, and finally the possibility that contributions from higher-order terms in spectral models can be effectively parameterized to produce adequate low-order models. Once questions such as these have been answered, we can turn to higher level, metamathematical problems such as determining necessary conditions for developing usable Galerkin approximations of the solutions to the partial differential equations and identifying alternative N-dimensional projections of the partial differential equations that might yield improved approximate systems.

Metamodeling has two aims. The first is to clarify the processes and the potential of modeling by developing an axiom and theorem approach to the study of models--the model of the modeling process we referred to above. Just as we showed that deductions from mathematical hydrodynamic models can be codified in axiom and theorem format, so we can envision such a structure for reaching and stating the conclusions of metamodeling. A very useful result for hydrodynamic models would be a theorem giving attractor structure as a function of model form. A companion metamodeling theorem might describe which aspects of attractor structure could be determined abstractly and which could only be found by simulation.

A second aim would be to develop a metamodel--a deductive structure that included but transcended the current collection of hydrodynamic models. A metamodel might be expected, upon specification of geometry and relevant exterior specifications, to produce either quantitative information or theorems about the behavior of the process.

As models of models, either the model of the modeling process or a metamodel would embody information about both the physical world and about human thought processes. In developing such metamodels, we would in part be modeling ourselves and learning how we think.

Appendix A

THE HURWITZ THEOREM AND BIFURCATION POINTS

RONALD GELARO

In general, the polynomial function

$$f(h) = h^n + H_1 h^{n-1} + \cdots + H_n \quad , \tag{A.1}$$

with real coefficients H_m is termed a Hurwitz polynomial if all its roots have negative real parts. To make this determination (Chetayev, 1961), we use the coefficients of (A.1) to form the table

$$\Delta_4\left\{\Delta_3\left\{\Delta_2\left\{\Delta_1\left\{\right.\right.\right.\right. \left\| \begin{array}{cccccc} H_1 & 1 & 0 & 0 & 0 & 0 \cdots \\ H_3 & H_2 & H_1 & 1 & 0 & 0 \cdots \\ H_5 & H_4 & H_3 & H_2 & H_1 & 1 \cdots \\ H_7 & H_6 & H_5 & H_4 & H_3 & H_2 \cdots \\ \vdots & \vdots & \vdots & \vdots & \vdots & \vdots \end{array} \right\| \quad , \tag{A.2}$$

in which all $H_m = 0$ if $m > n$ (n is the degree of f in (A.1)). On the main diagonal of the table are successively H_1, H_2, H_3, ... The principal diagonal minors Δ_i of (A.2) are denoted by

$$\Delta_1 = H_1 \quad , \quad \Delta_2 = \begin{vmatrix} H_1 & 1 \\ H_3 & H_2 \end{vmatrix} \quad , \quad \Delta_3 = \begin{vmatrix} H_1 & 1 & 0 \\ H_3 & H_2 & H_1 \\ H_5 & H_4 & H_3 \end{vmatrix} \quad , \ldots \quad , \tag{A.3}$$

which simply are the determinants of the subsets of (A.2) indicated by the brackets on the left side of the table. With this in mind we state Hurwitz's Theorem. The necessary and sufficient condition for the nth-degree polynomial $f(h)$ to have only roots with negative real parts is that all the following inequalities are satisfied:

$$\Delta_1 > 0, \quad \Delta_2 > 0, \ldots, \Delta_n > 0 \quad . \tag{A.4}$$

We recall that a possible bifurcation point is found by identifying a root λ_o of the characteristic equation $f(\lambda) = 0$ for which $\mathrm{Re}(\lambda_o) = 0$. In the present context, a bifurcation point may be identified by noting the conditions under which any one of the $\Delta_i = 0$, thereby implying that $Re(\lambda_o) = 0$ for some λ_o. For example, if the characteristic polynomial is a cubic equation of the form

$$\lambda^3 + e_1\lambda^2 + e_2\lambda + e_3 = 0 \quad , \tag{A.5}$$

then n = 3 and the table (A.2) becomes

$$\left\| \begin{array}{c|c|c|} e_1 & 1 & 0 \\ e_3 & e_2 & e_1 \\ 0 & 0 & e_3 \end{array} \right\| \quad . \tag{A.6}$$

Thus, the necessary and sufficient condition that $Re(\lambda) < 0$ for all λ is that the coefficients of (A.5) satisfy the three inequalities

$$\Delta_1 = e_1 > 0 \quad , \tag{A.7}$$

$$\Delta_2 = e_1e_2 - e_3 > 0 \quad , \tag{A.8}$$

$$\Delta_3 = e_3(e_1e_2 - e_3) > 0 \quad . \tag{A.9}$$

Bifurcation points are possible then if $e_1 = 0$, $e_1e_2 = e_3$, or $e_3 = 0$; in hydrodynamic problems, however, $e_1 > 0$ normally, so only the second and third equalities yield potential bifurcation points.

APPENDIX B

EUCLIDEAN ALGORITHM FOR FINDING COMMON ROOTS TO POLYNOMIALS

DAVID J. STENSRUD

The common root, or roots, to N polynomial equations in N variables can be determined by using the Euclidean Algorithm (van der Waerden, 1953). This algorithm involves a step-by-step elimination of the variables until a polynomial equation in one variable is obtained.

We begin by considering the case of two polynomial equations in two variables (Richards, 1959). We eliminate one variable from the two equations to derive a single equation in the remaining variable. Candidates for the common roots are found by solving the derived equation for the values of the retained variable, substituting these into the original two polynomial equations, and then determining the values of the eliminated variable. Although this procedure is essentially polynomial division (Richards, 1959), it allows a more straightforward identification of spurious roots.

We consider the two equations

$$F(x,y) = \sum_{k=0}^{m} \alpha_k(y)x^k = 0 \quad , \tag{B.1}$$

$$G(x,y) = \sum_{k=0}^{n} \beta_k(y)x^k = 0 \quad , \tag{B.2}$$

in which $\deg_x F = m \leq n = \deg_x G$ so that $\alpha_m(y) \neq 0$ and $\beta_n(y) \neq 0$. We note that we have written $F(x,y)$ and $G(x,y)$ in forms suitable for eliminating x. The first step is to eliminate the terms having the highest powers of x by writing

$$H(x,y) = \alpha_m(y)\, G(x,y) - \beta_n(y)\, x^{n-m}\, F(x,y)$$

$$= \sum_{k=0}^{\ell} \gamma_k(y)x^k = 0 \quad , \tag{B.3}$$

in which $\deg_x H = \ell < n$; thus we see that

$$\deg_x F + \deg_x H < \deg_x F + \deg_x G \quad . \tag{B.4}$$

Essentially, a common root (x_o, y_o) of $F(x,y) = 0$ and $G(x,y) = 0$ is also a common root (x_o, y_o) of $F(x,y) = 0$ and $H(x,y) = 0$ and a common root of $G(x,y) = 0$ and $H(x,y) = 0$. The only exceptions to this argument occur either when $x_o = 0$ or when y_o is a root of either $\alpha_m(y) = 0$ or $\beta_n(y) = 0$. Thus, from the common roots of either (B.1) and (B.3) or (B.2) and (B.3), we may recover the common roots of (B.1) and (B.2).

We continue to reduce the combined degree of the two polynomial equations by repeating the above procedure until we arrive at an equation in y alone. The roots of this equation can be easily found numerically. These roots are inserted into one of the original polynomial equations to obtain the candidates for the common roots. The above observation about common roots implies inductively that every common root of the original pair of polynomial equations appears among the candidates we have found. Finally, we determine which are actually roots by direct evaluation.

Algorithmically, we proceed as follows:

(1) Read $P(x,y) = 0$ and $Q(x,y) = 0$.

(2) If $\deg_x P > \deg_x Q$, then assign $G = P$ and $F = Q$;
else assign $F = P$ and $G = Q$.

(3) Apply (B.3) to obtain $H(x,y)$.

(4) If $\deg_x H = 0$ then go to (6); else assign $P = F$ and $Q = H$.

(5) Go to (2).

(6) Continue.

(7) Find roots $(y_1, \ldots, y_r)$ of $H(y) = 0$.

(8) Find common roots (x_o, y_o) of $P = 0$ and $Q = 0$ by substituting $y = y_1, \ldots, y_r$ into both $P = 0$ and $Q = 0$ of (1) and finding the common roots of the resulting polynomial equations in x.

As an example of the above algorithm, we take the pair of equations

$$P(x,y) = (y-1)(x+1) = x(y-1) + (y-1) \quad , \tag{B.5}$$

$$Q(x,y) = x^2(y-3) \quad , \tag{B.6}$$

for which $m = 1$, $n = 2$, $\alpha_0 = y - 1$, $\alpha_1 = y - 1$, $\beta_0 = 0$, $\beta_1 = 0$, and $\beta_2 = y - 3$. Thus it is obvious that $Q(x,y)$ has the highest power $n = 2$ of x. We eliminate x^2 by setting $F = P$ and $G = Q$ as in Step (2) and by forming the expression

$$H(x,y) = \alpha_1(y)\, G(x,y) - \beta_2(y)\, x^1\, F(x,y)$$

$$= (y-1)\left[x^2(y-3)\right] - (y-3)\, x\left[(y-1)(x+1)\right] = -\, x(y-3)(y-1) \quad , \qquad (B.7)$$

as in Step (3). Next, we determine whether x has been eliminated from H(x,y) as in Step (4). Because it has not, we set P = F = (y-1)(x+1) and Q = H = -x(y-3)(y-1) and return to Step (2). When we compare P(x,y) and Q(x,y) now, we find that the order of x is 1 in both equations. To eliminate x^1 from both equations, we calculate

$$H(x,y) = (y-1)\left[-x(y-3)(y-1)\right] - \left[-(y-3)(y-1)\right]x^0\left[(y-1)(x+1)\right]$$

$$= (y-3)(y-1)^2 \quad . \qquad (B.8)$$

In (B.8), we have produced a function depending only on y and so Step (4) sends us to Steps (6) and (7) at which we find the two roots $y_1 = 1$ and $y_2 = 3$. Following Step (8) we insert these two values of y into P(x,y) = 0 and Q(x,y) = 0, (B.5)-(B.6), and then solve these two equations for the associated values of x. For the root $y_1 = 1$, we find that P(x,1) = 0 for all x but that Q(0,1) = 0; thus $x_1 = 0$ and one common root is $(x_1,y_1) = (0,1)$. Similarly, for $y_2 = 3$, we have P(-1,3) = 0 but Q(x,3) = 0 for all x, and so the common root is $(x_2,y_2) = (-1,3)$. If we examine the curves P(x,y) = 0 (dotted lines) and Q(x,y) = 0 (dashed lines) in Fig. B.1, then we find that these curves do indeed cross at the calculated points (0,1) and (-1,3).

The above procedure can be generalized to N polynomial equations in N variables; we consider

$$\left.\begin{array}{l} R_{01} = P_1(x_1,\ldots,x_N) = 0 \\ \vdots \\ R_{0N} = P_N(x_1,\ldots,x_N) = 0 \end{array}\right\} \quad . \qquad (B.9)$$

Typically, we first apply Steps (1) through (6) of the above procedure to $F(x,y) = P_1(x_1,\ldots,x_N)$ and $G(x,y) = P_N(x_1,\ldots,x_N)$, where $x = x_N$ and $y = x_1,\ldots,x_{N-1}$, to obtain a new polynomial equation $R_{11}(x_1,\ldots,x_{N-1}) = 0$. We continue by eliminating x_N from the remaining pairs (P_j,P_N), j = 2,...,N-1 to obtain the

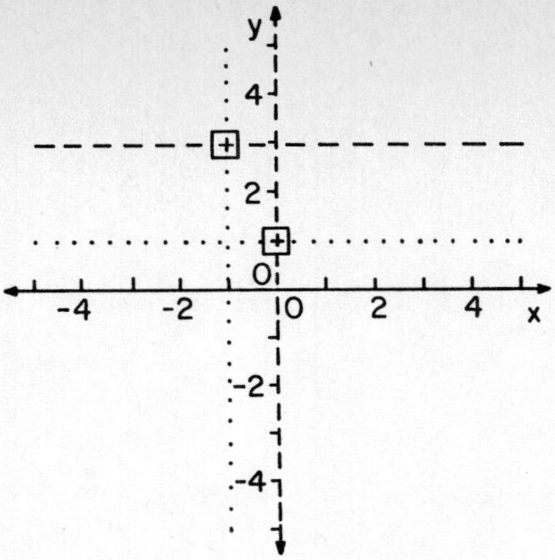

Fig. B.1 Curves of $P(x,y)=0$ (dotted lines) and $Q(x,y)=0$ (dashed lines) for the example given in (B.5) and (B.6). The points at which the dashed and dotted curves meet are indicated by squares at (0,1) and (-1,3). These are the common roots of $P(x,y)=0$ and $Q(x,y)=0$.

equations $R_{12}(x_1,\ldots,x_{N-1}) = 0, \ldots, R_{1,N-1}(x_1,\ldots,x_{N-1}) = 0$. Next we eliminate x_{N-1} as above to obtain the equations $R_{21}(x_1,\ldots,x_{N-2}) = 0, \ldots, R_{2,N-2}(x_1,\ldots,x_{N-2}) = 0$. We repeat this procedure to create at the kth step, the sets of polynomial equations $R_{k1}(x_1,\ldots,x_{N-k}) = 0, \ldots, R_{k,N-k}(x_1,\ldots,x_{N-k}) = 0$. Finally, after the last application, we obtain the single equation $R_{N-1,1}(x_1) = 0$. Then, we find the finite set S_1 of roots x_1 of $R_{N-1,1}(x_1) = 0$; next, we find the finite set S_2 of roots (x_1,x_2) of $R_{N-2,1}(x_1,x_2) = 0$ such that x_1 is in S_1. We continue inductively determining the finite set S_k of roots $(x_1,\ldots,x_k)$ of $R_{N-k,1}(x_1,\ldots,x_k) = 0$ such that $(x_1,\ldots,x_{k-1})$ is in S_{k-1}. Then S_N is a finite set containing all the common roots of $P_1 = 0, \ldots, P_N = 0$; the members of the set that are actually the common roots are found by evaluating all the polynomial equations in (B.9).

In singular cases the above procedure may fail because an infinite set S_k may be generated at the kth step. However, the original family of polynomial equations may be perturbed arbitrarily to one for which the above procedure works. The common roots to this perturbed family are close to the common roots to the original one.

APPENDIX C

THE METHOD OF ELIMINANTS FOR FINDING COMMON ROOTS TO POLYNOMIALS

DAVID J. STENSRUD

The method of eliminants is based on a theorem that states that two polynomial equations $p(x) = 0$ and $q(x) = 0$ have at least one root x_o in common if and only if a certain determinant E vanishes. To write this determinant, called the <u>eliminant</u>, we let

$$p(x) = c_0 + c_1x + c_2x^2 + \cdots + c_mx^m \quad , \tag{C.1}$$

$$q(x) = d_0 + d_1x + d_2x^2 + \cdots + d_nx^n \quad . \tag{C.2}$$

Then we form the $(m+n) \times (m+n)$ determinant given by (Walker, 1950)

$$\begin{array}{cc} & \begin{array}{cccccccccc} x^0 & x^1 & x^2 & \cdots & x^{m-1} & x^m & x^{m+1} & \cdots & x^{m+n-2} & x^{m+n-1} \end{array} \\ \begin{array}{c} 1 \\ 2 \\ \vdots \\ n \\ E = n+1 \\ n+2 \\ \vdots \\ n+m \end{array} & \left| \begin{array}{cccccccccc} c_0 & c_1 & c_2 & \cdots & c_{m-1} & c_m & 0 & \cdots & 0 & 0 \\ 0 & c_0 & c_1 & \cdots & c_{m-2} & c_{m-1} & c_m & \cdots & 0 & 0 \\ & \vdots & & & & \vdots & & & & \vdots \\ 0 & 0 & 0 & & & \cdots & & & c_{m-1} & c_m \\ d_0 & d_1 & d_2 & & & \cdots & & & 0 & 0 \\ 0 & d_0 & d_1 & & & \cdots & & & 0 & 0 \\ & \vdots & & & & \vdots & & & & \vdots \\ 0 & 0 & 0 & & & \cdots & & & d_{n-1} & d_n \end{array} \right| = 0 \quad . \end{array} \tag{C.3}$$

We notice from (C.3) that we may form the determinant one row at a time by successively shifting the list of coefficients of $p(x)$ to the right one column until the last column contains the coefficient c_m, and then by successively shifting the list of coefficients of $q(x)$ in the same manner. Alternatively, we may form the determinant by writing the coefficients of the polynomial functions $p(x)$, $xp(x)$, $x^2p(x)$, ..., $x^{n-1}p(x)$; $q(x)$, $xq(x)$, $x^2q(x)$, ..., $x^{m-1}q(x)$ in the appropriate columns.

Clearly, E can vanish only when the coefficients of p(x) and q(x) have special values.

To find these special values, we typically regard the coefficients of the polynomials as themselves functions of a second variable y. Thus, we suppose that p(x) = P(x,y) and q(x) = Q(x,y) are the pair of polynomial functions, and we write

$$P(x,y) = C_0(y) + C_1(y)x + C_2(y)x^2 + \cdots + C_m(y)x^m \quad , \tag{C.4}$$

$$Q(x,y) = D_0(y) + D_1(y)x + D_2(y)x^2 + \cdots + D_n(y)x^n \quad . \tag{C.5}$$

Now the eliminant E is a function of y, which in many cases can be determined using a symbolic manipulator. We conclude that the two polynomial equations P(x,y) = 0 and Q(x,y) = 0 have a common root (x_o,y_o) <u>only</u> when $E(y_o) = 0$. Moreover, if $E(y_o) = 0$, then there exists at least one value x_o of x such that (x_o,y_o) is a common root.

For the example given in Appendix B, we have the two equations

$$P(x,y) = xy - x + y - 1 = (y-1) + x(y-1) \quad , \tag{C.6}$$

$$Q(x,y) = x^2y - 3x^2 = x^2(y-3) \quad , \tag{C.7}$$

in which m = 1 and n = 2. If we decide to eliminate x from the problem, then there is at least one root if the following (1+2) × (1+2) determinant vanishes:

$$\begin{array}{cc} & \begin{array}{ccc} x^0 & x & x^2 \end{array} \\ E(y) = & \left| \begin{array}{ccc} (y-1) & (y-1) & 0 \\ 0 & (y-1) & (y-1) \\ 0 & 0 & (y-3) \end{array} \right| = 0 \end{array} \quad . \tag{C.8}$$

From expansion of the determinant, we get the condition that

$$(y-1)^2(y-3) = 0 \quad , \tag{C.9}$$

and so either y = 1 or y = 3 must occur.

Once the possible values of y are known, we can then calculate the values of x for which both P(x,y) = 0 and Q(x,y) = 0. If, for a given value of y, the values of x from P(x,y) = 0 and Q(x,y) = 0 are the same, then these values of x and y are the common roots. For the example (C.6)-(C.7), we have P(x,1) = 0 for all x and Q(0,1) = 0 for the case y = 1, and we have P(-1,3) = 0 and Q(x,3) = 0 for all x for the case y = 3. We conclude that the common roots are (0,1) and (-1,3). If we examine the curves of P(x,y) = 0 and Q(x,y) = 0 in Fig. B.1, then we find that these curves do indeed cross at the calculated points (0,1) and (-1,3).

REFERENCES

Abraham, R. and J.E. Marsden, 1967: Foundations of Mechanics. W.A. Benjamin, Inc., New York, 296 pp.

Ahlers, G. and R.P. Behringer, 1978: Evolution of turbulence from the Rayleigh-Bénard instability. Phys. Rev. Lett., 40, 712-716.

Alexander, J.C. and J.A. Yorke, 1978: The homotopy continuation method: Numerically implementable topological procedures. Trans. Am. Math. Soc., 242, 271-284.

Asai, T. and I. Nakasuji, 1973: On the stability of Ekman boundary layer flow with thermally unstable stratification. J. Meteor. Soc. Japan, 51, 29-42.

Atlas, D., S.H. Chou and W.P. Byerly, 1983: The influence of coastal shape on winter mesoscale air-sea interaction. Mon. Wea. Rev., 111, 245-252.

Aubrey, N., P. Holmes, J. Lumley and E. Stone, 1986: The dynamics of coherent structures in the wall region of a turbulent boundary layer. Report No. FDA-86-15 to the U.S. Office of Naval Research, 80 pp.

Bauer, L., H.B. Keller and E.L. Reiss, 1975: Multiple eigenvalues lead to secondary bifurcation. SIAM Review, 17, 101-121.

Boldrigini, C. and V. Franceschini, 1979: A five-dimensional truncation of the plane incompressible Navier-Stokes equations. Comm. Math. Phys., 64, 159-170.

Brown, R.A., 1972: On the inflection point instability of a stratified boundary layer. J. Atmos. Sci., 29, 850-859.

Brown, R.A., 1980: Longitudinal instabilities and secondary flows in the planetary boundary layer. A review. Rev. Geophy. Space Phys., 18, 683-697.

Brümmer, B., 1985: Structure, dynamics and energetics of boundary layer rolls from KonTur aircraft observations. Contrib. Atmos. Phys., 58, 237-254.

Brümmer, B. and M. Latif, 1985: Some studies on the inflection point instability. Contrib. Atmos. Phys., 58, 117-126.

Busse, F.H., 1981: Transition to turbulence in Rayleigh-Bénard convection. In Hydrodynamic Instabilities and the Transition to Turbulence, pp. 97-137, H.L. Swinney and J.P. Gollub (Eds.). Topics in Applied Physics, 45, Springer-Verlag, Heidelberg.

Busse, F.H. and J.A. Whitehead, 1971: Instabilities of convection rolls in a Prandtl number fluid. J. Fluid Mech., 47, 305-329.

Chaffee, N., 1968: The bifurcation of one or more closed orbits from an equilibrium point of an autonomous differential system. J. Diff. Eqn., 4, 661-679.

Chandrasekhar, S., 1961: Hydrodynamic and Hydromagnetic Stability. Clarendon Press, 652 pp.

Chang, H.R., 1983: Comparison of steady state transitions in truncated spectral and finite difference models of two-dimensional shallow convection. Ph.D. dissertation, Department of Meteorology, The Pennsylvania State University, University Park, PA, 175 pp.

Chang, H.R. and H.N. Shirer, 1984: Transitions in shallow convection: An explanation for lateral cell expansion. J. Atmos. Sci., 41, 2334-2346.

Chetayev, N.G., 1961: The Stability of Motion. Pergamon Press, 200 pp.

Chevalley, C., 1946: The Theory of Lie Groups, Vol. I. Princeton University Press, Princeton, 217 pp.

Chillingworth, D.R.J., 1976: Differential Topology with a View to Applications. Research Notes in Mathematics, 9, Pitman, London, 291 pp.

Clever, R.M. and F.H. Busse, 1974: Transition to time-dependent convection. J. Fluid Mech., 65, 625-645.

Clever, R.M. and F.H. Busse, 1978: Large wavelength convection rolls in low Prandtl number fluids. J. Applied Math and Physics (ZAMP), 29, 711-714.

Coddington, E.A. and N. Levinson, 1955: Theory of Ordinary Differential Equations, McGraw-Hill, New York, 429 pp.

Collet, P. and J.-P. Eckmann, 1980: Iterated Maps on the Interval as Dynamical Systems. Progress on Physics, I, Birkhäuser-Boston, Boston, 248 pp.

Constantin, P. and C. Foias, 1985: Global Lyapunov exponents, Kaplan-Yorke formulas, and the dimension of the attractor for two-dimensional Navier-Stokes equations. Comm. Pure Appl. Math., 38, 1-27.

Constantin, P., C. Foias and R. Temam, 1984: On the large-time Galerkin approximation of the Navier-Stokes equations. SIAM J. Numerical Analysis, 21, 615-634.

Constantin, P., C. Foias and R. Temam, 1985: Attractors representing turbulent flows. Memoirs of the American Mathematical Society, 53, No. 314, 67 pp.

Courant, R. and D. Hilbert, 1953: Methods of Mathematical Physics, Vol. I, Wiley Interscience, New York, 560 pp.

Curry, J.H., 1978: A generalized Lorenz system. Comm. Math. Phys., 60, 193-204.

Curry, J.H., J.R. Herring, J. Lonçaric and S.A. Orszag, 1984: Order and disorder in two- and three-dimensional Bénard convection. J. Fluid Mech., 147, 1-38.

Deardorff, J.W., 1964: A numerical study of two-dimensional parallel plate convection. J. Atmos. Sci., 21, 419-438.

Deardorff, J.W. and G.E. Willis, 1965: The effect of two-dimensionality on the suppression of thermal turbulence. J. Fluid Mech., 23, 337-353.

Drazin, P.G. and L.N. Howard, 1966: Hydrodynamic stability of parallel flow of inviscid fluid. Advan. Appl. Mech., 9, 1-89.

Dutton, J.A., 1973: The global thermodynamics of atmospheric motion. Tellus, 15, 89-110.

Dutton, J.A., 1976: The Ceaseless Wind: An Introduction to the Theory of Atmospheric Motion. McGraw-Hill, New York, 579 pp.

Dutton, J.A., 1982: Fundamental theorems of climate theory -- some proved, some conjectured. SIAM Review, 24, 1-33.

Dutton, J.A., 1986: The Ceaseless Wind: An Introduction to the Theory of Atmospheric Motion. Reprinted by Dover Publications, New York, 617 pp.

Dutton, J.A. and R.W. Henderson, 1982: Prospects for prediction of zonal wind oscillations. Preprints for Ninth Conference on Weather Forecasting and Analysis. American Meteorological Society, Boston, 315-322.

Dutton, J.A. and R. Wells, 1984: Topological issues in hydrodynamic predictability. In Predictability of Fluid Motions, pp. 11-44, G. Holloway and B.J. West (Eds.). AIP Conference Proceedings, No. 106, American Institute of Physics, New York.

Etling, D., 1971: The stability of Ekman boundary layer flow as influenced by the thermal stratification. Contrib. Atmos. Phys., 44, 168-186.

Faller, A.J. and R.E. Kaylor, 1966: A numerical study of the laminar Ekman boundary layer. J. Atmos. Sci., 23, 466-480.

Farmer, J.D., E. Ott, and J.A. Yorke, 1983: The dimension of chaotic attractors. Physica, 7D, 153-180.

Feigenbaum, M.J., 1978: Quantitative universality for a class of nonlinear transformations. J. Stat. Phys., 19, 25-52.

Foias, C., O.P. Manley, R. Temam and Y.M. Treve, 1983: Number of modes governing two-dimensional viscous, incompressible flows. Phys. Rev. Letters, 50, 1031-1034.

Fowlis, W.W. and R. Hide, 1965: Thermal convection in a rotating annulus of liquid: effect of viscosity on the transition between axisymmetric and non-axisymmetric flow regimes. J. Atmos. Sci., 22, 541-588.

Fraedrich, K., 1986: Estimating the dimensions of weather and climate attractors. J. Atmos. Sci., 43, 419-432.

Franceschini, V., 1980: A Feigenbaum sequence of bifurcations in the Lorenz model. J. Stat. Phys., 22, 397-406.

Franceschini, V. and C. Tebaldi, 1979: Sequences of infinite bifurcations and turbulence in a five-mode truncation of the Navier-Stokes equations. J. Stat. Phys., 21, 707-726.

Frederickson, P., J.L. Kaplan, E.D. Yorke and J.A. Yorke, 1983: The Lyapunov dimension of strange attractors. J. Diff. Eqns., 49, 185-207.

Friedrichs, K.O., 1965: Advanced Ordinary Differential Equations. Gordon Breach Science Publishers, Inc., New York, 205 pp.

Frøyland, J. and K.H. Alfsen, 1984: Lyapunov-exponent spectrum for the Lorenz model. Phys. Rev. A., 29, 2928-2931.

Fultz, D., R.R. Long, G.B. Owens, W. Boham, R. Kaylor and J. Weil, 1959: Studies of Thermal Convection in a Rotating Cylinder with Some Implications for Large-Scale Atmospheric Motions. Meteor. Monographs, No. 21, American Meteorological Society, Boston, 104 pp.

Gammelsrød, T., 1975: Instability of Couette flow in a rotating fluid and origin of Langmuir circulations. J. Geophys. Res., 80, 5069-5075.

Gelaro, R., 1983: Some topological aspects of parameterization in nonlinear spectral models of quasi-geostrophic flows. M.S. Thesis, Department of Meteorology, The Pennsylvania State University, University Park, PA, 228 pp.

Gelaro, R. and H.N. Shirer, 1986: A parameterization technique for nolinear spectral models. J. Atmos. Sci., 43, 671-687.

Grassberger, P. and I. Procaccia, 1983a: Characterization of strange attractors. Phys. Rev. Lett., 50, 346-349.

Grassberger, P. and I. Proccacia, 1983b: Measuring the strangeness of strange attractors. Physica, 9D, 189-208.

Greenside, H.S., A. Wolf, J. Swift and T. Pignataro, 1982: Impracticality of a box-counting algorithm for calculating the dimensionality of strange attractors. Phys. Rev. A, 25, 3453-3456.

Guckenheimer, J. and P. Holmes, 1983: Nonlinear Oscillations, Dynamical Systems, and Bifurcations of Vector Fields. Applied Mathematical Sciences, 42, Springer-Verlag, New York, 453 pp.

Henderson, H.W. and R. Wells, 1987: Calculating attractor dimensions from meteorological time series. To be submitted to Mon. Wea. Rev.

Hirsch, M.W. and S. Smale, 1974: Differential Equations, Dynamical Systems, and Linear Algebra. Academic Press, New York, 358 pp.

Hopf, E., 1942: Abzweigung einer periodischen Lösung von einer stationären Lösung eines differential-systems. Ber. Math.-Phys. Kl. Sächs. Acad. Wiss. Leipzig, 94, 1-22.

Huang, X-Y and E. Källén, 1986: A low-order model for moist convection. Tellus, 38A, in press.

Iooss, G. and D.D. Joseph, 1980: Elementary Stability and Bifurcation Theory. Springer-Verlag, New York, 286 pp.

Irwin, M.C., 1980: Smooth Dynamical Systems. Academic Press, New York, 259 pp.

Joseph, D.D., 1976: Stability of Fluid Motions, Vols. 1 and 2, Springer Tracts in Natural Philosophy, 27-28, Springer-Verlag, Berlin, 282 and 274 pp.

Joseph, D.D. and D.H. Sattinger, 1972: Bifurcating time periodic solutions and their stability. Arch. Rat. Mech. Anal., 45, 79-109.

Joseph, D.D., 1981: Hydrodynamic stability and bifurcation. In Hydrodynamic Instabilities and the Transition to Turbulence, pp. 27-76, H.L. Swinney and J.P. Gollub (Eds.). Topics in Applied Physics, 45, Springer-Verlag, New York.

Kadanoff, L.P., 1983: Roads to chaos. Physics Today, December, 46-53.

Kaplan, J.L. and J.A. Yorke, 1979: Chaotic behavior of multidimensional difference equations. In Functional Differential Equations and the Approximation of Fixed Points, pp. 228-237, H.O. Peitgen and H.O. Walther (Eds.). Lecture Notes in Mathematics, 730, Springer-Verlag, New York.

Kaylor, R. and A.J. Faller, 1972: Instability of the stratified Ekman boundary layer and the generation of internal waves. J. Atmos. Sci., 29, 497-509.

Kellison, S.G., 1975: Fundamentals of Numerical Analysis. Richard D. Irwin, Inc., 459 pp.

Kelly, R.D., 1984: Horizontal roll and boundary-layer interrelationships observed over Lake Michigan. J. Atmos. Sci., 41, 1816-1826.

Kirchgässner, K., 1975: Bifurcation in nonlinear hydrodynamic stability. SIAM Review, 17, 652-682.

Kloeden, P.E., 1986a: Minimal truncated spectral systems which preserve bifurcations. Z. Agnew Math. Mech., 66, 51-54.

Kloeden, P.E., 1986b: Asymptotically stable attracting sets in the Navier-Stokes equations. Bull. Australian Math. Soc., 34, 37-52.

Kloeden, P.E. and R. Wells, 1983: An explicit example of Hopf bifurcation in fluid mechanics. Proc. Roy. Soc. London, Ser. A., 390, 293-320.

Kolman, B., 1970: Elementary Linear Algebra. Collier-Macmillan Canada, Toronto, 255 pp.

Kolmogorov, A.N., 1958: A new invariant for transitive dynamical systems. Dokl. Akad. Nauk, USSR, 119, 861-864.

Krishnamurti, R., 1970a: On the transition to turbulent convection. Part 1. The transition from two- to three-dimensional flow. J. Fluid Mech., 42, 295-307.

Krishnamurti, R., 1970b: On the transition to turbulent convection. Part 2. The transition to time-dependent flow. J. Fluid Mech., 42, 309-320.

Krishnamurti, R. 1973: Some further studies on the transition to turbulent convection. J. Fluid Mech., 60, 285-303.

Kuettner, J.P., 1959: The band structure of the atmosphere. Tellus, 11, 267-294.

Kuettner, J.P., 1971: Cloud bands in the earth's atmosphere: Observations and theory. Tellus, 23, 404-425.

Ladyzhenskaya, O.A., 1969: The Mathematical Theory of Viscous Incompressible Flow. Gordon and Breach, New York, Second English edition translated by R.A. Silverman, 84 pp.

Landau, L.D., 1944: On the problem of turbulence. Comptes Rendu Acad. Sci. USSR, 44, 311-316.

Leray, J., 1933: Etude des diverses équations intégrales non linéaires et de quelques problèmes que pose l'hydrodynamique. J. Math. Pures Appl., 12, 1-82.

Lilly, D.K., 1966: On the instability of Ekman boundary flow. J. Atmos. Sci., 23, 481-494.

Lipps, F.B. and R.C.J. Somerville, 1971: Dynamics of variable wavelength in finite-amplitude Bénard convection. Physics of Fluids, 14, 759-765.

Loeve, M., 1963: Probability Theory. Van Nostrand, Princeton, New Jersey, 685 pp.

Lorenz, E.N., 1963: Deterministic nonperiodic flow. J. Atmos. Sci., 20, 130-141.

Lorenz, E.N., 1980: Noisy periodicity and reverse bifurcation. In Nonlinear Dynamics, pp. 282-291, R.H.G. Hellerman (Ed.), Annals N.Y. Acad. Sci., 357.

Lumley, J.L., 1970: Stochastic Tools in Turbulence. Academic Press, New York, 194 pp.

Malkus, W.V.R. and G. Veronis, 1958: Finite amplitude cellular convection. J. Fluid Mech., 4, 225-260.

Manneville, P. and Y. Pomeau, 1979: Intermittency and the Lorenz model. Phys. Lett., 75A, 1-2.

Manneville, P. and Y. Pomeau, 1980: Different ways to turbulence in dissipative dynamical systems. Physica, 1D, 219-226.

Marcus, P.S., 1978: Nonlinear thermal convection in Boussinesq fluids and ideal gases with plane-parallel and spherical geometries. Ph.D. Thesis, Ann Arbor, Michigan: University Microfilms.

Marcus, P.S., 1981: Effects of truncation in modal representations of thermal convection. J. Fluid Mech., 103, 241-255.

Marsden, J.E. and M. McCracken, 1976: The Hopf Bifurcation and Its Applications. Applied Mathematical Sciences, 19, Springer-Verlag, Heidelberg, 408 pp.

Mather, J., 1968: Stability of C^{∞} mappings III: Finitely determined map germs. Publ. Math. I.H.E.S., 35, 127-156.

Maurer, J. and A. Libchaber, 1979: Rayleigh-Bénard experiment in liquid helium; frequency locking and the onset of turbulence. J. Phys. Lett. (Paris), 40, L419 - L423.

May, R.M., 1976: Simple mathematical models with very complicated dynamics. In Bifurcation Theory and Its Applications in Scientific Disciplines, pp. 517-529, O. Gurel and O.E. Rössler (Eds.). Annals NY Acad. Sci., 316.

McLaughlin, J.B. and P.C. Martin, 1975: Transition to turbulence in a statically stressed fluid system. Phys. Rev. A, 12, 186-203.

Milnor, J.W., 1965: Topology from the Differential Point of View. University Press of Virginia, 64 pp.

Minorsky, N., 1962: Nonlinear Oscillations. D. Van Nostrand Co., Inc., Princeton, 714 pp.

Mitchell, K.E. and J.A. Dutton, 1981: Bifurcations from stationary to periodic solutions in a low-order model of forced, dissipative barotropic flow. J. Atmos. Sci., 38, 690-716.

Mori, H., 1980: Fractal dimensions of chaotic flows of autonomous dissipative systems. Prog. Theor. Phys., 63, 1044-1047.

Nese, J.M., 1985: Phase space structure and dimension of attractors of finite spectral models. M.S. Thesis, Department of Meteorology, The Pennsylvania State University, University Park, PA, 180 pp.

Nese, J.M., J.A. Dutton and R. Wells, 1987: Calculated attractor dimensions for low-order spectral models. J. Atmos. Sci., 44, in press.

Newhouse, S., D. Ruelle and F. Takens, 1978: Occurrence of strange Axiom A attractors near quasi-periodic flows on T^m, $m \geq 3$. Comm. Math. Phys., 64, 35-40.

Nitecki, Z., 1971: Differentiable Dynamics: An Introduction to the Orbit Structure of Diffeomorphisms. MIT Press, 282 pp.

Osledec, V.I., 1968: A multiplicative ergodic theorem. Lyapunov characteristic numbers for dynamical systems. Trans. Moscow Math. Soc., 19, 197-231.

Ostlund, S., D. Rand, J. Sethna and E. Siggia, 1983: Universal properties of the transition from quasi-periodicity to chaos in dissipative systems. Physica, 8D, 303-342.

Palis, J. and W. de Melo, 1982: Geometric Theory of Dynamical Systems: An Introduction. Springer-Verlag, New York, 198 pp.

Panofsky, H.A. and J.A. Dutton, 1984: Atmospheric Turbulence -- Models and Methods for Engineering Applications. John Wiley & Sons, New York, 397 pp.

Peixoto, M.M., 1962: Structural stability on two-dimensional manifolds. Topology, 1, 101-120.

Pyle, R.J., 1986: On modal truncations for branching temporally periodic solutions. M.S. Thesis, Department of Meteorology, The Pennsylvania State University, University Park, PA, 109 pp.

Rabinowitz, P.H., 1968: Existence and nonuniqueness of rectangular solutions of the Bénard problem. Arch. Rat. Mech. Anal., 29, 32-57.

Rayleigh, L., 1880: On the stability, or instability, of certain fluid motions. Scientific Papers, I, 474-487.

Richards, P.I., 1959: Manual of Mathematical Physics, Pergammon Press, 486 pp.

Riesz, F. and B. Sz.-Nagy, 1955: Functional Analysis. Translation by L.F. Boron. Frederick Ungar, New York, 468 pp.

Robbins, K.A., 1979: Periodic solutions and bifurcation structure at high R in the Lorenz model. SIAM J. Appl. Math., 36, 457-472.

Ruelle, D., 1979: Ergodic theory of differential dynamical systems. Institut des Hautes-Études Scientifiques Publications Mathématiques, 50, 27-58.

Ruelle, D. and F. Takens, 1971: On the nature of turbulence. Commun. Math. Phys., 20, 167-192.

Russell, D., J. Hanson and E. Ott, 1980: Dimension of strange attractors. Phys. Rev. Lett., 45, 1175-1178.

Saltzman, B., 1962: Finite amplitude free convection as an initial value problem -- I. J. Atmos. Sci., 19, 329-341.

Shirer, H.N., 1978: Bifurcation and stability in a model of moist convection. Ph.D. Dissertation, Department of Meteorology, The Pennsylvania State University, University Park, PA, 206 pp.

Shirer, H.N., 1980: Bifurcation and stability in a model of moist convection in a shearing environment. J. Atmos. Sci., 37, 1586-1602.

Shirer, H.N., 1984: On the dynamics of predictability. In Predictability of Fluid Motions, pp. 355-368, G. Holloway and B. West (Eds.). AIP Conference Proceedings, No. 106. American Institute of Physics, New York.

Shirer, H.N., 1986: On cloud street development in three dimensions: Parallel and Rayleigh instabilities. Contrib. Atmos. Phys., 59, 126-149.

Shirer, H.N. and B. Brümmer, 1986: Cloud streets during KonTur: A comparison of parallel/thermal modes with observations. Contrib. Atmos. Phys., 59, 150-161.

Shirer, H.N. and J.A. Dutton, 1979: The branching hierarchy of multiple solutions in a model of moist convection. J. Atmos Sci., 36, 1705-1721.

Shirer, H.N. and R. Wells, 1982: Improving spectral models by unfolding their singularities. J. Atmos. Sci., 39, 610-621.

Shirer, H.N. and R. Wells, 1983: Mathematical Structure of the Singularities at the Transitions Between Steady States in Hydrodynamic Systems. Lecture Notes in Physics, 185, Springer-Verlag, Heidelberg, 276 pp.

Shirer, H.N. and R. Wells, 1985: Steady states: Keys to classifying the routes to chaos. In Stability of Convective Flows, pp. 11-16, W.S. Saric and A.A. Szewczyk (Eds.). American Society of Mechanical Engineers, New York.

Sorokin, V.S., 1953: Variational method in the theory of convection. Prikl. Mat. Mekh., 17, 39-48.

Sparrow, C., 1982: The Lorenz Equations: Bifurcations, Chaos, and Strange Attractors. Applied Mathematical Sciences, 41, Springer-Verlag, Heidelberg, 269 pp.

Stensrud, D.J., 1985: On the development of boundary layer rolls from the inflection point instability. M.S. Thesis, Department of Meteorology, The Pennsylvania State University, University Park, PA, 125 pp.

Stensrud, D.J. and H.N. Shirer, 1987: On the development of boundary layer rolls from the dynamic instabilities. Submitted to J. Atmos. Sci., for review.

Stork, K. and U. Müller, 1972: Convection in boxes: experiments. J. Fluid Mech., 54, 599-611.

Swinney, H.L., 1978: Hydrodynamic instabilities and the transition to turbulence. Supp. Prog. Theor. Phys., 64, 164-175.

Swinney, H.L. and J.P. Gollub, 1978: The transition to turbulence. Physics Today, August, 41-49.

Swinney, H.L. and J.P. Gollub, 1981: Introduction to Hydrodynamic Instabilities and the Transition to Turbulence, pp. 1-6. H.L. Swinney and J.P. Gollub (Eds.). Topics in Applied Physics, 45, Springer-Verlag, New York.

Takens, F., 1981: Detecting strange attractors in turbulence. In Dynamical Systems and Turbulence, pp. 366-381, L.S. Young and D. Rand (Eds.). Lecture Notes in Mathematics, 898, Springer-Verlag, New York.

Temam, R., 1983: Navier-Stokes Equations and Nonlinear Functional Analysis. CBMS/ NSF Regional Conference Series in Applied Mathematics, 41, Society for Industrial and Applied Mathematics, Philadelphia, PA, 122 pp.

Tommre, J., D.O. Gough and E.A. Spiegel, 1977: Numerical solutions of single-mode convection equations. J. Fluid Mech., 79, 1-31.

van Delden, A., 1984: Scale selection in low-order spectral models of two-dimensional thermal convection. Tellus, 36, 458-479.

van der Waerden, B., 1953: Modern Algebra, Vol. 1. Translated by F. Blum, Frederick Ungar Pub. Co., New York, 264 pp.

van Storch, H. and G. Hannoschöck, 1985: Statistical aspects of estimated principal vectors (EOFs) based on small sample sizes. J. Clim. Appl. Meteor., 24, 716-724.

Veronis, G., 1959: Cellular convection with finite amplitude in a rotating fluid. J. Fluid Mech., 5, 401-435.

Veronis, G., 1966: Motions at subcritical values of the Rayleigh number in a rotating fluid. J. Fluid Mech., 24, 545-554.

Vickroy, J.G. and J.A. Dutton, 1979: Bifurcation and catastrophe in a simple, forced, dissipative quasi-geostrophic flow. J. Atmos. Sci., 36, 42-52.

Walker, R.J., 1950: Algebraic Curves. Princeton University Press, 201 pp.

Wells, R. and J.A. Dutton, 1986: Determination of bifurcating asymptotic behavior by means of truncated models in hydrodynamic systems. Bull. Australian Math. Soc., 34, in press.

Willis, G.E., J.W. Deardorff and R.C.J. Somerville, 1972: Roll-diameter dependence in Rayleigh convection and its effect upon the heat flux. J. Fluid Mech., 54, 351-367.

Wippermann, F., D. Etling and H.J. Kirstein, 1978: On the instability of a planetary boundary layer with Rossby number similarity. Bound. Layer Meteor., 15, 301-321.

Wolf, A., J. Swift, H. Swinney and J. Vastano, 1985: Determining Lyapunov exponents from a time series. Physica, 16D, 285-317.

Yorke, J.A. and E.D. Yorke, 1981: Chaotic behavior and fluid dynamics. In Hydrodynamic Instabilities and the Transition to Turbulence, pp. 77-95, H.L. Swinney and J.P. Gollub (Eds.). Topics in Applied Physics, 45, Springer-Verlag, New York.

Yost, D.A. and H.N. Shirer, 1982: Bifurcation and stability of low-order steady flows in horizontally and vertically forced convection. J. Atmos. Sci., 39, 114-125.

INDEX

Lecture Notes in Physics

Vol. 237: Nearby Molecular Clouds. Proceedings, 1984. Edited by G. Serra. IX, 242 pages. 1985.

Vol. 238: The Free-Lagrange Method. Proceedings, 1985. Edited by M.J. Fritts, W.P. Crowley and H. Trease. IX, 313 pages. 1985.

Vol. 239: Geometrics Aspects of the Einstein Equations and Integrable Systems. Proceedings, 1984. Edited by R. Martini. V, 344 pages. 1985.

Vol. 240: Monte-Carlo Methods and Applications in Neutronics, Photonics and Statistical Physics. Proceedings, 1985. Edited by R. Alcouffe, R. Dautray, A. Forster, G. Ledanois and B. Mercier. VIII, 483 pages. 1985.

Vol. 241: Numerical Simulation of Combustion Phenomena. Proceedings, 1985. Edited by R. Glowinski, B. Larrouturou and R. Temam. IX, 404 pages. 1985.

Vol. 242: Exactly Solvable Problems in Condensed Matter and Relativistic Field Theory. Proceedings, 1985. Edited by B.S. Shastry, S.S. Jha and V. Singh. V, 318 pages. 1985.

Vol. 243: Medium Energy Nucleon and Antinucleon Scattering. Proceedings, 1985. Edited by H.V. von Geramb. IX, 576 pages. 1985.

Vol. 244: W. Dittrich, M. Reuter, Selected Topics in Gauge Theories. V, 315 pages. 1986.

Vol. 245: R.Kh. Zeytounian, Les Modèles Asymptotiques de la Mécanique des Fluides I. IX, 260 pages. 1986.

Vol. 246: Field Theory, Quantum Gravity and Strings. Proceedings, 1984/85. Edited by H.J. de Vega and N. Sánchez. VI, 381 pages. 1986.

Vol. 247: Nonlinear Dynamics Aspects of Particle Accelerators. Proceedings, 1985. Edited by J.M. Jowett, M. Month and S. Turner. VIII, 583 pages. 1986.

Vol. 248: Quarks and Leptons. Proceedings, 1985. Edited by C.A. Engelbrecht. X, 417 pages. 1986.

Vol. 249: Trends in Applications of Pure Mathematics to Mechanics. Proceedings, 1985. Edited by E. Kröner and K. Kirchgässner. VIII, 523 pages. 1986.

Vol. 250: Lie Methods in Optics. Proceedings 1985. Edited by J. Sánchez Mondragón and K.B. Wolf. XIV, 249 pages. 1986.

Vol. 251: R. Liebmann, Statistical Mechanics of Periodic Frustrated Ising Systems. VII, 142 pages. 1986.

Vol. 252: Local and Global Methods of Nonlinear Dynamics. Proceedings, 1984. Edited by A.W. Sáenz, W.W. Zachary and R. Cawley. VII, 263 pages. 1986.

Vol. 253: Recent Developments in Nonequilibrium Thermodynamics Fluids and Related Topics. Proceedings, 1985. Edited by J. Casas-Vázquez, D. Jou and J.M. Rubí. X, 392 pages. 1986.

Vol. 254: Cool Stars, Stellar Systems, and the Sun. Proceedings, 1985. Edited by M. Zeilik and D.M. Gibson. XI, 501 pages. 1986.

Vol. 255: Radiation Hydrodynamics in Stars and Compact Objects. Proceedings, 1985. Edited by D. Mihalas and K.-H. A. Winkler. VI, 454 pages. 1986.

Vol. 256: Dynamics of Wave Packets in Molecular and Nuclear Physics. Proceedings, 1985. Edited by J. Broeckhove, L. Lathouwers and P. van Leuven. VIII, 187 pages. 1986.

Vol. 257: Statistical Mechanics and Field Theory: Mathematical Aspects. Proceedings, 1985. Edited by T.C. Dorlas, N.M. Hugenholtz and M. Winnink. VII, 328 pages. 1986.

Vol. 258: Wm. G. Hoover, Molecular Dynamics. VI, 138 pages. 1986.

Vol. 259: R.F. Alvarez-Estrada, F. Fernández, J.L. Sánchez-Gómez, V. Vento, Models of Hadron Structure Based on Quantum Chromodynamics. VI, 294 pages. 1986.

Vol. 260: The Three-Body Force in the Three-Nucleon System. Proceedings, 1986. Edited by B.L. Berman and B.F. Gibson. XI, 530 pages. 1986.

Vol. 261: Conformal Groups and Related Symmetries – Physical Results and Mathematical Background. Proceedings, 1985. Edited by A.O. Barut and H.-D. Doebner. VI, 443 pages. 1986.

Vol. 262: Stochastic Processes in Classical and Quantum Systems. Proceedings, 1985. Edited by S. Albeverio, G. Casati and D. Merlini. XI, 551 pages. 1986.

Vol. 263: Quantum Chaos and Statistical Nuclear Physics. Proceedings, 1986. Edited by T.H. Seligman and H. Nishioka. IX, 382 pages. 1986.

Vol. 264: Tenth International Conference on Numerical Methods in Fluid Dynamics. Proceedings, 1986. Edited by F.G. Zhuang and Y.L. Zhu. XII, 724 pages. 1986.

Vol. 265: N. Straumann, Thermodymamik. VI, 140 Seiten. 1986.

Vol. 266: The Physics of Accretion onto Compact Objects. Proceedings, 1986. Edited by K.O. Mason, M.G. Watson and N.E. White. VIII, 421 pages. 1986.

Vol. 267: The Use of Supercomputers in Stellar Dynamics. Proceedings, 1986. Edited by P. Hut and S. McMillan. VI, 240 pages. 1986.

Vol. 268: Fluctuations and Stochastic Phenomena in Condensed Matter. Proceedings, 1986. Edited by L. Garrido. VIII, 413 pages. 1987.

Vol. 269: PDMS and Clusters. Proceedings, 1986. Edited by E.R. Hilf, F. Kammer and K. Wien. VIII, 261 pages. 1987.

Vol. 270: B.G. Konopelchenko, Nonlinear Integrable Equations. VIII, 361 pages. 1987.

Vol. 271: Nonlinear Hydrodynamic Modeling: A Mathematical Introduction. Edited by Hampton N. Shirer. XVI, 546 pages. 1987.

Springer Series in Computational Physics

Editors: **H. Cabannes, M. Holt, H. B. Keller, J. Killeen, S. A. Orszag, V. V. Rusanov**

Computational Methods for Kinetic Models of Magnetically Confined Plasmas

By **J. Killeen, G. D. Kerbel, M. C. McCoy, A. A. Mirin**
1986. 77 figures. VIII, 199 pages. ISBN 3-540-13401-8

Y. N. Dnestrovskii, D. P. Kostomarov

Numerical Simulation of Plasmas

Translated from the Russian by N. V. Deyneka
1985. 97 figures. XIV, 304 pages. ISBN 3-540-15835-9

R. Peyret, T. D. Taylor

Computational Methods for Fluid Flow

2nd corrected printing. 1985. 125 figures. X, 358 pages
ISBN 3-540-13851-X

R. Gruber, J. Rappaz

Finite Element Methods in Linear Ideal Magnetohydrodynamics

1985. 103 figures. XI, 180 pages. ISBN 3-540-13398-4

C. A. J. Fletcher

Computational Galerkin Methods

1984. 107 figures. XI, 309 pages. ISBN 3-540-12633-3

R. Glowinski

Numerical Methods for Nonlinear Variational Problems

1984. 82 figures. XV, 493 pages. ISBN 3-540-12434-9
(Originally published as "Glowinski, Lectures on Numerical Methods...", Tata Institute Lectures on Mathematics, 1980)

M. Holt

Numerical Methods in Fluid Dynamics

2nd revised edition. 1984. 114 figures. XI, 273 pages
ISBN 3-540-12799-2

O. G. Mouritsen

Computer Studies of Phase Transitions and Critical Phenomena

1984. 79 figures. XII, 200 pages. ISBN 3-540-13397-6

O. Pironneau

Optimal Shape Design for Elliptic Systems

1984. 57 figures. XII, 168 pages. ISBN 3-540-12069-6

M. Kubíček, M. Marek

Computational Methods in Bifurcation Theory and Dissipative Structures

1983. 91 figures. XI, 243 pages. ISBN 3-540-12070-X

Y. I. Shokin

The Method of Differential Approximation

Translated from the Russian by K. G. Roesner
1983. 75 figures, 12 tables. XIII, 296 pages. ISBN 3-540-12225-7

Finite-Difference Techniques for Vectorized Fluid Dynamics Calculations

Editor: **D. L. Book**
With contributions by J. P. Boris, M. J. Fritts, R. V. Madala, B. E. McDonald, N. K. Winsor, S. T. Zalesak
1981. 60 figures. VIII, 226 pages. ISBN 3-540-10482-8

D. P. Telionis

Unsteady Viscous Flows

1981. 132 figures. XXIII, 408 pages. ISBN 3-540-10481-X

F. Thomasset

Implementation of Finite Element Methods for Navier-Stokes Equations

1981. 86 figures. VII, 161 pages. ISBN 3-540-10771-1

F. Bauer, O. Betancourt, P. Garabedian

A Computational Method in Plasma Physics

1978. 22 figures. VIII, 144 pages. ISBN 3-540-08833-4

Springer-Verlag
Berlin Heidelberg New York
London Paris Tokyo

Springer